A HEBRIDEAN OMNIBUS

D1363748

A HEBRIDEAN OMNIBUS

Lillian Beckwith

Decorations by Douglas Hall

Containing
The Hills is Lonely
The Sea for Breakfast
The Loud Halo

ARROW BOOKS

Arrow Books Limited
62-65 Chandos Place, London WC2N 4NW

An imprint of Century Hutchinson Limited

London Melbourne Sydney Auckland
Johannesburg and agencies throughout
the world

Omnibus edition first published by Hutchinson 1976
Arrow edition 1987

Printed and bound in Great Britain by
Anchor Brendon Limited, Tiptree, Essex

ISBN 0 09 954380 X

The characters in this book are not intended to be those of any living persons. The story of Johnny Comic first appeared in *The Countryman*

VOCABULARY

Bodach	Old man
Cailleach	Old woman
Cas chrom	The old Hebridean foot-plough
Ceilidh	A meeting for gossip and song
Ciamar a tha?	How are you?
Crack	A gossipy chat
Ealasaid	Elizabeth
Mo ghaoil	My dear
Pliach	A rough home-made dibber for planting potatoes
Skart	The shag, or green cormorant
Strupak	A cup of tea and a bite to eat
Tha e breagh or He breeah	It is fine
Tha e fliuch or He fluke	It is wet
Tha e fuar or He fooar	It is cold
Tha gu math	I am well

The Hills is Lonely

The Hills is Lonely

Lillian Beckwith

Decorations by Douglas Hall

Contents

1. *Arrival*

IF YOU have never experienced a stormy winter's night in the
Hebrides, you can have no idea of the sort of weather which I encountered when I arrived, travel-worn and weary, at the deserted little jetty
where I was to await the boat which would carry me across to 'Incredible Island'. It was a terrible night. A night to make one yearn for the
fierce, bright heat of an ample fire; for carpet slippers and a crossword
puzzle. Yet here I stood, alone in the alien, tempestuous blackness,
sodden, cold and dejected, my teeth chattering uncontrollably. On
three sides of me the sea roared and plunged frenziedly, and a strong
wind, which shrieked and wailed with theatrical violence, tore and
buffeted at my clothes and fought desperately to throw me off balance.
The swift, relentless rain stung my eyes, my face and my legs; it
trickled from my ruined hat to seep in cheeky rivulets down my
neck; it found the ventilation holes in my waterproof and crept
exploratively under my armpits.

Somewhere out on the turbulent water a light flashed briefly.
Peering through screwed-up eyes, I watched with fascinated horror as
it appeared and vanished again and again. With stiff fingers I switched
on my torch; the battery was new and the bright beam pierced the
blurring rain for a few yards. Quickly I switched it off. To a faint-
hearted landlubber like myself the sound of the sea was sufficiently
menacing; the sight of it was absolutely malevolent. Nostalgia overwhelmed me. Why, oh why, had I been so foolhardy—so headstrong?
And this was supposed to be for the good of my health! Why was I not
sitting with Mary in the cosy living-room of our town flat, dunking
ginger-nuts into cups of steaming hot tea and following from my own
armchair the exploits of my favourite detective? The second question
was simple enough to answer. The first presented more difficulty.

An illness some months previously had led my doctor to order me away to the country for a long complete rest. A timely windfall in the shape of a small annuity had made it possible for me to give up a not very lucrative teaching post in a smoky North of England town, and look around for a suitable place where, within the limits of my purse, I might, in the doctor's words, 'rest without being too lazy, and laze without being too restive'.

My advertisement in a well-known periodical had brought an avalanche of tempting offers. England, it appeared, was liberally dotted with miniature Paradises for anyone seeking recuperative solitude, and I had almost decided to remove myself temporarily to a Kentish farmhouse when the postman brought a letter which changed my plans completely. The envelope bore a Hebridean postmark; the handwriting, though straggly, was fairly legible, but the words themselves painted a picture as vivid and inviting as a railway poster. It ran thus:

Bruach.

Dear Madam,

      Its just now I saw your advert when I got the book for the knitting pattern I wanted from my cousin Catriona. I am sorry I did not write sooner if you are fixed up if you are not in any way fixed up I have a good good house stone and tiles and my brother Ruari who will wash down with lime twice every year. Ruari is married and lives just by. She is not damp. I live by myself and you could have the room that is not a kitchen and bedroom reasonable. I was in the kitchen of the lairds house till lately when he was changed God rest his soul the poor old gentleman that he was. You would be very welcomed. I have a cow also for milk and eggs and the minister at the manse will be referee if you wish such.

Yours affectionately,
Morag McDugan.

PS. She is not thatched.

Mary, reading the letter over my shoulder, dissolved into laughter. We were still chuckling when we went to bed that night, I to dream of a minister in full clerical garb, tearing frantically around a football pitch, blowing a referee's whistle, while two teams of lime-washed men played football with a cow's egg—a thing resembling a Dutch cheese—and an old man changed furtively in the kitchen.

Deciding privately to postpone acceptance of the Kentish offer, I wrote next morning to Morag McDugan, excusing myself to Mary by saying that a further reply might provide more amusement. I had to admit to myself, however, that the ingenuousness of the letter had so delighted me that the idea of a possible visit had already taken my fancy. The reply from Morag (already we were using her Christian name) did not disappoint us. Her advice regarding travelling arrangements was clear; obviously she had been instructed by a seasoned traveller, but her answers to my questions about quietness and distance from the sea, etc., were Morag's own.

Surely its that quiet here even the sheeps themselves on the hills is lonely and as to the sea its that near I use it myself every day for the refusals.

Mary's eyelids flickered.

'What does she have to say about the water supply?'

'*There's a good well right by me and no beasts at it,*' I read.

Mary shuddered expressively.

'I'm glad you're not going there anyway, Becky,' she said.

'I believe I am though,' I said suddenly, but I was thinking out loud, not really having made up my mind.

She stared at me, incredulous. 'But you can't, Becky!' she expostulated. 'Surely you can see that?'

'Why not?' I asked defensively. 'I'm interested in meeting people and finding out how they live and I've never yet crossed the border into Scotland.'

'Don't be a fool,' argued Mary. 'I admit the woman sounds fun, and so does the place; but it's ridiculous to let yourself be carried away like that. It wouldn't be in the least funny to live under the conditions suggested by those letters.'

'I'm sure it would be even funnier,' I replied, with a flippancy I was far from actually feeling. 'After all, there can't be many dual-purpose cows in the world and it's time someone did something to cheer up those poor lonely sheeps.'

Mary giggled. 'Don't be a fool!' she reiterated.

Her words goaded me to a decision.

'That's just what I'm going to be,' I replied.

Mary was not the only person to remonstrate with me on my decision to forgo the indisputable attractions of a Kentish farmhouse for the doubtful charms of a Hebridean croft. My doctor was equally incredulous when I told him of my plans.

'I don't think you're very wise,' he said seriously. 'Friends of mine who've been up in the Hebrides tell me the inhabitants are only half civilized.'

'Well,' I replied gaily, 'I'm going to find out for myself,' and added: 'Really, I'm quite determined.'

He stared at me for a few moments, then shrugged his shoulders and rose. 'In that case,' he warned me, 'I think you should let me inoculate you against typhoid.'

Inoculated I was, and now, standing embittered and lonely on the pier, I was heartily amazed that I could ever willingly have embarked on such a venture, and heartily glad neither the doctor nor Mary could witness my plight.

The light I had been watching drew unsteadily nearer and with sickening dread I realized that it belonged to the masthead of a tiny boat, and that its appearance and disappearance was due to the boat lifting and plunging on the huge seas. Slowly she lunged nearer, the dark outline of her bow leaping recklessly until it seemed impossible that she could come closer without being smashed to pieces on the stone jetty. But suddenly she was alongside and a figure clad in streaming oilskins and thigh-boots jumped ashore, a rope in his hands.

'Are you off the train?' he shouted as he hitched the rope around a tiny bollard.

The question was directed at me. 'Yes,' I yelled back. 'Is this the ferry?'

'Aye.' He spat with all the dignity of a man presenting a visiting card and obviously considered it sufficient introduction. 'Iss there anybody else for the ferry?' Again the question was for me and I peered vaguely into the surrounding darkness.

'I've no idea!' I yelled.

The man grunted. 'Wass there many on the train?'

Dimly I began to appreciate the degree of familiarity I must expect in my new surroundings.

'There were quite a few people on the train,' I replied, 'but they've all disappeared.' Impulsively I glanced behind and immediately regretted having done so, for the movement had deflected some of the rivulets along chilling new courses.

'Have you been here long?'

I felt that the questions were becoming pointless and was tempted to grossly overstate the ten minutes proclaimed by my watch. But I replied truthfully. Again the man spat.

'You'd best be gettin' aboard, then, if you're goin' the night,' he growled.

This was undoubtedly an example of the dourness I had been warned to expect from the Hebrideans, but to me at this moment it seemed particularly uncalled for. Apprehensively I groped forward. There was a surging gulf of water between the boat and the jetty and I was terrified of stepping down into it.

'Watch your step now!' commanded another voice, brisk and imperious, from the darkness, as I hesitated, waiting for the deck to leap high enough for me to clamber aboard without having to perform something in the nature of a gymnastic feat.

'I can't see!' I wailed. Almost before the words were out of my mouth I was seized by two strong arms and propelled unceremoniously over the gunwale and down into the well of the boat. The calves of my legs came up against something solid and I collapsed heavily. I managed to gasp out my thanks but need not have wasted my breath, for the men, having seen me and my belongings stowed safely aboard, went about their own business. Miserable with fright, cold and vexation, every muscle strained and taut, I clung grimly to the seat to prevent myself from being thrown overboard with each lurch of the boat. There were no other passengers. 'No one else,' I thought dully, 'would be such a fool as to cross on a night like this.' The thought galvanized me into action.

'I'm coming off!' I shouted. My voice shrilled with panic. 'I'm not going to cross tonight. It's too rough.'

'Ach, sit you down,' the answer came scornfully; 'you canna' go jumpin' on and off boats for fun on a night like this.'

'Fun!' I retorted angrily, and was about to tell them the extent of my pleasure when a suffocating stream of spray filled my mouth and effectively choked the words. The boatman may have intended his sarcasm to be reassuring, but before I could attempt further argument there was a staccato command, the men leaped aboard and the slowly ticking engine pulsed into life. We were off, and I must face whatever might come.

That we had left the jetty and were moving I could guess from the sound of the engine, but from the terrific impact of the waves on the bow I considered it more than likely that we were being driven back-wards. The boat seemed sometimes to rear supplicatingly on her stern, and then nose-dive so steeply that I was certain each time that her bow could never lift through the water again. My agonized thoughts compared the performance with that of Blackpool's 'Big Dipper', a thrill which I had endured once and subsequently avoided. This, however, was a succession of 'Big Dippers' and my stomach tied itself into knots at each abysmal plunge. While the boat rolled and pitched dramatically the sea belched over each gunwale in turn. Icy water was already swirling and eddying around my ankles. 'How much longer?' I wondered wretchedly. Soon I was sobbing and, in an excess of cowardice, praying alternately for safety and a quick death. I felt terribly sick but fear kept my muscles too tense to permit me to vomit.

· A dark shape loomed up beside me, and quite suddenly I knew that disaster was upon us; that this man had come to tell me to save myself as best I could; that the boat was sinking. I smothered a scream and, wrenching the torch from my pocket, looked wildly around for lifebelts. I could see none. The man continued to stand, still and silent, and I guessed that he too was gripped by a fear as strong as my own. I was shaking from head to foot.

'What is it?' I asked weakly.

'Tenpence.' His voice was crisply matter-of-fact.

'Tenpence?' My own voice burst from my throat in an incredulous squeak and relief flooded through my quaking body like a nip of hot brandy. I could almost have laughed. Foolishly I loosed my hold of the seat and a sudden lurch of the boat threw me heavily against him.

'Steady,' he reproved me.

'Tell that to the boat,' I replied pertly. With a feeling akin to elation I fumbled for my purse and handed the man a shilling. Gravely he sought the twopence change and handed it to me along with the ticket. The latter I promptly lost; but the two pennies I clutched like a talisman. It seemed fantastic. Twopence change on a night like this! Twopence change when I had been prepared to abandon my all! I began to feel quite exuberant.

The man disappeared and again I was left alone, but now I could at times glimpse the island jetty with its single light and what looked like a pair of car headlamps piercing the darkness beyond. Though I still had to cling to my seat as the boat performed acrobatics more suited to an aeroplane; though I was not one whit less cold and wet than I had been a few minutes previously, the purchase of a tenpenny ticket had given me new confidence; for had I not heard enough about the character of the Scot to be certain that the tenpence stood a good chance of reaching its destination safely? Otherwise I felt sure the weight of the money would have been left with my body, not added to heavy oilskins and sea-boots.

Like a steeplechaser that had scented its stable the boat romped alongside the jetty and I was promptly hauled out with as little ceremony as I had been stowed in. The headlights which I had noticed earlier had vanished temporarily, but now they flashed on again, spotlighting my woebegone appearance. The slam of a car door was followed by a rich masculine voice.

'Would it be yourself for McDugan's, madam?' it asked.

'It would,' I replied thankfully, almost ready to fall upon the speaker's neck.

'Come this way if you please,' the voice invited politely. 'I have the taxi you were wanting.'

A large overcoated figure picked up my two cases, shepherded me towards the headlamps and, with a flourish worthy of a Rolls, opened the door of an ancient roadster. It offered indifferent shelter, but I climbed in gratefully, and from somewhere in the rear the driver thoughtfully produced a rug which, though coarse and hairy and reeking horribly of mildew, was welcome if only to muffle the knocking of my knees. As we drove away from the pier the wind rushed and volleyed both inside and outside the car; silvery rain sluiced down the windscreen and visibility was restricted to the semi-circle of road lit by the headlamps. The driver, who chatted amiably the whole time, kindly informed me that the road followed the coastline most of the way, and I had to accept his assurance that it was a 'ghrand fiew in fine weather'.

For some miles the car ploughed noisily on, then it turned off abruptly into a ridiculously narrow lane, bounded on either side by high stone walls, vaulted a couple of hump-backed bridges in quick succession and drew slowly to a stop. I wondered if we had run out of petrol, for there were no lights or houses visible; nothing but road and walls and the rain.

'This is what you were wanting,' announced the driver, pushing open the door and slithering out from his seat. He could not have made a more erroneous statement. This was certainly not what I was wanting, but it looked, unfortunately, as though this was what I was getting.

Pulling his cap well down on the side of his face exposed to the wind and exaggeratedly drawing up his coat collar, he uttered a mild curse and flung open the rear door of the car, where he commenced to wrestle with my luggage. In the glare of the headlights the rain still swooped vengefully down as though each drop bore some personal animosity to each and every particle of the gritty lane. In all my life I had never seen such full-blooded rain!

With a despairing shudder I pulled my waterproof closer about my shoulders and peered anxiously over the driver's back, hoping fervently that he had stopped as near to the entrance gate as was possible. I was disappointed. On each side of the car the stone walls loomed up impenetrably, and I could see that it was not so much that the walls themselves were high, as that the road was a cutting, leaving an earth bank on either side thus forming a fairly inaccessible barrier of about six foot in height between the lane and the field.

'I can't see any entrance,' I complained fretfully.

The driver paused in his attempt to lever my second case through the door of the car. 'Oh no,' he assured me with nimble complacency; 'there's no entrance at all here, but you'll just climb over the wall, d'y' see? The house is beyond there.'

I could not have been more astounded had he told me I must wait for the drawbridge to be lowered! I began to realize that acrobatics were a necessary accomplishment for visitors to Bruach.

'I can't climb walls!' I protested, 'and that one is a good six feet high. Surely,' I went on, 'there must be some other entrance.'

'Oh surely, madam,' he replied in conciliatory tones, 'but the tide's in just now, and you'd be after swimming for it if you were going to use that tonight.' He permitted himself a sardonic chuckle.

'What a welcome!' I muttered.

'Ach, you'll soon nip over the wall easy enough,' the driver assured me blandly. 'I'll give you a leg up myself.'

Now while I do not wish to give the impression that my figure is in any way grotesque, I must disclaim that it is by any means the sort of figure which nips easily over six-foot walls. Agility is not, and never was, my strong point; my figure, though sturdy, being somewhat rotund for anything but a very moderate degree of athleticism. I viewed the prospect of climbing, even with a willing 'leg up' from the driver, with misgivings.

Despondently I climbed out of the car. The wind caught me off guard and almost succeeded in unbalancing me, and the rain recommenced its furious assault on my waterproof. From the darkness beyond and uncomfortably close came the pounding and sucking of breakers on the shore. To add to my dismay I perceived that a fast-flowing ditch coursed riotously along the base of the wall. I positively yearned for town pavements.

The driver nonchalantly stepped over the ditch (his legs were long) and pulled himself upwards. He was a tall man and the top of the wall was on a level with his nose. He turned an enquiring gaze on me.

'They'll be expectin' you likely?' he asked. I agreed that it was extremely likely, for I had sent Morag a wire announcing the probable time of my arrival.

Once again the driver turned to the wall, and gave a stentorian yell, the volume and unexpectedness of which outrivalled the storm and very nearly caused me to make a premature and undesirably close acquaintance with the ditch. Immediately a shaft of yellow light gleamed in the distance as a door was opened and a voice of equal power, though indisputably feminine, called out interrogatively. The driver answered and in spite of the violence of the weather a conversation was carried on, though as I could make out no word of it I concluded it to be in Gaelic.

The shaft of light was blotted out as the door was shut and then a lantern came swinging rhythmically towards us. A moment later a figure surmounted the wall and climbed quickly down to stand beside me. This then was Morag, my future landlady.

'Well, well, Miss Peckwitt is it? And how are you?' My hand was lifted in a firm grip and shaken vigorously and I only just managed to evade a full-lipped kiss.

'My, my, but what a night to welcome a body. Surely you must be drookit,' she lamented cheerfully. I thought that 'drookit' probably meant 'dead' and I agreed that I was—almost.

'Almost? Sure you must be quite,' she asserted. I decided that 'drookit' meant 'drowned'.

'Ach, but I have a nice fire waitin' on you,' continued Morag happily, 'and you'll be warrm and dry in no time at all.' The softened

consonants were very noticeable and to my Sassenach ears the rolled
'r's' sounded as over-emphasized as those of some opera singers.

Morag held up the lantern so that for a moment we were able to
study each other's faces and I was surprised, in view of her agility, to
see that hers was dry and wrinkled with age, while the wisps of hair
escaping from the scarf she had wound round her head were snowy
white. She dropped my hand and turned to the driver.

'Will we just swing her up and over between us?' she asked him.

'Aye,' agreed the driver shortly. I bridled and stepped back a pace
but, ignoring me, they bent and together swung my two suitcases up
and on to the wall. They were swiftly followed by Morag who lifted
them down to the other side; then, lissom as a two-year-old, she
leaped lightly down again. I gasped at the effortless ease with which
she accomplished the feat but her performance did nothing to allay
my own apprehension.

'Is there no other way?' I asked timidly.

'No indeed,' she replied, and pointed down the road; 'the wee gate's
down there, but the watter's up and all round it at this hour. It's a pity
you couldna' have come when the tide was out.' It occurred to me
that tides were going to play a very important part in my new life.
I smothered a sigh.

'Ach, but you'll find this way easy enough when you put your feets
to it,' Morag went on in an encouraging tone. 'Now come.' Cautiously I stepped across the ditch and put my 'feets' to it. 'Now then,'
directed my landlady with heavy pleasantry, 'one fine feet here . . .
now another fine feet here . . . that's lovely just . . . now another fine
feet here. . . .' Undoubtedly Morag believed her new guest to be a
quadruped. The driver who was waiting on the other side of the wall
to haul me over also clucked encouragement. I felt a firm grasp on
my ankle. 'Now just another feet here and you'll be near done,'
instructed Morag. She was right! In the next instant one of my 'fine
feet' slipped on the treacherous wet stone and I was left clinging desperately with my hands, my legs flaying the air, while the wind lifted
my skirts above my head and the rain committed atrocities on those
parts of my body which had not before been directly exposed to such
vengeance. The driver, seeing my predicament, came to the rescue
and gripping both arms firmly hoisted me bodily over the wall. My
feet landed on solid earth. Very wet earth admittedly, but I cared not
so long as I had to do no more climbing. Instantly Morag was beside

me. 'You're all right?' she enquired anxiously; 'you didna' hurt your-self?'

I assured her that I was in no way hurt; though I knew that, even if I had not suffered, my stockings at least were irreparably damaged.

'That's all right, then. I'll tell Ruari to see to your boxes directly.'

'Oh yes—Ruari,' I echoed, and had a fleeting vision of a freshly lime-washed Ruari braving this torrential rain, and began to feel better again. After all, I told myself, I had been roughly handled but then I had planned this as something of an adventure.

Opening my purse, I gave the driver his fare plus a moderate tip. He demurred at the latter but on my insistence thanked me courteously and pocketed it. 'It is indeed,' I thought, 'like coming to a different world, where even the taxi-drivers refuse to be tipped.'

Guided by Morag's lantern I followed her across the sodden grass, over cobblestones and into the tiny hall of the cottage where a candle burned lopsidedly in the draught from some hidden crevice. Taking off my dripping outdoor clothes I hung them on the antlers of a pathetic-looking stag's head. Morag opened the door of a room on our left and ushered me inside. 'The room that wasn't a kitchen' was a neat lamplit place with an immense fire burning brightly in the well-polished grate. Half on the fire, half on the hob, a kettle stood spouting steam and rattling its lid in ill-concealed impatience, promising a speedy brew of tea. A small table was spread with a white cloth and on it my supper was laid invitingly. After the appalling conditions outside the whole place gave a welcome so much greater than I had expected that I exclaimed over it impulsively. I dropped into a chair and ignoring its formidable creakings watched while Morag, with a self-satisfied smile on her face, busied herself about the meal.

My landlady was a small woman with a broad back which, though not exactly bent, gave one the impression that it was accustomed to carrying many burdens. The rest of her figure was hardly discernible beneath the bulk of clothing she wore, but her movements were lively enough despite a gait which I can only describe as 'running with one leg and walking with the other'. Her hair, as I have said, was white, her face wizened and freckled. Her eyes, when they were not being soulfully blue, were as mischievous as a small boy's, while her hands were horny as a man's, the stubby fingers resembling calcified sausages. Her clothes, or what I could see of them, consisted of a thick tweed jacket over a homespun skirt, the front of which was partially concealed by a now sodden apron, for she had apparently added nothing to her attire when she left the house to come to my assistance. I judged, however, from the proportion of bulk in relation to size, that there were in all probability a great many insulating layers between her skin and her outer garments, which were no doubt as efficient under Island weather conditions as the more conventional waterproof.

The tea brewed, Morag departed, having first assured herself that she could at the moment do nothing further for me beyond promising to stir Ruari into bringing my cases indoors. Accordingly, soon after she had gone I heard the front door bang, and even while I sat sipping my third cup of tea there was a rumble of voices followed by a thudding on the stairs which indicated that my bags were being carried up to my bedroom. I repressed a desire to peep. A few minutes later there was a knock on my door and Morag entered.

'I'm just sayin' I didna' bring Ruari and Lachy in to see you tonight, seeing you'll be awful tired,' she began. I protested feebly. 'You see,' she went on apologetically, 'Ruari's that deaf his shoutin' near splits the ears off you, and I'm after tellin' him to keep his mouth shut on the stairs for sure he grunts like a bull.'

'But who is Lachy?' I asked, stifling a yawn.

'Ach, he's the other half of the boat with Ruari,' explained Morag obscurely.

'And what time will you be for takin' your breakfast?' she asked. I suggested about eight-thirty.

'Half past eight,' she agreed; 'and if the Lord spares me I'll have your fire lit by eight then.' I glanced at her enquiringly.

'Aren't you feeling well then?' I asked.

'I'm feelin' fine,' she answered with some surprise; 'why, d'you think I'm lookin' poorly?'

'Not at all,' I rejoined hurriedly, 'but when you said "if the Lord spares me", I thought perhaps you were not feeling quite well.'

'I'm feelin' quite well tonight,' replied Morag piously; 'but who can tell if the Lord may call any one of us before the morn comes; and if He chooses to call me in the night then I canna' light your fire in the mornin', can I?'

'I rather take that for granted,' I said with a smile.

'Ah indeed, it's no wise to take anythin' for granted with the Lord,' she rebuked me, and then added determinedly: 'But I'll have your fire lit for eight certain if I'm spared,' and as though to underline the words she closed the door firmly behind her.

After the long journey, the fright, the bitter cold and now the warmth and food, I became unconquerably sleepy. Wearily I climbed the narrow linoleum-covered stairs to the bedroom which Morag had already pointed out to me. In the room a lamp had been lighted and burned dimly, but more than that everything appeared to be clean and comfortable I could not have told that night. Unpacking the minimum of necessities, I undressed and tumbled into bed, where I lay for a time listening to the storm outside. Conscious of a queer little thrill, I turned out the lamp. It was the first time in my life that I had actually used an oil-lamp and I was not at all sure whether to blow or keep turning the knob until the flame was completely extinguished. I managed a successful compromise, and as I dropped back on to the pillows and drifted into sleep I was aware of the rain spattering against the window and drumming with dogged persistence on the tiled roof.

2. *Initiation*

I AWOKE after what seemed a very short time to the realization that the rain had ceased and that chill, grey daylight was filtering through the lace curtains of my window. My head still echoed the rhythmic jogging of the train, for I am one of those unfortunates who, if they travel five hundred miles in actuality, travel at least another thousand during sleep.

The bed was cosy enough to make the prospect of leaving it seem unattractive and I lay sleepily surveying my room and listening with drowsy intentness to the sounds of the morning. There was a clanking of cans, which I assumed to be milk-pails; the impatient clucking and questioning of hens, interspersed with loud flutterings of wings; a strange intermittent wailing noise which I was quite unable to identify; doors opening and closing and dishes clattering: sounds which seemed to indicate that the Lord had seen fit to spare my landlady for another day's work, and also that the poultry still awaited their morning feed.

The hands of my watch were pointing to half past eight when there were footsteps on the stairs followed by a knock at my bedroom door.

'I've brought you watter and she's fine and hot,' Morag's voice announced.

'Take her away!' I entreated with an involuntary shudder. 'I shall wash downstairs where it's warmer.'

Morag began speaking again, but her words were drowned by an acrimonious bellow which reverberated up and down the stairs and almost dislodged me from my bed.

'Sorry,' I apologized when there was a moment's lull, 'but I didn't catch what you were saying.'

'That's just Ruari,' explained Morag with patient resignation, 'and I'm just sayin' he's fine and warm already for I have him blazin' up the chimney with a dose of paraffin.'

Her footsteps retreated down the stairs. After a moment of confused horror I succeeded in disentangling this rather surprising piece of information; though had I supposed my landlady to be capable of such villainy the strength of Ruari's bellow would undoubtedly have lent credence to her statement.

As I reached the bottom stair Morag came out of her kitchen bearing a steaming bowl of mash.

'Sure I hope you slept well after your long journey,' she greeted me. I agreed that I had.

'Something smells awfully good,' I observed.

'It's just the meal I'm after scaldin' for the hens,' said Morag; 'though it smells that good many's the time I'm takin' a lump of it for my own breakfast. Indeed it fairly makes my teeths watter.'

Although the latter part of her reply was patently untrue—over her shoulder I could see her 'teeths' adorning the dresser and they looked positively arid—I could not doubt the temptation of the smell, and had the bowl been a little cleaner I might perhaps have sampled it for myself.

Among the chorus of noises outside I again noticed the strange wailing call I had heard earlier.

'What sort of an animal makes that queer noise?' I asked.

The ghost of a smile curved Morag's lips. 'Why, that's my cockerel,' she explained.

'Really?' I said, then, seeing her smile broaden at my ignorance, added lamely: 'I thought cockerels always said cock-a-doodle-doo, but that one sounds as though he's been crossed with a circular saw.'

'Ach, he's just young yet,' she excused him; 'another six months and he'll be cock-a-doodle-dooin' as well as you can yourself.'

It became plain that my landlady was prepared for a long conversation but I could not, as she did, ignore the greedy clamour of the hens who, in their eagerness for food, had thronged the tiny hall and were endeavouring to reach perching positions on the edge of the mash-bowl. Out of consideration for the hens as well as concern for the state of the floor I decided to withdraw and hurried into my room.

Now, without the mellowness of lamplight and the contrast of the storm outside, it struck me as repulsively ugly. The floor covering was shabby; the two easy chairs were grey with age and, on closer examination, I discovered that their ability to support the human frame was due solely to the circumstance that a famous brand of margarine was packed in wooden boxes. A yellow-grained sideboard took up nearly the whole of one wall of the room; a dreadful monstrosity of a thing, which looked for all the world as though it had been set upon by someone suffering from a fit of delirium tremens, using as a weapon a paint brush dipped alternately in yellow ochre and black treacle.

The table was glaringly home-made and, though a cloth covered its major crudities, I was soon to learn that none of its four legs matched in shape or length and that the only way to keep it steady while eating was to balance it on my knees. The wallpaper, which last night had seemed self-effacing, now intruded its garish pattern of vermilion buttercups with a frieze of neglected false teeth, though the latter were no doubt meant to be autumn-tinted leaves.

Had I embarked on my venture with the full approval of my friends I might have permitted myself some doubts as to the probability of my remaining long with Morag. As it was I determined to look only on the more comforting side and, after reassuring myself that the curtains, the cushions and the tablecloth were fresh and clean, turned to admire the old-fashioned grate with its deep fire of glowing peat, the gleaming brass fire-irons and the clock which had already ticked its way through a century of time.

A knock on the door heralded Morag's appearance with my breakfast tray, the sight of which effectively dispersed any misgivings for the time being, and soon I was settling down to do full justice to the excellent meal she had provided. There was porridge—my first experience of porridge made with fresh-ground oatmeal—there was cream, thick, smooth and rich; there was sugar, though my landlady shook her head disapprovingly as I spooned the latter on to my plate.

'Ach, mo ghaoil,' she chided, 'but you were never meant to eat sugar with porridge. Sure it'll spoil the grand taste of it.'

'I should never manage it without,' I retorted and tucked into my well-filled plate with a most uninvalidish appetite.

Next a dish of succulent-smelling bacon and eggs was placed before me. As this had been keeping warm on the hob beside the fire

I easily ignored the fact that the dish was signed distinctly with a greasy black thumbprint. After all, had I not realized even while contemplating my Island sojourn that I could not afford to be over-fastidious? My suggestion that she should join me in a cup of tea, Morag accepted with alacrity.

'I don't know that I ever refused a cup of tea yet, supposin' it was my twentieth,' she admitted ruefully as she helped herself from the ample brown teapot. Subsequent experience convinced me that twenty cups per day was grossly understating Morag's capacity for tea, and that the enormous tea-caddy which dominated the mantelpiece in her own room was not there solely for ornament.

After breakfast, as the weather showed a distinct improvement, I set out on a tour of investigation. My own waterproof and shoes were still sodden from their experience of the night before, so my landlady offered me a spare oilskin and a pair of gumboots. I accepted them dubiously, fearing that the boots would be too heavy for my unpractised feet and that the oilskin would be only an encumbrance. But once the initial awkwardness had passed, I wished very much that my friends, particularly Mary, could see me as I clumped about in the strange outfit.

Out of doors the view was unimpressive, for though the rain had ceased it had merely given way to clouds of mist which rolled in from the sea and hovered sluggishly over the surrounding moors, intensifying the roar of the waves and curiously deflecting the sounds of the land. Morag, hopping eagerly about me with her odd gait, pointed out the approximate bounds of her domain; approximate because she shared a croft with her brother Ruari, Morag owning one-quarter and Ruari the remaining three-quarters, with no recognizable boundary between the two. I asked how they managed about letters, since both houses were number fifteen—the numbers being given to crofts only —and the surname common to both. The explanation was simple; the postman was thoroughly familiar with the goings-on of each household and could thus decide for himself which letters were for which person. He rarely made a mistake, but, all the same, I was delighted to learn that official correspondence was addressed to Morag at 'One-quarter of number fifteen', and to her brother at 'Three-quarters of number fifteen'. The preciseness of officialdom is commendable but it does look slightly ludicrous on an envelope.

We strolled down towards the elusive entrance gate, which turned out to be nothing more than a gap in the drystone wall across which was placed an old iron bedstead. Though the wind had dropped away to nothing and Morag murmured something about the tide being halfway out, the swell still slapped and sucked around the bottom of the three stone steps which led from the garden to the shore. Much as I disliked the idea of scaling walls, I decided that climbing would be less destructive to morale than being confined to the house except at negotiable states of the tide.

'It seems to be a choice of two evils,' I remarked sadly to Morag.

'Ach, by the time you've been here a month, you'll be leapin' over yon dyke like a goat,' she predicted cheerfully. Reflecting upon my performance of the night before, I had a vague suspicion that my landlady was being ironical.

For some minutes I had been watching a boat which was now pulling in to the shore a little to our right. Besides the man at the oars it contained five or six women of varying ages, each of whom nursed at least one large milk-pail. As the boat grounded, the women stepped into the water, grasped the gunwales and hauled the boat up the beach as though it were a light toy. In answer to my look of enquiry, Morag explained that some of the cattle were grazed on a small tidal island and, despite the tides being roughly half an hour later each day, the crofters preferred to wait and go by boat to milk rather than walk the two or three miles round the shore. The arrangement struck me as being haphazard, but I had not then discovered that in the Hebrides the cattle are wonderfully accommodating; that time is practically non-existent and that the clocks are as much out of touch with reality as are their owners.

The women milkers, frankly curious, stood holding their heavy pails. As much for their sakes as my own I decided to return to the house and there asked Morag to direct me to the post office.

'Well, you'll need to walk slowly, or she'll no be back from the milkin',' she instructed me.

'What time does she open then?' I asked, for it was nearly eleven o'clock.

'I believe it's nine o'clock rightly,' she answered, 'but the cows have to be milked and she canna' be in two places at once, can she now?'

I admitted the logic of her statement and, unwilling to incur the displeasure of the postmistress, I walked very slowly in the direction indicated to me, deriving a furtive and infantile pleasure from plodding through the deepest puddles and squelching through the thickest mud.

The crofters' houses, some low and thatched, some two-storied and slated, were scattered along both sides of the road. Through their open doors were wafted the sounds of clinking dishes, thudding feet and Gaelic voices engaged in fierce altercation; sounds which ceased with suspicious suddenness as I approached. Once or twice I turned quickly, hoping to see some hidden watcher betrayed by the twitch of a curtain, until I realized that there were no curtains to twitch. Inquisitive dogs appeared in every doorway; collies and cairns; some venturing so far as to smell at my heels, others content to hail me from the sanctuary of their own doorsteps. Here and there a tethered cow grazed, placidly indifferent to its restricting chain. Sheep nibbled contentedly in the circle allowed them by their short ropes. In front of one house a horse moved gingerly, revealing the fine-meshed chain stretching from its hind leg to a stake some distance away. A turkey gobbled forlornly and stood stork-like on one leg, its other leg being secured by a length of parcel string to a nearby bush. The crofters appeared to have brought the science of tethering down to a fine art, and every kind of animal seemed to accept a length of rope and a stake as a matter of course.

Surrounding each of the houses was a small plot of land bounded by a drystone wall, which in England we should call a garden, but which Morag had grandly referred to as 'the park'. This 'park' was distinct from the rest of the croft, which was itself also bounded by the inevitable drystone walls. In every case the entrance gate was achieved by knocking down a few of the stones and placing across the gap an old iron bedstead. Some of the bedsteads were ancient and rusted; others, obviously newly discarded, still sported their ornamental brass knobs and rings. They were of every conceivable pattern, so that I was able to amuse myself by trying to guess which design I should come upon next. That night, when I wrote to Mary telling her of my journey and my reception and impressions so far, I added: *Just imagine, every house I've seen has an old bedstead for an entrance gate and I've already counted at least twenty-two!*

A small sign, 'Post Office', led me to a corrugated-iron shed. I knocked on the door; there was no response, and despite repeated knockings the place remained still and silent. I looked again at the notice. Yes, it definitely said 'Post Office'. I continued knocking, but still nothing happened. A little way along the road some small boys were playing a scuffling game of football and, thinking that they might know the whereabouts of the postmistress, I went towards them. I was not really surprised to find that their football was a much battered brass bed-knob. They ceased their game as I approached, but my question stunned them into an embarrassed silence. I repeated it.

'She'll be at her house likely.' One boy vouchsafed the information shyly.

'Is the post office closed then?' I asked, gesturing towards the iron hut.

'That's not the post office just now.' The boy's voice strengthened as he gained courage. 'That's just the post office when there's tourists about in the summer. In the winter the stamps would all stick up with the damp in there, but she'll give them to you from her house.' He indicated a small cottage at the end of a cart track through one of the crofts, but a glance at my watch told me that the postmistress must remain undisturbed until after lunch. I quickly retraced my steps homewards.

In the cooking of my lunch Morag had excelled herself and once again the tablecloth was snowy white. The helping of meat was liberal enough for three appetites, but unfortunately it was served on an afternoon-tea plate, and even without the addition of vegetables the gravy was threatening to spill over the edge. I suggested a larger plate, hastily reassuring Morag, as I saw her woebegone expression, that it was not the inadequacy of the dinner that was disturbing me. Eagerly she hurried from the room, soon returning with an ordinary-sized plate which she was surreptitiously polishing on a corner of her apron. It was a pretty plate and I exclaimed delightedly at its attractive border of what I then took to be tiny yellow crocuses; their subsequent appearance and disappearance, however, was so perplexing that I reluctantly came to recognize them to be splashes of egg yolk, and was inordinately thankful that the green leaves at least showed signs of permanency. I complimented Morag on her cooking; the less said about her dish-washing the better.

I was awakened from my after-dinner doze by the noise of the front door opening and the rumble of a motor. Through the window

I could see a lorry, loaded high with coal, jolting slowly down the road past Ruari's house and towards the sea. I went into the hall where Morag was hurriedly tying a scarf over her head.

'It's yon man with the year's coal,' she grumbled in answer to my question; 'and here it is a Saturday too, the rascal! Another two hours and the tide will be takin' it away on me.'

I offered to help but, though it was plain from her manner that she would welcome assistance, Morag refused my offer after a disparaging glance at my neat suit. I changed into an old skirt and jacket and hurried outside. The tide was out now and the entrance gate was high and dry; beside it on the shingle a huge mound of coal had been dumped. Morag was already engaged in bitter recriminations with the lorry driver, whom I recognized as my taxi-driver of the previous evening. They broke off as I approached and the man greeted me with polite warmth.

'It's goin' to rain,' he told me cheerfully, with a knowing glance at the sky.

'Do you think so?' I asked.

'Certain to,' replied the driver emphatically. 'Now, Miss Peckwitt, I'll tell you a good weather sign: if ever you should see trees up in the sky you may be sure it's goin' to rain before very long.'

I thought that if ever I saw trees up in the sky I should expect to see pigs flying in and out of them; but I nodded and stared intelligently at a cloud-patched ceiling of grey, deeming it better to accept his prediction without comment.

'I canna' give you tea, if I'm to get this in before the watter's up,' snapped Morag to the driver.

The latter jumped hastily into the cab of the lorry. 'I couldn't stay for tea supposin' it was waitin' on me,' he retorted. 'I have two tons for the manse tonight yet.'

'Two tons for the manse?' shrilled Morag. 'They'll never take it from you tonight.'

'Then they'll do without it for longer than they care to,' said the driver with a sardonic chuckle. He let in the clutch and the lorry jolted away along the foreshore.

'So the taxi-driver is the lorry-driver too,' I observed to Morag as we set to work with shovels and pails.

'He's not just the taxi-driver and the lorry-driver,' replied Morag caustically, 'but he's the coal merchant, the carrier, the undertaker and the garage'; she counted off his trades on her fingers, 'and I don't know what else besides.'

I began to feel slightly embarrassed. 'He must be quite wealthy in that case,' I said.

'Wealthy?' she returned, 'Why, if I had as many halfpence as he has pounds I'd be comfortable for the rest of my life.'

I recalled the man's disinclination to accept my shilling tip and was glad that my exertions over the coal could account for the flush which spread over my neck and face.

'And swank!' continued Morag, rubbing salt into the wound. 'Why, he's that much swank on him as would suit a duke.'

Abruptly I changed the subject.

'How much coal is there here?' I asked, eyeing the prodigious heap.

'Two tons,' she lamented, 'and in less than two hours the tide will be away with it.'

It seemed an impossible feat for the two of us to transfer the coal from the shore to the coal-shed in under two hours. Morag must have read my thoughts.

'Ruari's away with his cow to the bull or he'd give us a hand,' she explained as we shovelled.

In all my life I have never performed such hard physical labour as I did during those two hours. The coal had to be carried pailful by pailful up the three stone steps and about ten yards beyond to a shed beside the henhouse. The day was dank and chill; our clothes were speckled with mist, but so fierce was our labour that we needed to work without waterproofs or even jackets. Morag wielded a workmanlike shovel, but I had to be content with a small fire-shovel that was of more ornament than use. After my sixteenth pailful my back ached, my arms felt as though they were being torn from their sockets and my 'funny bones' as though they had been beaten repeatedly with hammers; yet we had made little or no impression on that glistening black mound. Frenziedly we filled and carried, constantly glancing behind us at the line of water creeping inexorably nearer. All the time we worked my landlady discoursed on such subjects as the wisdom of teaching young girls mathematics; juvenile delinquency (a police friend in Glasgow had told her that 'galvanized deliquency had reached terrible propulsions these days'); and, inevitably, politics. I soon learned that Morag was an enthusiastic Tory; and

by the time the last pail of coal had been tipped into the shed she was
convinced that I was equally enthusiastic. The truth being that I had
no breath to express any opinion save a grunt.

By the light of a hurricane lantern firmly planted on the top of the
wall, and with the sea washing around our ankles, we scooped up the
last pailfuls from among the shingle. When daylight came we found
that we had scooped up a fair amount of shingle too, but by lamplight wet, black pebbles look remarkably like wet, black coal.

'My, but I'll be fallin' asleep in church tomorrow I'm that tired,'
said Morag as we plodded wearily up to the house.

'So you go to church?' I asked.

'Why, yes indeed,' she replied in shocked tones. 'I go whenever the
missionary's there to take the service.'

(Missionary?—I recalled the words of my doctor, 'people tell me
they're only half civilized up there'—but missionaries?)

'I thought you said in your letter that you had a minister,' I said.

'Surely, there's a minister for marryin' and buryin' and such, but
he's too busy to be takin' services here, there and everywhere. He has
missionaries to do that for him.'

'The missionary's not a minister then?'

'No, no, indeed!' She turned a pair of soulful blue eyes on me.
'Sure the missionary's wages aren't as big as the minister's, for he
doesna' feel the call of God till he retires from work and finds his
pension won't keep him,' she explained with startling irreverence.
'But the minister now, he's a true man of God. He starts earnin' when
he's quite a young man.'

After her piety of the night before, her guileless sarcasm shocked
me.

The next morning, my landlady, sober of mien and attire, placed
my breakfast before me. The weather, in direct contrast to the coal
merchant's prediction, showed a distinct improvement, but the
atmosphere was heavily Sabbatarian. When I offered to take the food
to the hens Morag merely nodded and thanked me meekly. Outside
I was relieved to find that the hens still had their weekday appetite
and scrambled eagerly for their food.

'Will you give a bitty to the cockerel under the creel yonder?'
requested my landlady in a sepulchral call.

I went to the henhouse where she pointed and there discovered
an upturned peat creel from which a cockerel's head was thrust

disconsolately forward. Having dropped plenty of food through a gap in the wicker-work I returned to the house.

'Why is the cockerel under the creel?' I asked. 'Is he sick?'

'It's the Sabbath,' Morag assured me piously, as though I was not already well aware of it.

'Yes,' I agreed doubtfully, 'but do you always put the cockerel under a creel on Sundays?'

'Yes I do!' she burst out, 'but there's plenty here as don't. Church-goin' folks too, and all they do on the Sabbath is to tether their cockerels with a piece of string.' Her eyes were flashing as she continued. 'I say if you live up to your religion then you must do the job properly and close him up altogether. Tetherin's only hippinocrasy,' she added severely.

I listened to her outburst with a show of concern, but was glad when a bubbling kettle compelled her to return to her own room.

Church service, it transpired, was held at the convenience of the missionary, not the congregation, and Morag asked me if I would prefer a late lunch or an early one. I plumped for a late meal and accordingly, a little before one o'clock, we set out; Morag garbed in black and wearing low shoes that revealed a pair of sturdy ankles. The church, she told me, was on the high road. I thought it strange that I had not noticed it on my stroll to the post office but I put it down to the mistiness of the morning, or perhaps to the counter-attraction of the bedsteads. Slowly and quietly we walked, as befitted the Sabbath, and at varying distances in front of us and behind us other figures in groups of twos and threes marched at the same devout pace. The men and the elderly folk were clad uniformly in sombre black; the young women and girls flaunted the excruciating blues and reds so beloved of the countrywoman, whatever her complexion.

It was not until we were picking our way along a muddy and refuse-strewn path that I realized from the subdued knot of people at its door that the ugly iron shed we were approaching was in fact the church.

'Why on earth don't they clean up the path?' I said to Morag.

'Aye, well, d'you see, the man who has this piece of land is of a different religion altogether and it just pleases him to make his dung heap in the path of them he calls the "unrighteous".'

At the church door we were greeted by a scissor-shaped man in an old-fashioned black suit.

'The precentor,' Morag said as he took my hand. Having previously been under the impression that a precentor was some sort of miniature organ I was quite interested to shake hands with a flesh-and-blood one, even though the flesh and blood were limp and chilly. His whispered welcome was scarcely audible. Around and about us the other worshippers also whispered, the fierce sibilance rushing and eddying through the tin church like wind through the tree tops. My own words acknowledging the introductions fell into their midst like thunderbolts.

A young man came forward in response to a nod from Morag.

'This is Lachy,' my landlady introduced him in a whisper, adding, 'the other half of the boat.'

I shook hands with a young man whose stocky, muscular figure was constrained by a tight navy-blue suit. His neck was disfigured by a large goitre which appeared to contend with an exceedingly tight collar for the privilege of choking him. Lachy, with punctilious politeness, and much to Morag's surprise, escorted us to our seats; and, having seen us settled, promptly sat himself down on the form in front. A couple of minutes later a vile-smelling woman nodded familiarly at the two of us and took the seat beside me.

I stared around the interior of the church, which was as uninspiring as the exterior, being furnished with several backless wooden benches on which numerous people slouched in impious attitudes. The place was disgustingly dirty; toffee papers littered the concrete floor; cobwebs festooned the beams of the iron roof; the plain glass windows were obscured by dirt, and, as there was no heating arrangement of any sort, it was evident that the fervour of the worship was expected to overcome the frigidity of the atmosphere. A small drunken-looking table, carved all over with initials, stood at the far end of the room and on its dusty top reposed a mouldering Bible. An ordinary kitchen chair and two tarnished brass oil-lamps completed the furnishings of the most squalid little House of God it has ever been my misfortune to enter.

From outside there came the noise of a motor followed by the slam of a car door.

'Here's the missionary,' whispered Morag.

Footsteps thudded up the muddy path and a few moments later an obese, pale-faced figure entered the church alone. He too was garbed in black, but more expensively so than the parishioners, and as he strode along the central aisle he had so much the air of a star performer appearing on the stage that I had to stifle a desire to applaud. Restrained hissings and obsequious flutterings echoed through the church but ceased abruptly as the missionary, reaching the table, turned to stare long and superciliously at the congregation. He spoke a few words which I could not understand, but as Morag prodded my waist and rose I stood up obediently.

The missionary, with legs widely straddled, one arm hidden behind his back and his eyes turned virtuously to the roof beams, began a prayer. Morag had intimated that it was to be a prayer, otherwise I should have thought it was the sermon, so long did it last. Colder and colder grew my feet, momently more agonizing became the crick in my neck, and still the vehement supplication and exhortation continued. I became aware of the sound of rustling paper behind me, then to the right of me, to the left of me and also in front. Morag thrust a bag of peppermints under my nose, thus adding her own particular rustle to what had by this time become a general one. Soon the rustling was replaced by a steady sucking which resounded from every corner of the building. I was sure that the missionary must be deaf if he could not hear it. At last the long prayer finished and we were able to sit down, whereupon the vile-smelling woman seized my hand, thrust two damp, warm peppermints into my palm and instructed me in a hoarse whisper to pass one of them on to Morag. I nodded and obligingly passed on both sweets.

The precentor now stood and, there being no organ or other instrument in the church, began to intone the paraphrase in a shaky tenor voice while the congregation, still seated, joined in demurely, their lips barely moving, their eyes fixed vacantly in front of them. Impressive as were the prayer and the paraphrase, the sermon which followed was even more so.

It began with the missionary standing very still behind the little table and treating the congregation to a prolonged combative stare. His eyes bulged; his lips pouted. He continued to stare silently for a while and then without the slightest warning he raised his fleshy fist and brought it crashing down upon the frail little table. The congregation flinched perceptibly.

'Someone has been here!' the missionary bellowed accusingly, and thirty or forty pairs of eyes stared in awed consternation.

Again he raised his fist above his head and brought it crashing down. Some of the women present appeared to shudder in sympathy with the table.

'Someone has been here!' he repeated in even louder tones.

I accepted another peppermint from Morag's proffered bag. For the third time table and fist met and now the voice rose to a thunderous roar:

'Someone has been here!'

There followed a significant pause and the walls of the church seemed to echo his words with tinny accusation. Clutching the table with fat, white hands, one of which was now ringed with grey dust, he dropped his voice to a gentle, sorrowful whisper.

'The Devil has been here,' he lamented. 'The Devil! The Devil I say, has been here!'

The repetition was irritating and was hardly complimentary to the previous Sunday's preacher. Furtively the missionary ran his tongue over thick lips; tears glistened in his eyes, and as he opened his mouth to speak again he almost lost the peppermint he was sucking.

'Don't ask me how I know.' His voice was rising again. 'Don't ask me how I know,' he repeated. 'But I know! I know! I know!' The sentence culminated in an ecstatic shout and, letting go the table which rocked unsteadily, his hands flayed the air like those of a man who has suddenly had the support snatched from beneath his feet. I wondered if he was holding the Devil responsible for all those toffee papers.

His brow was moist with perspiration; the tears had started to trickle down his cheeks; both his hands were by now exceedingly dirty and I was much relieved to see him produce a clean handkerchief; but instead of using it as I expected he held it in front of his mouth, disgorged the remainder of his peppermint, and bundled it back into his pocket. The tears were allowed to flow unchecked.

'Ahhhhh,' he breathed sadly. 'It is easy to smell the Devil amongst you.'

I almost giggled as the melodramatic words ran through my head like a play title: *The Devil smells of Peppermint*.

'Beware of the Devil in your hearts and in your homes,' he adjured us. 'Beware of the Devil who calls you out on Friday nights to listen to his luring music.'

A man whom Morag had pointed out as being the gamekeeper and the village piping enthusiast looked suddenly startled and a guilty flush suffused his face and neck.

'Beware of the Devil that teaches you to dance cheek to cheek, belly to belly, with strangers,' continued the missionary.

There was an aromatic gasp from the congregation, and the missionary, enamoured of his theme, licked his lips appreciatively. (Morag explained to me afterwards that the denunciation was occasioned by the introduction of the fox-trot and the one-step to the Island dance hall).

Dumbfounded, I fixed my gaze on the shoulders of 'the other half of the boat' and was astonished to see that they were heaving with mirth. I blinked rapidly but as my incredulous eyes travelled along the row of dark-clothed backs in front of me I perceived that several pairs of shoulders were shaking uncontrollably. I looked at the women. They all appeared to be staring piously into their laps, their mouths exaggeratedly prim. Catching an oblique glance from my landlady I saw that her eyes were merry as a child's. In fact the whole congregation, except for one obvious half-wit who sat tense and horror-stricken on the edge of a front pew, seemed to be nearly exploding with laughter. I stared steadily at the dirty floor.

At length the harangue ceased and the collection began. If the service had struck me as being crazy I was equally shaken by the manner of the collection. Two of the older members of the congregation produced little black velvet bags and made with what I thought to be irreverent haste towards the back seats, jostling and striving as one tried to outdo the other. Money dropped and rolled and was struggled for on the concrete floor, the collectors rising grey and dusty from between each row of seats. I dropped my contribution into the first bag thrust under my nose and received a savage glare from the bearer of the rival bag.

As soon as the collection was over the service was concluded and the worshippers shuffled out with dreadful solemnity. After the histrionic display we had just witnessed I felt that our exit could very appropriately have been accompanied by the slam of tip-up seats and a band playing the National Anthem. Outside the church chattering groups formed; they seemed to be waiting for something. They were.

The two collectors came outside and stood facing each other, their faces red and angry. Behind his back each held his full collection bag.

Simultaneously each extended a hand towards the other and demanded: 'Give me that bag!'

'What on earth is the matter with them?' I whispered.

'Well, it's the joint service that does it,' said Morag. 'They shouldn't give permission for joint services, for they always lead to trouble.'

It appeared that there was only one church in Bruach which had to be shared by two rival denominations. Everything went smoothly except for the collections. 'Last time they were after goin' round the back of the church and fightin' for it.'

'But surely the missionary——' I began.

'Ach,' said Morag, 'he'll not come out of the church till one of them goes back with the money.'

The combatants were becoming angrier, staring at each other defiantly. There seemed to be little prospect of ending the tension.

'They ought to toss for it,' I said flippantly.

Morag looked at me with admiration and then spoke out. 'Miss Peckwitt says you'd best toss for it,' she told them.

Miss Peckwitt wanted at that moment to become invisible; but I was surprised to find myself the centre of approbation.

'That's right! That's what they should do,' said the precentor, and everyone echoed his words, including the rival collectors. He extracted a penny from one of the bags.

'It was Miss Peckwitt that suggested it and as she belongs to neither side I think she should toss it,' he said. Meekly I took the penny.

'Now call out,' said the precentor. 'Which side will you have, the head or the man with the hayfork?'

They called; I tossed.

'Which side is it, Miss Peckwitt?' demanded the precentor.

'The man with the hayfork,' I said tremulously.

The scene was over; the loser handed over his bag with good grace and the winner disappeared into the church. Gradually the worshippers dispersed.

The sky was becoming overcast as we hurried home.

'What did you think of the service?' asked my landlady.

'That missionary of yours is just a witch doctor,' I said.

'Aye,' she admitted, 'but yon fellow's always the one for a good laugh.'

'Is that why people here go to church?' I enquired ironically.

Morag chuckled guiltily. 'Ach, no, it's no like that at all really,' she denied. 'It's just that man, the rest aren't like that at all. They say he's had too much religion. You know, one of these religious mannequins.'

It was dusk before we had finished our meal, so while my landlady rushed off to milk the cows I prepared the food for the hens.

'Don't forget the cockerel,' she reminded me as she disappeared with her milk pail.

I knew I should never forget the cockerel.

3. *Of Fare and Fishing*

MY STAY in Bruach lengthened from weeks to months and looked as though it might continue indefinitely, for the attractions of the Hebrides are indisputable and compelling; there were times when I felt I could not wish to forsake them for whatever England might offer in recompense. I soon surprised myself by becoming interested in agriculture generally and surprised my neighbours by my zeal in learning to milk, to plant and hoe potatoes, to make hay and even to scythe and to cut and carry peats.

The transition from town to croft life was accomplished without too much difficulty, though it was certainly not without its humorous side. Despite Morag's expert instruction, my early efforts were amateurish in the extreme: my haycocks, however painstakingly built, were wont to collapse; my corn-stooks curtsied; potatoes habitually impaled themselves on the tines of my fork; my scything was erratic to the point of danger—('You'll be hoppin' around on one feet if you thrust yourself about like that,' Morag continually warned.) However, perseverance brought some measure of skill and in time my offers of voluntary labour came to be accepted by the villagers with something akin to eagerness instead of sly mirth.

My own unfamiliarity with country folk and their habits was, if anything, outrivalled by the Bruachites' ignorance of English people, for Bruach was extremely isolated and, apart from a meagre sprinkling of tourists who came and went during the summer months, it was only the indefatigable researchers into crofting conditions who ever succeeded in negotiating the steadily worsening roads and penetrating the quiet seclusion.

The general impression seemed to be that 'the Englishman is a fool but his money is good', and during the whole of my Hebridean

sojourn I doubt if I gave the Islanders cause to alter that opinion.
I must admit that at first it comes as a shock to the egotism to realize
how far one is discounted merely because of being English, though
one eventually grows accustomed to it; so that I was not more than
ordinarily surprised when Morag, after telling me that a certain
woman had been married twice, replied, in answer to my observation
that I had heard the woman had been married three times: 'Aye, my
dear, so she has rightly, but the first one was an Englishman.'

The phenomenon of an Englishwoman actually resident among
them—and an uninquisitive Englishwoman at that—was enough to
arouse the curiosity of the crofters to fever pitch, and my movements
were followed by the populace as eagerly as the movements of
Royalty are followed by the Press. Trifling incidents which befell me
during my walks were already known to Morag before I returned
home, and inevitably her greeting would be some comment on the
day's adventures, such as: 'I'm hearing you met so-and-so by such
and such a place today,' or: 'They're after tellin' me that you near got
caught by the tide and had to paddle.'

This constant prying on my activities was naturally a little irksome,
but I assured myself that the interest was only temporary and soon
I should be able to enjoy my leisure without feeling myself to be the
cynosure of all eyes. As I have said, I knew practically nothing about
country folk!

Some of the stories concerning my initiation into Island life are
still told in Bruach today, and will, I am sure, continue to be told for
years to come. The story for instance of how, after volunteering to
collect a broody hen for my landlady, I struggled the whole length of
the village, one hand clutching one leg of a vociferously outraged
bird which flapped wildly above my head, the other hand shielding
my eyes from I knew not what. Morag, striving to compose her
features, met me outside the house.

'What fool gave you that?' she asked.

I explained with some irritation that the lady of the house had been
out and that the ancient grandfather and myself had chosen this hen
because it happened to be the only one sitting down at the time.

'Why, a broody hen should sit under your arm as quiet as a lamb,'
she told me, 'but that rascal you have there will no sit on an egg
supposin' you set a haystack on top of her.'

My spirits sank on learning that my errand had been in vain. 'What shall I do with her then?' I demanded, for the hen's struggling and clamouring showed no signs of decreasing.

'Let go of her leg,' counselled Morag, adding optimistically, 'she'll likely find her own way home.' I let go the leg and the hen, still squawking, flew heavily towards the sea.

'That's no a broody hen at all,' said my landlady. 'You can always tell a broody hen by her clockin'.'

A few days after this episode, I was passing a neighbour's garden when I happened to notice a sulky, bedraggled-looking hen which was being cold-shouldered by its companions. It looked distressingly familiar. I was sure in this case that Morag's optimism had not been justified and that it was up to me to do something about it, so sidling over the wall, in a manner that was fast becoming second nature, I cautiously approached the bird.

'Chuck, chuck,' I called seductively.

The hen appeared to have recognized me and, with a frenzied squawk which immediately stirred the rest of the hens into a screaming cacophony of terror, she took wing, scattering stray feathers as she flew, and disappeared behind a distant byre. I never saw her again. I doubt if her owner did either.

They tell too the story of the pet sheep.

It happened that I had taken a picnic lunch and had spent a long day exploring the moors. Evening was coming on by the time I started on the homeward road and I had not gone far when I heard a forlorn 'baa' and looking round saw a lone sheep hurrying towards me.

'Hello,' I greeted it, and as it 'baad' and rubbed itself against me in an ecstasy of recognition I knew it to be a motherless lamb which Ruari had brought home from the hill for his wife to bottle feed. The lamb had, not unnaturally, become the pampered pet of the household, cropping the grass of the park and running in and out of the kitchen like a frisky child. When it had grown into a fat and sturdy 'wether' it had become rather a problem and had to be banned from the house. Unfortunately, this did not discourage its devotion and it rarely ventured far afield, except to follow Ruari or Bella whenever they went to the well.

How the sheep had managed to stray so many miles from home I was at a loss to understand. Whether it really knew me or whether it would have thrown itself on the mercy of any passing human I could not be sure, but there was no escaping the fact that it was lost and that it was delighted to see me. I was certain Ruari would be missing the beast and wondering what had happened to it. Doubtless at this moment he would be out looking for it. With this in mind I unwound the scarf from my neck and tied it around the wether; then, feeling rather like the Good Shepherd and anticipating Ruari's gratefulness for having restored the lost sheep to the fold, I led the animal homeward. It was eager enough to be led and trotted obediently beside me all the way until, as we neared Ruari's house, I slipped my scarf from its neck and waited to see what would happen. Rushing forward delightedly, the wether bounded through the gate and, running up to the door of the house, commenced butting it with its horns, 'baaing' happily.

The door opened quickly and Ruari, obviously interrupted in the ritual of shaving, appeared on the threshold. I was just congratulating myself on my good deed when I was shocked to hear Ruari utter a curse which made me flinch and to see him put his boot against the thick fleece of the former pet and push it roughly away. He then embarked on an ear-stinging recital of the poor beast's pedigree, during which he got right down to fundamentals. Turning, he saw me.

'Look!' he commanded exasperatedly. 'Fourteen miles and more I trudged yesterday with that beast. Fourteen miles I took him to try would I lose him, and here he is back at my own doorstep within twenty-four hours!' A resentful oath bubbled again in his throat. 'Would you believe it, Miss Peckwitt, that a beast would know its way home from fourteen miles away?'

I replied feebly that I should have great difficulty in believing it, and Ruari, still muttering, drove the unhappy animal towards the byre.

With ears still singing I slunk away home where Morag awaited me. Almost the first words she said were: 'You'd best give me your scarf and let me wash it. It'll be smellin' awful strong of sheep likely?'

Before I had been long in the village I discovered that one of the essential differences between the English and the Hebrideans is that, in general, the former 'live to eat' and the latter 'eat to live'. There is a vast difference. The crofters ate sporadically, alternately gorging and fasting, while their eating habits made those of savages seem relatively elegant. As a consequence one saw otherwise healthy people looking as wishy-washy as a bowl of gruel; swallowing spoonful after spoonful of baking-soda or patent stomach powder, and if they were 'educated' punctuating their conversation with so many 'excuse-me's' that listening to them was like listening to the playing of a badly cracked gramophone record. In all my years in Bruach I never once met a crofter who regularly enjoyed his food. 'Sore stomachs' were such a frequent complaint that the job of the doctor must have been as monotonous as working at a factory bench, so busy was he kept cutting out identical pieces from an interminable procession of stomachs.

The fare was plain and shockingly lacking in variety. Except for the ubiquitous turnip, vegetables were practically unknown, the average crofter having as little inclination for the eating of vegetables as he has for the growing of them. So much is he in the thrall of his own fatalism that he will stand beside a plot of good cabbages and placidly assert that 'cabbages will not grow hereabouts'. So hypnotic are his mellow pathetic tones that the inexperienced are inclined to accept the truth of this astonishing statement despite the evidence of their own eyes.

In many ways my landlady, having been employed in the laird's kitchen 'till lately' (twenty-five years since!), was far superior to her neighbours both in the preparation and serving of meals, a circum-stance for which I was ineffably grateful. She had even progressed far enough to boil mint along with new potatoes, which she did, she said, 'because new potatoes is poisonous and the mint sucks the poison to itself'. However, the laird's menus struck me as having boasted scarcely more variety than those of his tenants, and I had some diffi-culty in persuading Morag that there were puddings other than rice and custard, and that there were more palatable ways of cooking young chicken than boiling it in a pot along with chunks of ancient turnip. She was always very anxious to please and accepted my sug-gestions without rancour, though she was inclined to dismiss the idea of serving a separately cooked vegetable each day of the week as eccentricity or, as she put it, 'city swank'.

Quite soon after I had arrived in Bruach Morag's own small stock of turnips had become exhausted and as we were then without veget-ables she suggested that I should pay a visit to 'Old Mac', who, at the age of eighty-four, had decided that it was time he started to save up in readiness for his old age. With this object in view he was reputed to have begun experimenting with the novel idea of growing veget-ables for sale to hotels on the mainland.

I set out for Old Mac's one chilly January morning. The moors were grizzled with hoar frost and the heather roots crisp under foot. A biting easterly wind frisked and rippled through the shaggy coats of the Highland cattle which grazed desultorily, one eye on the sparse grass, the other on the fence which barred them from the clustering buildings below, whence they were expecting their owners to appear bringing them filling bundles of hay. As I passed they lifted their heads hopefully and then, disappointed, returned to the task of filling their enormous bellies.

Dropping down the hillside I came upon Old Mac's croft, which was rush-grown and mossy, and decidedly unpromising-looking even to my inexperienced eye. The house itself huddled low into the hillside and from the single podgy chimney which pierced its grey thatched roof sprouted a wavering plume of peat smoke. I knocked on the door, over which drooped a dark moustache of battered ivy, and the old man's niece, a virago of about forty who also sported a dark moustache, appeared in answer to my summons. I acquainted her with my mission and, all smiles, she led me towards a small thatched shed where her uncle, white-bearded and as podgy as the chimney pot, sat—'marrying his potatoes', the niece explained. I thought I must have heard incorrectly but there the old man was, a heap of potatoes on either side of him. With serious concentration he took a potato from each heap, cut them into the required shapes with a meticulousness which would have been obscene in anyone less primitive, and then tied them together tightly with string. He hoped, he told me, to produce by this method a new variety which he intended to call 'Mac's Victory'.

Like Ruari, old Mac was rather deaf but, unlike Ruari, his speaking voice was inclined to be low and confidential. When the necessary civilities were over and the virago had departed to put on the kettle I repeated my errand. Mac shook his head.

'Turnips?' he said; 'it's no good tryin' for to grow turnips here.'

'Too sour?' I asked politely.

Mac glanced quickly towards the door from which came the sound of his niece's receding footsteps. He put a warning finger to his lips.

'Yes,' he agreed fervently. 'She's been like that ever since her operation. I don't know what's come over her.'

I had an uneasy feeling that the footsteps had paused.

'I mean the soil,' I put in hurriedly.

'Oh aye,' agreed Mac. 'Can't grow turnips.' He sighed deeply. 'The doctor said it might be her glands. I don't know . . . ever since her operation——'

'Did you ever try to grow turnips?' I persisted desperately in unnecessarily loud tones. To my relief the footsteps recommenced and then died away.

'Yes indeed! I grew turnips here one year and they was just like my fist.' He clenched a gnarled hand expressively.

I nodded.

'And I grew them again the next year and they was like——' He glanced impatiently about the shed but his eye lit on nothing suitable for demonstration and he continued: 'They was the size of my two fists together.' He hurled his knife into the potatoes and clenched his two fists together.

I smiled encouragement.

'And the third year I grew them, and they was just like my head,' he went on.

A cursory glance at his head showed me that it was certainly not lacking in size.

'Just like my head they was,' he repeated; 'but when I cut them open what did I find?'

He leaned forward earnestly and I rewarded him with a doubtful shake of my head.

'Well then, they was all rotten and maggoty inside,' he said disgustedly.

'Even more like your head,' I murmured jocularly. He stared at me, a quizzical frown between his eyes.

'Beg pardon?' he asked, grunting as he levered himself up from the potatoes to escort me to the house to drink tea.

'I just said it was a pity about the turnips,' I dissembled.

His finger went again to his lips. 'Yes,' he began, 'ever since her operation. . . . I don't know——'

We were almost at the door of the cottage.

'Come away in!' called the virago hospitably. She fixed me with a resolute smile, and I retaliated with equal determination.

I said goodbye to Old Mac and his niece after listening to the recital of a list of vegetables which included all I'd ever heard of and more besides, and which were bound to be failures on the Island because of the ravages of sun; rain; wind; mist; snow; hail; dogs; cows; sheep; horses; rabbits; deer; hens; blight; disease and tourists. From the way the old man referred to them I should have bracketed the last three together. It seemed that the growing of vegetables was an extremely hazardous business, and that Old Mac would be old indeed before he achieved his nest egg.

On my return home I wrote ordering a sack of carrots and one of turnips from a supplier on the mainland, and with these we managed tolerably well throughout the winter months. By the time spring came round I was heartily sick of both vegetables and an S O S was despatched to Mary, which resulted in the welcome arrival of a parcel containing peas, radishes, lettuce, cabbage, french beans and onions. ('I get funny with the smell of them,' Morag observed, pointing to the onions.)

The preparation of the vegetables Morag accomplished quite successfully with the exception of the beans and radishes, which items must have been strangers to the laird's kitchen. The beans she painstakingly shelled, cooking only the sparse brown seeds and throwing the pods to the hens, exclaiming contemptuously as she put them before me in an egg-cup instead of the usual vegetable dish: 'Sure they silly little peas is enough to crack the nails off a body.' The radishes were laboriously stripped of their colourful outer rind and served as a wan accompaniment to the lettuce. When I explained that they needed only washing, she commented: 'My, my! And I believe they'd be fine and comical if you can do that with them just.'

Due no doubt to the invigorating air of Bruach my own appetite soon became prodigious. My taste in food had always been catholic and I was able to enjoy the novelty and simplicity of the traditional Island delicacies. Porridge, which in town I had eschewed as being too heating, now appeared regularly on the breakfast table—and as regularly disappeared! Dulse soup, carragheen pudding (both seaweeds), I found fairly agreeable and also such things as boiled cormorant ('skart' as it was known locally) and many other kinds of sea fowl, though in some cases I must confess there was decided evidence of their marine habitat. Salt herring, which is the staple food of the crofters, sent me, after my first cautious mouthful, to the water bucket, where I drank more water in less time than I can remember ever having drunk before or since. The taste for salt herring, I venture to suggest, is rarely acquired. Indeed I maintain that to be able to enjoy salt herring one must first be able to speak the Gaelic, or, alternatively, to speak the Gaelic one must first have eaten plenty of salt herring. Which acts as the better throat abrasive I am not qualified to say, but before eating salt herring I think my voice would have been classified as 'soprano'. After I had eaten it my voice sounded to my own ears more like 'basso-profundo'.

Winkles, which during the winter months Morag picked for the London market, I managed to swallow after they had been boiled, but the prospect of letting them wriggle down my throat raw as Morag and Ruari did was too revolting to contemplate. Crabs, very much alive and wriggling, were put into the hot embers of the peat fire for about twenty minutes and then taken out and pulled to pieces with the fingers—a poker being used for all necessary tool-work. I soon became very partial to crab suppers and with practice grew adept at wielding the poker.

'Crowdie', a soft sour milk cheese, was very good when well made, though I could not fancy it served as a pudding with jam and cream; nor could I cultivate a taste for sugar instead of salt with my boiled eggs, which was the way the Bruachites relished them.

Sour milk was much drunk locally, but I had the townswoman's distaste for milk which is even slightly on the turn.

'I canna' understand you,' said Ruari one day, after I had watched him tilt a jugful of thick sour curds to his lips and suck them greedily down his throat. 'You townfolk now, you'd never think to eat a plum or an apple before it was ripe? Then why would you be drinkin' milk before it's ripe?'

I admitted that I had never thought of it in that way.

'Why, when I was for a time in England during the last war,' went on Ruari, 'I never saw a drop of ripe milk but except it was fed to the pigs. Everyone wanted this unripe new stuff straight from the cow. Ach, there's no good in that, except for the tea, and no as much taste in it as in a drink of water.'

During the summer months, when milk was plentiful and rich, Morag made butter—and such butter! In town I would have complained that it was rancid, but though its 'ripeness' stung my throat and I might have to swallow two or three times to every mouthful, I came to enjoy it as I had never enjoyed butter before. Morag's butter churn was a large sweetie jar with a hole in the lid. Through this hole went a rod about three feet long, at the bottom of which was a circle of wood with three or four holes in it. To make the butter Morag would sit on the edge of her chair, the jar, which would be about half full of cream, gripped firmly between her knees; then she would grasp the plunger and jerk it furiously up and down until the butter came. She reminded me of a jockey crouched grimly on the neck of his mount, his eyes fixed on the winning-post, while the illusion was intensified by the spatters of cream from the churn which spotted and streaked her face and hair, like the flecks of foam from a hard-ridden horse. The process sometimes lasted for hours and neighbours dropping in would obligingly take a turn at churning while Morag made tea. If she tired, my landlady would go to bed and resume her butter-making the next day or even the day after, and sometimes I would hear the 'plop! plop!' of the churn as a background to my dreams. It was a slap-dash way of butter-making—slap-dash in every sense of the word—but we nearly always got the butter, and it usually took longer to make than it did to eat!

Mushrooms in season grew abundantly on the moors and when the villagers heard of my fondness for them they persisted in bringing me all they could find. Day after day the mushrooms arrived, in milk-pails, in jam-jars, in dirty handkerchiefs and even dirtier caps. I ate mushrooms fried for breakfast; I ate them in soups; I concocted mushroom savouries; I experimented with the idea of drying them, but still I could not use all the mushrooms they so generously bestowed upon me. I was touched by the thoughtfulness of my new friends until disillusionment came with the discovery of their ineradicable belief that all mushrooms were deadly poison!

There were of course the dumplings.

There appears to be a tradition that a Scotch dumpling shall weigh at least ten pounds when cooked, no matter what size the household may be. It is fruity and spicy and is a noble sight when it is lifted from the pan in which it has been bubbling away for several hours and turned out on to the largest meat dish. Morag always used one of her old woollen vests, well floured, for a dumpling cloth as this produced a pleasing lacy effect on the outside. Ten pounds of rich fruit dumpling is a formidable quantity for two women to eat their way through unaided and whenever I saw one in preparation I knew I could look forward to a prolonged bout of indigestion. No scrap of it was ever wasted. The first day we ate it in steaming wedges hot from the pan and it was wonderful; on the following days we sliced it cold with a sharp knife and ate it either as cake or heated in the frying-pan for pudding. It was still good. Towards the end, when the pattern of Morag's vest began to take on a decidedly angora-like quality, we hewed the last craggy pieces, soaked them in custard and made them into a trifle. And that was the dumpling finished. I would heave a sigh of mingled regret and relief and put away my magnesia tablets—until the next time.

Fish, naturally, were there for the catching, but though when in England I had glibly prophesied to Mary that I should soon be doing my own fishing, I had never really expected the opportunity to arise. Fishing as a sport did not attract me in any way; I had not even held a fishing-rod in my hand. But 'Needs must when the Devil drives', and to my dismay there came a day when the butcher's meat 'went bad on him' and Morag, having developed a stomach ache, suggested that I should borrow a rod from Ruari and try my luck at catching a fish or two for the evening meal. She seemed to be so sure I could manage the task that, after a moment's hesitation, I decided that fishing might be as pleasant and profitable a way as any of spending an afternoon.

I went to see deaf Ruari, who by this time had become a very good friend of mine—if friendship can be said to exist between two individuals who resemble one another about as closely as a blast furnace resembles a candle. Ruari's powerful voice may at times have been an asset, but a few minutes conversation with him left me feeling bruised all over. It was said of Ruari, and I could well believe it, that his call for his stick and his dog was enough to put to flight the sheep on the far side of the hill. It was said that the cattle on the neighbouring island ceased their grazing and stared apprehensively about them when Ruari called home his own beasts. His dog, having had orders bawled at him since he was a puppy, would obey no command given in an ordinary voice, though he obviously possessed acute hearing. Ruari's voice was unique in my experience, and his habit of 'whispering' confidential asides was a source of embarrassment to everyone within earshot. On Sundays he was repeatedly adjured by both his wife and his sister to 'keep his mouth quiet' lest he should desecrate the Sabbath, and I had no doubt whatever that if Morag could have had her way her brother would have been banished to the creel along with the cockerel. But Ruari was a big man, and a determined one. His blue eyes topped by belligerent tufts of white eyebrows could be very fierce on occasion and when roused from his normal stolid good humour his red face beneath its feathering of white down would deepen to the colour of an over-ripe plum. He certainly would never be dominated by any woman.

This particular afternoon I found Ruari sitting on a kitchen chair in front of his house, his head supported by the ample stomach of the grocer-cum-barber, a cherubic octogenarian, who stood with wide-straddled legs in front of the chair and wielded a pair of scissors menacingly over Ruari's thin white hair. Against the wall of the house squatted a queue of patient but critical 'customers' of all ages and sizes, all alike in their indolence and shock-headedness.

I was greeted courteously and at considerable length, and when the subject of the weather had been completely exhausted and a polite interval had passed I collared Ruari's ear and made my request known. The waiting group concealed their smiles with difficulty. Women have for so long been nonentities in the islands that the idea of any woman, particularly a townswoman, going fishing appeared to them highly ludicrous. Ruari's voluble acquiescence was only slightly muffled by the barber's paunch, which shuddered visibly so that he stepped back a pace with the hurt look of a man who has received a low punch.

Ruari's wife Bella, having heard my voice, appeared in the door-way of the house and beckoned. Bella was pleasant and rubicund and had the shy, foolish look of the woman of seventy who had remained a virgin until she was sixty-five, for she and Ruari had married late in life. She accompanied me to the calf shed where Ruari's rods were kept, so that I might choose one for myself. The door of the shed stood wide open and inside a tousle-headed young boy sat on a log of wood, reading a comic which he held awkwardly in one hand. The other hand grasped a battered pail. I recognized the boy, chiefly by his insignificant nose, to be one of the clan of 'the other half of the boat'.

'Johnny here is waitin' on the calf to watter,' explained Bella with a bashful smile and in answer to my look of enquiry continued, 'He's awful sick with the red watter.' I was not at all sure which of the two occupants of the calf shed had the 'red watter' until Bella went on to tell me that red water fever was a very common ailment of young calves and that the only remedy was to 'make him drink his own watter'. This they intended to do and young Johnny was now engaged in earning a sixpence by waiting, pail in hand, for the calf to perform. The boy's hopes of his sixpence were apparently fast receding when we arrived on the scene, for so engrossed had he become in his comic that the calf had already foiled him twice. At our entrance, however, the beast woke from its torpor and almost before Bella had finished explaining it rose to its feet; there was a shout, and Johnny leaped forward and at last the precious medicine was safely in the pail.

'There now,' gloated Bella, 'you've brought him good luck; so soon as Ruari's finished with his hairs we'll give him the dose.' She took the pail and put it in a safe place.

I chose my fishing-rod under Johnny's careful supervision. It was of hazel and resembled a young sapling, to one end of which was attached a length of gut and a hook. I carried it outside into the sunshine and looked at it dubiously.

'Have you got any bait?' called the barber jovially.

I admitted that I had no bait and knew nothing about getting bait, or using it if I should get it.

'I'll come and get you bait,' offered Johnny, who evidently had not forgotten my help in the earning of the sixpence.

'Thank you,' I said. 'But aren't you waiting to get your hair cut?'

'Ach, they'll no be finished for a while yet,' he said, as he fell into step beside me.

I called my thanks to Ruari and Bella and, conscious of the surreptitious smiles of the onlookers, balanced the rod carefully over my shoulder and set off down the lane.

'I doubt she'll bring home a shark,' Ruari's 'aside' echoed down the lane and Johnny glanced anxiously at my face. I walked on indifferent, my companion padding silent and barefoot a yard or two to the side of me, wisely keeping his distance, for I was inclined to hurry, causing the fishing-rod to thrash around wildly.

We made our way to a rocky part of the shore and here my young friend pointed out a suicidal boulder which overhung the water, insisting, in spite of my protests, that it was the only good fishing place along the whole length of the shore. It began slowly to dawn upon me that, for the sake of his own reputation, Johnny intended me to catch some fish that day. I yielded hesitantly and with a good deal of trepidation climbed, skated and tottered to the top of the boulder, glad that my residence in Bruach had accustomed me to such exercise. Had I refused to go my youthful friend would doubtless have commandeered the fishing-rod for himself and I should have been relegated to the position of bait-seeker.

Meanwhile the boy was industriously investigating the deep pools among the rocks, grunting and wheezing the whole time like a man nine times his age.

'What is happening?' I called.

'Ahhh!' He gave a grunt which sounded more satisfied than the previous ones and held up a lively, wriggling crab. I felt a little nauseated when he wrenched off its legs and threw them into the sea, but the nausea was nothing to what I experienced when I saw him apply his mouth to the soft underpart of the body and dig his teeth so deeply into it that the shell almost sliced off a portion of his rudimentary nose.

'You'll die!' I gasped.

'I've been dead plenty times then,' he replied seriously.

I almost believed him.

For a few moments Johnny chewed with gusto and then, spitting out the conglomerate mass, divided it into equal portions, which he laid carefully on a flat rock. I had just begun to wonder what on earth had given me the idea that fishing might be a pleasant way to spend an afternoon when the boy whipped out some dirty grey stuff from his pocket and commenced to work it about in his hands.

'What is that?' I asked.

'Fleece,' he answered shortly and, commanding me to watch so that I could learn to do it by myself, he took my rod and proceeded to attach one of the disgusting little morsels of chewed crab to the hook and then to wrap it carefully with the sheep's wool.

'Goodness!' I ejaculated with a smile. 'Do fish need food and clothing then?'

He treated my remark with the contempt it deserved and handed me the rod.

'Now what do I do?' I asked.

'Put it out as far as you can,' he enjoined me.

Gingerly I stepped to the edge of the rock and prepared to do as my tutor advised. In vain I tried to recollect some angling photographs which might give me an idea how to cast; but perversely I could only recall a series of pictorial instructions on how to achieve a good golfing stance. I compromised by holding my rod as though it was a bayonet and I was about to charge.

Having always had the notion that anglers spent their time as Constable depicted them, sitting comfortably beside quiet, tree-shaded rivers, lazily swatting the occasional bothersome fly and carefully unhooking the occasional fish, I was totally unprepared for the rough and laborious business which I had undertaken. My rod was so long and heavy I felt I stood more chance of spiking my fish as it lay on the bottom of the sea than of hooking it near the surface. My feet were threatening at any moment to slip from under me and if this happened the slimy, seaweed-covered rocks would jettison me into the water like a helter-skelter.

'Throw it out,' insisted Johnny impatiently.

'I'm much too afraid I might follow it,' I argued.

'Ach, that's because you have shoes on,' he said with a scornful glance at my very good brogues.

Resignedly I laid down the rod and took off my shoes. Thank goodness I was not wearing stockings. 'The fish round here are very particular,' I remarked peevishly.

'Dinna' talk of the fish to their faces,' wailed Johnny in agonized tones. 'You'll never catch a fish if you talk of them by name.'

Groaning inwardly I took up the burden of rod again and as my glance rested on the water I glimpsed a swift iridescent shape in the depths.

'There's a fish!' I yelled shrilly. 'A fish! Look!' I turned excitedly to my companion. His expression was one of extreme anguish.

'There now!' he said sadly; 'you've gone and pointed at the fish, and surely it's that bad luck to point at a fish I'm thinkin' we may just as well go home.'

'Well I'm sorry,' I apologized; 'but you'll have to forgive me. I had no idea the fish were so self-conscious.'

He turned his back on me and went seeking another crab. 'You'll never catch a fish with your rod on dry land,' he threw at me over his shoulder.

Resolutely I lowered the road.

'Ach, that's no good at all. It's in the sea itself the fish are, not in the air.'

Johnny's continual reprimands began to get on my nerves. 'It is in the sea,' I retorted. 'Come and see for yourself.'

He came, and agreed that the hook was in the sea—just.

'Then you do it,' I said. He relented and taking the rod from my unresisting hands, he brandished it and sent the line out over the water. He then allowed me to take over. Nothing happened except that my rod became momently heavier and more difficult to handle; but there was some compensation in that I was able to admire a view of the village which I had not previously seen. The hills away to the right were dark and sombre, their peaks lost in the lowering clouds; the moors were dust coloured and by contrast the crofts looked richly green. In the distance I could see the roof of Morag's house and the gable end of what I decided must be Ruari's barn. Behind me, close to the shore, was a regular row of houses, only a few yards between each. 'Beach Terrace' I mused, and even as I watched a figure came out from one of the houses and waved. I waved back, a foolish action which very nearly caused me to meet the fishes in their own element. There was an audible titter from behind me and I concentrated again on my rod, which by now seemed to have grown from a sapling into a tree trunk. I remembered Ruari's jocose 'aside' and felt that it might yet turn out to be a prophecy. Certainly I seemed to have the right tool for the job.

'How shall I know when there's a fish on the line?' I called.

Johnny, who had got another crab and was busily preparing it, disgorged it into his palm. 'You can never mistake that.'

I invariably mistake the unmistakable. 'I might hook some sea-weed,' I hazarded.

'Seaweed doesn't pull and wriggle,' he replied.

Seeing that I was standing on a carpet of the stuff I was immeasurably thankful that what he said was true.

As though Johnny's words had been a sign, I felt almost immediately a sudden twitching of the rod which it was impossible even for a novice to doubt. I forgot the self-consciousness of the fish.

'A fish! A fish!' I cried. 'I have one here.'

'Bring him in then,' ordered Johnny, running towards me. 'Up with the rod.'

In the bustle of those few moments I was not quite sure what happened, but with a sudden onrush of strength I jerked at the rod, which came up in the air, the line flying like a kite behind it; I sat down heavily on a wet and glutinous cushion, aware as I did so that a silvery writhing missile was flying over my head and towards the houses beside the shore.

'Why, you'd be throwin' him right across the Island and into the sea the other side,' grumbled Johnny irritably.

'Was it really a fish?' I demanded.

'It was indeed,' he assured me, 'but if I don't get it quick it'll likely be hen food!' and skipped away in the direction in which the fish had disappeared.

'See if you can bait yon hook now,' he called. I looked at the hook; I looked at the bait; I looked at the sea, and decided that in this case, ignorance was bliss.

Standing up again I saw that in the garden of one of the houses two figures darted here and there as though seeking something. I had no doubt at all that one of the figures was Johnny, and in a few minutes he returned bearing proudly on the flat of his palm a silver-bellied fish of pathetic size.

'It's no a bad one at all,' he complimented me, caressing the fish gently with his other hand.

I asked him what sort of fish it was and he gave me the name in Gaelic. It sounded rather like 'brickbat'.

'What is it in English?'

'Ach now, I haven't the English for it.'

'Can one eat these sort of fish?' I asked him.

'Indeed you can. They're good. You should have it for your supper supposin' you get no more.'

I thought that might be quite a good idea.

'Where did you find it?'

'Under the gooseberry bush, just beside the manure heap in Kirsty McKinnon's garden,' Johnny said.

'Oh!' I said, abandoning the idea of a fish supper.

I offered the fish to Johnny. He refused politely, saying that they had 'plenty fish' and telling me that by the time I got home I would have an appetite for all the fish I could catch. I did not contradict him and, with one glance at the neat piles of chewed crab and then at the empty hook, he set about the task of re-baiting without further comment.

Thus in partnership we continued fishing for some time, I manœuvring the heavy rod while Johnny fielded very efficiently in the rear. It was at the moment of retrieving my third 'brickbat' that we noticed one of my shoes was missing. Together we searched, but in vain, and it became obvious that in the excitement of landing the fish one of my shoes had been kicked into the sea.

'Bother!' I said. 'If I've got to walk home barefoot I shan't have time for any more fishing.'

'Kirsty'll lend you a pair of her own shoes,' Johnny consoled me.

Remembering the size and more particularly the shape of Kirsty's feet I rejected the suggestion, feeling that my own would suffer less by going unshod than by being subjected to the torture of having the toes turned up very nearly at right-angles.

Slowly Johnny and I toiled homewards, he carrying the fish and the rod, and I, optimistically, carrying my remaining shoe. It took nearly two hours to cover the distance we had earlier covered in half an hour, and at times I felt that even Kirsty's turn-ups would have been preferable to the grazes and cuts I sustained as a result of encounters with limpet-covered rocks and over-familiarity with shell-strewn shingle.

'What sort of fish d'you like best?' asked Johnny abruptly.

'Plaice, sole, any sort of flat fish,' I replied.

He thought for a moment and then offered: 'I could show you how to flounder next week.'

'I've no doubt you could,' I replied with a forced laugh.

'Will I do that then?'

I glanced at his face. It was quite serious.

'What do you mean?' I asked.

'The flounders. They're good,' he replied. 'Flat fish they are and all you have to do is paddle out into the water when the tide's comin' in and wriggle your toes in the sand.'

'But how do you know when you find a flounder?'

'Ach, you can soon tell, for it's all smooth and slippery, and you just bend down quick and whip it up.'

'How deep is the water?'

'Not more than this.' He indicated a line well up on his thigh.

'I don't think I should take to floundering, but I'll give you a six-pence for every one you bring me,' I told him, and saw by the gleam in his eyes that I had said exactly the right thing.

After an absence of about four hours we reached Ruari's house again and I was relieved to find that Johnny was in plenty of time to get his hair cut. The knot of men, no longer shock-headed and indolent, but shorn and alert-looking, still hung about and they had been joined now by 'the other half of the boat'.

'Where's your shoe?' queried the barber, glancing from my bleeding feet to the one shoe which dangled from my hand.

'She's used it for bait,' chuckled Lachy, and was in no way quelled by my withering glance.

I received much congratulation on my catch and even more commiseration on the loss of my shoe.

'But you'll know better next time, and maybe you'll get better fishing.'

'If there is a next time,' I said doubtfully, but they mistook my meaning. (In point of fact there never was a next time.)

'Surely the tide will be right again tomorrow and the day after that too if the weather holds,' someone said as I turned to go.

'Sure the weather will be good.' One of the men spat with the air of making a profound announcement. The Bruachites put more animation into their spitting than they ever allowed to come into their speech. They spat expressively and with consummate skill.

'No it won't then,' someone contradicted him. 'Occasional showers with patches of smoke, that's exactly what the wireless says.'

'Ach, what do they know about the weather?' retorted the seer contemptuously. 'They have no influence on it at all. No influence whatever.'

I left them arguing and limped home where Morag awaited me on the doorstep.

'Ah, mo ghaoil,' she greeted me solicitously, 'what for are you dancin' around in your bare feets at this time of the evenin'?'

I assured her that I had never felt less like dancing, bare feet or otherwise, and held up the one shoe for inspection. 'I don't know why I bothered to bring it home,' I said.

'Ach, but you never know what treasure the watter might yield up in time,' she remarked, wagging her head mysteriously. 'It's just as well you brought it for what the sea takes away here it gives up there,' and strangely enough my shoe was eventually washed ashore, about a mile from where I had lost it.

I presented Morag with my catch. They were rather warm and limp, doubtless because Johnny, proud of the success of his pupil, had seized every opportunity to display them, with many tender caresses, as he expiated on their virtues to me and to everyone we had met.

It appeared that the fish were considered a delicacy in Bruach and my landlady expressed pleasure at the sight of them. 'In the Gaelic,' she told me, 'we have a sayin' that this fish is so good that the daughter is not expected to give it up even to her own mother.'

I decided not to relate the adventures of at least one of my catch.

'And how is your pain now?' I asked.

'Me, I'm just fine,' she replied, 'but you'll need to bathe your feets, my dear, or some of them cuts might go turnin' antiseptic.'

The next morning at breakfast I was confronted by a reproachful one-eyed glare from my share of the 'brickbats'. I glared back seeing not the fish but the mouthfuls of chewed bait; the seeking figures near the dung heap and Johnny's hot, grimy hands nursing the catch all the way home.

I said that I would prefer a boiled egg.

4. *The Funeral*

During the whole of my first year in Bruach there occurred no birth, marriage or death to disturb or enliven the leisurely amble of our lives. With the coming of the second autumn each of the three events came to pass, though not in that specific order.

The birth excited little interest beyond a sporadic procession of female visitors to criticize and admire the baby. The wedding was an insipid affair, the ceremony having taken place in a Glasgow register office, and, except for a complaint from the postman when he was called upon to deliver almost a mailbag full of sanguinary 'wee wee pokes of cake crumbs', it passed practically unnoticed. The death was easily the most impressive event of the year for due to the frequency of intermarriage everyone was related in some degree to everyone else. As a result the funeral necessitated the attendance of the community *en masse* and the occasion became virtually a general holiday. Now the Gael in holiday mood is irrepressible and, as he arrays himself in exactly the same 'best' clothes whether he is to attend a funeral or a festivity, it is perhaps not surprising that he shows a tendency to combine the two.

The news of the death of Ian Mor, the old fisherman, came one dull October morning when Morag brought in my breakfast tray. Ian Mor had lived with his two sisters in one of the houses which I had dubbed 'Beach Terrace', and, as he had always been a strong, healthy-looking man, his 'being changed' had come as rather a shock to everyone in the village. To everyone, that is, except myself; I could feel little surprise at the death of a man who had passed the allotted span by at least nine years. Rather was I inclined to wonder how the villagers, in view of their seeming disregard for their physical well-being, managed to live so long.

'And he was such a fine man,' Morag lamented tearfully. 'A good Christian and a good fisherman.' She wiped the sleeve of her cardigan across her brimming eyes.

It was the custom, my landlady went on to tell me, for everyone to pay their last respects to the corpse and, though I was loth to do so, she eventually prevailed upon me to accompany her on a visit of condolence to the bereaved sisters. Thus it was that in the twilight of the evening before the funeral we set out for the house in 'Beach Terrace'. The melancholy of the occasion was increased by the fact that it was raining; the steady relentless rain that makes the grass and the trees and even the sea itself look tired and defeated. Morag had donned her largest oilskin and with it a cloak of intense piety which effectively prevented her from being her usual voluble self. For some time we plodded heavily and silently across squelching crofts and along boggy footpaths until, irritated by the solemnity, I tried to draw out my companion by asking about the deceased fisherman's youth. The experiment was successful.

'Indeed he was very fond of myself at one time,' she confided, a trace of coyness in her voice. 'Why, he'd even made a song for me.' (In Bruach the 'making of a song' for one's sweetheart was of far more importance than the giving of an engagement ring!) Love's ardour had cooled, however, when Ian had learned that Morag's father was not going to be particularly generous in the matter of a dowry for his daughter, and the final break had come when Ian had called one evening to 'do his wee bitty courtin'', and Morag, instead of sitting beside him on the bench, had set him to carrying manure for the potatoes.

'He was that vexed because I put too much manure in his creel that he never came near me again, and that was the end of it.' The resigned sigh which followed this recital was expressive of my landlady's conviction of the fickleness of all sweethearts.

'Whatever came over him, I don't know,' she continued sadly, 'but he started to get religion. I always used to comfort myself afterwards that maybe I spoiled him with too much manure, but he came near to spoilin' me with too much religion.'

The subject of Ian Mor was summarily dismissed from the conversation as a figure approached us from the opposite direction, doubtless returning from the same errand as that on which we were bound.

'Who on earth can this be without a waterproof on an evening like this?' I asked.

Morag made a noise approximating to a snort.

'Sure it's yon fool Dugan Ruag. He'd be the only one to care naught for rain such as this,' she replied.

Dugan Ruag, hands in the pockets of his tweed jacket, paused as we drew closer and I had no difficulty in recognizing the 'precentor'.

'Here, Dugan,' Morag greeted him. 'It's a wonder you're not under the ground yourself, man, with no coat on and a day like this.' The threat combined with the allusion to the prospective funeral made the man spit contemptuously.

'Me? I've been wet since the day I was born near enough, and never taken no harm,' he replied.

'I've seen him in a coat but once in his life,' Morag admitted to me.

'You have once? Then if you've seen me in a coat she must have been blowin' a gale on us. Man! I'd wear a coat for the wind, but the rain!' He spat again and glanced confidently at the leaden sky. 'The rain itself would no hurt me.'

'I'm no so sure,' called Morag over her shoulder as Dugan, with elbows pressed close against his body and chin tucked well down, continued on his way. To me she remarked: 'In all the years I've known that man, and there must be over sixty of them, there's few have seen him in a coat, and yet he's never needed a doctor in his life.'

I wondered if peat smoke has an effect on the human skin like tanning on a cow hide, for there was no doubt that many of the Bruachites seemed to be well-nigh impervious to rain.

We reached the house of the late Ian Mor and pushed open the door of the kitchen to receive a restrained welcome from the two sisters, who immediately set about preparing a strupak. While the tea was brewing Morag followed the younger sister upstairs to view the corpse but, though invited to go with them, I shook my head, electing to stay in the kitchen with the elder sister to whom I proceeded to offer my condolences.

'Indeed it was spiteful of him to go and die on us like that,' she replied, with a touch of asperity in her voice.

I reminded the old lady that her brother had lived to a good old age.

'Old age, indeed!' she expostulated with some bitterness, 'he could have been looking after us for ten years and more yet. There's plenty does.'

'He certainly looked very fit the last time I saw him,' I said.

'Aye, aye,' she agreed, 'and who'd have thought now that a little thing like pleurisy could have killed him; and him as strong as a bull.'

'Yes, he did look strong,' I conceded.

'Indeed, that's true enough, but ach! that doctor!' She expressed her contempt for the doctor by a vindictive poke at the fire. 'If I could have got the vet to him instead of that doctor,' she continued to my amazement, 'I truly believe he would have been alive and out fishin' at this minute, instead of lyin' up there senseless in his bed.'

'Do you really think so?' I asked, too much taken aback to think of anything else to say.

'Yes I do,' she replied with an emphatic nod. 'Why, when our old cow had pleurisy didn't the vet cure her of it in no time at all? And she after havin' a calf regular each year since?' She glared at me intimidatingly as she continued: 'And if he could do that for our cow then I'm no doubtin' but what he could have done the same for our brother.'

I suggested, somewhat diffidently, that the two cases were not identical.

'That's what the vet said when I sent him the telegram,' she answered.

'Of course it would be quite different,' I began, but she silenced me with a peremptory flourish of the dish cloth.

'Same cause, same cure,' she observed epigrammatically. She swabbed the table top vigorously for some minutes before saying with biting scorn: 'I'm tellin' you that doctor couldna' cure a corn on your toe without cutting off your foot and if he cut off your foot and buried it, likely as not it would grow into a poisonous weed.'

I was saved from further confidences by the re-entry of Morag and the other sister who were closely followed by Johnny the bus-driver and Lachy of the boat. Presently the two sisters led the men upstairs, while Morag and I remained in the kitchen. From the room above came the sound of heavy footsteps.

'Johnny and Lachy have come to take Ian down to the sofa in the parlour,' my landlady explained.

'Doesn't the undertaker do that on the day of the funeral?' I asked.

'Well, he would likely,' she replied, her voice dropping to a whisper, 'but d'you see the coffin won't go up these narrow stairs, and the undertaker doesna' care one bit. He just takes hold of the corpus by the feet and drags it bump, bump, bump down the stairs whichever way it'll come best,' She illustrated her words horrifically with a fist on the table.

'Oh no!' I protested.

'Ach, indeed he does, and folks doesn't like it, you know.'

'I should think not!'

'No, they don't,' she repeated; 'they say they never seem to get the noise of it out of their ears for weeks afterwards. That's why the men try to get them down before yon fellow can lay his hands on them.'

At that moment the door of the kitchen opened and the two sisters came inside. They closed the door firmly behind them. The noises in the bedroom above increased, and were followed by the sound of slow, halting footsteps on the stairs, and the scuff of garments against the wooden walls. I tried hard not to listen.

'The weather seems to be improving,' I said desperately.

My companions merely nodded, their whole attention being riveted on the performance without.

'Steady there!' That was Lachy's voice, respectful and quiet.

'Up your end a bit.' That was Johnny, purposeful and businesslike. 'Now over this way a bit.'

Suddenly there was a choking gurgling sound followed by a fit of violent coughing, which caused the four of us in the kitchen to stare questioningly at the door and then at one another.

Johnny's voice, now plaintive, filled the passage: 'Lachy, you damn fool! Lower your end a bit; that was his big toe nearly halfway down my throat.'

From the stairs came Lachy's voice raised in remonstrance:

'For God's sake let him down a minute!'

There was a significant pause and then the ominous noises began again. This time, except for a suspicious-sounding thud, there was apparently no mishap, and a few minutes later Lachy and Johnny burst into the kitchen. Both were inhaling deeply at the cigarettes in their mouths. Johnny made a beeline for the water-pail, helped himself to a ladleful and tilting it to his lips drank deeply.

'Did you manage him all right?' asked one of the sisters unnecessarily.

'Aye, so we did,' exploded Johnny, panting and shaking his head like a swimmer after a cold plunge. 'By God I'm tellin' you that many's the corpse I've carried, but that's the first time I've been forced to swallow one.' He banged down the ladle heavily. 'Bah! What a taste!'

'Whisht!' said one of the sisters, while the other repeated: 'Oh God! Oh God!' over and over again, but whether as an imprecation or an invocation I could not guess.

Johnny and Lachy, after drinking the tea which had been awaiting them, were armed with the gift of a bottle of whisky and departed to dig the grave. They reassured the anxious sisters, one of whom was worried 'in case they should get Ian taken all that way and then find no hole to put him in', that with the stimulus of a bottle of whisky there was bound to be plenty of labour.

'I'm after takin' the bus anyway,' said Johnny; 'so there's plenty will come along just for the ride.'

Other people began to arrive and Morag and I prepared to take our leave.

'It's funny Old Farquhar hasn't been near since Ian died,' said the sister who saw us to the door. 'I don't believe he can have heard yet.'

Thus obliquely she suggested that we should take upon ourselves the task of acquainting Farquhar with the news of Ian's demise and, as the rain had stopped, bringing a bright starry sky with a full moon on the point of rising, we readily agreed.

Old Farquhar was the tatterdemalion of the village, who passed a hermit-like existence in a secluded little corrie a couple of miles away from the nearest habitation. I had seen him infrequently, and then always hurrying awkwardly in the opposite direction. I was hearing of him constantly, for in addition to his being something of a bard he was reputed to possess the 'second sight', but I had not yet met him and, as his was a character obviously worth investigation, I was not averse to taking this opportunity of doing so.

To reach Farquhar's house we had to pass by the graveyard. The empty bus stood outside and we could not help being aware that somewhere beyond the trees an extremely merry party of grave-diggers were already engaged upon their task.

'Dig first and drink after!' called Morag, with a hand cupped to her mouth, but there was no response and the sounds of merriment continued unabated.

Farquhar's cottage when we reached it appeared to be nothing more than a dilapidated barn, and, in spite of Morag's reiteration, I could not at first believe that it was actually occupied by a human being. It was stone built and thatched, but the latter was black with age and part of the house seemed to have fallen away altogether. A space in the wall which had at some time been a window was now partly blocked with a barrel, from the chinks around which there eddied drifts of peat smoke.

Morag called out and then opened the door. Hesitantly I followed her into a room where an old man sat at a table slicing a loaf with a large clasp knife. He looked up as we entered and, brandishing the knife in welcome, bade us be seated. My companion lowered herself on to a plank supported by two more barrels and introduced me to Farquhar, a scarecrow of a man whose clothes hung raggedly on his gaunt, bony frame. As he shook my hand his blue eyes gazed at me with quick intelligence from deep in his lean, dark face, the skin of which was fissured and brown as the bark of an ancient oak.

Morag and our host immediately started to compare reminiscences of Ian Mor and, as their conversation lapsed into the Gaelic, I was at leisure to examine my surroundings. The room, though rude, was surprisingly warm with the heat from an enormous peat fire which glowed on an open hearth; the smoke curled upwards to be caught by yet another barrel suspended from a beam and guided through a hole in the thatch. By no means all the smoke escaped this way; quite a lot still eddied about the room, but peat smoke can be thick indeed before it becomes unpleasant. Apart from the table and the plank upon which we were sitting, the only furniture was the barrel on which Farquhar himself was seated when we arrived. The floor was a jig-saw pattern of driftwood of all shapes and sizes, and in all stages of decay. There was no sign of a bed and I wondered if there could possibly be another room in which Farquhar slept, or if he slept on the plank we now occupied. Illumination was provided by a candle which stood, supported by a cake of its own grease, in the centre of the table. Beside the loaf of bread was a jar of jam, a paper of butter, some oatcakes and a saucer of crowdie. Evidently we had interrupted Farquhar at his evening meal but, in no way put out, he gestured enthusiastically towards the oatcakes and jam, telling us as though it was a recommendation that he had made the former himself; he was already wiping a horny finger round the inside of two handle-less cups 'to chase out the dust' before Morag, noticing my frantic signals, managed to convince him that we could not possibly drink another cup of tea or eat one mouthful of food. He was sorely disappointed at our refusal and obviously considered that he was being slighted; but I felt that I had gone through enough for one night. For the life of me I could not have swallowed food in that house.

As Farquhar talked animatedly I noticed that he continued to cut and butter slices of bread, until he had sliced up the whole loaf. It seemed an enormous meal for one old man but, before he resumed his own repast, he deliberately placed one of the buttered rounds at each corner of the table farthest away from him. I had by that time become accustomed to the eccentricities of some of the older crofters but, as Morag had distinctly told me that Farquhar had always lived alone since he was capable of doing so, I rejected the idea that the rounds were set there for a brace of memorable family ghosts. My thoughts were busily engaged in seeking a reasonable explanation for his action when I glimpsed a stealthy movement and, turning, saw two beady eyes followed by the head and body of a large rat appear over the corner of the table. Stifling a scream I jumped up on to the plank.

'There's a rat!' I gabbled hysterically. 'A rat! A rat! He's taken your bread!'

Morag pulled at my skirts; Farquhar stopped eating and stared at me; only the rat remained completely self-possessed.

'Surely,' answered Farquhar mildly. ' 'Tis for him that I'm after puttin' it there.'

'You put it there for a rat?' I stammered in awed incredulity. 'Is it poisoned then?'

'Indeed no,' replied Farquhar, 'but I always put something out for him when I take my own food and he knows it well.'

'Why?' I asked weakly.

'Because if I didn't he would come up here and pinch mine,' answered the old man philosophically.

I gripped Morag's arm as a second rat appeared at the opposite corner and took away the remaining slice of bread.

'That's his wife,' Farquhar explained, but I was too upset even to pretend an interest in rodent relationships.

'Is it just two pets you have?' I asked, gingerly lowering myself to the seat.

'Ach indeed no!' Morag answered for him. 'Sure all the rats in the village is welcome in Farquhar's house.' She turned to the old man. 'I hope the rest are as well trained as those two.'

Farquhar shook his head in sorrowful denial.

I made desperate signs that I wished to go home, but courtesy forbade brief partings and so it was some agonizing minutes before I made for the door with what Morag afterwards referred to as 'indigent haste'.

'Come again any time, Miss Peckwitt,' Farquhar called; 'and don't be afraid of the rats,' he chuckled. 'Rats is all right. I always know what to expect from a rat, and that's more than I can say of any other body in this village.'

'What did you think of that now?' queried Morag when we were a safe distance from the house.

I made no reply.

Morag laughed. 'He's got some sense though has old Farquhar,' she said.

'That's not my impression of him,' I retorted.

It was now past midnight; the sky had cleared completely and a brilliantly full moon sailed placidly on an indigo sea. The distant hills were crested with silver and away to our right Rhuna Island appeared like a handful of crushed black velvet dropped carelessly on the water. We walked quickly, for the night was cold. A rabbit darted across my path and I jumped as though shot.

'It's no a rat,' comforted Morag. I guessed that Miss Peckwitt and the rats would soon be making a good ceilidh story.

As we neared the burial ground we saw that the bus still stood outside.

'Good,' said my landlady; 'maybe we'll be able to get a lift home.'

A murmur of voices reached us and turning into the ill-kept graveyard we went towards them, picking our way through tufts of weed and evading the cluttering branches.

Suddenly Morag pulled me to a stop.

'Listen!' she commanded.

I listened with a quaking heart, uneasy among the shadowed grey tombstones and the sibilant rustling of trees. The voices became distinct.

'My, you near had that one.'

With relief I recognized Lachy's voice, for the second time that evening.

'Try again.' That was undoubtedly Johnny. 'Maybe you'll get it this time.'

There was a sound as of a pebble falling, followed by an exclamation of disgust, and then Lachy's voice again: 'Your turn, Angus.'

Morag held my arm tightly.

'What on earth can they be doing?' I whispered fiercely.

Cautiously edging our way between drunken tombstones and avoiding innumerable rabbit burrows, we moved forward, guided by a strong aroma of whisky which had completely overcome the customary dank and musty smell of the graves, to come upon a spectacle as macabre as that of the graveyard scene from *Hamlet*. Lachy, Johnny and Angus were crouched together in a devout-enough-looking group and were staring as though hypnotized at a wooden cross about ten yards in front of them. I too stared at the cross, for spiked carelessly on top of it was a widely grinning human skull.

'Throw!' Johnny's voice broke out imperiously into the temporary silence.

Angus drew back his arm, a pebble hit the skull, and Lachy, going forward to inspect the target, gave a shout of admiration: 'Good for you, man! That's only five teeth he has left now.'

'Good-oh!' ejaculated Johnny. 'We'll finish him off tonight yet.'

To come across three grave-diggers playing Aunt Sally in the moonlight with a human skull as a target was a shattering enough experience, but I had yet to appreciate the full horror of the situation. Morag stepped forward bristling with indignation.

'Why! Johnny, Lachy, Angus!' she addressed them with withering scorn. 'I'm ashamed of you! Grown men like yourselves, and nothin' better to do when you're supposed to be diggin' a grave for a poor man, than be playin' games with a corpus.'

The three men looked sheepish, but only for a moment.

'We've finished diggin' the grave,' Lachy replied pertly.

'Show me, then,' demanded Morag.

We followed them towards a clump of bushes a few yards away and looked down at a grave which was no more than two feet deep. Beside it lay a large sod of turf which had been rolled around a tree-trunk, Swiss roll fashion.

'Surely if you don't put him deeper than that the dogs will have him out by the mornin'!' Morag reprimanded, throwing out her hands in a gesture of despair.

'He'll be all right there,' said Johnny brusquely.

'He will not,' answered Morag; 'why did you no put him over there where there's more soil?'

'Because it's so boggy over there now that the first shower of rain will float him out,' replied the undaunted Lachy.

'It's only one bottle of whisky we got and it's only one grave we're diggin',' put in Angus.

Morag sighed heavily.

'Anyway,' continued Lachy, 'even diggin' that far we've dug up one body, so it must be plenty deep enough.'

'Who would that be?' asked Morag with sudden interest.

'You remember yon fellow who was drowned in England about twenty years ago, and they did somethin' to his body and sent him up here?'

'So I do,' replied Morag; 'Euan Beag that was surely?'

'Aye, well it was him.'

'Indeed.' Morag sucked in her breath impressively. 'And what has he kept like?' she asked, curiosity overcoming indignation.

'He was just as good as new,' answered Johnny, and the other two echoed his words.

'And you had to bury him again?' pursued Morag.

'No, we didn't yet.'

'You didn't? Then what did you do with him?'

'Ach, he's just there,' answered Lachy, pointing; 'in the bushes there behind where Miss Peckwitt is standin'.'

Miss Peckwitt moved very quickly away from the bushes.

'He's kept so well all these years, he'll keep a good while longer, so we'll put Ian Mor in and then put Euan Beag on top of him. That's the best way to keep the dogs out.'

The logic of Lachy's argument seemed to appeal to Morag, but she was a little disturbed in case someone might find the body under the bushes.

'Ach, stop frettin',' Angus chided her; 'we covered him over well with bracken and twigs, and there's nobody will find him there unless they tread on him first.'

I followed very closely on the heels of my companions.

'Who's that?' Morag stopped and pointed to a mound that was conspicuous by its neatness.

'That's Donachan, that was,' said Lachy in words strangely reminiscent of a famous petrol advertisement.

When we returned to the site of the Aunt Sally Morag went straight up to the skull and, taking it down from its perch, examined it critically.

'Where did you get this?' she enquired.

'Same grave,' said Lachy nonchalantly. 'We found three of them altogether. That one was on the top.'

With renewed indignation Morag turned on the bus driver.

'Why, Johnny! This is your poor great-grandfather, and indeed if he'd been alive this day, I'm tellin' you, you'd no be darin' to play skittles with his teeths.'

This statement was received in a contrite silence which lasted perhaps three seconds.

'Well, I wish I'd inherited his teeth,' said Johnny with unseemly levity.

Morag looked at the skull affectionately, turning it round in her hands as a fond mother might display a pretty doll to a child.

'There's not a mite of him you've inherited,' said Morag tartly. 'You're no half, no, not a quarter the man he was.'

Johnny shuffled uncomfortably from one foot to the other.

'Where's the rest of him?' Morag demanded.

Johnny pointed and Morag handed him the skull with the injunction that he must put it back with the rest of his great-grandfather.

'Not till we've finished our game,' insisted Johnny. 'I've got twenty cigarettes on it, and he canna' feel anythin' now.'

Morag clucked despairingly.

'You shouldn't make people dig graves if you don't like what we do here,' began Lachy argumentatively.

'Why, people must die and graves must be dug,' Morag interposed regretfully.

'Why shouldn't we just burn them?' asked Angus.

'D'you mean we should all be incriminated?' Morag's voice rose shrilly.

'Aye indeed.'

'Angus Mor Ruari! May the Good Lord forgive you for your words,' prayed Morag with infinite pathos. 'I hope nobody will have the wickedness to incriminate me when I die, or I'll haunt them sure as I'm here.' With this threat she drew herself up stiffly. 'Why,' she taunted them as she turned to go, 'to incriminate anybody is as wicked as murderin' them.'

I followed her out of the graveyard, after one hasty glance over my shoulder which showed me the target being replaced and the men preparing to take up their positions. Morag evidently saw it too, for she paused and shouted warningly: 'Johnny! See and don't leave your great-grandfather lyin' around or the seagulls will have him for sure.'

The next day, which was cold and blustery, we gathered at the house on the shore to see Ian Mor on his last journey.

'It'll be the minister himself to bury him,' said Morag; 'the missionary is laid aside.'

'He's dead d'you mean?' I asked.

'No, no, he's just laid aside through illness.'

By the time we arrived the coffin had already been brought from the house and had been placed on two kitchen chairs in front of the door. I recognized in the black-clad, bowler-hatted undertaker my friend the taxi-driver. He was moving with solemn decorum among the cluster of mourners, shaking hands, muttering greetings, and, to judge from the expressions of some of the people, indulging in some pretty humorous wisecracking at the same time.

The minister, wearing a black overcoat and hat, a striking canary-yellow muffler and brown boots, arrived in due course and insisted upon shaking hands with everyone lengthily and boisterously. The preliminaries over, he took up his station behind the coffin, and the men, except for those not directly under the minister's eye, doused their cigarettes and bowed their heads reverently, though only the undertaker removed his hat. The women began to leak out of the house to congregate in a colourful knot in the doorway. They commenced to knuckle their eyes with hard, work-coarsened hands and to sigh and moan, faintly at first and then louder, but their grief, despite quite genuine tears, seemed almost mechanical. Their expressions remained alert and watchful; their eyes, darting here and there, missed nothing of what was going on. Shortly after the service had begun, two latecomers—young girls dressed in blatant reds and blues —came galloping up, their faces glowing with the exercise and excitement. Without ceremony they pushed their way through the crowd of men and insinuated themselves into the huddled group in the doorway. They turned to face the coffin and miraculously their faces had become composed into masks of condolence.

It was sometimes difficult to hear the words of the service above the rustle of wind in the trees, the plashing of waves on the shingle, the wailing of the women and the mocking chorus of the seagulls as they hovered and wheeled above us. There was a glut of herring in the loch and the presence of the seagulls caused much discomfiture to the mourners who, from time to time, lifted irreverent heads to glare with savage apprehension at the offenders. Imperturbably the minister droned on, though when he came to the words 'and the years of our age are threescore and ten' I got the impression, both from his tone and his countenance, that he was feeling rather cross with Ian Mor for having cheated him out of a job for nine years.

The service over, the men began to form themselves into a long double line. The first six grasped the handles of the coffin and, with the nearest male relative of the deceased man to lead the coffin by a silken cord, the procession moved off at a leisured pace. The minister, after bidding everyone a cheerful farewell, jumped into his car, which, after a preliminary grumble of its engine, leaped forward impatiently to envelop the mourners in a cloud of smoke before it disappeared into the distance. Some of the women remained to comfort the bereaved relatives and to fortify themselves with cups of tea; others chose to follow the cortège at a discreet distance. Morag suggested that we should take a short cut to the burial ground and thus save ourselves the fatigue of following the winding road. This we did but though we were separated from the funeral procession by some distance it was not too far to disguise the fact that for such a procession it was decidedly hilarious. There was not, as I had been led to believe by some writers on the Highlands, anything in the nature of a quarrel or a fight at any time, either in progress or even brewing. On the contrary, joviality was the keynote of the day. The men, even those carrying the coffin, puffed unconcernedly at cigarettes and laughed and chatted as they walked; stopping at every telegraph pole to change bearers. At one time, when only a drystone wall was between us and the road, I heard one of the mourners call out: 'Lachy Murdy says he's cold.' Instantly the reply came: 'Let's take out the corpse and put Lachy Murdy in—he'll be warm enough in there I doubt.'

Loud laughter rippled along the line, Lachy Murdy himself laughing louder than anyone.

At the graveside there was no prayer or service whatever. The coffin was stripped of its ornaments by the undertaker and earth was thrown on top of it by any man who could find a spade. It was all done with as little ceremony as a dog inters a bone, and those not actively engaged in shovelling attended desultorily to the graves of their kinsmen, uprooting weeds and throwing them indifferently on to the surrounding graves. Old men, pipes in mouths, shambled among the tombstones, spitting recklessly.

As the earth shovelling progressed I heard Lachy call a halt and point towards the clump of bushes beside which I had stood the previous night. I glanced at Morag. Her eye was fixed steadily on Johnny whom we had observed to pause once or twice and to cast furtive glances about him. I wondered if he had mislaid his great-grandfather.

'Let's go now,' I implored my landlady.

She turned a distasteful glance on the rest of the women who were hanging round the grave like voracious seagulls round a fish pier.

'There, look at that!' she said. 'Ian Mor was a bachelor and there's more women at his funeral than ever I seen before. Indeed,' she went on pointedly, 'they've been chasin' him all his life and now they've chased him to his grave.' The promptness with which she agreed to my suggestion that we return home made it plain that she herself was not going to be accused of such forward behaviour.

That night both Lachy and Johnny were among those who dropped in at Morag's house to ceilidh. Naturally funerals were the main topic of the conversation.

'Come, Morag,' said Lachy, pulling out a bottle of whisky from his pocket. 'Give us some tots and we'll have a drink.'

'What'll we drink to?' someone asked.

'We'll drink to the hope that the rest of the people to die here from now on will have been ailin' for three months or so before they go.'

'That's a terrible thing to wish for,' I ejaculated. 'Surely you yourself would not care to be ill all that time?'

'Indeed but I would,' retorted Lachy.

'But why?' I asked.

'Because I know fine how heavy folks are when they die suddenly,' said Lachy candidly. 'It's no fair on the folks who have to carry when a corpse hasn't lost a bit of weight first. Just look at Ian Mor,' he continued, warming to his subject. 'Seventeen stone that man was and ill less than a week. It's no right I'm tellin' you. It near killed some of us today the weight of him.'

'That's right enough,' agreed Johnny fervently, and his words were echoed with approbation by every other man present.

'You sounded as though you were being killed,' I said drily.

'We ought to have a bier that can be drawn by a horse in this place,' said Lachy, ignoring my sarcasm.

'A what?' demanded Ruari, a hand to his ear.

'A bier—a horse bier,' vociferated Lachy.

'There's no enough beer for the men in this place without givin' it to the horses indeed,' roared Ruari amid laughter.

Morag changed the subject. 'Miss Peckwitt was tellin' me she was awful shocked that none of you men took off his hat when the service was on,' she told them, her lips quirking faintly.

Several pairs of astonished eyes were turned on me.

'Take off our hats?' repeated Lachy foolishly. 'Why now would we do that? Our heads were not hot!'

'The undertaker took off his hat, I noticed,' put in someone.

'Aye,' answered another, 'tryin' to shame us folk into followin' suit so that we'd catch our death of cold and make plenty of work for him I doubt. Ach, but we're too wise here for that sort of caper.'

They were indeed too wise altogether.

5. *The Cattle Sale*

'IF I'M spared,' remarked Morag one hazy morning in early spring, 'I'll be after puttin' the stirk to the sale on Friday. Will you be comin' with me?'

'I will,' I replied promptly as I spooned thick yellow cream on to my steaming porridge. 'But where is the sale and how do we get there?'

Morag poured out two cups of tea from the pot and taking one for herself sat down on the edge of the sofa.

'The cattle float will be takin' him on Thursday evenin',' she explained, 'and we'll folly by bus on Friday mornin'.'

I was infinitely relieved that the few shreds of dignity I had managed to retain were sufficient to prevent there being any suggestion that I might occupy a spare stall in the cattle float.

'But I thought you had only one stirk and surely you said that was a female?' I said.

'So I did,' elucidated Morag, 'and so he will be when she's older you understand?'

I nodded wisely, accepting the fact that it was not nature but the Gaelic language which was responsible for the beast's being temporarily an hermaphrodite.

'You'll need good boots to your feets and a good stick to your hand,' warned my landlady seriously. 'Why, there's some of them beasts that wild, they'd be ridin' you round the ring on their horns for nothin' at all.'

I put down my cup and stared at Morag. The sight of the most placidly grazing cow had always been sufficient to fill me with trepidation; the prospect of horn riding I viewed with complete terror.

'Then count me out,' I said decisively. 'I've neither the figure nor the inclination to become a toreador.'

'Ach, you can always stay out of the field if you've a mind,' cajoled Morag, who loathed going anywhere at all without a companion.

I relented, though not without misgivings, but stressed most emphatically that I had a mind.

'In that case,' went on my landlady nimbly, 'will you 'phone for me from the new kosk to tell the cattle float to come.'

Morag claimed to be 'feart to death' of the 'phone, so, after giving a hand with the breakfast dishes, I went up the road towards the post office beside which stood the new telephone kiosk. This was a very recent arrival in Bruach and its installation had naturally excited a good deal of interest. Almost immediately it had become a popular evening rendezvous for the youth of the neighbourhood and, within a few days, or even hours, countless people were to be observed busily popping in and out, lifting the receiver, dialling numbers and indulging in prolonged and apparently cordial conversations with unseen friends; all regardless of the fact that the 'phone was as yet connected to nothing more responsive than the outside of the post office wall.

Though on arrival the kiosk had been an unimpressive pink, Lachy, who was by way of being the village odd job man, had soon transformed its pallidness into a vivid and arresting red. It was perhaps regrettable that for such odd jobs as Lachy deigned to undertake he would accept no payment but whisky; and as he always insisted on drinking the wages before commencing the work the results of his labours were frequently somewhat startling. On this occasion Lachy excelled himself, and even Bruach had been astonished when, next morning, unsuspecting crofters opened pillar-box red doors to discover striped sheep, cows with fiery horns and hens that looked as though they had been crossed with flamingoes. Lachy had succeeded in 'painting the town red' with a vengeance. But though Bruach was surprised, it was in no way dismayed. The escapade was dismissed with a philosophical shrug of the shoulders, sometimes with a smile, and in nearly every case it was left to the weather to remove, or at least modify, the damage. Only two of the villagers showed distinct signs of wrath. One was Kirsty, the gaunt and prim-mouthed spinster of 'Beach Terrace', who had had the misfortune to leave a pair of combinations and a chaste white nightgown hanging on the clothes line overnight, with disastrous results.

'When I came to gather them in, Miss Peckwitt,' she told me, with tears of indignation in her eyes, 'I fell down on my knees on the grass, for I thought the Lord Himself had struck at me for wearin' such fancy underwear.'

The other was the over-sized, over-aged schoolmistress who was seen the next morning in full pursuit of the miscreant, furiously pelting him with threats, with insults, and with cauliflowers from her carefully tended garden—cauliflowers which had overnight exchanged their blonde heads for red ones.

As to the success of the actual 'odd job,' one could perhaps best judge from the following notice which appeared a day or two later in the window of the post office:

WANTED: Boy *under sixteen* to scrape paint off glass in kiosk

It was some weeks now since everything had been made ship-shape and Bruach had been connected with the outside world. To all but the excessively righteous it was a welcome link, and though the latter professed to regard it as an implement of the Devil their condemnation did not extend to their being rung up by friends.

As I came in sight of the kiosk, an old man, leaning heavily on two sticks, shuffled with laborious haste from one of the low-roofed cottages and along the road in front of me. Reaching the flamboyant red door, he managed with some difficulty to pull it open, and with even more difficulty to insert himself inside. I sighed. Old men of the Bruach variety were not as a rule adept in the use of modern inventions like the telephone and I realized that it might be some time before I could contact the owner of the cattle float. I had by now acquired the Hebridean brand of patience so, lighting a cigarette, I settled myself contemplatively on the lichen-blotched stump of an old gate-post to watch the mist, like a grey vagabond, ragging itself across the hills and sending groping fingers down into the hidden corries. Every few minutes I glanced behind to watch progress in the kiosk. The old man appeared to be an extraordinarily restless conversationalist. My first glimpse showed him to be writhing convulsively from side to side in a manner suggestive of a hula-hula dancer. Another time he seemed to be embracing the telephone so closely that it looked as though he must be attempting either to swing from it or to wrest it from the wall. I was of course perfectly well aware that men are much inclined to strike attitudes when using the 'phone, but this old man had hardly progressed far enough to achieve such poise.

On the other hand, even the most agonizing rheumatic pains could surely not account for his contortions? I waited and waited; my watch ticked on; I threw away the butt of my third cigarette; the wraith-like mist crept inexorably nearer, yet still the performance in the kiosk continued.

Feeling rather puzzled, I got up and moved closer. The old man, catching sight of me, waved a bland greeting and I saw that he had not yet lifted the receiver. I answered his wave with a friendly smile, hoping that he might thus be encouraged to enlist my help in his difficulty, which was probably nothing more serious than the inability to find the correct number in the directory. The smile had its effect and, grunting and sighing noisily, he pushed open the door, collected his sticks, manœuvred himself carefully through and hobbled a few steps towards me.

'Excuse me, Miss Peckwitt,' he began with bashful humility, 'but can you tell me if it's true that I haff a spot of green paint on the side of my face and under my chin?' He turned the left side of his face towards me, tilted his chin, and awaited my comments. I examined his face critically, and was able to assure him that so far as I could see there was not the slightest trace of greenness about him.

'Ach, they was just haffin' me on then up at the house,' he said ruefully. 'Just after haffin' me on they was, the rascals; and me haffin' to come all this way for to see.' He grunted again gustily. 'And what a job I'm after haffin' with my rheumatics to try would I get to see under my chin.'

'Aren't you going to use the 'phone then?' I asked him.

'Me?' he asked with pained surprised. 'Me? Why indeed, I couldna' use that thing to save my life.'

After again bemoaning the cruelty of his family in forcing him to such exertions, just because he 'was after makin' a bitty mess paintin' the house door green again', he lumbered off home, and I was able to take his place in the kiosk. I did not realize until I was inside that in addition to the telephone it was fitted with a small mirror—a luxury which so many crofter homes lacked. At last I understood the reason for all those one-sided telephone conversations.

For several hours on the Thursday evening preceding the sale, the rain came down in torrents, but by Friday morning there seemed to be a faint prospect of the day developing into a reasonably fine one.

The ditches on either side of the road still gushed exhilaratedly as Morag and I, clad in waterproofs and armed with stout sticks, hastened towards the bus-driver's house. The hills loomed darkly through a billowing mantle of cloud; behind us the tawny washed moors stretched interminably, and a chill eddying breeze whispered terse messages to the trembling bog cotton.

The bus was due to leave at 7.30 a.m. and at 7.25 a.m. my companion and I were comfortably settled on one of the front seats, watching the grey blanket of sky being swept northwards to reveal elusive shafts of sunlight which patterned the dark water with pools of silver. At a quarter to eight we still sat, or rather I still sat, no longer enraptured by the swift changing panorama, but thinking yearningly of the extra cup of tea I should have had time for if only I could have known that the bus-driver was going to lie so long abed. Morag had gone on a reconnoitring tour but now she appeared at the door of the bus.

'He's no out of his bed yet, the scamp,' she said. 'I think we'd best give him a shout.'

I alighted from the bus and stood with Morag in the road.

'Johnny!' Morag called as she would call a cow three miles distant. 'JOHNNY! JOHNNY!' We called in unison, but the house remained still and silent. We called repeatedly.

'We could do with our own Ruari here now,' sighed Morag.

I felt a twinge of pity for Johnny and climbing aboard the bus I found the horn and pressed it several times. The strident hoot should have awakened the dead, but Johnny must have been more than dead. We were wondering how next to proceed when a loud hail from down the road made us turn in that direction and we saw Padruig, the old road-mender, labouring up the hill towards us on his way to an eight o'clock start.

'Why, surely the man's no sleepin' through all that noise?' he greeted us querulously. 'I could hear you bletherin' away down at my own house there.'

'Call yourself then,' commanded Morag as he paused beside us. Padruig, thus invited, threw back his head and gathered himself for the effort.

'JOHNNY!' His stentorian shout shamed us into silence, but was as little productive as our own efforts had been. He tried again, but with the same result.

'Well now, what d'you think of that?' he asked, turning to us in amazement. 'Indeed I've a good mind to drive off the bus myself and give him a good fright,' he added threateningly.

'You canna' drive,' jeered Morag.

'I can so,' argued Padruig with some vehemence.

'You can no,' insisted Morag. 'You canna' drive a bus anyway.'

'And why not?' demanded Padruig.

'Because,' said Morag crushingly, 'you havena' got a public convenience licence and you canna' drive a bus without one.'

Padruig opened his mouth to repeat his shouts but as though struck by some sudden suspicion turned to gape foolishly at Morag for some seconds.

'JOHNNY!' This time Padruig's voice was augmented by a handful of flints which he hurled vindictively against the bedroom window. The combination had the desired effect, and instantly the window was thrown open and a stream of Gaelic issued forth. I gathered, from Morag's anxious glance towards me, that it was mainly maledictory.

'Get you out of that, man,' Padruig cut short Johnny's diatribe. 'It's gone eight o'clock.

'Eight!' Johnny's voice was incredulous. 'Whose time is that? God's time, Government time or daft time?'

'Daft time,' answered Padruig evenly, 'and isn't it daft time the mails are goin' by anyway.'

'Oh my God!' gasped Johnny. (I should perhaps explain that locally 'God's time' was Greenwich time; 'Government time' was British Summer time, and 'Daft time' was the scornful designation for British Double Summer time.)

'You'd best bring your bed with you, you're that fond of it,' chided Padruig mercilessly as he stumped off along the road to his work.

Johnny, ignoring the insult, addressed Morag, 'Go you into the kitchen and get the kettle on, Morag,' he said peremptorily; and as his dark head disappeared through the window Morag and I hurried to the back door of the house, which opened unresistingly. Together we set about lighting the Primus stove.

Johnny, in shirt sleeves, his braces hanging down the back of his trousers and his shoes unlaced, came clattering down the stairs, seeming in no way ashamed of his *déshabille* or disturbed by the fact that two of his intending passengers were busily preparing his breakfast half an hour after the bus should have left. Hastily he poured some of the hot water from the already steaming kettle into a cup and commenced shaving at reckless speed. Morag brewed tea with the remainder of the water while I searched in a cupboard for something to eat. I found a couple of oatcakes and fed them to Johnny as he fastened his braces with one hand and dabbed a towel over his face with the other.

'You've cut yourself,' I told him as he wiped a smear of blood across his cheek.

'Damn!' he muttered and held a handkerchief to the cut.

'Sticking plaster?' I suggested helpfully.

'Ach, there'd be none,' said Johnny with disgust. 'There never is in this place.'

'A stamp?' put in Morag. Johnny indicated the wallet in his jacket pocket, from which Morag extracted a twopenny stamp and, after licking it, carefully stuck it over the cut.

'You'll do fine,' she told him.

I thought it an appropriate treatment for a mail carrier and extremely effective in both senses of the word.

We waited only while Johnny swallowed two or three mouthfuls of scalding tea, then hurrying outside we clambered again on to the bus. Almost immediately it leaped forward as Johnny, not giving the engine a moment to warm up, let in the clutch. At last we were off, forty minutes late it is true but Johnny was, through experience, an expert at catching up on lost time.

There were several halts along the road, where we loaded up with parcels, mailbags and impatient passengers, and with such careless abandon were all these stowed aboard that Morag complained a little fretfully that, 'You didna' know if it was a pillar-box or somebody's grandfather would be landin' in your lap next.'

Some of the passengers were at first inclined to testy remonstrance regarding the lateness of the bus, but Johnny, with his foot hard down on the accelerator, soon put them in their places both literally and figuratively speaking, and before we had covered more than a few yards even the most wrathful of them seemed to have lost either the desire or the ability to argue. Like some mad demon the bus pounded, rocked, bumped and thundered along the road. My insides felt as though they were being pulverized and for the first time that morning I ceased to yearn for that missed cup of tea.

We reached the post office with only two minutes to spare, and here the passengers, their peevishness forgotten, entered gleefully

into the spirit of the affair. Tumbling out of the bus they rushed the
sacks of mail into the sorting office, where, anxious to ensure the
utmost celerity, they stood menacingly over the harassed sorters.
Astonishingly the task was completed just as the clock finished
striking the hour and, though the postmaster's baleful glare should
have annihilated Johnny, the latter remained sublimely indifferent.
He stood, hands in pockets, whistling tunelessly, his stamped face
looking remarkably at home in such a setting.

'You'd best lace up your shoes,' said Morag in an undertone as we
passed near him on our way out.

Johnny treated us to a benevolent smile.

Still slightly breathless, Morag and I made in the direction of the
sale yard, which was situated, as were most things of importance in
the Island, in close proximity to a public bar; a fact which no doubt
accounted for there being no sign of the presence of humans, though
many sheep and cattle were tied to stakes around the low wall of the
field.

Together my landlady and I leaned on the wall, each examining
with an anxious eye the qualities of the various beasts. Morag's interest
was for the comparative condition and therefore likely price of her
own stirk; mine arose purely from cowardice.

An old car rattled to a stop in front of the entrance to the field, and
a couple of men with the brisk air of those who are intent only on
making money stepped from it. Simultaneously groups of flushed
crofters began to emerge from the adjacent bar, and without preliminaries, as far as I could see, prices were being called and business
had begun.

I left them to their bargaining, and wishing to look for specimens
of wild flowers I wandered along the road towards a promising-looking
clump of trees. They proved on investigation to be mostly hazel,
though here and there a rowan waved its exquisite fronds in the
capricious breeze. Beneath them the celandines grew in profusion
and a gleam of sunlight catching the wet grass transformed it into
a shimmering carpet of diamonds. Leaving the trees I ambled slowly
across the road to sit on a large stone which, in Morag's youth, had
been used for weight-lifting contests by the Bruach males on their
way homeward after a sale. It was a pleasant spot for meditation and I
lingered some time watching the burn below tearing its swift, loquacious way towards the sea. Above me a pair of buzzards circled with

superb grace, their plaintive mews mingling with the liquid notes of the curlews which echoed eerily among the desolate hills.

Suddenly from the distance there came a loud shouting and, glancing uneasily over my shoulder, I saw with horror that a distracted bull or cow was careering madly along the road in my direction. It ran erratically, weaving from side to side, and making wild sweeps with its enormous horns at two furiously snapping sheep dogs which raced on either side. Some way behind the cow but obviously in pursuit tore a frantically gesticulating figure whose shouting had attracted my attention. As the figure perceived me the shouting and gesticulating were intensified.

For one awful moment I was transfixed with fear but the realization that I was being warned to run for my life galvanized me into action. I do not believe it would be any exaggeration to say that in spite of my heavy gumboots I was across the road in one bound and into the wood, and in another I was up in the top of the most dependable-looking hazel tree I could see. Certainly I could recollect afterwards a sensation of flying more than of climbing, and I felt I might more reasonably claim to be an ex-mate of Tarzan than an ex-schoolmarm. Quaking with fear, I clung to my perch while the noise of hooves and the incessant altercation of the dogs drew nearer, passed, and faded into the distance. I was shakily descending the tree when a voice assailed me in voluble Gaelic and I espied the elderly pursuer of the cow advancing, red-faced and truculent, towards me. My boots touched earth, but so formidable was the old man's countenance that I was tempted to repeat the climb. Without preamble he began to address me eloquently and though he spoke in Gaelic I had the uncomfortable feeling that much of the eloquence was vituperative.

'Please say what you have to say in English,' I told him with as much hauteur as I could command.

At once he became confused and apologetic.

'Ah, my, my, you have no Gaelic is it? Indeed and I'm after mistakin' you for one hereabouts. Ach, but you've no Gaelic.' He looked at me pityingly.

'What were you saying to me then?' I asked.

'I was just sayin' if only you would have stood still in front of the cow and waved your arms at her she'd have taken fright at you and would have turned back likely.'

I pondered the compliment carefully.

'Now d'you see,' he continued, his voice full of pathos, 'I'll never turn her before she gets home, and it's fourteen miles the day already I've driven the beast.'

I condoled with him suitably, but had to admit that I was afraid the cow might have tossed me if I had stayed within reach. My excuse seemed to puzzle him for he blinked thoughtfully for a few seconds.

'I don't believe she would have,' he said seriously, 'but even supposin' she had tossed you there would have been no malice in it—no malice at all. She's not a cross cow by rights.'

I was wondering if it felt any different to be tossed by a unmalicious cow than by a malicious one when the old man spoke again.

'What a pity you had not the Gaelic,' he said mournfully. 'I could just as well have shouted to you in English, and then maybe I wouldn't have had all this trouble for nothin'.'

We commiserated with each other at some length on our joint misfortunes before he could bring himself to continue his forlorn trek homeward.

'What were you up the tree for?' he rounded on me just as I was hoping I was rid of him and, strange as it may seem, I could not think on the spur of the moment of a plausible reason why a middle-aged woman should be up in the top of a tree, for I was not willing to confess the full extent of my cowardice. Providentially the man went on to answer his own question.

'Lookin' for nuts were you?'

I grasped at the straw and nodded affirmation.

'Ach!' he burst out derisively, 'there'll be no nuts there till September or after.'

At my affectation of surprise he permitted himself a short bark of laughter. 'No, no,' he repeated. 'Not till September, so you've started climbin' a few months too soon.'

Pleased with his joke he plodded off down the road in the wake of the recalcitrant cow.

Deciding that it was time for me to go in search of Morag, I returned to the sale yard and there found my landlady. She was in high spirits, her stirk having sold at a good price.

'Didn't you say something about there being sheepdog trials here today after the sale?' I asked.

'So there was to be,' replied Morag, 'but they tell me they've been cancelled.'

'Why is that?'

'All I heard was that the sheep had broke out of the pen and they'd been chasin' the dogs all over the place. They must have been a wild lot of sheep that, and the poor dogs have had an awful time with them.'

There was very little activity at the sale yard by now: most of the beasts had been disposed of and the knots of arguing men—an inevitable occurrence whenever Gaels fraternize—were already beginning to move off. I noticed the butcher, an immense man, leading a tiny calf by a tiny piece of rope. He reminded me of a portly matron airing her Pekingese.

Morag was eager to hurry me off to the hotel for lunch and there we ate our meal in the kitchen with the cook who was a good friend of hers. The hospitality of the Islander is proverbial, and it is, or seems to be, accepted that their hospitality extends beyond their own larders to those of their employers, so the excellent meal cost us nothing.

As we sat sipping our after-lunch cups of tea, the cook rose and opened a door which gave on to a small passage. Through this passage was the bar and it was possible both to see and hear the barman serving drinks to the assembled crowd. The cook considered this excellent entertainment and assuring us that it was 'as good as a concert', she settled herself in a chair placed as near the door as possible.

Most of the male population of Bruach were present in the bar along with many others I did not know and all were in good trim; full of beer and whisky and, to begin with, bonhomie. Gradually as more whisky was consumed the voices became first argumentative and then threatening. One or two were heard soothing or cajoling, while every now and then the barman himself intervened on a note of warning. In the midst of a particularly noisy dispute the outside door of the bar was flung violently open and for a moment every voice was hushed. Then the clamour broke out afresh as the newcomer was recognized. But this time it sounded to be congratulatory. From my position I could not see who had entered, but the cook whispered excitedly:

'My, my, if yon isn't Hamish Mor himself.'

'It is so?' gushed Morag ecstatically.

'It is so,' reiterated the cook.

Edging forward I saw that the cause of all the acclamation was a tall well-made man with fiery red hair peeping from under his cloth cap. Like a conquering hero he strode up to the bar counter while on all sides people pressed about him effusively, shaking his hand vigorously, and interspersing their salutations with commands to the barman to ply the newcomer with drinks. Only an odd one or two of the customers, seeming to find their own drinks suddenly distasteful, slunk towards the door and sliding round it disappeared unobtrusively. Meanwhile Hamish Mor, utterly unperturbed, was downing drinks as fast as his friends could pay for them. I asked Morag why he should be so popular.

'Ach, you'll no be knowin' him,' she told me. 'He's no from the village at all.' Her tone was like a rebuff.

'They're making a great fuss of him,' I observed.

'Aye indeed, and so they might, for a better man never lived,' breathed the cook reverently.

'Do they always treat him like this?' I persisted.

'No,' replied Morag guardedly.

'Then why today?' I asked. 'Is it his birthday or has he won a medal or something?'

Morag sighed. 'No,' she said, 'but today he's just come out of prison.'

'Prison?' I echoed incredulously.

'Aye, prison,' she confirmed.

'What was he convicted of?' I asked.

'Assault,' interposed the cook shortly.

'Assault? Who did he assault?'

'He threw the barman out of the window there,' the cook replied with a languid gesture towards the bar.

'Which barman?'

'Why, the one that you see there now,' said the cook with a touch of impatience.

I ventured a further peep round the door. The barman appeared to me to be a dissolute-looking fellow of the type that makes a woman's flesh creep and a man's fists tingle, but even so the behaviour of the crowd seemed too cruel. I watched carefully as with impassive countenance he served drink after drink to his assaulter, every drink paid for by the admiring company, who continued to jostle one another for the privilege of patting Hamish Mor on the back and wishing him, rather pointedly: 'Better luck next time!'

'Sure Hamish was for killin' that barman, was he not, Morag?' said the cook with a tinge of regret in her voice.

'I suppose that is why the wretches are wishing him better luck next time,' I retorted drily.

'Aye, I'm thinkin' Hamish will be killin' that barman one of these days yet,' asseverated Morag and added hurriedly, 'that is if the Lord spares him.'

The cook and Morag continued to discuss Hamish and his perfections while I listened with one ear to their gossip and with the other to the tragi-comedy of the bar.

'D'you mind that summer Hamish signed the pledge?' asked the cook with a chuckle.

'Aye, I mind fine,' replied Morag.

'Three days he kept off the whisky,' said the cook reminiscently.

'Three days? Three weeks it was more like,' corrected Morag.

'Three days it was,' maintained the cook stoutly.

'What happened then?' I interposed.

'Why, Hamish was lyin' in his bed that night when he hears the thrush singin' outside. "Drink well, Hamish, drink well, Hamish," says the thrush, "drink all the time." '

The two women laughed together.

'And bless me,' went on the cook, 'but Hamish jumps up. "To Hell with the missionary!" says he. "When the birds in the trees are tellin' a man to drink it canna' be wrong." So he comes here—two o'clock in the mornin' it was—and he knocks us up and tells us what he'll do to us if he doesn't get a bottle or two of whisky there and then.' The cook lifted the corner of her apron to wipe the tears of laughter from her eyes.

Hamish's message seemed to me to be an odd interpretation of the call of the thrush, but then I remembered that the bird, unlike myself, would be fortunate enough to have the Gaelic.

'D'you mind that time the artist told Hamish he wanted to paint him?' asked Morag of the cook.

'No, I don't mind that at all,' replied the other. 'Indeed I never heard of that.'

'He was only a poor wee soul,' said Morag, 'and Hamish looked down at him. "Wee mannie," says he, "if you dare to lay a brush on me I'll kick the pants off you." '

The sound of our laughter attracted the attention of the bar customers. Quickly the cook pushed the door. 'We'll just keep it shut while we finish our strupak,' she said, 'or they'll be wantin' in here with their drink.'

When the door was opened again, Hamish had left and with him the merriest of the drinkers. The atmosphere now was decidedly less convivial. Of the remaining occupants of the bar, I had no difficulty in spotting Lachy's red, flushed face and also the pale cadaverous one of Alistair the shepherd. There appeared to be some sort of argument in progress between the two.

'Lachy, my lad,' I heard Alistair say with complete amiability, 'if you say that to me again, I'll throw you out the door.'

'Alistair, my boy,' replied Lachy with equal affability, 'I'll say it to you again, and if you don't like it I'll smash your head through the counter.'

The argument terminated in a brief but cyclonic disturbance among the lounging figures; the barman shouted and the amazed crowd parted to reveal a dazed and vanquished shepherd pulling splinters of the bar counter from his hair. Lachy bent and solicitously assisted his victim to rise.

'Lachy, my boy,' began the shepherd respectfully, 'you kept your word, man, and I'm one as respects a man who can keep his word.' He turned to the barman. 'Two doubles quick now, and we'll feel the better for it,' he commanded.

Soon the erstwhile combatants were tossing off two doubles, topping them with another two, and, with arms entwined about each other's shoulders, were already proceeding into the next stage of the argument which, according to the cook's experience, they would not be long in reaching.

'Goodness! Here it is three o'clock in the evenin' and time we were makin' for home,' broke in Morag, as she caught sight of the clock.

'My, how the clock runs away with the time,' said the cook politely.

We said goodbye, and were shortly being ushered through the main doorway of the hotel as though we were honoured guests, I trying hard to look as though I had paid for my dinner.

We had to pass by the public bar entrance where I saw on the road several scraps of material of different colours. Morag, seeing the direction of my glance, bent down and picked up one of them.

'Aye, but it's always like this after a sale,' she said.

'It's the neckband of a shirt, isn't it?' I asked.

'It is so,' agreed Morag, 'and I've a good idea this one belongs to our Ruari.'

'But how on earth?' I began, when my question was cut short by a commotion inside the bar; the door burst open and out tumbled Lachy and Alistair, fighting mad once again. Lachy flung off his coat; Alistair had already discarded his. For a moment or two the men glared at one another ferociously and then each, with one swift movement that could only have been achieved with practice, pulled his clean cotton shirt up and over his head, leaving the tight cuffs around his wrists and the neckband around his neck. There was no need to finish my question.

'Come on!' said Morag, oblivious of the fact that I was already a few yards ahead of her. 'Best leave them to fight it out.'

We had agreed that our best plan was to walk on homeward until we were picked up by the bus. In this way we should avoid being crowded and also miss most of the drunks, who, according to Morag's reckoning, would by that time have been dropped off, knocked out or put to sleep in the rear. Also it would save us having to wait about for the bus as the time of its departure even on normal days was well-nigh unpredictable. We set off at a brisk pace and had not gone far before we overtook Donald Beag, one of the crofters, shepherding in front of him an unusually docile black-faced ewe and her two tiny lambs. Now I must admit that there had been a time when the sight of curly little lambs provoked in me a sentimental leaning towards vegetarianism, but after a year or so of heather-fed mutton I am afraid the sight of them merely made my mouth water. Donald was glad of our company and so that he might keep pace with us he urged on the sheep by beating his side with his artificial arm, the gleaming hook of which aroused memories of Barrie's infamous captain. The Great War which had deprived Donald of his arm had in recompense provided him with a fund of stories of his experiences, which he was always ready to relate, but now he listened avidly while I recounted the story of the runaway cow.

'My, my,' he exclaimed as I finished, 'you mean to tell me you havena' the Gaelic yet then?'

I told him that my knowledge of Gaelic was limited to such phrases as 'Kamera-ha' and 'Ha-goo-ma'.

'Indeed and it's surprising how far that bit itself will take you supposin' you have no other words of the language,' said Donald, with a wisely reminiscent smile, and embarked on a war anecdote to illustrate his words.

He was once, he told us, in a trench with a couple of dozen other soldiers when a shell came over and not one but himself was left alive. He picked himself up and started to walk away from the trench, but though he walked and walked he met with no living soul. He walked until dusk and then, espying the ruins of a house, he made towards them. Just as he reached them a figure jumped from behind a wall, held up its arms and shouted, '*Kamerad, Kamerad.*'

'Ach, well,' continued Donald. 'There was a good few Gaelic speakers in our regiment at that time, so I just holds out my hand and says, "Ha-goo-ma". As soon as I'd said it we both stared at each other and then we both turned and ran like blazes in opposite directions.'

Donald chuckled at the memory. 'Ach, but I was sorry enough afterwards I can tell you,' he went on. 'For I'd sooner have had a German to talk to than nobody at all, and I daresay that with the Gaelic we might have understood each other pretty well.'

As Donald's story came to an end we were drawing level with an elderly man who was making repeated attempts to drive an emaciated cow before him. It was fortunate that he had not far to go or he would have stood little chance of getting the beast home.

'What on earth came over the man to buy himself a beast like that?' muttered Morag under her breath. 'It looks as though it started to shiver when the frost came and it's still frozen into its shiver.'

I thought it an apt description, but Donald was not to be outdone.

'You need to get a rope on that cow quickly,' he shouted to the owner.

'A rope?' The old man looked bewildered. 'Why, she's that quiet she has no need of a rope.'

'It's no to quiet her she's needin' it,' said Donald with brutal candour, 'it's to keep her from fallin' to pieces.'

The man glowered in reply and as the sheep were in better condition than the cow we soon left him behind. Some distance in front of us we could see a knot of people and animals progressing slowly along the road. I have never been able to determine whether the crofters walk slowly so as not to distress the animals they herd, or whether the animals walk slowly out of consideration for the crofters they lead. Whichever way it was I had learned that, short of brutality, it was impossible to hurry either a crofter or his cow. As we drew abreast of them we were hailed delightedly by the jovial red-faced drovers, many of whom I remembered having seen quite recently in the bar. They were decidedly merry and seemed quite unconcerned whether they reached home that night or the next day. Bottles were soon being extricated from jacket pockets and proffered confidentially. Had glasses been obtainable Morag and I would have had great difficulty in refusing their generosity but fortunately they accepted the fact that bottles were for the privileged, or not so particular, menfolk.

Much interest was focused on Murdoch, a white-haired old bachelor, who was riding a horse purchased at the sale.

'Why did you buy a new horse?' asked Donald. 'Was your other one not good enough?'

'No,' replied Murdoch, 'she wasn't very good at the ploughin' this year.'

Morag was quick to defend the old horse. 'Well, she was gettin' old,' she scolded Murdoch, 'and you must expect horses to disintegrate with age.'

No one seemed to think this characteristic of old horses in the least peculiar, and I waited in vain for Donald to offer his suggestion of a rope.

'Your own horse is gettin' old at that,' Murdoch told Donald.

'Indeed she is not,' retorted Donald indignantly. 'My horse put in three bags of potatoes for me only last week.'

'Did you see yon cow Ian Tearlaich had bought?' asked someone in reference to the bag of bones we had lately passed.

'So we did,' replied Morag, 'just one big bellyache that beast is and nothin' more.'

The train of men and beasts strung itself out along the road; cows bellowed and from time to time calves tried vainly to elude their new owners.

'We'll just stay and wait here for the bus,' suggested Morag, and as we had already covered a good distance I willingly agreed.

At that moment one of the drovers treated us to a conspiratorial wink.

'Why is Angus givin' us the wingéd eye?'whispered my companion.

Angus pointed gleefully at Murdoch, who sat with unshakable confidence astride his surprisingly quiet horse. The old man's back was comfortably rounded, his hands were deep in his pockets and his outsize feet swung loosely on either side. Angus went alongside and put his hand on the saddle.

'Sure, Murdoch, it's yourself that's havin' the nice ride home now, is it not?' he teased.

'So I am,' agreed Murdoch cordially. 'She's a nice quiet horse indeed for an old man like myself.'

'And you with the biggest flat feet in the place to take you home too,' went on Angus.

Murdoch laughed self-consciously.

Before I realized what was happening Angus had stealthily lifted the saddle, placed his lighted cigarette under and dodged quickly away. Instantly the horse reared, pawed the air desperately for a few seconds and then, to the delight of the wildly cheering drovers, galloped madly along the road with Murdoch clinging to its mane like grim death and swearing comprehensively. The startled cattle scattered to right and left.

'You fool!' I flung at Angus as I took off in the wake of the runaway, feeling certain that the old man would come to some harm. I ran quickly but not having had the same incentive my performance was much less impressive than that of the horse.

Rounding a bend I was in time to see Murdoch being flung, or flinging himself, from the back of his mount on to the grassy verge of the road and some minutes later, closely followed by the gamekeeper, I came upon his prostrate body. Murdoch lay quite still and though I could see no blood I was quite sure that he was injured in some way. Gingerly I began to examine him. By this time the rest of the men had left their cattle to look after themselves and had arrived on the scene. They stood watching in a subdued silence while Morag, who had come panting in their rear, prodded exploratively at the prone figure.

'He's no dead but I believe he's unconscience,' she pronounced.

'D'you hear that now?' The gamekeeper turned on Angus with simulated rage.

'Ach, you couldna' kill that one without shootin' him first,' rejoined Angus lightly; 'and supposin' you shot him dead you'd still have to go and knock him down afterwards, his feet are that flat.'

A gust of relieved laughter swept the onlookers.

'It was a crazy thing to do,' I cut in tartly. My rebuke brought a completely unrepentant smile to Angus's ruddy face.

The gamekeeper tried again: 'It was a fool thing to do,' he stressed reproachfully; 'and you're lucky he's only been knocked unconscious. He could easily have been hurt badly.'

After that inane observation I gave up trying to bestir in them any feelings of remorse.

Someone bethought himself to go and catch the horse, which by now had rid itself of the cigarette and was grazing quietly, utterly indifferent to the fate of its owner.

The bus opportunely arrived at that moment and Murdoch was deposited on the top of a snoring pile of inebriates who were in turn bedded on a mattress of bulging mailbags. His condition was the cause of much levity and even when, still unconscious, he was being carried home by four of the more sober of the Bruachites it seemed to have occurred to no one but myself that the man might have sustained serious injury. As it was quite possible that the four carriers would tire of their burden before they reached Murdoch's house and that the invalid, like the old woman with the pig, would 'never get home that night', I insisted on accompanying them. Morag came too and we were present to see Murdoch taken off to bed by indifferent relatives who seemed in no way surprised to see their kinsman being brought home insensible. I gathered that it was the rule rather than the exception for Murdoch to be in this condition after a sale, and my proposal that a doctor be sent for was received with icy disdain.

After taking a welcome cup of tea, Morag and I set off home. The night was patchily dark and there was again a threat of rain in the scudding clouds through which a fugitive moon peeped anxiously. I remembered I had a torch and had just retrieved it from the bottom of my handbag when a savage scream rent the stillness of the night, and out from one of the cottages a white shape staggered. My companion and I stopped still and in the beam of the torch saw a middle-aged woman clad only in a nightgown. The woman's eyes were sunken and staring, her grey unkempt hair fell in wisps over her dirt-streaked face. Her hands tore convulsively at her breast and her mouth moved soundlessly.

'It's Barbac,' whispered Morag, but I had already recognized the figure, despite the fact that when I had first met her she had been a plump and pleasant little woman, with only a slight inclination to neurosis. A long illness coupled with careless nursing had affected her brain, and now here she was, a wasted gibbering lunatic. Her plight was shocking but at this moment the sight of her made me shudder.

'Go back to your bed, Barbac,' Morag entreated softly, 'go back to your bed.'

A man appeared and, taking the unresisting woman by the arm, led her back to the cottage with silent resignation. The incident had shaken Morag nearly as much as myself, and it was not until we were on our own doorstep that she spoke again.

'Indeed it's a pity when people go like that,' she said sadly.

I agreed wholeheartedly.

'Sure,' she went on, 'I would sooner lose my hearin' or my sight than I would lose my sanitation. I believe to lose one's sanitation would be the end of everythin'.'

The following day I called at Murdoch's house to ask how he fared, for I was still the only one who was in the least worried by his mishap. I was assured that he was 'fine except for a sore head', and this was apparently of such frequent occurrence that I realized my enquiry was not tactful. On the contrary, my concern was regarded as a reflection on Murdoch's capacity to hold his drink.

Later I called at Lachy's home to collect some wool for Morag. Lachy was there, his jaw much swollen. He also complained of a 'sore head'—a 'sale head', interpreted his mother pithily. It was not long before we heard the voice of Alistair the shepherd and Lachy was quick to invite his recent opponent to come in for a strupak. Both Alistair's eyes were black and he had a cut on his nose.

'Lachy, my boy, they tell me we was fightin' like bulls yesterday,' said the shepherd contritely.

'We was?' asked Lachy, tenderly feeling his jaw.

'Aye, it's true they're sayin'.'

Lachy inspected his knuckles critically.

'Ach, if we was fightin' it was no us fightin',' expounded the shepherd.

'No?' queried Lachy.

'No, 'twas the drink inside us that was fightin',' said the shepherd importantly.

Their heads nodded in unison as each studied the other's wounds, and then Lachy let out a self-satisfied chuckle.

'Well, Alistair, my boy, I'd say from the look of you that my whisky was stronger than your whisky.' He gave me an audacious wink. 'D'you not think so?' he asked me.

I declined to give an opinion and after politely refusing the invitation of Lachy's mother to stay and 'take a drink of milk from the cattles', left them to their raillery. At several of the houses I passed on my way home a solitary shirt hung limply on the clothes line. Each shirt was devoid of cuffs and neckband!

6. *Patients and Patience*

THE paralysing effect of an influenza epidemic which swept the village was the means of my obtaining a far deeper insight into the customs and living conditions of the inhabitants than I could possibly have obtained in ordinary circumstances. The epidemic temporarily incapacitated the nurse and deluged the doctor with work; so daily Morag and I, who were lucky enough to escape infection, sallied forth to make beds, to wash dishes, and in some cases, where the illness had struck most severely, to do a good deal of the house and croft work besides. It was fortunate that I had by this time learned to milk, but, though most of the women exclaimed favourably at the degree of skill I had acquired, most of the cows expressed grave doubts as to my ability; doubts which often resulted in the milk-pail being a much different shape at the end of the milking than at the beginning!

During this period of ministration to the sick I discovered that Morag's mother had been regarded as the 'medicine woman' of the village, and, as the daughter was expected to have acquired much of the mother's skill or 'magic', my landlady's remedies were often much in demand. It soon became evident to me that her advice and instructions were adhered to far more conscientiously than were those of the doctor. The latter, who was by no means unaware of the attitude of the crofters towards his profession, accepted the position with amused tolerance and between the amateur and the professional there existed a friendly rivalry which neither the one nor the other would allow to be affected by the continuous badinage of their patients. Naturally, we saw a good deal of the doctor at this time; constantly encountering him in and out of sick rooms; and though in me he expected to find an ally, I was already too conscious of the efficacy of Morag's prescriptions in contrast to his own to prove a particularly staunch one. Indeed I was inclined to suspect that he himself had more faith in the simple traditional remedies than in his own involved treatments, especially so when I overheard him asking my landlady what she recommended for rheumatism.

'Thicker soles on your boots, boy,' she advised him, with a disapproving glance at his dressy town shoes.

'I cannot get strong shoes on my feet they're so swollen,' countered the doctor.

'The swellin' would come down if you rubbed your feets with eel fat a time or two,' said Morag, and though the doctor pretended scepticism he insisted on driving us home, where, after allowing himself to be persuaded to take a 'wee strupak', he offhandedly reintroduced the subject of rheumatism. Morag, taking the hint, searched in the cupboard and then brought out a small bottle of yellowish-brown oily stuff which she handed to the doctor. There was a contemptuous smile on his lips as he accepted it, but nevertheless the alacrity with which he pocketed the bottle convinced me that a good deal of his manner was assumed purely for my benefit.

Though in the opinion of the crofters the doctor's medical skill was negligible, his presence in the sick room was as welcome as it was at the ceilidh. He drank their tea, capped their jokes and criticized their cattle—he was generally considered to be a better vet than doctor—and probably his camaraderie contributed as much to the recovery of his patients as anything he might give them from a bottle. Personally I found the doctor refreshing, for, whatever his faults may have been, he had at least retained a character. He was clever and he knew it; he liked whisky and he drank it—in quantity; he ate his food with more gusto than grace and the evidence of it could be seen all down the front of his waistcoat. His sense of humour was puckish, and his contempt for the English, despite the fact that he had married an Englishwoman, permeated much of his conversation; before I had been acquainted with him for half an hour, he had embarked on a story of his student days in which he claimed to have got the better of a supercilious Englishman.

It was during the university vacation, he told me, and the doctor was roaming the hills herding his father's cattle, when two tourists, a man and a woman, approached him. The doctor was barefooted and bareheaded and was clad, as he himself put it, 'in a well-ventilated pair of breeks and a shirt with more front than back in it'.

'Hello, young fellow!' said the Englishman condescendingly.

'Good afternoon,' answered the doctor politely.

'And do you live around here?' asked the man archly.

'I do,' replied the doctor.

'And do you go to school?'

'Sometimes I go,' the doctor admitted.

'I see you have a book under your arm. Can you read?'

'A little,' said the doctor hesitantly, though the book happened to be an advanced medical textbook.

'Ah!' The man turned and conferred in low tones with his companion and then addressed the doctor once more. 'And can you count?' he asked.

'Er, yes,' faltered the doctor.

'Very good!' exclaimed the man. 'How much can you count?'

The doctor looked puzzled.

'Tell me, my boy, how many people there are here just at this moment. You, myself and my wife. How many is that?'

'One hundred,' answered the doctor after a struggle.

The man and his wife laughed derisively. 'Come, come, my boy. How do you make that out?' they remonstrated.

'Well,' explained the doctor, turning to go, 'there's myself, that's one.'

'Yes?' the couple waited in amused expectancy.

'And there's yourself and your wife—you're the two nothings. Good day to you both.'

Never before or since, it seemed, had the hill been so strangely quiet as it was in the following moments. Whether or not the story was true I cannot say, but I do know that the doctor possessed an enviable gift for disconcerting people whom he regarded as being impudent, and I am forced to admit that my countrymen seem to regard themselves as having the right to interrogate the Islanders much as a policeman might interrogate a suspicious character.

Of all the intractable patients that we helped to nurse during the epidemic, Murdoch was by far the most difficult. He was by turns haughty, mischievous, crafty and ingenuous. One day he would decide he was at death's door and would be amenable to every suggestion; the next he would not only be out of bed, but visiting a neighbour's house to read the newspaper. When he had exhausted

the news he would crawl back to his own home and would again
make rapid strides towards death's door, where, moaning piteously,
he would remain until the time for delivery of the next newspaper.
Why Murdoch would never go to the length of buying his own paper
I do not know, but then many of the crofters' little economies are
entirely incomprehensible to the outsider.

Murdoch's two elderly sisters had also been taken ill with the
influenza at the same time as himself, but they were all three fairly
well on the road to recovery when I called one day to milk their cow
and to make their tea. As soon as I pushed open the kitchen door
I could hear voices coming from Murdoch's room, one of which
belonged to the doctor. After a word to the sisters I set about preparing the tea-trays and was engaged on this task when the door leading
from Murdoch's room was opened and the doctor, winking furiously,
beckoned me to accompany him. His expression prepared me for
some sort of joke and as I followed him through to the bedroom
I wondered what it could be.

'Well, Murdoch,' said the doctor, 'I'll be away now as Miss Beckwith's come to make your tea.'

Murdoch lay back on his pillows and greeted me with a benign
smile.

'Just you see and keep on taking your medicine,' the doctor told
him.

'Aye, that I will, Doctor. I feel the better of that medicine indeed,'
replied Murdoch earnestly.

'Did you take it in the morning?' asked the doctor.

'Aye, I did,' said the old man.

'And after your tea?'

'To be sure I did.'

'And did you take it last night after supper?'

'Certainly I did,' nodded Murdoch solemnly.

'Murdoch!' accused the doctor suddenly, 'you're a b—— liar!'

Murdoch sat bolt upright and fixed the doctor with a pair of
startled eyes.

'Doctor,' he declared with touching dignity, 'wouldn't I swear
before God I did as you said. I'm tellin' you I took it three times
yesterday and twice this day already, and there's no more than half
the bottle left now. I swear it indeed.'

Murdoch lifted up his hand as though taking the oath and I was sure that even the doctor would be convinced that the old man was telling the truth.

'Murdoch,' repeated the doctor sternly, 'I'm telling you you're a liar.' He produced a bag of peppermints, offered it to me and then popped one into his own mouth. Murdoch scrutinized the doctor's face.

'Am I indeed a liar?' he asked, an unrepentant smile beginning to touch his lips and eyes.

The doctor extracted a bottle of medicine from his bulging jacket pocket and set it on the table beside the bed. 'There now,' he announced triumphantly, 'though I brought your medicine along with me on Tuesday, I forgot to leave it for you, and when I got back home I found it still in my pocket. You old rascal, you didn't even miss the stuff so I know fine you're a liar.' He folded his arms across his chest and stood smiling down impishly at his patient's discomfiture which was brief indeed.

'Why then I must be a liar,' admitted Murdoch equably. 'But fancy me been suckin' at an empty bottle these three or four times. It just shows how poorly I've been.'

'Empty bottle!' exploded the doctor with feigned wrath. 'You old bodach, you've never sucked at an empty bottle in your life. I'll guarantee that any bottle you've sucked was more than half full; but, you devil, you'd sooner take your medicine from the barman than from the doctor.'

Murdoch chuckled appreciatively. 'I'd take the medicine all right if you'd dose me with the right stuff,' he retaliated.

The doctor grunted non-committally. 'If you're quite comfortable I'll be on my way,' he said.

'Comfortable!' echoed Murdoch. 'I'm comfortable enough except for my feets.'

'What's wrong with your feet?'

'Indeed my feets and my legs is as red as the dove's with the cold,' the old man said plaintively. 'I canna' seem to keep the warmth in them.'

'You must be dyin' from the feet upwards then,' retorted the doctor callously.

'That wouldn't be true now would it?' pleaded the old man.

'And why not?' asked the doctor, indifferent to Murdoch's sudden woebegone expression. 'It's well over seventy you are, isn't it?'

'Just a year or two over,' muttered the patient with a sidelong glance at me.

'Ah well, maybe a hot-water bottle will save you this time,' said the doctor with a laugh. I laughed too, but more with the desire to comfort, and Murdoch, taking courage, joined in wholeheartedly.

After seeing the doctor to the door and collecting the tray from the kitchen, I returned to the invalid to find him eyeing the bottle of medicine distastefully. 'I wonder what's in that?' he asked me.

'You'll soon find out,' I told him.

He removed the cork, sniffed once or twice and then, carefully replacing the cork, offered the bottle to me, in case I should catch the influenzy and be in need of a dose. Upon my refusal he respectfully bade me to throw the bottle in the sea on my way home.

'But you should take it,' I argued, 'it will do you good, otherwise the doctor wouldn't give it to you.'

'Ach, that joker!' Murdoch said scornfully. 'It was for my sisters I had to send for him rightly, they was that bad with the influenzy; and if they'd gone and died on me, and me not after havin' the doctor to them, they'd have been grumbling at me for the rest of their lives.'

He reached for his pipe. 'Whisky's the stuff for me,' he resumed. 'I'd be dead many times over if it wasn't for the wee dram I take every night of my life.'

I did as much as I could for Murdoch and his household and was on my way home when Morag's voice hailed me from a neighbouring cottage.

'Can you give me a hand in here?' she beseeched. 'There's all of them sick and not a body to do a hand's turn.'

I followed her into the cottage and into the one and only bedroom where 'all of them'—father, mother, nine children and the daughter-in-law—were compressed into three beds. The father and mother along with two of the younger children occupied one of the double beds; the other was shared by three girls and three boys, head to tail, while the married son and his pregnant wife looked almost comfortable in the comparative spaciousness of a single bed. All the beds were littered with paper-back novelettes and tattered comics, which some of the occupants had been reading avidly as we entered, despite the fact that there was little light filtering through the deep, yellow, lace-screened window. The room was sickeningly hot, for it was impossible to open the window and Morag had a big peat fire blazing in the grate.

By the time we had tidied the beds and I had collected several bruises from the iron bedsteads I was feeling that I should soon be in need of attention myself.

'Why d'you cramp yourselves like this?' asked Morag. 'Why are you no usin' the recess bed in the kitchen.'

'But it's more fun when we're all together,' the mother replied evenly. 'It's kind of lonely for those in the kitchen.'

'Fun' seemed a strange description of their plight, but those who were not too ill to appreciate it were obviously quite content.

I was glad when Morag suggested that I should make some tea, and escaped thankfully to the relative coolness of the kitchen, where, as I buttered scones already baked by Morag and waited for the kettle to boil, I marvelled at the crofter's ability to endure discomfort, which is as often due to choice as circumstance.

I was in the act of setting the teapot to warm when a shout took me back to the bedroom. One of the younger invalids wanted to vomit and while Morag held the child away from the bed I was requested to seek the necessary receptacle. Going down on my knees I drew from under the bed what I imagined was the chamber, only to discover it to be a tightly packed bowl of salt herring—part of the family's winter supply. A burst of hysterical laughter greeted its appearance and, pushing back the bowl, I tried again. Gingerly I slid out another bowl of a slightly different shape. This was the cause for further merriment.

'That's the milk settin' for the cream,' shrieked the lady of the house joyously. 'Annie promised she'd come and make butter for us tomorrow.'

I replaced the bowl of milk and again poked warily under the bed; my explorations being accompanied by gusts of unrestrained laughter from the beds. My fingers touched a bundle of clothes, a small barrel, some wood, a pile of books and then, thank heaven! earthenware. This proved to be the utensil I was seeking and drawing it forth with a flourish I thrust it towards Morag. But the pantomime of my attempts to find it had reduced the small invalid to such a state of helpless mirth that all thoughts of being sick had been banished.

'My, that was as good as a tonic,' gasped the patients feebly as they wiped away tears of laughter with the edges of blankets.

An hour or two later, after we had made our happy family as comfortable as we could, Morag and I set out for the home of 'Padruig the daftie'. The word 'daftie' in the islands covered a multitude of mentalities. It was applied to the repulsive, misshapen imbeciles who were capable of nothing but vice, but also included the innocuous souls like Padruig who, if his income had been five thousand pounds a year instead of five thousand pence, might have been classed as merely eccentric. My acquaintance with Padruig was slight, for, though I had at various times noticed him shambling in and out of the houses of the neighbours, he was very shy and reserved and had seen to it that we never came within speaking distance. I knew, of course, that he lived in a tiny two-roomed cottage which he shared with his half-wit brother Euan. I knew that until three months previously they had been looked after by their very attractive sister but, on her marriage, she had left them to fend for themselves. Padruig was reputed to be immensely strong and to do those jobs which he was capable of doing remarkably well. Despite his simplicity he was well behaved and was, except in moments of excitement, an upright and devout Christian.

His brother Euan was a different character altogether, for, on the death of his parents, he had had the misfortune to be sent to live with a reprobate old uncle who had taught the boy nothing except a comprehensive vocabulary of vulgar abuse and profanity. The uncle had possessed such a violent temper that no one had felt inclined to interfere, and thus it was that Euan acquired a language peculiarly his own. For instance he referred to a man quite inoffensively as a 'he-bugger', a woman as a 'she-bugger', a dog as a 'hairy-bugger', and a bird as a 'feathery-bugger', and so on. After the death of his uncle Euan returned home and Padruig, whose vocabulary was extensive enough when occasion demanded, set himself the task of thrashing the evil out of his poor brother. So effective was his punishment that Euan, instead of refraining from the use of oaths, found it easier to refrain from speaking. This he did whenever possible, substituting a rapid blinking of the eyes for the words he did not utter.

Morag nudged my arm as we stumbled along the tortuous little path that led to Padruig's cottage. 'He talks awful wild sometimes,' she warned, 'but don't be laughin' at him to his face or you'll upset him.'

I promised not to laugh.

'And don't talk to Euan at all if you can help it,' continued Morag. 'If he was to swear in front of you, the Lord knows what Padruig would do to him.'

Reaching the cottage my companion pushed open the door and entered. I was about to follow, ducking my head to save banging it against the low roof, but recoiled as a dreadful stench assailed my nostrils.

'Padruig, Padruig,' Morag chided the unseen occupants. 'You and your ferrets! The smell of them is near knockin' Miss Peckwitt over backwards.'

Cautiously I started forward again, circumnavigating the large wooden chests which impeded the entrance both of people and of light. Morag motioned towards the chests. 'Ferrets,' she explained in a whisper, but I had already discovered four of the little horrors for myself.

'And you're feelin' better today, are you, Padruig my boy?' asked my landlady brightly as she crossed the kitchen. The room was incredibly dark and smoky and at first I could make out nothing but the dim glow of a fire, though there was still ample daylight outside.

A man's voice answered hoarse and low: 'I'm better now. I'm for gettin' myself up tomorrow.'

'You are not!' contradicted Morag flatly.

'I am so,' maintained the voice firmly. 'I got to sweep the chimbly.' Morag accepted the announcement with a sigh.

'Here, I've brought Miss Peckwitt to see you,' she said, adroitly changing the subject.

With difficulty I groped my way across the kitchen; past a wooden bench on which I was just able to discern the figure of Euan sitting motionless as a statue; past a large barrel on top of which stood a water-pail, and as my eyes became accustomed to the gloom I managed to make out the shape of a recess bed in the corner where Padruig himself reclined. His horny hand grasped mine and shook it lengthily.

'I'm goin' to light the lamp,' said Morag in a business-like tone and turning to Euan she commanded him to blow up the fire so that she could make a wee oatcake or two for their tea. Euan jumped up instantly, but instead of taking a pair of bellows, as I expected him to, he dropped down on his knees, puffed out his cheeks and commenced to blow on the fire with such prodigious gusts that his eyes threatened to start out of his head at any moment. The dim glow showered sparks and blossomed gradually into a flickering flame which in contrast to Euan's madder-hued cheeks looked positively anaemic.

'It's that dark in here I canna' see if you're well or dyin',' grumbled Morag as she put a spill to the wick of a miniature oil-lamp. 'Sure if you don't throw them ferrets in the sea soon, they'll be takin' the bed from under you,' she admonished Padruig.

I smiled at Padruig and his gentle brown eyes smiled back at me shyly.

'Are you hearin' from Lexy?' Morag enquired as she set the lamp on the mantelpiece and, taking a basin from the meagrely equipped dresser, scooped up some oatmeal from the barrel.

Padruig nodded.

'Did you get someone to read it for you?' asked Morag.

Again Padruig nodded and, pointing to the mantelpiece, asked Morag to hand him an envelope which was hiding demurely behind a glass net float. Holding the envelope in his hand he pointed eagerly to the stamp.

'All the waitresses in Glasgow has them little caps on their heads,' he told me, indicating the tiara worn by the Queen.

'Do they?' I asked stoically.

'Turn up that lamp a bitty, Euan,' Morag's voice interrupted, 'I canna' see whether it's my hands or my feets I'm stirrin' with.' Euan did as he was told and then returned to his seat on the bench.

Padruig spoke again. 'It's darker than this in Buckram Palace,' he said.

'In Buckingham Palace? Is it really?' I asked in astonishment.

'Yes,' he asserted, nodding his dark bullet head emphatically. I nodded wonderingly in return.

'I been to England once,' Padruig continued, watching my face intently.

'You did?' I asked, giving him nod for nod as well as I was able. 'How nice that must have been. Did you enjoy yourself?'

'Yes, yes.' His own nodding was becoming extraordinarily vigorous. I doubted if I could keep pace.

'I went to Buckram Palace to see the Queen.'

Helplessly I glanced at Morag, but she was busily occupied in pouring melted fat into the bowl of oatmeal.

'You did? You were very lucky,' I said faintly.

'Yes, up lots and lots of steps I been.' Padruig was still staring at me with concentrated attention and I risked a sober nod.

'Ever so many steps,' he continued. 'Up, up, up.' He demonstrated on the blanket with two of his stubby fingers how he had laboured up the steps of 'Buckram Palace', pausing every now and then to ensure by an anxious glance that I understood him.

'Just give me a hand with this,' Morag broke peremptorily into a brief but awed silence. Thankfully I moved over to the table. She put a finger to her lips and frowned expressively: and, guessing that she was again imploring me not to laugh, I shook my head reassuringly, for I was not so much amused as amazed by the tale. On the bed Padruig was still engrossed in climbing the innumerable steps of 'Buckram Palace', while from the bench the almost toothless Euan watched him with wide, fascinated eyes.

'We get to top.' Padruig waved an expressive arm above his head, and out of the corner of my eye I saw Euan ogle the rafters.

'And what did you find then?' I asked him, feeling rather like the inquisitor of the pussy cat who went to London.

'Chairs!' burst out Padruig. 'Chairs!' he repeated, 'hundreds and hundreds of little red armchairs all in rows. As true as I'm here.' He leaned earnestly towards me as though doubting my credulity.

'Really?' I murmured politely. 'And the Queen? Where did you see the Queen?'

'The Queen,' echoed Padruig rapturously. 'My, my, beautiful she was. Beautiful just.' He sighed lingeringly. 'But it was so dark in Buckram Palace,' he went on, 'that the Queen herself had to run in front of everybody with a little torch, and show people which was their seats.'

'Really!' I quavered.

'And what did you take for your breakfast, Padruig, my boy?' My landlady's voice broke opportunely into the recital and, giving Padruig no chance to reply, she pushed a cup of tea and two or three hot buttered oatcakes into his hand.

I subsided on to the bench beside Euan, refusing the tea Morag had proffered, which I was quite sure would be ferret flavoured. Suddenly Euan uttered an exclamation and jumping to his feet he charged recklessly through the outer door, muttering under his breath words which sounded suspiciously maledictory. I wondered what I had done and looked questioningly at Morag.

'It's his ducks,' she told me. 'He has one duck and one drake and he thinks the world of them just. But they plague the life out of him, always gettin' into the wee bit garden Padruig takes so much care of, and if Padruig catches them there he'll be for killin' them. Is that not right, Padruig?'

Padruig, his mouth crammed to capacity with oatcake, grumbled confirmation.

'Sure,' continued Morag, 'Euan spends most of his time chasin' them ducks away from Padruig's garden, and when he's chased them far enough he has to go and seek for them for fear they'll run away on him.'

As Morag was speaking she was rinsing soiled dishes in the remainder of the hot water from the kettle and, taking a cloth which was grey with age, I dried them and put them back on the dresser. Morag then started to tidy up but as the room was so austerely furnished the amount of actual tidying needed was negligible. The house may, as Morag claimed, have been spotlessly clean—if one excepted the ferrets—but there was so little illumination, either natural or artificial, that it was impossible for the casual observer like myself to tell whether it was clean or filthy.

Before we went I pointed to an extremely handsome bird-cage which was suspended from the ceiling on the far side of the room. It was a beautiful cage, shining and clean, its ornate brassy decorations gleaming like gold, but to me the thought of a creature so sun- and freedom-loving as a bird incarcerated in such gloom was distressing.

'Your bird is very quiet,' I observed.

Morag prodded me hastily. 'He has no bird,' she told me, hurrying me out of the house.

Outside there was still enough daylight for us to see Euan returning to the byre, shepherding in front of him two plump, waddling, quacking ducks. He stood and smiled at us vacuously.

'Fine ducks,' I commented.

'Bloody fine ducks,' Euan agreed blissfully.

'Euan!' interposed Morag in tones that shrivelled the half-wit into abjectness.

'What do you feed them on?' I enquired.

'Duck eggs, Missed,' the reply came with prompt servility. (Euan had never made up his mind whether to address me as 'Miss' or 'Mistress', but his compromise of 'Missed' was, I suppose, as apt a designation as any other for a middle-aged spinster.)

'Duck eggs?' I echoed foolishly. 'Where do you get them?'

Euan bestowed on Morag a look that was eloquent with pity. 'The ducks lays eggs,' he elucidated. 'Best Bl—— Best food for ducks, Missed.'

'Yes, of course,' I agreed wanly, faced with the eternal problem of which came first.

We were well out of range of the house before I asked Morag why she had nudged me at the mention of the bird-cage. She told me that Padruig had seen the cage at an auction sale some years ago and had fallen so much in love with it that he had insisted on buying it.

'There's nothin' in the whole of the village that gets a quarter of the care that cage gets; if he isna' paintin' it he's polishin' it, and if he's no polishin' it he's tattin' with it some way or another.'

'I wonder he doesn't want a bird to keep in it,' I said.

'Indeed if a bird set foot in that cage Padruig would wring its neck,' replied Morag seriously.

The next day Padruig kept to his intention of leaving his bed and when Lachy and I passed the house in the early afternoon we saw him preparing to sweep the chimney by means of a large bunch of heather and a stone which were tied to one end of a rope.

'He ought not to be doing that,' I told Lachy. 'He hasn't really recovered from his flu.'

'Ach, we'll just keep behind the dyke here and see he doesn't come to any harm.'

We watched Padruig, who may have been feeling as dizzy as he looked, climb with the aid of a flimsy ladder on to the roof and fling his arms passionately around the single chimney pot. After clinging desperately for a few minutes he decided it was safe to let go with one hand with which he began to manipulate the rope.

'How does he sweep the chimney with that arrangement?' I asked Lachy, who explained that the stone was lowered down the chimney and was then removed by a confederate inside the house. The confederate then pulled on the end of the rope until the man on the roof shouted the signal to stop; the cleaning being accomplished by each man hauling on the rope in turn, thus causing the bunch of heather to scrape up and down the chimney and dislodge the soot.

'Ready!' We heard Padruig's stentorian shout, but unfortunately Euan, who should have been ready to remove the stone and pull, had just noticed that his ducks were bent on entering Padruig's beloved garden and had rushed off after them, hurling murderous-looking boulders and colourful abuse. Padruig, discovering the desertion of his accomplice, pulled furiously on the rope, climbed wrathfully down from the chimney and also gave chase. His abuse was equally colourful and the boulders he threw looked just as murderous. It was only the target that was different!

A few minutes later Padruig returned dragging a crestfallen Euan by the scruff of the neck. Again he ascended the roof and again, with the deliberateness of a star performer in a play, he made his preparations.

'Right!' he bawled down the chimney, but the recalcitrant ducks had grown impatient for their feed and were already engaged on their investigation of the garden. With a stream of curses and an utter disregard for Padruig's instructions, Euan chased the two ducks down towards the burn. Padruig's language as he descended from the roof a second time and took off after his errant brother outrivalled Euan's worst.

Lachy and I made our presence known.

'I'm goin' to tie him to the end of the rope when I get him, and jiggle him up and down the chimney,' Padruig panted as he passed us at a vengeful trot.

'I believe he means it, too.' laughed Lachy.

By what means Padruig eventually completed the chimney sweeping I have no idea, for I had to be on my way, but when I returned later that afternoon a sinuous column of blue smoke was ascending serenely from the chimney, and the satisfying fragrance of burning peat lingered warmly in the chill air. I caught sight of Euan, who, with many furtive glances at the house, was shooing his duck and drake towards their evening quarters in the cow byre.

'He Breeah!' I called.

With a guilty start he whisked round to return my greeting. He looked very chastened—and very black!

It was about a month or so later when I met Euan again. He was staying alone in the house, Padruig having gone to spend a holiday with his newly married sister on the other side of the Island.

'Well, and how are your ducks?' I asked him, after I had made the necessary enquiries as to his brother's health.

'Bugger died on me,' he replied despondently.

I was suitably astonished. 'When was that?' I asked.

'Soon,' he answered with a lachrymose nod.

I wanted to commiserate but was at a loss to know which tense to commiserate in.

'But you still have your drake?' I said.

'Yes, yes.' He started off towards the house, obviously expecting me to follow, but I was slightly surprised when, beckoning to me eagerly, he disappeared into its dark depths. I wondered if, in Padruig's absence, the drake had ousted one of the ferrets, and after taking some deep breaths of fresh air and doing some rapid eye-blinking I warily poked my head and shoulders round the door into the kitchen. Immediately a frenzied quacking and hissing broke out in the gloom of the far corner and even before I could make out the wildly swinging cage and the outline of its occupant's head darting and feinting in all directions, I guessed that Padruig's cherished toy had become the new refuge for Euan's equally cherished drake. Recalling Morag's prophecy I hoped for the sake of both Euan and his bird that Padruig would not return without due warning.

I had taken my leave of Euan before remembering that I had omitted to ask after the health of his recently married sister. I turned to him with the enquiry.

'Her buggered, Missed.' The profane affability of the reply made me wince.

'Whatever is the matter?' I asked.

Euan lifted his shoulders in a prolonged fatalistic shrug. 'He-bugger, she-bugger, quick come little-bugger,' he informed me with remarkable frankness.

I walked for some distance before I permitted myself to consider his extraordinary statement, which persisted in running through my head like an oft-repeated formula. I was shocked to find myself walking in time to the words just as one unwittingly walks in time to a band playing in a city street. I shook myself and changed step resolutely.

I had to change step three or four times before I finally reached home.

7. *Seagull*

Seagull, which was the name of the boat shared by Lachy and Ruari, was used for inshore fishing, lobster creeling and for the occasional tourist trade. She was slow and heavy and, like a Cheshire beauty, broad in the beam. Her insides were spangled with fish scales which, though decorative, were inclined to be somewhat odorous; her engine was capricious but only slightly more so than her crew; her name was inapt, for she looked as much out of her element on the water as would a bedroom slipper floating on a bathtub.

The frequent invitations I received from Ruari and Lachy to accompany them on their trips were flattering in the extreme, though I must frankly admit that, once aboard, neither of the men seemed to be aware of my presence. They addressed me seldom and left me more or less to my own devices, and I was perfectly content that it should be so. Seasickness never troubled me in *Seagull*, nor did I ever reach the stage which Morag described as being 'sick of the sea but not sick in it'. Sometimes I would take a darra and lower it hopefully into the cool, green water, and was thrilled when it came in again, as it sometimes did, with half a dozen or so rainbow-hued mackerel writhing on its hooks. Sometimes I would help haul in the creels but was always careful to retire to a safe distance while Lachy tied the vicious claws of their occupants. Invariably I dragged a spinner after the boat and, to the amazement of the crew, who thought they knew everything there was to be known about fishing, hooked all kinds of fish ranging from dogfish to salmon. The latter of course we always threw back into the sea as the law demands. By what method we managed to obey the law and still have the salmon for supper is nobody's business.

Though Ruari and Lachy could reasonably be described as intrepid sailors there was an underlying nervousness about them which revealed itself in the altercation between them which continued incessantly. If Ruari saw a cormorant, Lachy swore it was a porpoise. If Lachy saw a rock, Ruari contended that it was a seal and on more than one occasion *Seagull*'s keel was scraping against the back of a 'shark' before one or the other would give way and admit that that particular shark had been marked on the Admiralty chart for the past twenty-five years.

It was one bright morning in early spring that Morag limped into my room having, as she said, 'gone off her anchor' the night before when looking for the cow.

'Ruari's after takin' a great lump of them jolly gees to the hills and then he'll be after collectin' some cattle from Rhuna and he's sayin' you'll get with them if you've a mind,' she informed me. (Morag always expressed quantity in 'lumps', whether she was speaking of manure, cheese or humanity.) Messages from Ruari reached me via his sister, for, though my company was not despised, it was beneath the male dignity to issue invitations to non-Gaelic-speaking females. I accepted with alacrity even though, as I told Morag, I had no idea what 'jolly gees' might be.

'Jolly gees? Why, they're yon fellows who hammer little bits off the hills and then fancy they can tell the Lord Himself how the earth was made,' Morag replied.

'Geologists!' I exclaimed. She nodded.

'It's awfully good of Ruari to take me,' I remarked as my landlady was about to signal my acceptance.

'You should see the size of the stones he'll need to put into the stern for ballast if he doesna' take you,' she replied with devastating candour.

I felt momentarily deflated, but even deputizing for a few stones acted as no damper to my enthusiasm for the trip. Rhuna, shaped like a crumbly brown bread sandwich with a bite taken out of it, had always fascinated me, and though I had hinted many times to Ruari that I should like to visit it he had so far fobbed me off with one excuse or another. I was swallowing breakfast as quickly as I could when Morag came back into my room.

'There they go,' she muttered resentfully, pointing through the window at the straggling party of men, each armed with a capacious rucksack, who were picking their way down to the shore.

'Don't you like them?' I asked carelessly.

'Like them? Indeed I do not!' she replied with unaccustomed vehemence. 'Climbin' like spiders all over the hills and tap, tap, tappin' with they little hammers. One of these days we'll wake up in the mornin' and find no hills left.' She snapped her fingers expressively and went out of the room, leaving me to wrestle with the remains of a tough kipper and an imagination that tried to picture an army of 'jolly gees' engaged on their gargantuan task. I finally abandoned the kipper and, pulling on a warm coat, started off for the shore. Before I was halfway I was arrested by an affronted bellow from Ruari.

'Six legs I had last night! Six legs I had and none but two have I got this mornin'. Who's taken my legs? How am I goin' to manage without my other four legs now?' he declaimed.

Ruari was as yet invisible to me and so also was the recipient of the tirade.

'Taken and chopped them up for firewood I'll be bound!' His bludgeoning voice apprised the world in general of the probable fate of his four spare legs.

Arriving, a little breathless, at the shore, I found an enraged Ruari holding aloft two 'legs'—small logs of wood used for hauling the dinghy over the rough shingle—for the bewildered survey of the party of geologists who, I felt certain, were less impressed by the substance of the complaint than by the volume of it. Actually, when the time came, Ruari and Lachy managed very well without the four missing legs and soon they and myself and the geologists had been rowed out to where *Seagull* lay wallowing gently at her moorings. We stowed ourselves aboard and the engine, after resisting the power of Lachy's muscles for a time, yielded suddenly to the power of Ruari's vocabulary and, overcoming a slight preliminary fretfulness, settled down to the task of propelling us to our destination.

The hills for which we were bound looked cold and remote, their wintry peaks appearing to jostle one another for a glimpse of the morning sun, which transformed the sky into a rippling canopy of blue and gold. The geologists stared towards them speculatively, their minds no doubt occupied with formations and faults, bridging the gap of millions of years. I stared reflectively, dwelling only on the past hundred years of their history. Ruari and Lachy stared at them indifferently, merely as an object in the course they were setting; and bickered eternally.

We passed a dilapidated old boat, swinging sluggishly at her mooring; a seagull poised, aloof and graceful, on her masthead.

'She'd be the better of a coat of paint,' I observed, using the Bruach idiom.

'If he leaves her there much longer the seagulls will soon paint her white for him,' retorted Lachy meaningly.

Except for the fact that the weather was rather cold it was a perfect day for our sail. I enjoyed the feel of the engine labouring beneath my feet; the sight of the bow cleaving its way through the water which curled and splashed on either side. I liked to try to identify the different sea-birds as they bobbed and ducked in the ripples, and to watch the seals or porpoises or even a venturesome otter.

All too soon we reached the tiny jetty where the geologists were to be put ashore and, after arranging to pick them up at six o'clock in the evening, Ruari headed the boat seaward and set course for the island of Rhuna.

'It's deep watter all the way,' Ruari told me. 'Would you like to try your hand at steerin'?'

'Certainly I should,' I replied and grasped the tiller confidently.

'Just fix your eye on that end of the island and steer straight for it,' he instructed. It looked child's play, and I sat with one arm thrown negligently over the tiller, adopting Ruari's own habitual attitude when steering. The two men, thus released from duty, went to the forepeak of the boat and were soon occupied in inspecting tackle. I fixed my eyes on the point indicated by Ruari and concentrated on steering a straight course, which is infinitely more difficult than it looks. The boat chugged steadily, but only the water falling away on either side of the bow showed that we were not at anchor, for Rhuna seemed to be coming no nearer. The scenery was breathtakingly beautiful even for eyes that had feasted long on such glory. The Bruach hills and moors, hardly yet aware of the tentative prodding of spring's green fingers, offered an intricate patchwork of browns and greys. Rhuna and her companion isles, which a loitering winter had left sprinkled with snow, reposed lightly on the strangely still water, looking as fragile as meringues on a baking board, needing only a palette knife slipping under them to lift them cleanly from their calm, blue base.

A lacerating 'aside' from Ruari brought me back to reality with a bump.

'She steers a course as crooked as a dog pissin' in the snow,' he confided to Lachy.

Stunned by the criticism, I stared at the two men. Lachy's face crimsoned with embarrassment and from the awkward position of his elbow I judged that he had just dealt Ruari a vigorous dig in the ribs. The latter, looking slightly sheepish, became absorbed in the complications of rope splicing. I turned round to see for myself the narrow lane of bubbles which marked *Seagull*'s wake and though I had to accept the veracity of Ruari's statement it was not until the following winter that I was able to appreciate the aptness of his simile.

Somewhere about one o'clock in the afternoon we crept into the sequestered bay of Rhuna. The island was dotted here and there with ruined habitations, outside which lounged their equally ruined inhabitants. On the shore awaiting us were Murdoch and Angus, who had rowed over in a big, flat-bottomed barge of a boat early that morning and who now stood guard over half a dozen or so uneasy-looking cattle. Murdoch regarded himself as the 'big' cattle man and, as none of the official buyers ever crossed to Rhuna, he looked upon it as his own private gold mine, buying cattle there cheaply, ferrying them over to Bruach and thence to the mainland sale yard, where he usually reckoned to make a hundred per cent profit.

A young boy appeared from one of the cottages and whispered a few words to Murdoch who translated them into an invitation to come ashore and take a 'wee strupak'. There were a few feet of water between *Seagull* and the shore and Angus, wading out in thigh-boots, offered me a piggy-back. I refused, for the water looked shallow enough and Angus's propensity for practical joking was too well known for me to be taking risks. I slipped off my boots and stockings and climbed over the side. The water was shockingly cold and of course much deeper than it had appeared; the shingle was slippery and the gunwale of the boat was a long way off, but willing hands grasped my shoulders and I was soon hauled ashore, my legs pink and tingling and my dress sodden only as far as the waist. I smothered the impulse to race to the cottage and toast myself in front of the fire, remembering that the Bruachites always spoke of the inhabitants of Rhuna as being 'mad as I don't know what', a description which was in no way reassuring to one cognizant of the very moderate degree of sanity in Bruach itself. I therefore matched my pace to that of the men, which for me necessitated a rigorous exercise of muscle control, their walk being as deliberate and meticulous as a slow-motion film. One foot was put forward and then, after separately relaxing each muscle of the calf, it was slowly lowered to the ground heel first. When it was certain that the ground was flat enough and safe enough for the whole foot, it was trusted with the man's weight and the process repeated with the other foot. In heavy thigh-boots or hill-boots the ritual might have been both prudent and necessary; with bare wet limbs and an empty stomach it was excruciating.

After what seemed an interminable time we reached the house to which we had been invited and were greeted with the utmost cordiality by a grey-haired crone of incredible age, who then presented her mother, another grey-haired crone of even more incredible age. Suspecting that the introductions might continue *ad infinitum* I glanced covertly into the shadowy recesses of the room, wondering what vision of decrepitude I might be confronted with next. Fortunately the introductions ended there and 'mother', with many smiles, suggested I should come away in and dry myself through. Taking the chair she drew forward I proceeded to carry out her suggestion. The younger crone, with pursed lips, and eyes darting here and there, busied herself brewing tea while the elder jabbed a knife viciously into a jar of jam, spread the confection lavishly on thick slices of bread and butter and shop biscuits; then seized the delicacies with sticky, dirt-ingrained fingers and urged them upon us. The young boy who had brought us the invitation was, in an agony of shyness, trying to insert his stocky little body into the crevice between the dresser and the wall, his limpid brown eyes watching my every movement as though I were a creature from another world, as perhaps I was. I wondered if he could possibly be the son of the less incredible of the crones, for my stay in the Hebrides had already taught me that it was not impossible for the recipient of the old age pension to use it for the purchasing of a layette!

While I munched and drank and my clothes steamed, I examined the room, which was reasonably clean. It boasted no ceiling except for the rafters over which lay the dark thatch and from which hung various species of dried, salt fish, a bundle of rabbit skins, a herring net and an iron girdle. The fireplace was of rough stone and the peat fire burned upon the flat hearth. A chimney pot saved it from being what is known as a 'black house', but so inadequate was the tiny window that the designation was merited. The furniture was a replica of what I now expected to see in the homes of the crofters who did not cater for tourists, namely a bench, table, dresser and the one wooden chair upon which I was now sitting. A long blue curtain covered an alcove in which was probably a recess bed. There was no clue to the number of people in the household. It might have been only the three I had met or it might have been a dozen.

The men, having finished their tea, put down their cups and stumped outside to begin the task of loading the protesting cattle into the likewise protesting boat. I too stood up and thanked my hostesses for their hospitality, but as the loading looked like taking some time they pressed me to stay and steam my skirts for a little longer in front of the fire. The mother questioned me courteously about my stay in Bruach, plainly disbelieving that I found the remoteness to my liking. They were both astounded when I told them I actually enjoyed the wild weather and was in no hurry to go back to England. Though they gave every appearance of accepting my statements I got the impression that they could imagine only two reasons why a woman should choose to settle down in Bruach: either that she was running away from the police, or else escaping from a lurid past. My plain homely features probably inclined them to the former belief.

In my turn I questioned them about their own lives. Did they differ much from those of the Bruachites? It seemed not.

'You haven't many places to cayley,' I said. They admitted there was little of what could be called 'good cayleying'.

'I suppose you have lots and lots of books here,' I began, resolving that in return for their kindness I could perhaps send them some.

Mother drew herself up haughtily.

'No indeed!' she answered frigidly. 'None at all.'

'No books? You don't like them? How strange!' I said.

'It's no strange at all.' The daughter's denial cut witheringly into an atmosphere that had changed suddenly from the cordial to the antipathetic. I puzzled as to what on earth I had said to upset them.

'I should have thought you would have had plenty of books,' I began, but the mother cut me short.

'Forty-five years I've lived in this house and never a bug did I see in it yet,' she asserted indignantly.

'Good heavens no!' I expostulated, glancing round fruitlessly to see if there was a book of any sort I might use as an illustration. 'Books,' I repeated desperately. 'Printed pages, magazines, reading books.' My cheeks burned; I was mortified that they should think I would repay their generosity by making such an aspersion.

To my immense relief the two women relaxed simultaneously and indulged in quite genuine laughter.

'I thought for a minute you must be one of them social women we used to get comin' round askin' questions about bugs and childrens and things.'

'Do they really do that?' I enquired mirthfully.

'Aye, indeed they do,' nodded the old mother. 'One comes to me and she says she'll tell me how to bring up my thirteen childrens.'

'You have thirteen children?' I asked.

'Aye, so I had,' admitted the old woman proudly.

The daughter giggled. 'Tell Miss Peckwitt what you told the woman,' she implored her mother, and the latter continued the story eagerly.

'Says she to me, "How many childrens?" "Thirteen," says I. "How many have you?" She looks at me surprised. "Why, none at all," says she. "Well," says I, "go you away and have fourteen and then maybe I'll take some notice of you when you come back here and tell me how to bring up my thirteen." '

The shouting of the men broke into our laughter and hurriedly taking my leave I ran down to the shore where Lachy and Ruari were waiting to stow me into an impatient *Seagull*. The engine was already throbbing and as soon as I was aboard we started off, the poor old boat struggling valiantly to tow the rowing-boat with its quivering, snorting cargo of cattle. Even to my unpractised eye it looked decidedly overloaded, for not only was it crammed full of beasts but the bottom had been partly filled with shingle so as to provide a level base upon which the animals could stand. I said as much to Murdoch who was perched on the bow of the towed boat, his coat-tails almost touching the water.

'Ach, cattle's got sense; they're not like humans,' he retorted with so much acerbity that I concluded he himself was a little apprehensive.

For perhaps a mile we plodded on without mishap and then *Seagull* started to roll; so also did the cattle-boat.

'It's the tide rip!' roared Ruari. 'I told you we'd meet it. By God! you'd best watch out now.'

Murdoch answered with a cool nod and taking out his beloved pipe he began to fill and light it methodically. His position on the bow looked precarious but, refusing to show the least sign of perturbation, he settled the pipe more comfortably in his mouth and puffed at it with satisfaction. I turned to watch the weaving line of the tide rip coming nearer and nearer. How the catastrophe happened I never really knew, but it was probably due to a sudden movement of some of the beasts coinciding with a particularly severe roll of the boat. I heard first a concerted yell from the *Seagull*'s crew and wheeling round saw that the heavily laden rowing-boat lay over on her side with the sea pouring in over her gunwale; that the cattle were struggling in the water and bellowing with terror, and then, after a moment of anguish, that the boat had vanished beneath the waves. Fortunately someone had the presence of mind to slash the tow-rope or *Seagull* might have suffered the same fate. It was not until some moments later that I realized there was no sign of Murdoch.

'Murdoch!' I screamed and scanned the water for a trace of him among the panic-stricken beasts who were already swimming strongly and most sensibly back towards Rhuna. It seemed an age but must have been only a matter of seconds before Murdoch's white head appeared some twenty yards away from the side of the boat and, despite the dreadful anxiety of the moment, I remember noticing how large and red and bulbous was his nose. Angus, Ruari and Lachy stood staring stupidly at the scene, their attitudes expressive of something very like indifference.

'Can he swim?' I shouted distractedly.

'No,' answered Lachy, and pinioned my two arms behind my back as I tried to slip off my coat. 'No you don't,' he said firmly, 'one corpse is enough.'

'He won't be a corpse if you'll let me go,' I argued, but Ruari turned angrily upon me.

'Stay where you are!' he commanded. 'We can throw him a rope.'

'For God's sake throw it then!' I sobbed, feeling sick with panic and frustration. 'Don't let him drown. Do something!'

In the space of the last few seconds, or perhaps at some equally perilous moment in his career, Murdoch had apparently learned to tread water, since he remained visible for a considerable time. Angus grabbed a coil of rope and threw it towards the unfortunate man. The aim was excellent; it fell within a few inches of Murdoch, but as Angus had forgotten to keep a hold of the other end it was wasted effort. Murdoch's voice came plaintively over the water: 'I canna' keep this up much longer. Save me! I'll drown!'

'It'll take more than a bit of watter to drown you,' comforted Ruari, and picking up an oar he hurled it with such accuracy that it looked as though he intended to put Murdoch out of his misery quickly rather than assist in his rescue.

There was no shadow of doubt that Murdoch was in imminent danger of drowning before our very eyes and yet, in spite of the seriousness of the situation, one half of my mind was conscious that the whole episode smacked of farce. Fortunately, however, Murdoch managed to grasp a second oar that was thrown; another coil of rope went out to him, this time with all four of us hanging on to the end, and he was safely hauled aboard, where he gasped and shivered for some minutes. He seemed comparatively undaunted by his experience and taking a flask of whisky from his pocket he tipped it to his lips and drank deeply.

'Did any of you see my pipe?' he asked when he was sufficiently stimulated. 'It was in my mouth when I went down.'

Murdoch contrived to be ludicrous even in the most unsuitable circumstances. The four of us shook our heads.

'There was somethin' in your mouth when you went down,' said Lachy, 'but whether it was your heart or your pipe I couldna' tell.'

'Indeed it was my pipe,' responded Murdoch.

'Ach, then I expect you swallowed it,' said Lachy.

'I did not then,' replied Murdoch. 'My insides would be warmer than they are now if I'd swallowed my pipe—it was lit, I tell you.'

Everyone laughed rather more than the remark or the occasion warranted, and though Murdoch that day came within an ace of losing his life, or so it seemed to me, I never heard him refer to the incident except to bemoan the loss of the best pipe he'd ever had.

The mishap caused some delay in our programme and there was talk of taking Murdoch and Angus along with us to pick up the geologists. I, maintaining that the old man should get into dry clothes as soon as possible, prevailed upon Ruari to deliver him to his family before he should involve us in any more hair-raising experiences. As soon as this had been accomplished, *Seagull's* bow was turned once more towards the hills. We were already an hour later than the time we had promised to return and when we again chugged into the little sheltered harbour there was neither sight nor sound of the geologists. Ruari stopped the engine and the sudden quiet pressed on our eardrums. Lachy stepped ashore.

'Give a shout,' he urged Ruari, and straightway Ruari let forth a bellow which split the intense quiet like a bomb and resounded among the hills for some moments afterwards. There was an echoing sound, scratchily feeble, in return, and after tying the boat the three of us went along the steep track towards it. It was not long before we met two of the geologists tottering down towards us, carrying between them a heavy sack.

'What the devil!' began one of the men truculently, but was soon subdued by Ruari's suave but picturesque excuses for our late arrival. 'Well, we'll go and round up the others,' the geologist replied sulkily. 'We've all been down to the jetty once, but when we found you hadn't turned up we thought we might as well keep working until you did.' He gestured towards the heavy bag which had been dropped on first seeing us. 'Here,' he instructed Ruari imperiously, 'you can carry that down to the boat and put it aboard.'

The two left us to go in search of the rest of their party while Ruari, with Lachy's assistance, lifted the sack on to his back. Ruari, as I have said before, was a strong man but his load was a heavy one, and he was quite distressed by the time we eventually reached the jetty. He deposited the sack with a bump on the rocks and rubbed his back tenderly.

'My God! That sack's so hard and heavy you'd think it was stones they had in it,' he grumbled.

'It is stones,' answered Lachy, who was more familiar with the ways of geologists.

'Stones?' Ruari almost spat. 'I'll give them stones if they try to play tricks like that on me,' he threatened. He looked at me for confirmation.

'Of course they're stones,' I told him, my face breaking into a smile at his outraged expression. He eyed me suspiciously from beneath knitted brows and his fingers plucked at the string which tied the neck of the bag. Out of the corner of my eye I perceived the party of geologists coming out of the dusk down the track towards the boat. Lachy saw them too.

'Look,' I told Ruari. 'If you don't believe me you can ask them for yourself, for here they come now.'

But Ruari had the sack open and was fingering the samples of gneiss and gabbro which would no doubt afford material for research for many months to come. He turned menacingly towards the approaching group. 'You buggers!' he yelled angrily. 'I'll teach you to play a joke like that on an old man. You ought to be ashamed of yourselves!' And before anyone, least of all myself, realized his intention he had turned the bag upside down and tipped the whole of its contents into the water.

There was a heartrending groan from the weary geologists and some of them raced forward impetuously in a vain attempt to save the treasure they had so industriously gathered. Their groans tailed off into sighs and their sighs melted into a stricken silence as they sank down hopelessly on the nearby rocks and stared dispiritedly at the ever-widening circle of ripples on the water where their treasure had disappeared. Ruari continued to glower at them with implacable wrath. I glanced uneasily at Lachy who was bending over the engine of *Seagull*, an unlit cigarette between his teeth and a superfluously intent expression on his face.

'Ruari,' I began timorously, feeling it incumbent on me to say something, 'they were not just ordinary stones. These men were not playing a joke on you. They're samples,' I floundered as Ruari bent his chilly gaze on me, 'specimens for studying,' I faltered.

'Is that so?' asked Ruari in somewhat mollified tones. I nodded.

'Yes, these men are students,' I persevered. 'They get a degree for this sort of thing.'

The words 'students' and 'degree' Ruari understood at once. He turned with a conciliatory smile to the group of scowling men.

'Well, if that's it now you must excuse me, but I thought it was a nasty bit of a game you were playin' on an old man, makin' him carry a big bag of stones down the mountain side,' he apologized magnanimously. 'But ach,' he went on, 'it's lucky indeed I havena' thrown away the sack itself and I'll have it full for you in a couple of minutes just.'

The geologists, still in a state of mental and physical overthrow and utterly bereft of speech, stared glumly while Ruari bent and began to fill the sack with shingle from the beach.

'That's no good!' the leader found his voice. 'For heaven's sake let's get home!' he snapped sullenly.

'Ach, but it's no trouble at all,' Ruari declared, with an extravagant flourish of his hand, 'and what harm I've done I must try to undo as best I can.'

'You're a damn fool!' returned the irate one ungraciously, and snatching the sack from Ruari clambered gloomily aboard *Seagull*.

'Well if I mustn't, I mustn't. I dare say you know best yourselves,' murmured Ruari with a puzzled nod.

As soon as the rest of the party were aboard we cast off and *Seagull* gambolled ponderously towards the Bruach shore. Talk was desultory, for Ruari was surprisingly abashed after his experience, while Lachy and I hovered between profound sympathy and irrepressible mirth.

It was an exceedingly melancholy party of 'jolly gees' who were landed at Bruach and who climbed stiffly and slowly up the brae towards the special bus which awaited them. Ruari watched them go, a sly expression on his face. 'Yon men are fools,' he observed as he baled out *Seagull* while I secured the tiller.

'It's you who were the fool,' I told him. 'You should have known that the stones wouldn't be ordinary stones.'

'Me? A fool?' exclaimed Ruari indignantly. 'Is it me that's the fool, when they've had to hire my boat to take them again tomorrow?'

'You wretch!' I chuckled.

'I'm thinkin',' said Ruari, cocking a speculative eye at the cloudless horizon, 'that we're in for another fine day tomorrow. You'll be comin' with us again, Miss Peckwitt?'

'No,' I said with a shudder. 'I can't face that crowd again.'

Ruari turned to Lachy who had just come alongside in the dinghy to take us ashore.

'What was you talkin' about to yon man?' he asked.

I had noticed that Lachy seemed to be having quite a voluble conversation with one of the geologists while he was taking them ashore.

'Ach, he wasn't a geologist at all,' replied Lachy. 'He called himself a cartyographer or somethin' like that.'

'A what?' demanded Ruari.

'A cartyographer,' repeated Lachy. 'I had some fun with him I can tell you.'

'How was that?' asked Ruari.

'Well, he was wantin' to know all the place names in Gaelic and in English,' said Lachy.

'But I distinctly saw you pointing to Rhu Corran, and calling it
Allt Rhunan,' I accused.

'So I did,' agreed Lachy cheerfully. 'And I told him Corry Dhy was
Cnoc Dhanaid, and plenty others wrong besides. The old nosey parker
he was.'

Ruari chuckled appreciatively.

'But Lachy,' I expostulated feebly. 'If he said he was a cartographer
you should have told him correctly. It's very important.'

'Ach,' said Lachy scornfully, 'what does he want to know the right
names for? He doesn't live about here at all. He's only after makin'
a map.'

8. *A Ceilidh*

THE acquisition of the Gaelic is, I believe, a necessity for those who wish to lead a full life in the Hebrides, and accordingly I purchased a Gaelic grammar and set myself the task of mastering the idiosyncrasies of that much-exalted tongue. Languages have never been my strong point but having the advantage of actually residing and conversing with natural Gaelic speakers, I estimated that by the end of three months I should have achieved a reasonable degree of fluency.

'It's quite easy to learn,' encouraged one of the accepted scholars of the village when he heard of my intention. 'The Gaelic is pronounced exactly as it is spelled so you will not find it half so difficult as other languages.'

I was enormously cheered by his words and was tempted to cut my estimate to six weeks, but the discovery that 'Cnoc' was pronounced 'Crock', 'Dubh' as 'Doo' and 'Ceilidh' as 'cayley' convinced me that his statement had been somewhat misleading. When I found that a simple phrase like 'I have a cat' is in the Gaelic distorted to 'A cat is at me' I felt that I must double my original estimate and, even so, doubted whether I should ever realize that to say 'The dog is at me' indicated possession and not attack.

Previous to commencing the study of Gaelic I had noticed that the inhabitants always seemed to be slightly nonplussed by my formal English greeting of 'Good morning!' or 'Good evening!' Naturally I used 'Good morning' as a salutation, not as an observation on weather conditions, and I was not to know then that in such matters the Gael believes in being specific. In my anxiety to say the right thing I asked Morag to tell me the Gaelic way of wishing people 'Good day'. She, taking me literally, taught me to say 'He Breeah', a phrase which, I later learned to my dismay, meant 'It is a good day', in the sense that 'the weather is fine', and it was singularly unfortunate that for practically the whole of that season there were no days when 'He Breeah' could have been called a suitable greeting. Through rain and cold, through wind, hail and snow, 'He Breeah!' I called gaily, and received in reply politely bewildered 'He Breeahs' from dejected figures whose boots squelched wetly and from whose sou'westers the rain streamed steadily. 'He Breeah!' I greeted the embittered roadman as he sheltered in his inadequate little hut from the merciless flurries of sleet which swept incessantly up the valley. 'He Breeah!' I hailed startled milkmaids as, blue-fingered and red-nosed, they huddled miserably under the cows' bellies, seeking refuge from the torrential rain.

The villagers accepted my misuse of the phrase with amused tolerance and were unfailingly complaisant, as is their way, but my suspicions were at last aroused when one old soul, battling homeward against a fierce north-westerly gale, her sodden cape billowing wildly in spite of her effort to restrain it, returned my 'He Breeah' promptly and then added conscientiously, 'But there's a fearful lot of wet along with it now, isn't there?' That night I learned to say 'He Fluke' (it is wet) and 'He Fooar' (it is cold) and by so doing ensured the finest spell of warm dry weather that the Island had experienced for some years.

Though my Gaelic studies were not conspicuously successful they did at least help me to understand the propensity of my new friends for investing anything and everything with the masculine or feminine gender, for, like French, the language has no neuter. A shoe for instance is a 'she', while a coat is a 'he'. The professions are all masculine, though the noun 'work' is feminine. (It is easy to understand the significance of this when one has lived in the Hebrides for a short time.) The circumstance that an object might be feminine in the English language yet masculine in the Gaelic added to the confusion, as did the complications of soft and hard consonants and shortened vowels; and when I heard of cows with calves at foot being referred to as 'he' I began to doubt very much whether anyone among the Bruachites was capable of classifying sex with any certainty.

This use of either the masculine or the feminine gender persisted among the crofters even when speaking English, and I was frequently considerably agitated on hearing remarks which seemed to suggest all manner of nefarious or ludicrous practices.

'When he's done barking, Ruari's going to hang him on the clothes line for an hour or so,' I overheard Bella telling Morag one day, and was greatly relieved to discover that 'he' was nothing more animate than a fishing-net. For one like myself, possessing only a limited capacity for controlling my countenance, there were agonizing moments such as the occasion when I met an old crofter and his wife stumping morosely along the road. The weather, which earlier had looked promising, had turned treacherously to rain and as we paused to commiserate with one another on this fact the woman bent down to tie her bootlace. Her husband studied her bent back, a lugubrious expression on his lined face. 'Yes,' he grumbled disconsolately, 'and I did think we'd have got to the peats today, but it's no use now she's gone and turned wet on me.' I need hardly point out that in this case the weather was the 'she'.

Apart from the curious idiom I was often disconcerted by the precise old ladies who, having little knowledge of English except for the English of the Bible, attempted to converse with me in distressingly scriptural language, utterly oblivious of the fact that many Biblical words are not used in polite conversation these days.

To familiarize myself with the language and thus help along my Gaelic studies, I should have acquired the ceilidh habit. These ceilidhs, which were really nothing more than the impromptu dropping in of neighbours, were going on almost every night of the autumn, winter and spring, but whereas most writers on Highland subjects deem it their duty to depict the ceilidhs with a romantic pen—lamplight; peat fire flames playing on a cluster of honest friendly faces; rich Highland voices, joking, singing and story-telling; cups of tea and home-baked scones—I was never able to forget that the room was likely to be ill-ventilated; that the tight-packed bodies would be hot and unbathed; that the pipe-smoking old men would be spitting indiscriminately; that the boots of the company would be caked with dung and mud; that more than one of my neighbours might be belching with threatening violence, and the clothes of others reeking of stale peat smoke and sour milk. As a consequence I was inclined to view the ceilidhs with disfavour; so that I was not at all pleased when Morag relayed to me a most pressing invitation to attend such a gathering at the home of the village's pet widow. I was tempted to refuse point-blank but, recalling that the house in question was comparatively large and airy and that the widow herself was an exceptionally genial lady, I decided that I might do worse than accept.

Morag was delighted, and about nine o'clock on a bright, starlit November evening we sallied forth. All day there had been a sharp frost and now our footsteps rang with a clear, staccato echo instead of the customary sloshing plod. A silvery glow behind the hills heralded the rising of the maturing moon and suddenly and impressively it emerged above the dark peaks, spilling light and shadow with superb artistry into the tranquil valley. My companion and I walked briskly; not because we expected to be late for the ceilidh—that would have been well nigh impossible as the Bruachites kept astonishingly late hours—but because of the invigorating effect of the chill air. Morag, never at a loss for some topic of conversation, pointed out various dwellings and amused both herself and me by recounting stories of their occupants past and present. Just as we came abreast of a low, thatched house on the high road the door was flung open and a woman of demi-john proportions stood silhouetted in the lamplit space. Morag immediately called out a greeting which was shrilly returned by the fat woman, along with the additional information that she would be catching us up presently.

'Yon's Anna Vic,' said my companion. 'You'll know her likely?'

I certainly knew Anna Vic both by sight and reputation. Ruari had described her to me as being 'so fat that if you saw her on the skyline you didna' know if it was herself or two cows standin' side by side', while Lachy asserted that 'if you can see daylight between the ankles then it canna' be Anna Vic'.

'She is indeed a very big woman,' I said.

'Aye, and her heart's the biggest part of her,' replied Morag warmly. 'My,' she continued with barely a pause for breath, 'but she holdᵉ a lot of water that one.'

'Who does?' I gasped.

'Why, that fine rainwater tank beside the house there,' answered my landlady, inclining her head towards the house we had just passed. 'I must be seein' about gettin' one of them for myself.'

Our ears were assailed by a piercing shout and, turning, we beheld the panting Anna Vic waddling after us like an excited duck.

'How fast you walk,' she grumbled pleasantly as she toiled along beside us, but neither her corpulence nor our speed proved the slightest impediment to her conversational powers.

'Why,' she panted after a little while, 'it's warm enough walkin', but in the house I was feelin' the cold terrible. Indeed I was sittin' that close over the fire that when I came to put on my stockings my legs was tartan with the toasting I'd given them.'

We laughed, and so entertained did she keep us that it seemed no time at all before we were pushing open the door of the ceilidh house where we found several people already comfortably ranged in front of an enormous peat fire. On the inevitable wooden bench sat Alistair the shepherd, Angus, Murdoch, Adam the gamekeeper and one-armed Donald. Roddy and Callum, the hostess's bachelor brothers, sat determinedly in their favourite armchairs. A wooden chair was shared awkwardly by twin sisters whom I had already christened 'Giggle' and 'Sniggle'; Johnny the bus-driver was perched precariously on one end of the roughly hewn kerb, while Elspeth, the young schoolteacher, sat, with arms akimbo and knees locked virtuously together, on a corner of the table, her feet resting on a low stool. Greetings were exchanged and the men, after catching the intimidating eye of our hostess, executed a sort of 'general post' as they outdid one another in their anxiety to make room for us. We settled ourselves on a horsehair sofa drawn close to the fire; the conversation was resumed and in no time at all Anna Vic and Morag were involved in an argument with Donald as to the price of whelks for the previous season. I listened impartially, being far more interested in the setting than in the dispute.

The room was cosily warm; the mellow lamplight, reflected by the varnished wood walls, whitened the hair and smoothed the wrinkles of the aged, while it burnished the hair and enhanced the already ravishing complexions of the young. On the gleaming hob two sooty kettles spouted steam and beside them a magnificent brown teapot squatted complacently. Against one wall stood a homely dresser bedecked with gay china, and flanked on either side by 'Vesuvius in Eruption (daytime)' and 'Vesuvius in Eruption (at night)'. On the opposite wall, nearly surrounded by its festoon of weights and chains, hung an old-fashioned clock, its pendulum lazily swinging the night away; its ticking rivalled only by the repetitive sniffs of the company, for sniffing is as sure an accompaniment to a ceilidh as is the popping of corks to a champagne party.

Tea and biscuits began to circulate and the conversation ranged from such topics as the prospect of winter herring to the existence of witches; from the price of whisky to the efficacy of willow bark for cold sores; from the condition of the cattle to the miraculous traffic lights of Glasgow. It was Murdoch who regarded the latter thus, explaining carefully to his unsophisticated audience that: 'When the lights is blue the cars can go; when they're yellow they can still go; but when they're red!' the old man's fist dropped expressively on to his knee and his voice became emphatic. 'Why 'tis just like a tether on their wheels,' he told them, 'and they canna' move, no not an inch!' After one glance at his spellbound audience he added knowledgeably: 'It's the electric d'you see?'

It was plain that Murdoch believed the secret of the traffic lights to be a powerful electric ray which effectively immobilized all engines in the vicinity, and it says much for Glasgow motorists that Murdoch, who had studied them intensively during the fortnight he had spent in the city, had apparently never seen a car 'jump' the lights.

'Have you ever seen them?' he asked me.

'Yes,' I told him. 'We have them in England too.'

Murdoch regarded me with a sceptical stare. 'Is that so?' he murmured with polite disbelief.

Tea drinking was well in progress when the rampant Lachy burst into the room, followed by Euan the half-wit. Without ceremony Lachy snatched the stool from beneath Elspeth's feet, ignoring her sudden collapse as blandly as he ignored her profane remonstrance. He seated himself on the major portion of the stool and generously allowed Euan to make himself comfortable on the remaining two inches. The latter opened his mouth to begin a vituperative protest but a quelling glance from his hostess not only silenced his protestations but also appeared to paralyse the muscles of his jaws, so that he sat for the remainder of the evening staring stupidly before him, his mouth with its one front tooth gaping as rigidly and seductively as a baited mousetrap.

So far as I was concerned Lachy's arrival was inopportune, for the discussion had turned to old country cures—a subject in which I was intensely interested—and I had made mental notes of numerous, half-remembered remedies. As I have mentioned previously, Morag's mother was reputed to have possessed great skill in concocting medicines from plants, but Morag always appeared embarrassed when I tried to pump her for information. It was as though she was ashamed to confess her knowledge. Tonight, however, she was not averse to discussing the subject and I heard her prescribe sea urchins for the cure of asthma; scabious roots for jaundice; plantain leaves for poultices and plasters; clover heads for cancer, and a fantastic-sounding remedy for a soaring temperature as in the case of fevers, etc., which was to split and fry a red herring, then to tie the halves to the soles of the patient's feet. This treatment, though claimed to be efficacious, was considered to be rather drastic and was accompanied by the warning that in the case of an adult the fish should not be left on the feet for more than twenty minutes by the clock; while in the case of a child ten minutes was the maximum for safety, otherwise it might do more harm than good. I hope I may never have occasion to try out this cure; nor, for that matter, would I care to try out the recommended cure for piles, which was to 'sit in a bucket of pneumonia every night for half an hour before going to bed'.

The manner of Lachy's entrance had thrown everyone into a state of expectancy and though I attempted several times to bring the conversation back to cures my efforts were unavailing.

'D'you know who I've just seen?' the newcomer demanded.

Everyone professed ignorance.

'I saw Hamish MacAlistair Oulliam,' announced Lachy dramatically.

His statement was greeted with cries of 'Oh, my, my!' and 'Surely not after all this time?' and 'Whoever was expectin' to see him again indeed?'

'Well, he's home again this night, true as I'm here,' affirmed Lachy. There were even more exclamations and in the middle of them he turned to me.

'You never knew Hamish MacAlistair Oulliam, did you, Miss Peckwitt?' he asked, and then continued: 'No, you couldn't have.'

I had to admit that I had never heard of Hamish MacAlistair Oulliam.

'Well, I'm tellin' you, Miss Peckwitt,' he explained solemnly, ' 'tis three years now since that fellow—and he was only eighteen or thereabouts at the time—he jumped on a sheep and away he went and not a soul has seen breath, nor line, nor trace, nor shape of him from then until he walked into his own house tonight.'

As I have said, the talk during the evening had touched upon various aspects of the supernatural; I had listened to the most impressive tales of present-day fairies, tales which would be vouched for by witnesses still alive and of impeccable character. As a result I was in a particularly receptive mood, but even so the existence of an enchanted sheep which could carry away a man was too much for my prosaic mind. Covertly I studied the circle of intent faces, watching for the slightest quirk of the lips or glint in the eye to confirm my suspicion that the story was a deliberate attempt at pulling my often too-susceptible leg. I could, however, discern nothing in their expressions save profound interest.

'I don't believe a word of it,' I said decisively.

My words brought a chorus of indignant and sorrowful rebukes from the company.

'Why, there's plenty knows the truth of it,' they told me.

'Indeed,' someone insisted, 'he'll like as not be tellin' you the truth of it for himself soon enough.'

Their earnest asseverations were obviously made in the sincere belief that the sheep had indeed run away with the man, but try as I would my faltering imagination boggled, first at the idea of any sheep being able to carry on its back even the smallest of men, and then at the possibility that, even in such a wild part of the country, the steed and its rider could disappear completely for three years. It was a tale for the superstitious Gael or an infants' school; not for a town-bred Englishwoman.

'Sheep don't do that,' I insisted. 'It's not possible.'

'They don't?' Murdoch enquired haughtily. 'I'm tellin' you, Miss Peckwitt, if the sheep is carryin' a mixed cargo she might be away for even five years. It all depends on the cargo and the Company.'

The ensuing silence was broken by a snatch of song. So long as the Gaels stick to their own melodies I like to hear their singing, there being a primitive and unrestrained passion in their music which perfectly expresses the spirit of the wild hills and lonely glens of their land, and completely suits the curious vibrancy of their untrained voices. Listening sometimes I had the vague feeling that the beat of the tom-toms was missing, so strangely reminiscent are some of their songs to those of native tribes.

Adam the gamekeeper was considered to be Bruach's best male singer and it was he who started now, nodding the beat of the music to himself as he sang, and interspersing each verse with a colossal guttural sniff which twisted his nose like the thong of a whip, and jerked his head up from his chest like a marionette on a string.

Everyone joined in the choruses and I could not help noticing that the mannerisms and facial expressions of all the singers were almost identical.

It was the custom for every person present at the ceilidh to be asked to sing, and it was equally the custom for everyone to deny that he or she could sing. Giggle and Sniggle were addressed when Adam had finished.

'Come on, girls, what about a song from you?'

Giggle and Sniggle hung their heads shyly and of course giggled and sniggled in unison. They undoubtedly would have provided a long-drawn-out duet of giggling and sniggling had there been room enough on the chair for them both to breathe out at the same time. Persuasion having proved fruitless in their case, Elspeth was next entreated.

'Come now, you Elspeth, you're a good singer.'

Elspeth too hung her head and giggled. 'I can no sing,' she disclaimed unenthusiastically.

'You can so.'

'Ach, I can no.'

'Indeed you can so.'

Thus the cajolery and contradiction continued and between each unconvincing denial Elspeth surreptitiously but very determinedly cleared her throat in preparation for the song she had every intention of singing throughout every one of its fifteen verses.

As the night wore on the singing and the gossiping became more sporadic until there was only the voice of Anna Vic, who for the greater part of the evening had been regaling our patient hostess with shrilly despairing confidences regarding the shortcomings of the fat woman's youngest son. Her affronted voice pierced a temporary silence.

'Supposin' I stand on my head he won't do it for me,' she complained. There was the echo of a sardonic laugh from Lachy.

'Supposin' you stand on your head, nobody would notice the difference. You're the same shape either way up.'

His quip was received with a roar of laughter from the assembled company and the fat woman looked momentarily uncomfortable. The shepherd, still grinning widely, got up to go. He was tired, he told us, after having had such a heavy day, 'there'd been that many docks chasin' ships all over the hills'. He directed a meaning glance at

Murdoch who was reputed to own the worst sheep-worrying dog in the district; but, affecting to be deaf, the old man continued to stare steadily at the fire.

'The merry dancers are puttin' on a good show tonight,' called Alistair as he went out; 'it means a change in the weather one way or another.'

Morag and I decided that it was time we also should be making a move, and Johnny, Lachy, Angus, Anna Vic and Murdoch, though loth to break up the ceilidh, made up their minds to come with us. The night was still clear and the slightly toothachy moon sailed serenely along through a froth of white cloud. From behind the hills rose the flickering green-gold cone of the Northern Lights, its apex directly above our heads.

'Aye, aye, a change in the weather right enough,' confirmed Murdoch as he minced along in front of us, holding his pipe to his mouth in the manner of a small child blowing bubbles. We three women followed, arms linked together, and behind us came Johnny, Lachy and Angus. The talk eddied from one to another and the background to our conversation was the sucking rasp of the breakers on the shingle and the infrequent cry of some night-flying bird. And then we became aware of another sound: a weird, rhythmic, burring wail which none of us could identify.

'Good God! Whatever's that?' burst out Anna Vic apprehensively.

After pausing to listen we decided that the noise was coming from somewhere along a stretch of road now under repair. The men turned their steps inquisitively in that direction and we followed, keeping close to their heels, dropping our voices to whispers. The noise grew gradually more distinct and was now punctuated by an eerie, choking moan. Anna Vic clutched at my arm, but whether it was for her own comfort or mine I could not tell. If it was the former she was likely to be disillusioned, for after the evening's ghost stories my nerves were not exactly steady. After walking for some distance the men halted and we were at once relieved and surprised to hear Murdoch's asthmatic chuckle. Following the direction of his pointing finger, we saw, a short way in front of us, a dark mass which we soon identified as the small hut where the 'gaffer' of the roadmen lived. It was from the hut that the strange noise was coming.

'My, but that man can snore,' declared Johnny with grudging admiration.

Anna Vic's tightly held breath escaped in a thankful sigh and she slackened her hold on my arm.

'He must be ill,' I said.

'Not him,' replied Murdoch sagely. 'It's whisky that makes him snore like that, not sickness.'

'How that man can drink!' Angus observed in accents of awed humility.

'You should have seen him on Friday,' said Lachy. 'He was that drunk it took four of us to get him over from the bus to his hut. And when we got him inside, Johnny here lights the Primus to make him some tea to try would it sober him up. There was no watter, so we had to take a pail and go to the burn and by God! when we got back we found the old bodach sittin' on top of the lighted Primus itself.'

'Indeed it was lucky for him he'd sat in a few bogs on the way home,' said Johnny, taking up the story, 'or he'd have been in a worse mess than he was.'

'Was he burned bad?' demanded Murdoch.

'Burned? Him?' asked Lachy incredulously. 'Why, when we pulled him off the stove he said he must have been sittin' in a patch of thistles some time. Thistles!' went on Lachy. 'Can you believe it? And the bottom burned out of his pants and his backside as red as a cock's comb in spring. I'm tellin' you that fellow has a skin like the sole of a tackety hill-boot.'

Lachy's enthusiastic description of the gaffer's misadventure lasted while we retraced our steps to the road.

'My, but he's a character that one,' remarked Murdoch. 'And I've never in my life seen a man that's wilder in his drink,' he added respectfully.

'He doesn't have to get drunk to get wild,' interpolated Johnny. 'He wanted to smash my face in the other day because I told him the Government would lose the next election.'

'Aye, aye, he's a staunch Tory,' averred Murdoch.

'And so you are yourself for that matter,' muttered Johnny sulkily.

'And why shouldn't I be?' demanded Murdoch with some heat. 'People that's lived as long as I have is always Tory. You grow in sense as you grow in years you know.'

Johnny retaliated with some incoherent remark reflecting upon the senility of the Tory party in general and the comparative youthfulness of Socialism.

'Socialism! Why, I'd sooner have rheumatism than Socialism. It's easier to c-cure,' stuttered Murdoch, who had never felt the slightest twinge of either malady. 'You young people,' he went on, 'shouldn't be allowed to have a vote at all, and then Socialism would never have come to fret us in our old age. You have no sense at all,' he finished disparagingly.

'I'm no so young,' objected Johnny. 'I'm gettin' on for forty.'

Murdoch spat with elaborate contempt. 'Forty!' he exclaimed scathingly. 'Forty!' he repeated. 'Chicken's age is forty. You shouldn't get your vote till you get your old age pension. You should qualify for the two of them together.' Haughtily he resumed his place at the head of the procession and ventured no further remark until he wished us good night at his own bedstead gate.

'So Johnny's a red-hot Socialist,' I observed when Murdoch had gone.

'Aye,' put in Lachy, 'he's been a good Socialist all his life except on polling days.'

Johnny laughed self-consciously.

'That was one of those social nosey parkers we had on the trip today,' resumed Lachy.

'You got a trip today?' asked Morag with surprise.

'Aye, we did, and the social woman was pretty seasick I can tell you.'

'What did you do with her?' asked Johnny.

'There was nothin' I could do with her,' replied the other indifferently. 'She was done for. All I could do was drag her up the beach and leave her above the tide.'

'Oh, but you should have done more than that for the creature,' scolded Morag. 'Could you no have done somethin' to try would you bring her round?'

'Me? Bring her round?' echoed Lachy. 'Why should I try bringin' her round?' And then apparently divining a reason for Morag's admonition he added with materialistic reassurance: 'It was all right, I didn't need to bother, she'd already paid her fare.'

The talk of sickness in humans veered to the far more important topic of sickness in animals. We reached the dyke and as I was about to 'leap' over it, Morag began asking minutely about a cow of Lachy's which had been ailing for some time.

'It's no right for her to go on like that,' he told her. 'She's old and she's sick and I've made up my mind I'm goin' to shoot her in the mornin'.'

Morag agreed that it was high time the beast was disposed of and later, when I was filling my hot-water bottle, she emphasized, in reply to my question, that Lachy could be trusted to make a far easier and better job of putting the beast out of its misery than would the 'Cruelty'.

During the night, as Murdoch and the Aurora Borealis had foretold, the wind changed its direction and brought with it a couple of hours of torrential rain from the west. By morning the ground was again sodden and the blackcurrant bushes stood sadly in the middle of a sheet of water.

'And did you shoot your poor old cow?' I asked Lachy when I met him.

'No, I did not then,' he replied morosely. 'I believe I'll have to be gettin' the Cruelty to do it yet.'

I felt that I understood. 'It cannot be very nice to have to shoot an animal you've had all these years and grown fond of,' I suggested sympathetically.

'Ach, it's no that at all.' Hastily Lachy repudiated the suggestion that his failure to accomplish the deed had been in any way due to sentiment. 'I was goin' to shoot her right enough,' he went on stoutly, 'but when I came to do it I found she'd gone and got damp in the night and swollen so big I couldna' push her into the gun.'

He resolved this statement of patent impossibility by producing for my inspection an undeniably swollen, but far from effeminate-looking, shot-gun cartridge!

9. *The Dance*

I studied the carelessly scrawled notice in the window of the
grocer's shop; the black crayon lettering on a roughly torn sheet of
white wrapping-paper looked like a child's first attempt at printing.
The poster was somewhat overshadowed by another one which
advertised a 'Grand Sale of Females' on the following Saturday. This
was of no interest to me personally as it referred only to a sale of
heifers, but the dance 'warning' was definitely worth attention. I
translated the 'no splitting' into a very prudent desire on the part of
the organizers to avoid either the concert or the dance being a financial failure, as might be the case if a separate charge were made for
each.

The demand for soap flakes was a little puzzling, but I had lived
long enough in Bruach to appreciate that many of their customs had
survived from Biblical times, and though I had not yet observed
the practice it was not wildly improbable that solicitous hand-
maidens would, with true Biblical courtesy, bathe the feet of
all patrons on arrival. The 'D.V.' struck me as being anomalous,

but from reports I had heard of the dance secretary's flagrant misappropriation of funds, I knew that its position on the notice was significant.

The organized social activities of Bruach were practically non-existent; a circumstance which was partly due to there being no public hall of any kind, and partly to the fact that both the head schoolteacher and the council representative were so Calvinistically opposed to entertainment that they would perjure themselves pink to prevent the schoolroom being used for anything but its everyday purpose. It was fortunate, therefore, that a neighbouring village which boasted a nebulous and often lethargic 'Committy', and also a disused barn which was styled grandiloquently as the 'Public Hall', would occasionally exert itself sufficiently to sponsor a concert or a dance—generally in aid of some obscure charity—and would invite the patronage of any Bruachites who might feel so inclined. The prospect of such entertainment invariably aroused a good deal of interest throughout the district and almost every inhabitant, except those prevented by religious scruples or rheumatic twinges, could be relied upon to attend. In the present case the 'Committy' was evidently determined to excel itself and a beauty competition would undoubtedly prove an irresistible attraction for young and old.

Pushing open the creaking door, I ventured into the poorly lighted shop where a boy in a threadbare brown kilt and dung-caked tennis shoes stood resting his face on the counter, while from behind the counter the grocer himself dexterously manipulated a pair of scissors over the boy's dark head.

'Well, well, well! Good afternoon, Miss Peckwitt,' the grocer greeted me, in tones which tried to deny that I had, for the past five minutes, been undergoing his close scrutiny from between a pair of hand-knit socks and a showcard advertising warble-fly dressing. As he spoke the head on the counter jerked upwards, but it was instantly rammed down again by the grocer's impatient fist.

'Be still you, Johnny!' threatened the amateur barber, vindictively grasping a handful of the boy's hair. 'You be tryin' to turn round and stare and it's this big bunch I'll be after cuttin' off.'

The head, which I now recognized as belonging to my erstwhile fishing instructor, remained obediently rigid. The grocer treated me to a prodigious wink.

'This is what comes of leavin' your hair to a Saturday to get it cut,' he muttered banteringly. 'And then it's such a rush you're in to get it done for the Sabbath, eh, Johnny?'

The head on the counter grunted and as the grocer diligently resumed his task I watched with fascination while an irregular-shaped patch of Johnny's scalp was laid almost bare and the sheaves of crisp, black hair fell stiffly on to the counter. The grocer, stimulated by my interest and sublimely confident of my admiration, continued to snip and chat pleasantly until one half of Johnny's head resembled fine sandpaper and the other half a gale-battered hay-cock; then I was treated to a second wink.

'There now, what d'you think of that, Miss Peckwitt?' he asked, laying down the scissors with an air of finality. 'Does that not look handsome?' And to the boy: 'Run you away now, Johnny, I've finished.'

Johnny, without raising his head, ran an explorative hand over his hair and let out a muffled groan.

'Away with you,' repeated the grocer, pushing the boy's shoulder, 'I'll finish the rest on Monday.'

The boy's head did not move, but a snigger squeezed its way out from between it and the counter.

'Very well.' The tormentor relented with a smile. 'But you'll have to wait until I've given Miss Peckwitt what she's wantin'.'

The head nodded uncomfortable acquiescence but I insisted that the hairdressing should be completed before I was attended to. I was, I declared, in no hurry whatever. But, I pointed out, this could not be said of a diminutive fellow of about seven years of age who had darted breathlessly into the shop on my heels and who had since stood, studiously ignored by the grocer, tapping a half-crown discreetly on the edge of the counter. My reminder made the grocer fix the boy with a repressive frown.

'What are you wantin' all in your haste, Ally Beag?' he asked sharply.

'I'm wantin' half a pound of bakin' sody,' whispered Ally Beag with a terrified glance in my direction.

'It's near seven o'clock,' said the grocer severely. As the shop made no pretence of closing until around eight or even nine o'clock, I was puzzled by this seemingly irrelevant remark. 'What's your mother wantin' with bakin' sody at this time on a Saturday night?' he continued, still frowning fiercely.

Ally Beag wilted visibly. 'She's wantin' it for bakin' scones,' he faltered.

The grocer's eyebrows shot up. 'She is indeed?' he asked superciliously. 'Tonight you say?'

Ally Beag nodded in awed confirmation.

'No she is not then,' gloated the grocer. 'She's goin' out to ceilidh with Anna Vic this night, and it's fine I'm knowin' she'll no have time for bakin' scones as well.' He paused, and stressing his words by tapping the scissors on Johnny's head, continued: 'It's bakin' scones on the Sabbath she'll be if I give her sody tonight. Go you home and tell her I've no bakin' sody till Monday,' he commanded, and then added cryptically, 'she'll understand.'

Ally Beag's freckled face reddened, but as he made no attempt to argue it is possible that he too suspected his mother's intention to desecrate the Sabbath. With eyes fixed despairingly on the grocer's unyielding countenance he sidled slowly out of the shop.

'If it had been her stomach she would have got it,' the grocer excused himself virtuously as he resumed clipping. 'I'm no a man to deny a thing when there's real need.'

After a few minutes had elapsed a crestfallen Ally Beag returned and silently helped himself to three damp-looking loaves from the cardboard box beside the counter. With eyes downcast he again proffered the half-crown and the grocer, with a righteous pursing of his lips, accepted the money and clapped the change on to the counter. The vanquished Ally clasped his burden of loaves to his chest and slunk out of the shop watched by the grocer who squinted at him from between the shelves of the window and nodded his head knowingly. I should mention that the grocer was an Elder of the church and the duty of an Elder (in addition to preventing the minister from becoming too secular) is to discourage the deviation of the flock from the path of righteousness. How he could reconcile his Calvinistic piety with the poster displayed in his window was one of the inconsistencies of Bruach which I never managed to fathom.

When Johnny's scalp was shining beneath what was no more than the merest suggestion of stubble, he was released and, while the barber surveyed his handiwork, the victim, with a sheepish grin at me, vigorously rubbed shape and colour back to his crushed apology for a nose. With his arm the grocer swept the dark mass of hair from the counter and, as Johnny skipped away, he turned to me with a smile of unctuous enquiry.

'Half a pound of baking soda,' I said audaciously, though baking soda was not one of the items on my list. Perhaps I imagined the flash of chagrin which touched his heavy-lidded eyes. I think I must have done, for there was no trace of hesitation or reluctance as he reached up to the shelf and handed me a packet already made up. Apparently my soul was beyond hope of redemption.

'You'll get some apples and pears if you're wantin' them,' he offered magnanimously. 'They came yesterday on the bus.'

'Good!' I exclaimed. 'I love them both.'

'Aye,' he agreed quietly, 'I know that fine.'

I must explain that fruit of any kind could rarely be obtained in Bruach, and when it was available it was rationed like golden sovereigns.

'It's queer about the pears though,' the grocer remarked conversationally as he lifted the basket on to the counter for my inspection. 'D'you see there's somebody been and taken a bite out of each one of them.'

He held up the pears one by one. Every pear, though otherwise perfect, bore the indisputable imprint of teeth—and very good teeth too.

'What a disgusting thing to do!' I commented, mentally reviewing the dentitions, both false and true, of the neighbourhood. The grocer, who had two front teeth missing, was obviously not the culprit.

'Yes indeed, it's a shame right enough,' he agreed as he carefully replaced them in the basket. 'But you see, Miss Peckwitt, the bus-driver swears they was perfectly all right when he took them on, so it can only have been someone from round about here who's been at them.' And as I was wondering why he offered that as consolation he added ingenuously: 'Of course, if it had been anybody from the main-land I daresay I might not have been able to sell the half of them.'

I said I would take a pound of apples.

'You have good teeth yourself,' he complimented me tactlessly as he weighed out the fruit.

Huffily I refuted the implication, whereat he protested with suspicious vehemence that such a thought had never entered his head. This assertion he immediately contradicted by letting slip the information that his enquiries had shown I had not been among the bus passengers. My innocence must, however, have been proved to his satisfaction for I would undoubtedly have been classed as a tainted mainlander and consequently the pears would have been totally unsaleable.

There is no point in brooding over insults in Bruach. 'So there's going to be a concert and dance,' I managed to say pleasantly.

'Oh yes indeed,' admitted the grocer, and with an obvious shock of recollection he reached into the window and discreetly turned the notice front to back so that the advertisement should not profane the Sabbath.

'I'm glad they've given us due warning,' I said.

'They'd need to do that,' he answered with complete seriousness. 'Folks has to make their plans.'

'Why the soap flakes?' I asked.

'To make the floor slippery,' he explained; 'though I'm thinkin' it's whole bars of soap they'll need for fillin' up the holes where the rats have eaten through.'

I wondered why they did not use french chalk.

'French chalk?' he echoed. 'I don't sell that. What like of stuff would that be?'

I enlightened him regarding the properties of french chalk but he was not impressed. Soap flakes, he maintained, were the best thing in the world for sticking to the men's tackety boots. 'Makes them lighter about the feet,' he added. It was my turn to be supercilious.

The prospect of a dance where one's partners were likely to be wearing tackety boots was not inviting to me, but it acted as no deterrent to the rest of the village. Very soon after the appearance of the notice and the announcement that voting for the Beauty Contest was to be left entirely to the men, the lassies, with smiles and coquetry, were beginning to woo the male population as assiduously as a prospective M.P. woos his constituency. If the grocer could be believed, there was a noticeable increase in the cosmetic trade, which hitherto had been a despised and slow-moving sideline, relegated along with the picture postcards, toilet rolls and souvenirs, to the unplumbed (except in the tourist season) depths of the shop. If Lachy could be believed, five damsels had already offered to pay for his ticket if he would promise them his vote and with placid impudence he expressed his intention of accepting all five offers. Even the Gaffer, who was a case-hardened bachelor if ever there was one, complained of being disturbed by the nightly serenading of female voices, while even the village half-wits claimed to have discerned a strange tendency to amiability in girls who had previously greeted them with sarcastic reflections upon their shortcomings.

The lassies taunted one another mercilessly with the sole design of calling attention to one another's imperfections. They posed; they hung on every word their menfolk uttered, contriving to be gay, alluring or brazen as occasion demanded; they frizzed their hair; they rolled their eyes and batted their eyelids; they studied dress catalogues intently; they experimented liberally with lipstick and face powder and, not forgetting the time-honoured way of ensnaring men's hearts, they concentrated a little of their attention on the baking of scones and oatcakes. And the men, well aware of what was going on, and the reason for it, watched the artifices and subterfuges of the aspirants with cool, enigmatic smiles.

As the day of the dance drew nearer I was constantly coming upon people of all ages and sizes, and of both sexes, furtively rehearsing dance steps. At the peats one day I watched from behind a convenient hillock while a hefty maiden in gumboots and tattered skirt tripped awkwardly round the stack, gathering up the peats and throwing them into the creel as she went. As the creel on her back filled the steps became less recognizable but even when it was quite full she refused to give in and my last glimpse showed her striving to strathspey her homeward way across the sucking bog.

Some days later, when rounding a bend in the road, I came upon a gang of lusty roadmenders who, despite enormous iron-shod boots, were jigging and posturing their way through a 'Dashing White Sergeant', their shovels and picks deputizing for female partners. The music was being supplied by the Gaffer, who performed with less skill than enthusiasm on a miniature mouth-organ, while a short distance away a forsaken steam-roller panted its indignant chorus of protestation. When the musician tired he announced that it was past five o'clock, whereupon the men, ignoring his energetic denunciation of their desertion, abruptly abandoned their 'partners' in a clattering heap beside the road and melted away. Sourly the Gaffer pocketed his instrument and walked over to the steam-roller. There was a final puff from its tiny chimney, a long-drawn-out sigh, and then silence.

'Are you going to the dance?' I called out.

'Not me,' replied the Gaffer scornfully. 'There's too many women and too much beer drinkin' at them dances.'

The latter part of this remark coming from a man who so recently had been too drunk to know whether he was sitting on a lighted Primus stove or a thistle was confounding.

'Don't you believe in drinking?' I asked him.

'Not beer,' he replied. 'Beer drinkin' will kill a man quicker than anythin' else.'

'Is that so?'

'Surely it will,' he said authoritatively. 'Just the other day for instance I had word from two of my friends tellin' me they was dead. Two of them mind you and beer drinkers both of them.' He shook his head sadly. 'Yet look at me,' he continued as we paused for a moment beside his little hut: 'I bin a whisky drinker since I was twelve. Gallons of it I must have drunk in my time and never a minute's pain or illness as a result.'

As he bent to open the door of the hut my attention was caught by the vivid circle of tartan which provided the seat of his otherwise drab trousers.

The day of the concert was cold but dry; the night was even colder. Dusk was only beginning to creep over the mainland hills and only one star twinkled faintly as Morag and I, having decided not to risk being crowded into the ramshackle bus, set out to walk to the 'Public Hall'. We took a short-cut across the crofts; past low thatched byres where cattle chains clinked companionably; past crude little sod huts where hens questioned and ducks quacked apprehensively; past a potent-smelling dung heap—at least I should have gone past it had I not been lost in contemplation of the night sky and had not my companion been engrossed in the contents of a neighbour's clothes-line. Morag skirted the dung heap by inches. I ploughed into the middle of the beastly thing.

'Oh darn!' I ejaculated crossly, peering down at my filthy shoes and stockings.

'Ach, dinna' be frettin',' comforted Morag. 'Likely it'll keep your legs warm.' She giggled. 'Keep your chin up. Isn't that what the English say when they're in trouble?'

I admitted it was and kept my chin up, but it was not fortitude but the stench of the manure which forced me to take her advice so literally.

Reaching the high road we met the postman's sister who was also on her way to the concert. The meeting reminded me that I had been expecting a letter to which I particularly wished to send a speedy reply, but the excitement of the evening had ousted it from my mind until this moment.

'Goodness!' I said in dismay. 'I should have waited for the postman. I was expecting a letter.'

'I don't suppose there'll be any mails tonight,' the postman's sister explained kindly, 'or only very few, anyway, for my brother's intending to go to the concert.'

'Oh,' I said with some surprise, 'doesn't he deliver the mails when there's a concert then?'

'Why, no indeed, how could he get the mails done and the concert beginnin' at eight o'clock?' she asked reasonably.

I admitted that it would of course be impossible. 'But,' I persisted foolishly, 'what happens if someone is depending on a letter? I mean, what if there should be something really important? How would he know?'

The contempt of her glance withered me from the top of my permanently waved head to the toes of my manured feet.

'Well then,' she reproached me icily, 'do you think, Miss Peckwitt, that my brother has never been to school? D'you think he is not able to read?'

I grovelled abjectly, denying that I had intended any such implication, and Morag, rushing to my aid, reproved the woman for believing that Miss Peckwitt would suggest such a thing. Why, didn't Miss Peckwitt know fine the post could read, and write too? Didn't she know he always signed the receipts for her registered parcels himself instead of troubling Miss Peckwitt to do it? Slightly mollified by Morag's words, the sister condescended to change the subject. Her manner, however, remained frigid and I believe that she never really forgave me for what she considered to be an outrageous reflection upon her brother's education. Morag explained later that the present postman's predecessor had in actual fact been unable to read and this perhaps had led the sister to be slightly touchy on this point.

'How did he manage to deliver letters if he couldn't read?' I asked.

'Surely he just used to give us the bundle and we'd choose our own,' replied Morag.

Despite the mishap at the dung heap we were in good time for the concert, the hall being only about half full when we arrived.

'Come and we'll get a good seat,' said Morag and hurrying forward she laid claim to two portions of a long wooden bench with drunken-looking legs, on to which we lowered ourselves experimentally. I thought I had seen the benches somewhere before.

'They're the seats from the church,' explained my companion.

'I'm surprised the missionary allows them to use the church seats for a concert,' I said. 'Does he approve of this sort of thing?'

'No, no, indeed,' responded Morag, 'and they wouldn't have got them if he knew anythin' of it.' She went on to explain that the 'Committy' had just helped themselves to the seats without so much as a word to the missionary; an undertaking which, considering that the Mission House lay on the road between the church and the Hall, must have been accomplished with a good deal of stealth. I said as much to Morag. Her expression as she turned to me was a remarkable blend of pity and mischievousness.

'Sure you can trust the missionary to keep his eyes shut if there's a thing he doesna' want to see,' she said, and added guilelessly: 'He's no bad really like that. I'll say that much for him.'

We continued to sit on our unsteady 'pew' for a long time; Morag rising every now and then to wave a greeting to some friend on the other side of the hall; but it was not until about a quarter of an hour after the concert was due to start that the place began to fill with any rapidity. People began to gather in groups and, indifferent to the compelling pianoforte chords which issued from time to time from behind the stage curtains, became absorbed in conversation. Without warning the curtains suddenly swept apart and the audience prepared to give the stage a proportion of its attention. After a moment, how-ever, the curtains swung purposefully together again, a performance that was greeted with piercing whistles and derogatory Gaelic phrases from the back of the hall where the gossiping groups showed little sign of subsiding.

'Ach, they're only practisin' to see will the curtains work.' A cloud of hot peppermint and whisky assailed us as a large, fiery-faced youth leaned forward to give us this titbit of highly confidential information. His statement was borne out by the fact that for the ensuing ten minutes the curtains continued their career of advance and retreat, achieving with practice and a little lubrication a performance which ranged from the weightily majestic to ecstatic abandon, and disclosing to the interested spectators nothing more inviting than a deserted stage. Everyone was the more startled therefore when, after a particularly impressive meeting, the curtains were parted by a bowing figure, resplendent in full Highland garb, who announced that the concert was about to begin and that the first item on the programme was to be a song entitled 'Blast you, Euan, can't you leave that alone!' This title was later corrected to 'The Bonnie Bonnie Hoose o' Airlie', the mis-statement apparently having been caused by the sudden decision of the curtains to recommence their cavortings—presumably at the instance of one Euan—coupled with the misfortune that the announcer happened to be standing on the hem of one of them and had narrowly escaped being precipitated on to the bald head of the illustrious chairman, who sat, rigid with importance or terror, in the centre of the front row. It was also explained that their own pianist having been taken ill, we should accord a warm reception to the local cobbler who had volunteered to act as accompanist. At this juncture the stocky figure of the cobbler who, according to Morag, had 'picked up the piano' during the war, burst with flaming cheeks on to the stage and, ignoring the grateful plaudits of the audience, commenced to manœuvre the piano into a suitable position much in the manner of a gun crew manœuvring a bogged gun. Satisfied at last, he struck a few chords in a very professional fashion—his own profession—and thereafter pounded away with such violence that he had perforce to pause every now and then to suck his bruised fingers. There was no doubt about the warmth of the cobbler's reception. The audience cheered themselves hoarse (judging from the voices of some of the singers, I rather think they did too), and did not desist until the first artiste appeared on the stage, when they settled themselves into their seats with a thoroughness which was, under the circumstances, definitely risky.

It surprised nobody I think when, after the first couple of songs, the rest of the artistes decided to perform unaccompanied, and the cobbler thus released shambled to his seat, explaining to his admiring supporters that he'd have been better if he hadn't been loadin' the sheep these last few days and gettin' his hands soft with the fleece grease.

The singers, most of whom were attired in Highland dress, delivered their repertoires with serious concentration, and the audience, except for the unquenchable groups at the back of the hall, listened with rapt attention until in the middle of a spirited rendering of a 'waulking song' a strident scream from Anna Vic shattered our ears. The interruption revealed that Murdoch, who was trying to accustom himself to a new pipe, had been so carried away by the performance that he had thoughtlessly knocked out his pipe on the low collar of Anna Vic's dress, thus sending a stream of hot ash down the unfortunate woman's neck. Still exploding volubly the fat woman was escorted from the hall by her two daughters, one of whom, encouraged by titters and advice from all sides, tried unavailingly to hold the dress away from her mother's ample back. The singer, undeterred by the wandering attention of his audience, continued valiantly, and it was not many minutes before the maltreated Anna Vic was back again, casting indignant glances on a highly amused Murdoch but seeming little the worse for her experience. She stubbornly refused to resume her seat and remained standing for the rest of the concert, but whether her determination was due to apprehension or blisters I could only conjecture.

There were many songs sung that night, some of them with more vigour than skill, the choruses being taken up by everyone present with fervid uproariousness and each being acclaimed with a verve and enthusiasm that was as damaging to the seating accommodation as it was to the ear. There was, too, a comedian, who pleased the audience immensely, though they smothered their mirth in their handkerchiefs and received every joke in a desolate silence. For a time the comedian struggled along manfully but, despairing at last of evoking even a single audible titter from his listeners, his patter soon faded into insignificance and he retired defeated from the stage.

When the curtains had closed for the last time we shuffled out slowly in twos and threes, to gather in the usual chattering clusters. From inside the hall came thuds, bangs, giggles and melody, the inseparable accompaniments of the busy Gael, which told us that the floor was in process of being cleared for dancing. I was introduced to a dry, aloof-looking woman who had acquired, at some period of her life, a spurious Oxford accent with which she now proceeded to afflict me. We were invited to take tea at her house during the interval and as our throats were parched after the heat and the choking smells of the hall we were both extremely glad to accept.

'Wasn't the singing good?' asked our hostess as she handed out the steaming cups of tea.

'Indeed but my hands is sore with the clappin',' answered Morag fulsomely.

'Mine too,' replied the woman. 'What did you think of the concert, Miss Beckwith?'

'I'm afraid I didn't think much of it at all,' I replied bluntly.

'Well now, neither did I,' rejoined Morag easily.

'No to be sure.' Our hostess accomplished the *volte face* without so much as the flicker of an eyelid. 'I've heard better singing than that in my own house.'

'Yet you've just been saying your hands were sore with clapping,' I taxed them.

'Of course we clapped,' agreed Morag plausibly, 'but d'you see they've come a long way to sing for us, and they think they're awful good, anyway. It wouldn't be right to disappoint them.'

'No indeed,' responded our hostess feelingly, 'one couldn't do that. But myself, I'm not so keen on these Mod medallists, they sing too much like the wireless.' (A Gaelic 'Mod' is the equivalent of the Welsh Eisteddfod and is held for the competitive singing of Gaelic.)

'No more am I,' affirmed Morag, her mouth crammed full of buttered oatcake. 'They sound more like seagulls with larningitis.'

'What a pity people didn't give the comedian any encouragement,' I said, when the two women had ceased to laugh. 'I felt rather sorry for him and some of his jokes were quite good.'

'He was a good laugh, right enough,' they agreed.

'But nobody laughed aloud at his jokes,' I said.

'Ach, but you canna' be laughin' at a man to his face just as though he was a sort of animal,' replied Morag.

I pointed out that comedians thrive on laughter, but our hostess cut me short.

'No, but that's just the English way of it,' she corrected. 'It's not our way.'

'We leave the laughter to the English,' tittered Morag, 'the same way as we leave them the love. Why, the way English folks goes on about fallin' in love you'd think love was a thing you could put into a parcel and take home with you.'

'Haven't you ever loved anyone?' I asked.

'There's not such a thing as love,' she said.

'You've been married,' I told her. 'Weren't you in love with your husband?'

'In love! In love! Listen to it I tell you. Indeed it's true I've been marrit. I marrit a good enough man and he had a good enough wife in myself and between us we had five children. What for would we be wantin' love for as well? Surely I know as much about love as I know about 'lectricity and I want nothin' to do with either of them if I can help it.'

So spake the practical Morag, and it was difficult to believe that hardly less than an hour ago I had seen her dabbing furtively at her eyes during the singing of a particularly sentimental song.

Some time later, having taken leave of the Oxford accent, who was not coming to the dance until she had seen her old father safely to bed, we returned to the hall. It was soon evident that the majority of the revellers were still drinking strupaks with their friends or, in the case of the menfolk, drinking illegal whisky at the nearby hotel, for except for a listless group of females who had draped themselves round the doorway like wilted flags, the place was strangely deserted. The girls aroused themselves briefly from their torpor to greet Morag and me and then sank back into attitudes that seemed to add to the general lifelessness of the place rather than detract from it. Inside the hall lights were burning, but there was no sound from within. I looked at my watch. The dance had been advertised to begin at eleven o'clock and it was now half past that hour.

'What's happenin'?' Morag addressed the bevy of girls who stared dully in reply.

'It's the band,' one of them at last managed to answer.

'The band? What's wrong with the band?' asked Morag.

'They're out at the back there fightin' like bulls,' the girl said morosely.

'They're fightin'? Why is that?'

The girl who had volunteered the information shrugged her shoulders apathetically. The rest remained comatose. The band was having a fight, and the fact was accepted philosophically as though to be 'fightin' like bulls' was a characteristic habit of all dance bands.

'It's swearin' to strangle one another they was a few minutes ago.' Another girl jerked herself to life momentarily and threw out this piece of intelligence with gloating satisfaction.

'How many players are there in the band?' I asked, visualizing something in the nature of a musical rugger scrummage.

'Three,' answered the first girl; 'the pipes, the fiddle and the melodeon.'

'And who's swearin' to strangle who?' asked Morag.

'Ach, the fiddle says he's for stranglin' the melodeon and the melodeon says he's for stranglin' the fiddler.'

'And the piper?'

'He's too drunk to strangle anybody but himself.' The girls sniggered smugly.

My landlady and I had, while extracting this information, become aware of varying sounds of battle which emanated from somewhere at the back of the hall.

'I'm goin' to take a look,' said Morag bravely, and hurried towards the scene of conflict.

'I wonder what has happened to the M.C.?' I asked the girls after ten minutes had ticked by, and there was still no sign of the dance beginning.

'He's out at the back too,' the girls told me. 'He was tryin' to stop them from quarrellin', but they take no heed of him at all.'

Being confident of Morag's ability to quell the musical strife and noticing that the girls still hugged their packets of soap flakes, I suggested that we should do whatever we were expected to do with them. 'Just empty them on the floor as you go in,' they told me. I led the way in and they proceeded to tear open the packets and strew the contents on the floor. Conscientiously I followed suit.

The grocer's statement that the floor needed whole bars of soap to fill up the rat-holes was certainly not far wrong. There were some treacherous holes and even those parts of the floor which the rats had left alone were splintered and rough. Boards creaked and groaned and in places black mud oozed up between the joints as they gave under our weight. It could not by any stretch of imagination be called a dance floor, but I daresay it was good enough for tackety boots.

More people began to arrive and just as we had finished our nose-tickling task Morag appeared on the threshold solicitously shepherding two tragic and muddy figures: one with a black eye and bleeding nose; the other with a swollen chin and a gory ear. They were closely followed by the M.C. supporting or being supported by a rotund and beaming piper, who was assuring everyone happily that he had succeeded in persuading the two musicians to postpone strangling each other until after the feshtertivities, for it was a shame if folks wash to be dishappointed. (His last words, I assumed, referred to the dance and not to the strangling duet.)

Thus inauspiciously the dancing started and there were some of us who wished before the evening was very far advanced that the piper's powers of persuasion had not been so successful, for the erst-while combatants seemed to have imbued their instruments with their own disharmony and our ears were assaulted by an incessant riot of discordancy which Morag aptly described as being 'worse than a bullin' cow'. Regardless of strife the dancers leaped and stamped their way through innumerable schottisches and reels, their shrill 'yeeps' and screams outrivalling the frantic efforts of the belligerent instrumentalists who, with carefully averted eyes, played with the single-mindedness of two greyhounds chasing a hare and with much the same result; the fiddle invariably reaching the winning post two or three bars ahead of his antagonist.

The piper who 'spelled' the fiddle and melodeon was determinedly hilarious and did not degenerate until shortly after the refreshment interval, when his piping developed an alarming bubbling undertone, an intrusion which the M.C. dismissed as due to there being 'so much beer got into the pipes they won't play right', and while first aid was rendered to the instrument the piper himself was permitted to sleep off his excesses at the rear of the stage, from whence his nasal organs continued to accompany the dancing with only slightly less sonorous-ness and decidedly more rhythm than had been discernible in his previous efforts.

A bashful young blood was quick in offering to make up for the piper's lapse and produced for this purpose an ordinary mouth-organ. A dance was duly announced and entered upon by the dancers but except for a chord at the beginning and another at the end the only indications that there might be a musical accompaniment were the bulging eyes and the distended cheeks of the musician and the position of his eyebrows which were a good two inches above normal.

The announcement that voting in the Beauty Contest was due to begin released all the musicians temporarily and the fiddle and melodeon were escorted from the stage in opposite directions by anxious friends. The girls meanwhile were requested to form a circle in the centre of the room and the men were handed pencils and paper and asked to record their votes. I had been asked to present the prizes, so I now made my way to a small table at the front of the stage, upon which a box of lace-edged handkerchiefs and a pair of silk stockings—the first and second prizes—were displayed, together with several half-bottles of whisky and one or two boxes of cigarettes which were to be spot prizes. The efforts of the M.C. to persuade the circle of girls to perambulate and display their charms were unavailing; they either huddled together in exaggerated modesty, as false as it was infuriating, or stood with heads bowed in attitudes of knock-kneed shyness, yet resolutely ogling the men from beneath lowered eyelids. Various ribald remarks percolated through the buzz of talk, and then the M.C. gave instructions for the papers to be collected. 'And the pencils,' he added meaningly, as some of the men endeavoured to secrete the latter in breast pockets. Capfuls of paper were soon being emptied on the table and between us the M.C. and I went through them.

'Number sixteen!' announced the M.C. and, amidst a roar of applause, number sixteen, a hefty buck-toothed young woman, sturdy as an oak and just about as supple, came lurching ferociously towards the stage. Clumsily she negotiated the steps, or rather failed to negotiate them, and tripping over the top one clutched my proffered hand desperately as a support rather than as the salute I had intended it to be. I congratulated her solemnly and handed over the prize but, overcome by an excess of shyness, she was unable to articulate even the most perfunctory acknowledgment. The M.C. also shook her hand and the dancers, seizing the opportunity for fun, clamoured that he should kiss the winner. The two looked at each other and then away again. The M.C. smiled fatuously. The girl shook her abundant hair over her flaming cheeks.

'Kiss!' The clamour became insistent, and dutifully the M.C. obeyed, but as he too was preceded by very pronounced buck teeth it was a difficult feat to accomplish. The noise of the impact put my own teeth on edge.

'Number twenty-eight,' called the M.C. next, and with another burst of applause the second prize-winner came lumbering forward like a frenzied calf into a sale ring. Buxom, scarlet-faced and perspiring, she was afflicted with a wall-eye, thick ankles and a depraved taste in scent. Her thick red hair was adorned with a posy of white flowers which, as I reached hastily for a handkerchief, I identified as the ramsons, or wild garlic. She shook my hand limply, grinned gummily and, evading the proffered hand of the M.C., plunged down the steps to her friends.

It may be suspected that the men were perpetrating a colossal joke, or that the girls had won their votes more as objects of compassion than of admiration. But this was not so. The Islanders viewed beauty purely from the utilitarian standpoint. For a woman to possess allure she had first to possess bulk, for in windy climates a thin or normally developed woman has distinct disadvantages. Anna Vic's husband was a much envied man, particularly during hay harvest, because not only could his wife carry immense loads on her broad back but on breezy days he could build quite substantial hay-cocks in the shelter provided by her girth; less fortunate men with skinny wives had either to leave their hay at the mercy of the weather or build it in low cocks through which any rain would soak in no time. There could be no doubting that the men had chosen according to their desires.

The next prize was a bottle of whisky for which tickets had already been sold. The winner was a tall, pasty-faced, Bruach youth who I had hitherto glimpsed retiring clandestinely around the backs of houses, or disappearing into convenient cattle byres. Tonight he was in no mood for self-effacement and swaggering up to the stage he took his prize, pulled out the cork, and then walking to the centre of the floor he held up the bottle, threw back his head dramatically and drained the contents at one single draught. I fully expected him to drop down senseless but instead he stalked majestically to the open door and in a reedy but penetrating voice demanded naïvely: 'Where's that bloody policeman? Isn't it his job to be lookin' after drunks like me?' As though in answer the uniformed policeman appeared in the doorway, his face split from ear to ear by a grin. The prize-winner lurched forward and took him most companionably by the buttons of his tunic. 'I'm Duncan MacAllister,' he asserted in accents that were rapidly becoming more blurred. 'And I'm that drunk I'm not fit to be at large. I ought to be locked up where I'm safe.'

In spite of the policeman's obvious reluctance, Duncan grasped his arm compellingly and amid jeers and encouragements the two disappeared. Dancing was resumed, and when, about half an hour later, the policeman returned alone, he was heard confiding to enquirers that he'd got so fed up with Duncan hangin' round his neck and insistin' on bein' jailed that he'd pushed him in through a little narrow window at the back of the hall, told him it was a prison cell and cleared off as quickly as he could. It transpired that the 'little narrow window' belonged to the ladies lavatory!

At three o'clock in the morning the dancers were still in fine fettle and old men and young men, dowagers and damsels, were capering about the soapy room with the exuberance of two-year-olds, the fervour of their dancing banishing the missionary and his prophecies of Hell-fire to the regions of their inspiration. The men had discarded their jackets, collars and ties and were dancing in shirt sleeves, their expressions a mixture of ecstasy and bliss. At the commencement of each dance they approached the girls with condescending masculinity, using the same phrase, the same peremptory voice and intonation when requesting them to dance as they used when they wished to move an obstinate cow. It sounded suspiciously like the English farmer's 'Get up there, Daisy!' The roadmen were much in evidence, inches of their sunburnt bull-necks emerging above constricting neck-bands, their shirts soaked with perspiration. Boisterously they skipped and vaulted about the uneven floor, wielding their partners as they had wielded their picks and shovels, though I should say that the latter had received the more consideration. Their dancing was an ungainly combination of capers, lunges and caprioles and was attended by an incessant chorus of male and female shrieks; the former rapturous, the latter agonized. It struck me that none of the roadmen had changed his boots. Lachy, hot and dishevelled, pranced vengefully across the floor brandishing his two partners as though he was practising for 'tossing the caber' rather than leading them through the intricacies of a 'Dashing White Sergeant'. Johnny was being propelled hither and thither by Elspeth the schoolteacher; his legs looked as though they were moving mechanically; his eyes were tight shut. It was quite possible that he was fast asleep! Watching the dancers I recalled a phrase of the 'warning' notice—'lassies now's your chance to shine'. The lassies were certainly shining and if they had not mopped their pretty faces profusely (borrowing one another's handkerchiefs for the purpose) they would have shone a good deal more; the perspiration showed as dark patches which reached from the armpits almost to the waistlines of their flimsy blouses. The wooden walls of the room were running with condensation; the air was blue with tobacco smoke, and cigarette butts and empty packets were being trodden and kicked around the floor by the feet of the dancers. At the end of each dance the men dropped their partners as though they were hot—perhaps the simile is not inappropriate—and hurried outside.

At one time during the evening I ventured outside myself for a breath of fresh air and was surprised to hear the sound of a spade being plunged into earth.

'There's Miss Peckwitt.' The remark came out of the darkness and a moment later Lachy's voice was asking me if he'd 'get a shine of a torch'. Obediently I went towards the voice and found a group of men gazing with puzzled intensity at a newly turned patch of earth. Lachy bent down, unearthed a bottle, and held it in the beam of the torch.

'That's no ours, Lachy,' said Johnny who was also one of the group.

'What brand was ours then?' asked Lachy.

'It was no that one anyway,' insisted someone; 'haste and put that back.'

'Then were the hell is ours?' asked Lachy irritably as he replaced the bottle and covered it over. 'I'm damty sure it was somewhere here we put it.'

He set to work again in a slightly different spot and this time his digging brought to light a bottle which they were all satisfied was their own.

'I have another one I buried earlier over by the dyke there,' said Johnny. He turned to me: 'Miss Peckwitt will be thinkin' it's awful strange to be buryin' the drinks,' he said ruefully, 'but you canna' dance with bottles in your pockets and you canna' trust folks here when it comes to whisky.' He addressed Lachy again. 'Come and we'll get my bottle while we have the light,' he said eagerly.

'Not on your life,' replied Lachy. 'Leave that one where it is for now. We'll drink this one first—it won't take long.'

It certainly did not take them long and within a short time they were again borrowing my torch. How many bottles of whisky had been buried in the grounds of the hall that night I had no idea, but whenever I went in search of fresh air there was always one group or another busy digging.

'How is it that there happens to be a spade at the hall?' I asked Johnny. 'Surely the committee don't provide that, do they?'

'Of course they don't,' he rejoined. 'We picked it up from the burial ground on our way here.' And misunderstanding my look of surprise he went on: 'It's all right, we're goin' to put it back on our way home.'

'The trouble with these girls is that they canna' dance,' grumbled Lachy as we sat watching the progress of an aptly named reel. His wandering eye fixed briefly on a full-blooded young siren who had draped herself sinuously over a couple of chairs and was raking the 'stag lines' with hungry eyes. 'That's the only one here who knows how to dance properly,' he finished. I recognized the girl as the missionary's daughter.

I pointed to an extremely pretty girl with a glorious mop of blonde curls. 'Who is she?' I asked.

'Ach, she doesn't rightly belong here at all,' said Lachy, and after a few minutes cogitation whispered: 'Not properly she doesn't—one half of her comes from Glasgow.'

The next dance was one which was utterly unfamiliar to me and though I studied the steps of the revellers I could see no two couples who followed the same pattern. 'Tripping the light fantastic' might have been a fair description of some of the steps executed by the more lissom of the damsels, but 'fantastic' was the only adjective applicable to those of the rest of the dancers.

'Come and dance,' invited Lachy.

'I'm sorry, I'm quite unable to do this one,' I apologized.

'Neither can anybody else,' said Lachy; 'but who's worryin' so long as we enjoy ourselves.'

It was difficult to refuse Lachy because he was always much too ready to feel that he was being snubbed, so I suffered myself to be bobbed and bounced through something that might have been a jig but was more akin to a judo lesson.

'I like the way you townsfolk seem to be able to dance on your toes,' panted my partner admiringly.

'You're dancing on them too,' I replied with a ghostly chuckle that was half irony and half agony.

'Me? Dancin' on my toes?'

'No,' I retorted brutally, 'on mine.'

'I thought I must be,' said Lachy simply, and with no trace of remorse; 'I could tell by the way your face keeps changin'.'

'What did you think of the evening's beauty?' I enquired as we sank exhausted into our seats.

'She'd make a damty fine heifer,' he said dispassionately.

'She wasn't your choice, then?'

'No indeed. It was the one with pink hair I voted for.'

I had long since discovered that colour shades in Bruach bore no resemblance whatever to those recognized by the rest of the world. A red and white cow, for instance, is known as a 'grey beast'; a black one will be described as 'blue'; but pink hair was worth investigation. I asked Lachy to point out the freak. For a few minutes he scanned the weaving dancers and then he pointed to a young girl with pale, sandy-coloured hair who was at that moment engaged in executing a frolicsome schottische. She caught our glance, waved cheerily and continued dancing with zest. I was surprised to see her there for it was only recently that I had heard she had secured a good post as a lady's maid in Edinburgh. I mentioned this to Lachy.

'Oh, but she had to give it up and come home,' he replied. 'Did you not hear? She's been on the club for a few weeks now.'

'Is there something wrong with her?' I asked dubiously, my eyes following the girl's fast-moving, nimble figure.

'Indeed there is!' said Lachy. 'Did you not know she has terrible rheumatics in her feets? My, I hear it's that bad sometimes she can hardly put her legs under her.'

The lassie had 'her legs under her' tonight all right, and it looked to me from the way she was skipping about the floor that she might have the legs of a few other people under her before very much longer. My own shins were already bruised after encountering her as a neighbour in a 'Strip the Willow'.

'How did you like the second prize-winner?' I demanded of Lachy.

'Oh, she wasn't bad,' he said. 'Her hair was all right. That's real Highland hair.'

'That's real hennaed,' contradicted Morag who had just seated herself on the empty form beside us. 'I'm tellin' you, Miss Peckwitt, that second prize-winner is the girl Lachy has a fancy for marryin'.'

'It is not,' repudiated Lachy. 'I'm after marryin' nobody but an Englishwoman like Miss Peckwitt here. They're good workers the English.'

At five o'clock, the floor was noticeably clearer and even the younger dancers were beginning to show signs of fatigue. There being no more prizes to present, Morag and I decided we could unobtrusively withdraw from the festivities. We were tired, I more so than my landlady for she had done little but sit and ceilidh during the whole evening. Rescuing my coat from the packed cloakroom, I flung it

over my shoulders, and was following Morag to the door when suddenly a wild-eyed figure burst into the room.

'The hotel's on fire!' he bellowed. 'Help! Help!'

The response from even the most jaded dancers among us was
immediate, and in less than a minute the hall was emptied of dancers,
onlookers, officials and musicians and we were all racing as fast as we
could in the direction of the hotel. The smell of burning soon met our
nostrils, and, callous as it may seem, it was a welcome change from the
pungent odour of soap flakes and sweat I had been breathing all
evening. As we rounded the corner we came upon the hotel, where
one of the garret windows sprouted fierce tufts of flame and billowing
clouds of smoke.

The policeman, hatless and jacketless, was already attempting to
form the revellers into a bucket chain, assuring everyone meantime
that he had despatched someone to ' 'phone for the Brigade'. His task
was well nigh hopeless, for the Bruachites and their neighbours were
nothing if not fierce individualists and they retained their individualism even in the face of fire. He might just as easily have tried to
organize a chain of live eels as organize a chain of Gaels. His exhorta-
tions, entreaties and threats were in vain; the crowd obeyed their own
inclinations entirely, clinging tenaciously to the belief that personal
effort would always be superior to communal effort. The few who
were not bewitched by the conflagration seized pails and ran to the
loch, but the blazing lights of the hotel were so dazzling after the
darkness that people and pails were constantly colliding and at least
as much water was spilled on the ground as eventually reached the
flames.

'Them lights near takes the eyes out of you,' coughed Morag as she
came over to join the knot of women whom I had more or less
coerced into forming a straggled and inefficient chain. But even with
the eyes near out of her she was worth at least three of the other
women. Her presence shamed them into action; her tongue stirred
action to alacrity, and soon buckets and jugs were passing to and from
the loch. Several men stood by, their admiration divided between the
burning building and the bucket chain.

'What can I do? What can I do?' The distracted hotel housekeeper
ran out from the kitchen and stood wailing, and wringing her hands,
in the midst of the confusion.

'Get me half a dozen darning needles to stick into some of these louts!' shrilled a voice which I was faintly surprised to recognize as my own. From the way the spellbound watchers were electrified into activity it might have been supposed that the darning needles had been produced forthwith.

'Get into the chain will you!' the sorely tried policeman shouted as he descried an old man, the occupant of a thatched cottage dangerously near to the burning building, returning from the direction of the loch.

'I will not then,' retorted the old man defiantly. ' 'Tis my own chamber I got and 'tis my own watter that's in it, and 'tis my own bit of flame I'll be after quenchin'.'

The reply typified the attitude of the crowd and, with a despondent shrug of his shoulders, the policeman watched the lone fire-fighter trotting purposefully in the direction of the cottage, his utensil held in front of him as though he was a competitor in an egg-and-spoon race.

Tired as everyone must have been, we worked like Trojans that night but, though every utensil a hotel could provide was commandeered for fire-fighting, our efforts had only a negligible effect on the flames. If the helpers had directed their energies as efficiently as they wagged their tongues we might have accomplished more, but the Gael's inability to co-operate is congenital and his loquacity is, if anything, increased by peril or panic.

Over an hour later there was a cry of relief as a small, grey van slid elegantly towards the hotel and braked to a decorous halt. Then began a scene which could only have been described as high comedy.

'He Breeah!' The driver, who was in fireman's uniform, greeted us all with true Hebridean politeness, unfailing though sometimes exasperating. He and his two mates alighted from the van, and, bestowing confident smiles on the bunch of sodden fire-fighters, seemed undecided whether to come and shake hands with each of us in turn.

'My, but what a time you've taken,' complained one of the onlookers peevishly.

'Indeed, and you're lucky we're here at all,' the driver responded with some heat. 'Didn't the fool who gave the message forget to tell us where was the fire?' He turned to his mates. 'What a job we've had knockin' up folks all the way to find where we should go.' (At that time in the morning I am quite sure that many of the crofters would

have told them where they should go—and in no uncertain terms.)
The driver's mates nodded agreement and I wondered if, having now
arrived at the scene of the fire, they had yet noticed it.

At this moment the policeman, harassed and sooty, raced impetuously towards the fire engine.

'Put everythin' you can up there!' he commanded. 'It's ragin' like
a furnace.'

The fireman-driver, who was obviously also in command, looked
through the policeman's broad chest.

'In my job,' he retorted coolly, 'it's me that says what's to be
done.'

The policeman received the rebuff in silence and turning to the
bystanders, who, upon the arrival of the fire engine, had forsaken
their utensils, he beseeched them to bring their pails and follow him.
About a dozen men obeyed and tore after the policeman into the
hotel, where, a short time later, we could see them charging in and out
of the upstairs rooms, silhouetted like figures on a frieze.

With a deliberateness that was probably thorough, but was nevertheless irritating to the onlooker, the firemen coupled up their hoses
and started the engine of the pump. The youngest of them, a lean
youth with a mop of cherubic curls peeping from beneath his stiff cap,
lumbered heavily towards the hotel with a length of hose. By this
time the policeman and his retinue were throwing linen and blankets
through the open windows, to be salvaged by willing hands below.

'Right?' called the chief fireman to the cherub.

'Right!' replied the cherub. He positioned himself to direct a jet
of water at one of the windows when, without warning, he went
down beneath a large double bed mattress which hurtled from somewhere above.

'Hi!' yelled the crowd, while gesticulating rescuers ran to extricate
the fireman.

'Hi!' they yelled again as the rescuers themselves were buried
beneath a veritable shower of mattresses, all aimed with a precision
that would under other circumstances have looked suspicious.

'What's happened?' asked the chief fireman curiously.

'They've flattened him,' supplied an onlooker equably.

'Flattened him?' echoed the chief with a bellicose glance at the
window where the policeman had last appeared. 'What for? He's done
no wrong.'

Meanwhile the second fireman ran forward with his own hose, but as he crossed the lawn he too was knocked for six, not by a mattress but by a large wardrobe which someone, in an excess of zeal and panic, had thrown recklessly from a second-floor window. Two anxious faces appeared at the window from which the wardrobe had descended but their concern was for the fate of the furniture, not for the unfortunate fireman who lay prostrate in the middle of the lawn; a lawn which his still-gushing hose was quickly transforming into a miniature lake.

The chief fireman, furious at the treatment his men had received, was still standing beside the engine excitedly flinging orders at all and sundry. What the orders may have been nobody knew, for of course nobody took the slightest notice. The policeman reappeared on the scene.

'Look here, man,' he addressed the chief witheringly; 'what's the use of pouring water into the cellars when it's up in the roof the fire is. A hose on the roof will have it out in no time.'

'You've near killed my mates,' retaliated the chief angrily. 'Now what d'you expect me to do about your fire?'

'Me? Killed your mates?' demanded the policeman, who was quite unaware of the mishap to the firemen. 'Well, it's likely they'll have more life in them dead than alive. But if you don't get up there quick I'll report you,' he went on savagely.

The chief fixed his adversary with a pair of horror-stricken eyes. 'Me?' he expostulated. 'Me? Go up on that bloody roof?'

'Why not?' returned the policeman with admirable restraint. 'That's where the fire is, isn't it?'

It looked for a moment as though the chief was about to dissolve into tears, but instead he hitched up his trouser leg and turned abjectly on the policeman.

'Have you seen that?' he asked piteously, displaying his wooden leg for inspection. 'Can you rightly expect a man like me to go clamberin' and climbin' stairs, let alone roofs?'

'Oh no, that's different.' At once the policeman was contrite. 'You'd best give me the hose and I'll go up myself,' he offered.

'Are you sure you'll manage?' asked the chief considerately.

'I'll manage,' returned the policeman through clenched teeth, and ran forward to take up his duties as chief fireman.

As he had claimed, a hose on the roof had the fire out in a

comparatively short time. Within an hour the threatening flames were subdued and the charred and dripping ruin of the roof emerged from the pall of smoke. A fine drizzle of rain began to help along the good work.

'Come round to the kitchen,' said Morag. 'There's tea for everybody there.'

Thankfully we adjourned to the kitchen where we found the two injured firemen who, having been rescued from their predicament and given first aid, were now reclining comfortably in easy chairs beside the stove and regaling themselves liberally with whisky supplied by a grateful proprietor. They were, someone explained, 'waitin' on the ambulance takin' them to hospital'. They were obviously hoping the ambulance would be a long time coming.

The policeman, with torn shirt, was hardly recognizable under his grime as he tottered into the kitchen and dropped into a chair.

'I think I've sprained my wrist,' he muttered. Someone pressed a roll of bandage into my hand and I bound up his wrist as well as I could. 'God! What a night!' he said as his chin sank wearily on his chest.

The experience being safely over, cups began to clatter merrily and the night's adventures were gone through over and over again in detail, as people sipped tea and poked whole biscuits into their gabbling mouths.

'The sooner the ambulance comes and these men get skilled attention the better it will be for them.' A high authoritative voice briefly silenced the hurly-burly of the kitchen. The two firemen directed baleful glances at the speaker and hastily replenished their glasses; the crowd resumed their chatter.

'Oughtn't we to get hold of the nurse?' I asked the policeman.

'Impossible,' he replied. 'The nurse is on holiday in Glasgow.'

'Well, what about the doctor?' I persisted. 'Is he on holiday too?'

The policeman permitted himself a grim smile. 'In a way he is,' he said. His smile broadened into an expansive grin. 'I had to lock him up on Thursday—drunk in charge again.'

It was long past breakfast-time when Morag and I set out to walk home, there being no sign of the bus anywhere.

'I wouldn't have minded bein' a bitty crowded to save havin' this walk on top of the night we've had,' mourned my landlady, and as I dragged beside her along the stony path with the brittle heather stems rasping against the remains of my silk stockings I sincerely echoed her sentiments.

The drizzle was by this time showing signs of developing into a real downpour and the newly turned potato and corn patches were speedily changing their pale dun colour for a moist blackness. The rain sizzled through the sparsely leafed bushes and in the grey murk above a skylark soared, pouring out melody as though compelled to rid itself of its jubilation before it could bear to seek shelter. The burn rippled sportively under the old lichen-patterned bridge.

'Them's voices,' said Morag suddenly, and leaning over the parapet we beheld the 'fiddle' and the 'melodeon', one arm embracing their instruments and their free arms embracing each other. They were making repeated claims that ' 'twas my fault sure as I'm here', and so engrossed were they in their new friendship that neither of them was aware of our presence. We thought it wiser not to disturb them.

'They look very comfortable in spite of the weather,' I said.

'They should be comfortable,' replied Morag. 'Did you no see it was the piper himself they was sittin' on? He's one that won't get wet anyway.'

We did not go to bed when we reached home but busied ourselves with the sedentary tasks of the house. The letter I had been expecting was duly delivered by a red-eyed and befuddled postman, somewhere about lunch-time. I managed to summon up enough energy to take my answer up to the pillar-box. On my way home I perceived a group of tired men sheltering just inside the doorway of Lachy's cow byre. They included Duncan the whisky drinker and, remembering his performance of the previous night and also the policeman's remedy, I called out to ask him how he had liked his spell in prison.

Duncan grinned pallidly. 'Prison's all right,' he said. 'But them damty wardresses won't give a man a minute's peace and quiet.'

10. *Mary's Visit*

It had been, if I remember rightly, during breakfast one morning in our flat, soon after the proposal of my migration to the Hebrides, that Mary, with her customary bluntness, had raised the subject of sanitation. It was a subject which I had at the time been reluctant to discuss, largely I suppose because I knew instinctively that one could not expect such refinements as flush lavatories in isolated country villages, and just at that particular hour I recoiled from envisaging the only alternative.

On my arrival in Bruach Morag had soon introduced me to the niceties of rural sanitation, pointing proudly to a horridly conspicuous little hut, painted a torturous pink and almost surrounded by an abundant growth of nettles, which stood in splendid isolation at the far end of the 'park'.

'I empty her in the sea every day,' Morag had said, and I had immediately enlightened Mary as to the nature of the 'refusals'. 'When I knew you was comin',' continued my landlady, 'I painted her all over inside and out, and I got Ruari to shift her from where she was beside the hen house over to here.' She chuckled briefly. 'And bless me, but the fool didna' realize the paint was wet, and he comes up behind her, puts his two long arms around her, lifts her up and carries her to where she is now,' she finished triumphantly.

I was a little confused by her recital and it must have seemed to her that I was not sufficiently impressed by her brother's feat.

'If you dinna' believe me, just take a look at her behind and you'll see the shape of Ruari on her yet,' she assured me earnestly.

I at once feigned a convincing interest in Ruari's prowess, for the menacing appearance of the nettles completely overruled the impulse to 'take a look at her behind'.

166

The 'wee hoosie', as Morag called the lavatory in my presence—
though when I happened to overhear her mentioning it to Ruari one
day she referred to it by a far more robust name—looked exceedingly
fragile and, I imagine, depended a good deal for support on the large
heaps of stones which were piled anyhow against its sides; it was
possible that the nettles also made some slight contribution to its
stability. Ventilation was lavish, and at night one was thankful for the
ubiquitous cycle lamp—a candle would not have remained alight for
an instant in the fierce draughts. The door, I found to my dismay,
could not be secured except by means of a piece of string looped round
a rusty nail: a flimsy and far from reassuring arrangement, but when
in occupation the numerous ventilation holes gave advance glimpses
of any intending visitor, and a throaty cough at an opportune moment
was all that was necessary to divert the would-be intruder to the
pursuit of an imaginary bird's nest or an industrious weeding of the
garden. So far as Morag and I were concerned the arrangement
worked admirably, but during a visit from one of my landlady's male
relatives—a fellow utterly lacking in sensitivity—I so nearly coughed
myself into an attack of laryngitis that I insisted on purchasing a
handsome and effective brass bolt, and prevailed upon Ruari to fix it
on the door. Ruari undertook the task with thinly disguised scorn
but his subsequent remark that the door would be 'the better for that
bit of strengthenin'' convinced me, in spite of Morag's silent criticism,
that my one and ninepence had been well spent.

The supply of toilet paper was erratic, the grocer receiving a con-
signment only once a year, at the beginning of the tourist season, and
when that was exhausted Morag attempted to remedy the situation
with an accumulation of well-thumbed periodicals covering an
extensive range of subjects. I ensured an adequate supply of toilet
rolls by post but I must admit that my education, during the summer
months at any rate, was enormously improved by the regular perusal
of the magazines. Before I had been in Bruach a year I was well versed
in such subjects as: 'How to prepare the ideal growing mash for
newly weaned pigs'—this was wasted study as there were no pigs in
Bruach, at least not the four-legged ones; 'How to distinguish a pipit
from a skylark'; 'How M.S., Glasgow, could cure his headaches' and
'Housewife in Perth' could avoid getting chilblains, and 'How to make
a scruggin cake'—though I never discovered what scruggins might
be. I could even recite parrot-fashion the correct shades of make-up

for blonde, brunette and red-head, and also reel off a list of the historic monuments of Scotland with hardly a pause for breath. I like to think that some day the information may prove valuable.

It was not until my second summer in Bruach that Mary decided to risk visiting me in my new home, and directly she announced her intention Morag and I began a belated but furious onslaught on the spring cleaning and the enhancing of improvements which had originally been undertaken in my honour. I had of course become inured to many of the crudities of Island life, but I could still recall my own repugnance on first coming into contact with many of the accepted arrangements, and I had no wish to give Mary the impression that I had become completely degenerate. Though Morag's house was one of the cleanest in Bruach, that which passes for cleanliness in the Hebrides would be looked upon as slovenliness by the average urban housewife, so my landlady and I scrubbed, polished and mended and at intervals wielded moulting paint-brushes with more vigour than skill.

'My, but you do come in handy,' Morag exclaimed admiringly after one of my artistic orgies had transformed the drab brown stair-case into a glistening and unsullied white.

After the house, the next objective was the 'park', which besides half a dozen tall rowans and what Morag described generously as a 'seeds mixture grass'—though 'weeds mixture' would have been my more fitting description—boasted only a few ancient blackcurrant bushes which to my knowledge had never produced anything more attractive than curled leaves and earwigs. Ruari, having been per-suaded to lend a hand, mowed grass steadily, and just as steadily emitted a comprehensive stream of expletives as his scythe came up against an appalling number of stones which, if he could be believed, had been hidden there with deliberate and spiteful intent. It was a thrill for me to watch the superb effortlessness of Ruari's rhythmic, graceful swing; it was an education for me to listen to the effortless-ness of his abuse. In desperation Morag went out to him.

'Ruari, shut your noise,' she implored. 'Miss Peckwitt's after hearin' every word you say.'

'If she don't like it she can come out here and cut the grass herself,' replied the undaunted Ruari, and carried on swinging and swearing without noticeable pause.

Gradually, our labours showed their effect. The garden no longer resembled a garbage dump, and after I had enjoyed the privilege of seeing Ruari 'wash down with lime' the house itself looked as spick and span as it was possible to make it.

'Everythin' in the garden's lovely,' trilled Morag inspiringly, the evening before Mary's expected arrival, but I was glaring at the 'wee hoosie' whose garish pinkness had, by my efforts, now been modified to a sober green.

'I wish,' I remarked testily, 'that you had left the "wee hoosie" where it was beside the hen house instead of having it moved to its present position.'

'In that case, I'll tell Ruari to shift her back as soon as he has a moment,' promised my landlady confidently.

'Oh no!' I entreated hurriedly, mentally coupling Ruari's deafness with his genius for doing the wrong thing at precisely the wrong moment. 'I beg of you, please leave it where it is.'

'Ach, but he'll do the same as he did before, I expect,' rejoined Morag. 'He'll just up with her in his arms and away.'

That was exactly what I was afraid of.

'No,' I replied firmly. 'Please don't mention it to him at all.'

'Just as you like,' agreed Morag with resignation, and so the "wee hoosie" with its dado of nettles remained where it was.

The following day I made the trip to the mainland to meet Mary, whose determinedly optimistic mood was reassuring. Her arrival coincided fortunately with a spell of fine though blustery weather, but unfortunately with the breakdown of the only available hire car. The driver, though promising to do his very best to provide a substitute, had not been particularly hopeful, so it was an immense relief on our arrival at the pier to see his smiling face blooming above a flamboyant suit of dissonant checks. I introduced him to Mary and this being accomplished he condescended to busy himself with our luggage, only pausing to suggest cheerfully that he would not mind waiting while we took a cup of tea at the nearby tearoom. I could see that Mary was already favourably impressed, and was quick to point out that this willingness to oblige was a common trait among the Islanders. Our tea was excellent, the waitress who served was smiling and efficient, and I congratulated myself that Mary would soon come to understand the fascination the Island held for me. Feeling refreshed and full of pleasant satisfaction we were emerging from the tearoom when a funeral hearse, sombre and stately, drew up at the door. Mary gave it a startled glance and I managed to recollect that in England one does not expect to see a hearse parked outside a café while the driver goes for a cup of tea. I felt a little explanation was necessary.

'I told you they're very unsentimental about funerals, didn't I?' I began, 'and this hearse has probably come all the way from Glasgow. You never know how far they may have travelled and I expect the driver . . .' The rest of my words died away for it was at that moment that I beheld the driver. Eager and effusive, he climbed down from the driving-seat and greeted us for the second time that day.

'Enjoy your tea?' he asked hospitably, and without waiting for an answer turned to Mary. 'I've put your luggage aboard, miss,' he told her happily. 'There's nothing I might have forgotten now, is there?'

I turned to my companion. Never, 'while the Lord spares me', shall I forget the expression on Mary's face as she stared, not at the coffin she expected to see, but at her own suitcases and parcels piled neatly among the silver appointments. I experienced a moment of dismay as I realized suddenly the full force of the shock she was about to receive when the driver should fling open the glass doors and wait courteously to give us a 'leg up' inside. Of course it was all my own fault for I had taken great pains to impress upon the driver the necessity of providing some alternative form of transport to the broken-down taxi. I was prepared for a journey by lorry, by the cattle float, or even a borrowed horse and cart, but never in my wildest moments had I dreamed that anyone would think of substituting a hearse for a taxi. No doubt at first my own expression was equally tense, but, having grown accustomed to the unorthodoxy of Island transport and the general indifference to death, I was very quickly able to accept the situation with something approaching equanimity, even to see the humour in it.

'There's nothing else for it except Shanks' pony,' I whispered urgently to Mary.

'Does he expect us to go in that thing too?' she demanded in outraged tones. I nodded.

The driver discerned our hesitation. 'You two ladies can just sit in front with me,' he said, accompanying his invitation with a grin of ineffable superiority. 'It's only the wife's old mother I have there and she'll go in the back with the luggage easy enough.' He motioned blithely towards the cab of the hearse and, after a circumspect peep,

I was able to confide to Mary that the 'wife's old mother' was neither coffined nor embalmed, but, on the contrary, appeared to be exceedingly agile. As if the words were a signal the old woman bustled obligingly out of her seat and, though I felt rather doubtful as to the propriety of allowing one obviously so much nearer the grave than myself to go joy-riding in the back of a hearse, I was relieved when she refused to accept my half-hearted suggestion that I should take her place.

'It's quite comfortable, my dear,' she told me, her old face wreathed in smiles. 'You see, with it bein' for the corpuses it has to be nice and bouncy.'

'Come on,' I muttered inflexibly to Mary. 'It's our flat feet if you don't.'

Yielding reluctantly, she allowed herself to be handed with decorous solicitude into the front seat where she stayed, stiff and straight, for the whole of the journey. The hearse, after an *arpeggio* on the horn for the benefit of the crews of several fishing-boats, started off at an irreverent speed, and as he accelerated the impenitent driver discoursed upon the superiorities of the hearse above all other forms of transport, remaining callously indifferent to the rigid anxiety of Mary's face and a silence between the two of us which could only be described as deathly.

Morag, her face expressionless, was waiting for us as we drew to a majestic stop beside the wall. She eyed Mary uneasily, but I hastened to explain in an aside that my companion's aloofness was due not to hauteur but to the shock of having to travel in a funeral hearse. The uneasiness was instantly replaced by a smile of warm welcome. While Mary was being introduced to Ruari, I paid the driver (the exact fare) and, while Morag and Ruari were wrestling with the luggage, I turned to the 'wife's old mother', who by now had been hauled out of the glass doors and was ready to resume her place beside her son-in-law. I hoped she had been comfortable.

'Och aye, nobody could mind dyin' for a ride like that,' she replied.

'That one,' commented Morag sourly as the hearse disappeared, 'she'd say anythin' just to get folks to hire the hearse for their funerals. And as for that driver fellow, he's after swankin' round the place in it ever since he bought it. Indeed you'd think it was for takin' folks to Heaven itself instead of to the burial ground.'

She examined our clothes closely. 'It's to be hoped he cleaned it out after takin' yon calf to the sale in it this mornin', she said.

'Oh surely not!' protested Mary.

'Surely indeed,' asseverated Morag. 'And isn't he after takin' the scholars to school in it these three days past?'

The experience being safely over Mary was able to smile wanly. We negotiated the wall with an adroitness that was on my part due to long practice and on Mary's part to long legs, and soon the two of us were eating bacon and eggs and oatcakes and chattering away as though it was only yesterday we had said goodbye. Eagerly we fired question after question at each other, and outside in the whispering rowans a thrush echoed us interrogatively. Sleep overwhelmed us before even a tenth of our confidences had been exchanged, and as soon as we woke the next morning our tongues were at it again. Mary was still tired after her long journey and the two of us sat lazily beside the open window after a late breakfast, our conversation outrivalling the scandalmongering of the starlings on the chimney pot.

Suddenly Ruari's bellow assaulted the walls of the house like a battering ram.

'My, but that man shouts loud enough to wound a body,' we heard Morag complain, as she opened the door. The two voices continued in high altercation for some minutes and then a momentary quiet was followed by a perfunctory tap on the door. Morag burst into the room, but as she never allowed distress of any kind to interfere with good manners, she began by hoping we had enjoyed our breakfast. We assured her that we had.

'Is anything the matter?' I asked.

Morag looked apologetically at Mary. 'It's yon man,' she said plaintively, 'they're after tellin me' he's runnin' all over the place stabbin' all they cattle.'

'Good gracious!' Mary and I ejaculated together.

'I'm wonderin' if you'd help me take my own beasts to the hill?' Morag went on. I nodded assent.

As I have said earlier, Bruach possessed more than its fair share of mental defectives but I had not so far heard of one who was afflicted with bovicidal tendencies. That the position was serious we judged from Morag's manner, so I jumped up from my chair and pulled on gumboots (necessary because of the inevitable bogs which, unreasonable as it may sound, are always more numerous the higher one climbs). Mary watched me with wide-eyed astonishment.

'Shall I come with you?' she asked in a voice that invited refusal.

'No,' I told her. 'You lock the door after us and you'll be all right. He won't come here.'

I was not in the least apprehensive about her safety but was in fact secretly rather pleased that she should so soon learn how 'handy' I had become with the cattle.

Morag had already reached the cow byre and there I sped after her. A slam of the house door indicated that Mary was following my instructions.

'If you'll take the stirk, I can take the cow,' said Morag as she deftly untied the two beasts, and in a jiffy we and the animals were out of the dark byre. I assumed that as the stabber was beyond control we should be taking the beasts to some appointed place in the hills where the men of the village could combine and act as a bodyguard until the maniac was got under control.

'Which direction?' I called, as the stirk, his tail stiff as a poker, galumphed impetuously across the 'park'.

'To the glen,' she answered.

With an ominous bellow the beast bounded forward and as I grasped his head-rope firmly our memorable trek began. To say that I took the stirk to the glen that day would be an utterly erroneous description of our journey. It would be more correct to say that the stirk took me, for, winding the cattle on the hill, he raced off like a thing demented, and, like something equally demented, I careered after him, resolutely hanging on to his rope. Behind me I thought I heard Morag shout, but it was quite impossible for me to check the beast in his mad flight. Out of the corner of my eye I saw old Murdoch wheeling a barrow-load of manure from his byre and as we flashed past him he nearly overturned the barrow in his astonishment.

'Where are you away to?' he shouted.

'I'm taking the beast to the glen,' I yelled back, as I panted in the rear of the stirk's exuberant rushes. The echo of a cynical laugh fell upon my throbbing ears.

Over the hill my charge and I tore with heedless abandon, plunging through intimidating bogs, vaulting lightly over ruined dykes and sailing airily over peat hags until I began to feel that one at least of my

progenitors must have been a deer. Never before had I been conscious
of possessing legs that moved like wheels, but like wheels they worked
that day. Round and round they went as though they were jointless
and muscleless, until I was doubtful if I could ever stop them from
going round and round. It would perhaps have been an exhilarating
experience had I been in the mood and training for it, but I was in far
too much of a panic about the stabber for there to be the faintest
possibility of enjoying myself. To me the trek was a nightmare,
though to Bruach it subsequently became an epic: one eye-witness
relating that 'Indeed I didn't know it was a woman at all he had with
him. It looked like some cow flyin' one of they big kites.'

At length we reached the glen where a motley collection of
cavorting cattle were mooing and lowing in every key from double
bass to falsetto, and a number of conspicuously idle men squatted in
the heather. The stirk, his flanks heaving, stopped dead in his tracks,
lumbering only a couple of paces forward when I, having half his
number of legs and consequently less efficient braking power, can-
noned forcibly into his stern. Gasping, I collapsed on the ground, my
throat feeling like emery paper. Ruari's thundering voice penetrated
my exhaustion.

'You shouldn't have set the beast a pace like that,' he reproved me;
'it's bad for him.'

I glanced reproachfully in his direction, too breathless to disclaim
responsibility in the matter.

'Will they be all right here?' I asked Lachy when I had regained
sufficient breath to speak intelligently.

'Aye,' replied Lachy, who was always prominent among any
loungers, 'I daresay he'll attend to it soon.'

I possibly looked as enlightened as I felt.

'Who will?' I asked.

'Why, the vet of course,' responded Lachy. 'Isn't that what you've
brought the beast for?'

Comprehension dawned slowly and, dragging myself wearily to
my feet, I went over to where a knot of spectators were clustered
about a belligerent but securely held cow. I had already made the
acquaintance of the veterinary surgeon; an Edinburgh man with
a keenly developed sense of humour.

'Is it you who's the maniac running about "stabbin' all they
cattle"?' I taxed him with mock severity.

The vet glanced significantly at the hypodermic in his hand. 'I believe it must be,' he said with a wry grin. 'Watch how I do it.' Clipping a tiny patch of hair from the cow's neck, he inserted the needle.

'Testing for tuberculosis,' he muttered, 'and dashed high time too.'

Silently I cursed the literalness of Morag's descriptions. It was by no means the first time they had caused me stress and embarrassment; probably it would not be the last. My landlady herself arrived at this moment, rather breathless and more than a little anxious for my welfare. She too chided me on my unseemly haste.

To save us the tedium of waiting, the vet obligingly 'stabbed' our two beasts and, that done to everyone's satisfaction, he turned to a mangy black cow which was being led forward by a decrepit old man whom I knew as Shamus Beag.

'He has a nasty cut on his udder,' I heard Shamus telling the vet, and saw the latter bend down to examine the cow.

'I don't like that at all,' he said as he straightened up again. 'There's an awful queer smell about it.' Again he bent down and sniffed. 'It doesn't smell right at all.' He frowned deeply. 'Have you been putting anything on it, Shamus?' he asked.

'I have so,' admitted Shamus. 'Indeed I have the stuff here with me now.' Fumbling in his capacious pocket he produced a tube and held it out for the vet's inspection. I did not need to glance twice to recognize the alluring label of a much advertised and highly scented vanishing cream. The vet took a cigarette and clamped it between his twitching lips.

'Why on earth d'you go putting stuff like that on a cow's udder?' he asked Shamus.

Shamus, ignoring the ribald comments of the interested spectators, scratched vigorously at the sparse hair beneath his cap.

' 'Tis all what I could get from the tinks when they was round,' he explained with grave simplicity. 'And I do believe it's been doin' him good.'

'Maybe, maybe,' agreed the vet quickly as he snapped shut his cigarette-case. 'But look here, Shamus, I'll send you some better stuff than that for the cow. You can give that scented stuff to your wife.'

Shamus directed a puzzled glance at the speaker. 'My wife has no cut on her——' he began.

'No!' interpolated the vet loudly. 'For her face of course.'

'My wife has no cut on her face,' replied the old man with a slow shake of his head, and then added innocently: 'That would be her mouth.'

Laughter gurgled among the onlookers and the vet cupped his hand around the match flame to try and hide his own furtive smile.

Shamus bade everyone an indifferent farewell and plodded away with his cow.

The calm of the morning had by this time given way to a bullying breeze that frisked our hair and tore at our jackets. Leaving the cattle to find their own way home Morag and I retraced our steps across the moors. Mary unlocked the door with a scared face.

'Everything all right?' she enquired.

I nodded briefly.

'Your friend must be awful nervous,' said Morag in my ear, for naturally she had not heard my parting instructions to Mary.

'Yes,' I whispered treacherously, 'I'm afraid she is.'

Poor Mary! Already she was beginning to think that 'Bedlam' was a more apt name than Bruach for the village, but my explanation of the lunatic stabber and a description of my own hectic cross-country flight sent her into peals of laughter.

'Becky,' she prophesied joyfully, 'I do believe you'll make an Olympic runner yet.'

For the remainder of the afternoon and until late in the evening I lay on the sofa in a lethargy born of exhaustion. Mary was quite content to rest also and as she sat by the window in the growing dusk, sipping her hot milk supper, she said: 'You know, Becky, I believe your Island does have a certain charm in spite of its uncouthness.'

I grunted sleepily.

All day the wind had been steadily rising and now it had whipped itself into a full summer gale. Mary stared fascinatedly at the rowan trees bowing themselves to its onslaught.

'I say, Becky,' she began suddenly, 'I saw some funny white birds fly past the window then. What could they be?'

'I don't know,' I said, and reluctantly heaving my aching limbs from the comfortless sofa I went to the door. There was still some daylight left in the sky, for the summer twilight of the islands lingers long—too long. I peered outside and could see no sign of any birds, but even as I watched some white shapes hurtled by me. Calling to

Mary I propelled her round the end of the house and down the 'primrose path'.

'There's one sure thing,' I gloated. 'I may some day make an Olympic runner, but you'll never make an ornithologist. There! Look at your "birds".'

Mary's eyes followed mine, and we both burst out laughing as we stood watching the 'wee hoosie' where the boisterous wind, having sought and found the brand-new toilet roll, was now mischievously whipping it through one of the larger ventilation holes and tearing it into garlands which caught in the branches of the dark trees, making them look like gaunt presbyterian spinsters attired for some stygian ball. Streamers of migratory toilet paper whisked away up the village to festoon themselves around clothes-line posts, chimneys, byres and even on the horns of a perplexed cow. I called to Morag and she, seeing what had happened, skipped nimbly across the grass, intent on retrieving stray wisps of the precious paper. She came to me offering a crumpled armful, which I accepted only to sacrifice it to the appetite of the storm.

'My, but that's a shame,' Morag reproached me as the last length of the roll, now unwound to its extremity, sailed swiftly towards the hills. But I only smiled at her concern and made a mental note to keep to that particular brand of toilet paper, for the manufacturer obviously gave good value for money—there seemed to have been miles of it.

'Well, I think it's spiteful of her then,' said Morag.

'Who?' asked Mary, but a dig in the ribs from me warned her not to pursue the question.

In the privacy of our own room I explained that it was the wind that was 'spiteful' for having taken away the toilet roll.

'The wind is a "she" then?' asked Mary.

'It depends who you happen to be talking to,' I told her. 'It's a "she" with Morag; it might easily be a "he" with the next person you meet. They don't waste time on trivialities like sex.'

'What a language,' said Mary.

'What a people,' I murmured.

We finished our supper and were going upstairs to bed, pausing to say good night to Morag who was standing just inside the outer doors watching a car with unnecessarily bright headlights tearing up the road.

'That's the taxi-driver and his wife and a crowd of other folk goin'
off to the dance,' she informed us conversationally.

'Oh,' I said innocently, 'then he must have managed to repair the
taxi at last?'

'Not him,' said Morag serenely, 'that's the hearse itself they was in.'

11.   *Getting Ready for the Wedding*

'In the spring,' sings the poet, 'a young man's fancy lightly turns to thoughts of love.' But in the Hebrides that is indeed no truism. In the spring the crofter's materialistic fancy turns to planting, for though he can contemplate a future without love, a future without potatoes would be unendurable. It is for this reason that weddings, for the most part, are confined to the autumn and winter and, because he is invariably in no hurry for marriage, the terms 'autumn' and 'winter' are frequently symbolic of the time of life at which he chooses to take the fatal step (except in those cases when, in polite language, the bride finds it necessary to prepare the layette before the trousseau).

One autumn a whisper began to percolate through Bruach that it was to witness a wedding and before the rumour had circled the village three times it had become an established fact. Bruach was indeed to have a wedding; a real white wedding with bridesmaids, hotel reception, and even printed invitation cards. Morag sniffed contemptuously at the last piece of information.

'Them things is just a waste,' she said. 'When my own daughter was married in Glasgow she sent out them cards and she had R.I.P. printed on the bottom of them so she'd know how many was comin'.' She shook her head sadly. 'But nobody did—they're so ignorant about here.'

There had already been two or three weddings during my stay in Bruach but being of the sort just referred to in parentheses they had involved little more than a clandestine visit to the mainland, a few hurried minutes at a register office and, on the return home, had meant nothing more romantic than the addition of an extra pair of hands to the *ménage* of the in-laws more in need of labour or less cramped for room. In this case however the bridegroom was a doughty young fisherman of not more than thirty years of age and the bride, who was only a few years his senior, an attractive waitress from the hotel in the neighbouring village; a village moreover which boasted not just a church, but a church with a belfry and an organ. The hotel had undertaken the catering for the wedding breakfast and never before had the Bruachites enjoyed such an exciting prospect. From the first spectral whisper until at least a year after the solemnization of the event weddings, past, present and future were the sole topic of conversation wherever one went.

'Ach, but weddings isn't like they used to be,' lamented the old folk. But Anna Vic, whose wedding had taken place as recently as thirty years previously, spiritedly refuted the criticism.

'Indeed after my own weddin' my Uncle Roddy and my Uncle Hamish was missin' for three whole days,' she argued firmly. 'And where did we find them at last but in yon Allta cave. Barricaded themselves in they had, with crates of beer and whisky and them vowin' they wouldn't come home till they'd drunk their way out.'

The uncles Roddy and Hamish, their patriarchal appearance betraying no indication of their riotous youth, were present to hear and corroborate the fat woman's assertion.

'And we near managed it too,' said Roddy proudly, turning his flushed face away from the fire for a moment. 'There was but one full bottle left when you found us.'

'So there was,' agreed Hamish, nodding reflectively. 'And if the beer and whisky was as good today as then, I'm no doubtin' but what we could do the same again.'

'Whist, whist!' counselled some of the women, with doubtful glances at me.

'And for the three nights it was freezing solid and everyone thought they'd be very near dead with the cold,' went on Anna Vic indomitably.

'I never remember bein' warmer in my life,' objected Hamish, directing a satisfied stream of spittle into the glowing peats.

'I should think not,' put in the roadman sarcastically. 'Why, man, it's thirty years since and amn't I still findin' empty bottles in that cave?'

His remark was greeted by a chorus of delighted chuckles which lingered until Lachy was heard asking if anyone remembered the Skean wedding. It appeared that everyone did.

'Tell Miss Peckwitt about that one, Lachy,' said Johnny, and Lachy, needing no further persuasion, embarked on his story.

'This weddin' at Skean,' he began. 'We was all there most of us, and the bride and bridegroom was standin' nice as you like in front of the minister. Well that bridegroom was as drunk as blazes. He was that drunk it was the best man havin' to hold him up from behind all the time—and he had a job to do that. Of course the minister he'd been born and reared in the place as you might say, so he didn't mind at all that the fellow was drunk. "Will you take this woman?" says he.

' "I'll take her for a whiley," says the man. "Just till I get tired of her."

' "You're that drunk you don't know what you're sayin'," the minister tells him. "I know your own mind better than you do yourself." So he carries on with the service without botherin' to ask the fellow again. Ach well, everythin' was all right till after about six months the fellow goes back to the minister.

' "I'm tired of this woman," says he. "I'm wantin' to get rid of her."

' "Man, you can't do that," the minister tells him.

' "I can so," says the fellow. "It's the conditions I took her on and there's all my friends and relations at the church will swear that I made it plain to you I was only takin' her on those terms."

' "Man, man," groans the minister, "I would be thrown out of the Church entirely if it was known I'd married a man as drunk as you were yourself that day."

' "I'm no carin' what happens to you," says the fellow. "But I want to be rid of this woman so that I can get a good milk cow. I canna' afford both."

' "Listen here," says the minister, "I have the best milk cow on the Island, and if you'll keep your mouth shut and keep the woman I'll make you a present of the beast."

'Of course the fellow knows that fine, that's just what he was after. He wasn't tired of his wife at all and it was just a put-up job between the two of them. At the end of another six months he goes again to the manse and says he's wantin' a horse; a bit later on he's needin' a good ram, and so on. The Lord himself knows what he might have got with time, but the poor old minister went and died on him. I wouldn't be surprised if it was worry that killed him,' finished Lachy complacently.

Naturally I doubted the truth of the story but strangely enough everyone was well acquainted with the couple concerned and their admiration for the husband's astuteness was patent.

'How long ago did all this happen?' I asked.

'Ach, not more than twenty or twenty-five years back,' replied Lachy, 'and that man's a rich man now, Miss Peckwitt.' I was not surprised.

The Bruach wedding, though not scheduled to take place until some weeks after I had first heard of it, managed to interfere with my own plans, for I had decided to pay a prolonged visit to Mary and I was expecting to stay in England until after the New Year. But this wedding promised to be too interesting to miss and consequently I announced my intention of cutting short my holiday so as to be present. Straightway I was deluged with commissions to purchase innumerable articles from the English shops, for, not withstanding their contempt for the English as a race, the Bruachites were firmly convinced of the superiority of English merchandise. The requests were made diffidently but with a pathetic optimism that made refusal impossible, and my shopping list grew longer with each day that passed. The bride-to-be wanted a pair of white silk stockings, a lacy handkerchief and, blushingly, a pair of pink frilly garters. She had, she told me, already procured her dress, veil and shoes from one of the mail order firms which, to the best of my belief, specialize in supplying outlying places with outmoded fashions at outrageous prices. Giggle and Sniggle, who were to be bridesmaids, wanted head-dresses—blue ones.

'Very nice,' I complimented them, for they both had pretty blue eyes. 'And are your dresses blue too?' But they didn't yet know. The dresses were being purchased second-hand from a shop in Glasgow, 'seein' as they'll only be needed the once', and the colour would depend on what the store could provide. My suggestion that they wait until the dresses arrived before deciding on the colour for the accessories was received with an indulgent smile. 'Any colour suits blue,' they told me loftily, and, with a resigned sigh, I entered the blue head-dresses on my list.

Morag wanted gloves—black ones.

'For the wedding?' I murmured.

'They'll do me for church and funerals too,' she replied.

Lachy, still hankering after an English wife, pressed me to bring one back for him.

'Blonde or brunette,' I asked jocularly with my pencil poised ready.

'Ach, I'm no carin' one bit,' he said. 'I'm willin' to take whatever you bring for I think by now you know my tastes pretty well. Just be sure she's no wearin' one of them weeks.' It took me a moment of puzzled thought before I could translate 'weeks' into 'wigs'.

Kirsty, the gaunt and wrinkled spinster, peeped shyly in through the door one evening shortly before my departure. She clutched a paper in one hand.

'I can never get a hat that will suit me,' she mourned as we settled down to a strupak, and anyone who had ever seen Kirsty's homely features could well believe her complaint. 'See, will you get me a hat like this one,' she continued, nervously unfolding the paper and pointing to an advertisement which depicted several hats of alluring designs. Her dry, knobbly finger came to rest on one of them. 'A peek-a-bo style', ran the caption, 'a debutante's dream'. I studied it carefully, trying hard to visualize it surmounting Kirsty's tired face from which all trace of the debutante had vanished a quarter of a century ago.

'I think I will suit it, don't you?' she enquired timidly.

'What colour were you wanting?' I asked evasively.

'My coat is brown and I was thinkin' blue would go awful nice with it.' Her tones became apologetically firm and as any attempt at argument would have been construed as unwillingness to make the purchase for entirely different reasons, I merely nodded and ventured only an apathetic suggestion that green might look better.

'But my eyes are blue, and they say blue-eyed people always suit blue,' she replied with childlike candour. Her pale eyes met mine briefly and slid away again and, not for the first time, I cursed the authors of the 'twopenny loves' with their inevitable blue-eyed heroines, wearing the equally inevitable 'little blue dress' which 'deepened the colour of her forget-me-not blue eyes'. Fatalistically I folded the paper and tucked it inside my shopping list which by this time had grown to considerable length.

The very evening before my departure I was doing some last-minute ironing when there came a timid knock on my door and in response to my invitation there entered Euan the half-wit. I was very surprised to see him, for though he sat sometimes in Morag's kitchen he had not so far invaded the precincts of my own room. His presence was by no means welcome, but having by this time resided long enough in the Hebrides to have acquired a little of the Gaelic courtesy, I suggested half-heartedly that he should take a seat. In reply Euan swallowed twice, grinned widely, but remained standing awkwardly beside the door. Deeming it wiser to ignore him until he chose to speak, I carried on with my ironing.

'You go England?' His voice jerked into my thoughts as I slid the iron carefully between the intricate frills of a blouse.

'Yes, I am,' I agreed.

Euan blinked rapidly in acknowledgment, but said nothing more.

'Are you wanting me to get you something?' I asked banteringly, being well aware that he had no money of his own.

'Yes!' The word burst from him with startling vehemence and was followed by a number of convulsive swallows.

'Well, tell me what it is and I'll do my best for you,' I encouraged, and overwhelmed with pity for his feeble-mindedness resolved that if it was at all practicable I would get what he wanted.

'Bring me——' he stuttered pleadingly, his eyes starting so far out of his head that I expected them to drop on to the floor at any moment.

'Yes, bring you what?' I coaxed.

'Donkey!'

I stared at Euan so long that the iron scorched an ineradicable angle on my blouse.

'A donkey!' I exploded. 'What sort of a donkey?'

'With legs,' he replied timorously.

'Do you mean a real donkey?'

He nodded and blinked vigorously, but words failed him. They nearly failed me.

'Goodness gracious! I couldn't possibly bring you a real donkey,' I told him. 'How on earth do you think I could manage with a donkey on the train?'

His expression changed abruptly from eager anticipation to utter dejection. Slowly, and without another word, he turned and, closing the door quietly behind him, crossed the passage to Morag's room. It was not until some minutes later that I heard her sending him home. When the outer door had closed after him Morag herself entered my room. The first thing I asked was whether Euan had told her of his request that I should bring him a donkey.

'So he did,' she replied, 'and I was askin' him if he'd ever seen a donkey to be pesterin' you to bring him one.'

'And has he?' I enquired.

'He was sayin' no he hadna' rightly but he thinks a donkey looks like a squashed horse. He doesna' think you've seen one either.'

'Me?' I echoed. 'Why not?'

'Well, he was sayin' if you'd ever seen a donkey it's fine you'd be after knowin' it wouldna' need to go on the train. He says you'd know that it has its own legs and can walk.'

'I wonder what he expects me to do with it?' I asked drily. 'Ride on it, walk beside it, or hitch it on to the back of the train?'

Morag laughed. 'Ach, but Euan doesna' know but what England's any further away than Shuna,' she excused him. Her eyes came to rest on my open, neatly packed bags on the sofa. 'So it's all ready for off you are,' she observed.

'Yes,' I told her. 'But I shall leave my cases open and pack the crushables at the last moment.'

She nodded, briefly confirmed the rest of the arrangements for the morning, and said good night.

After a broken night during which my sleep was continually interrupted by dreams that the clock had stopped or had failed to ring; that my luggage had mysteriously disappeared; or that I had mislaid my purse and was unable to pay for my ticket, the strident burr of the alarm startled me into wakefulness. I lit a candle, slid reluctantly out of bed and threw a dressing-gown around my shoulders. As I poked my feet into bedroom slippers I became hazily aware of the sounds of most unusual activity downstairs. There was the noise of windows being thrown open, doors flung back on their hinges and a muffled roaring, coupled with the acrid smell of smoke.

'Come quick, Miss Peckwitt! My house is on fire!' I doubt if there is another sentence in the English language which can galvanize a person into activity as quickly as that which my landlady had just uttered. Frantically I tore downstairs and bursting into my room was confronted with the sight of a tremendous fire which raged in and around the grate, while a deluge of glowing soot cascaded from the chimney on to the floor and smouldered fiercely on the linoleum.

'Shut the door and the window!' I commanded, recollecting the instructions I had once seen on a cigarette-card. Obediently Morag leaped to the window and shut it down with such a bang that the two

lower panes of glass shattered. The next few minutes were utter confusion. Morag sensibly grabbed a brush and swept the red-hot soot
towards the hearth and immediately the odour of singeing bristles
mingled with the choking smoke. I grabbed pails and raced down to
the sea but, as luck would have it, the tide was out and it was quite
impossible to fill the pails unless one waded until one was almost
knee-deep—no enviable task on a dark, cold and frosty morning.
With two full pails and a torch it is difficult to race and I should have
known better than to try to leap up three steps at a time. I fell heavily
and the chill water flowed round and under me before I could arise.
Back to the sea again to refill my pails, one of which now leaked
shockingly, and with as much speed as could be combined with
caution I hurried back to the house. Morag was still sweeping for all
she was worth, that is if pushing soot about with a bald and smouldering broomhead can be called sweeping. The room was so full of smoke
that it was well nigh impossible to see. I sluiced the water over the
floor, but during my absence the tablecloth had caught fire and the
wallpaper above the fireplace was rapidly browning with the heat.

'Run for Ruari!' sobbed Morag. 'Run for him quick.'

Seizing the tablecloth I flung it outside to burn away harmlessly
on the grass, and then ran for Ruari. There is no doubt that there are
times when deafness seems to be the worst affliction anyone can
suffer. Certainly I thought so as I pounded at the door of Ruari's
house and flung handfuls of pebbles at the window, but though I had
the assistance of the dog, who from his kennel contributed to the
uproar to the full extent of his capacious lungs, there was no acknowledgment from within. Discovering that the door was only latched
I went inside, continuing to yell unceasingly for Ruari. The only reply
was a duet of serene, undisturbed snores from above. I climbed halfway up the stairs, still calling; I gained the landing; I went into the
bedroom from which the snores were coming and grasping Ruari's
flannel-clad shoulder shook it vigorously. With my mouth close to
his ear I entreated him to wake up and come and help. At last aroused,
he shot upright with such suddenness that his head bumped my
teeth.

'Wuff, wuff, wuff!' he spluttered as might a bulldog that has been
compelled to take a cold plunge.

Quickly I explained what had happened, insisting that the house
was in imminent danger. With surprising speed one of Ruari's legs

appeared from under the bedclothes but, recollecting himself, he hastily tucked it in again.

'I canna' get dressed with a woman watchin' me,' he said reprovingly.

'Sorry,' I said, and retreating from the room started downstairs.

'Hi! where are you goin' with that torch?' came a shout. 'I canna' see what shape I am and where is my clothes without a light, can I?'

Returning to the bedroom I found Ruari, still a little dazed, sitting on the edge of the bed in his nightshirt. At the sight of me with the torch he immediately scrambled back beneath the clothes, pulling them right up to his chin.

'Woman, woman!' he chided me. 'Let me get into my breekis in private will you!'

'But I can't see my way down again without a light,' I retorted. 'I don't know my way about your house in daylight, never mind in the dark.'

We effected a compromise by my holding the torch round the edge of the door into the bedroom while the rest of my body stayed outside.

'Is your eyes shut?' demanded Ruari.

'Of course!' I snapped back.

Muttering and breathing heavily, he attired himself in clothes which were, I suspected, both in quantity and quality, more suitable for an expedition to the North Pole than for wrestling with a fire in a neighbouring house. Having accomplished this much he decided to wake Bella who had slept profoundly throughout the disturbance.

'Come and get watter to quench Morag's fire,' he bade her shortly. As we hurried downstairs Bella's querulous voice pursued us, demanding to know how she was going to see to dress herself without a light. I affected not to hear: it was no concern of mine that Ruari and Bella made a habit of staying in bed until daylight.

'Wait now while I get my boots on,' said Ruari as I made for the door and, while I seethed with impatience, he retrieved his boots from under a chair and sat down leisurely to put them on. As soon as he had tied the second bootlace I bounded outside and bolted back to Morag's, leaving him to be guided by the glow of the fire, which could now plainly be seen through the windowless window. Once again I recalled the instructions on the cigarette-card.

'Salt!' I shouted, rushing into the room, 'plenty of salt to dout the fire.'

'My God!' whimpered Morag, 'I used the last pailful of it only yesterday for the herrin' and I havena' as much left as will salt the potatoes.'

Ruari appeared, and with a determination born of panic Morag seized his ear.

'Salt!' she yelled in her turn. 'Get me salt, plenty salt!'

Ruari shook his head. 'We have none,' he replied flatly, 'we hadna' enough for all the herrin' we got and the grocer has none either.' His hand went to his ear as though to protect it from further savagery.

Morag's expression was tense. 'We'll need to sacrifice the salt herrin',' she decided heroically.

I shook my head doubtfully, for though I am at all times only too willing to sacrifice salt herring I wondered if salt in this form would serve the same purpose. Before I could voice my doubts Ruari had charged off into the shed, had heaved the heavy barrel from its corner and, spurning my inefficient help with an untranslatable growl, was stumbling with it back into the house.

'Clear oot the way!' he warned Morag and she, dodging nimbly into a corner, only just managed to avoid the cataract of herring, salt and liquor as Ruari hurled the contents of the barrel on to the fire. There was a fierce sputtering, and choking smoke billowed out once more into the room; the house began to smell worse than a kipper factory, but the fire was considerably quelled and by the time a strangely attired Bella arrived with more water and wet sacks, the steady roar had become fretful and was gradually, but unmistakably, subsiding. Daylight was breaking as we carried more water to douse the hot walls and the charred linoleum and Ruari climbed up on the roof to ram wet sacks down the chimney from above.

'Why did you start that?' he demanded truculently as soon as we were able to breathe again.

'Indeed wasn't I in such a fret to get Miss Peckwitt's breakfast, and then this spiteful old fire goes sleepy on me,' exclaimed Morag with a malevolent glare at the red-hot grate. 'I was wantin' her to have a nice bitty warm before she went out, so I dosed her with plenty paraffin and bless me but puff! the old bitch went and flies away up the chimbley.'

Summoning a wan smile, I glanced at the clock, and Morag, seeing the direction of my glance, climbed on a chair and rubbed the coating of soot from the glass with a corner of her apron. It was exactly the time my train should have been leaving the mainland station. 'Why, you've gone and missed your train,' she remarked superfluously.

'So I have,' I agreed as I wearily surveyed the sooty contents of my suitcases, and collected my freshly ironed crushables for re-laundering.

'Oh well,' said Morag comfortably; 'that's the very first time I've felt sure that old chimbley was really clean.'

No further calamity occurred to prevent me from setting off for England the following day and after an uneventful journey the train drew into the station of my home town where Mary was awaiting me. The return to town life was exciting and I revelled once more in 'all modern conveniences'; in the wearing of light shoes; in nice peaceful church services, and in eating thin bread and butter. My shopping expeditions were amazingly successful, though the pink frilly garters necessitated some diligent seeking. We unearthed a sumptuous pair at last in a decaying little shop in an insignificant side street; they were speckled with rose buds, bordered with lace, and tufted with swans-down, and I could be very certain that the bride-to-be would be enchanted with them. Kirsty's 'debutante's dream' was purchased and despatched to her in a debonair hat box. The bridesmaids' head-dresses, very blue and very beguiling, were packed safely in the bottom of one of my cases. Eventually all the items on my list were scored through—Lachy's wife and Euan's donkey excepted—and I could safely concentrate on my own plans.

For some time I had been toying with the idea of purchasing a small car for use in Bruach, and now I set about putting my plan into action. As I explained to Mary, I was tired of being allotted a space in the cattle float or distorting my body to fit into the backs of inadequate vans on the very frequent occasions when the Bruach bus was unfit for service. The hearse too was still a disturbingly regular feature of Island transport and, though up to the present I had always been fortunate enough to have the seat beside the driver, I could not help feeling a little apprehensive that the time might come when this would prove impracticable. I was lucky enough to purchase an old Morris two-seater car which we promptly christened 'Joanna', and at once I embarked on a course of driving lessons from a reputable instructor. At the end of a few weeks I was confident of my prowess and, saying goodbye to England, 'Joanna' and I set off, a little uncertainly to begin with perhaps, on the four-hundred-mile journey to Bruach, intending to reach our destination rather less than a week before the wedding.

The sensation of homecoming which I experienced when I drove 'Joanna' off the ferry boat and introduced her to the Island—the crossing was mercifully calm—was strange indeed for a town-bred Englishwoman. The charm of the Island struck me afresh and, although it was December and what slight breeze there was stroked my cheeks with icy fingers, I drove with both windows of the car lowered, and drew deep, eager breaths of the fresh, invigorating air. To the left of me the loch stretched out, placid and still, reflecting the dark, rain-washed hills, the anchored fishing-boats, and the slow flight of the homeward-bound gulls. The setting sun was no more than a sliver of vermilion above the horizon, while to the north the rapidly purpling sky was laced with brilliant green. I was glad to come upon the first thatched houses of Bruach looking for all the world like sturdy brown mushrooms that a snail has eaten its way through; from the snail hole curled the now familiar blue of peat smoke mingling its fragrance with that of scorching flour, reminding me that it was Saturday evening and the Sabbath baking would be in progress. Bringing 'Joanna' to a stop beside the wall, I jumped out, and a beaming Morag came hurrying to greet me. It would have been churlish to try to avoid the embrace she had so obviously determined upon and, before it was over, Bella had appeared, to bestow upon me similar evidence of affection, while a flushed and smiling Ruari waited impatiently to shake my hand with ferocious warmth. The fervour of the welcome from all three of them was impressive and made that which I had received in England seem frigid by comparison. It was difficult to repress a feeling of elation, for the geniality of the Gael, despite its lack of sincerity, is an endearing trait. While the women prodded my limbs to see if I had lost weight, and enthused over 'Joanna' and over my new clothes, Ruari busied himself with my cases. Back again in my own room I was fussed over and petted and repeatedly assured that my company had been very much missed, and by the time I was ready for bed that night I was feeling so flattered by their attentions that I experienced no regrets at all that town life was once more behind me.

My return was the signal for a chain of visitors who came to welcome me, to inspect me, and to hear the latest news from England. Among the first were the bride and bridesmaids. All three professed themselves delighted with the purchases I had made for them and were eager to tell me that the bridesmaids' dresses had arrived from the second-hand shop. Though neither the shade nor the style of the dresses was identical, as they had been hoping, the girls were plainly thrilled. 'One is a sort of pink,' they told me, 'and the other is a sort of orange'—a colour combination which filled them with rapture and me with regret. Not far behind the bridal retinue came Kirsty, no less enamoured with the hat I had sent her from England, which I was to be permitted to see her wearing on the following Sunday. Hard on Kirsty's heels came Padruig and Euan. Once again I had to endure the former's description of his visit to 'Buckram Palace', and during the recital Euan, apparently bearing me no ill-will after my failure to bring him a donkey, sat watching me with eyes full of dog-like devotion.

'Euan doesn't seem to be fretting that I haven't brought his donkey,' I observed to Morag after they had left.

'But he thinks you have brought him one,' she replied.

'What!' I exclaimed feelingly. 'How can that be?'

'Indeed havena' the boys been after tellin' him you brought one back for him and that he's to come to Ruari's croft here tomorrow to practise will he ride it?'

'That really is the limit,' I said angrily. 'Goodness only knows what they've let me in for now. I shall be having the fellow trailing me all over the place.'

'Ach, they've let you in for nothin',' she soothed. 'The boys has borrowed a park deer from over the other side of the Island and they're after tellin' Euan it's an English donkey. That was the idea when they put him up to askin' you for a donkey in the first place.'

I discerned a touch of the combined genius of Lachy, Angus and possibly Johnny in the ludicrous plan and vowed vengeance on all three of them.

'It'll be all right,' continued my landlady, 'Euan's never seen a donkey.'

Having emphatically refused to stay and witness the meeting of Euan and the deer, I have only my landlady's narrative as to the eventual outcome of the escapade. She, almost delirious with laughter, described the spectacle vividly and, as may be expected, in language peculiarly her own. It appeared that while a few of the men—Angus, Lachy and Johnny prominent among them—held on to the deer, Euan was persuaded to throw his leg over the saddle. As soon as he complied the men let go their hold and the deer, with prodigious leaps and bounds, made for the hills. Miraculously, no one attempted to explain how, the jockey had managed to cling on and, accompanied by the vociferous encouragement of the onlookers, was carried fully a third the length of the croft before he slid over the beast's stern and landed flat on his back in the mud. The deer fled precipitately and was soon out of sight and Euan, after slapping the mud from his trousers and retrieving his cap, flew in pursuit. He too was soon lost to sight and it was two hours later that the gamekeeper reported having seen him—still running.

It was a relief to me to hear that Euan had eventually returned and to know that the poor fellow was in no way hurt.

'He'll never forgive me,' I complained.

'Forgive you? Why should he forgive you?' argued Morag. 'He thinks it's a wonderful donkey. He's done nothin' but boast and swank of his English donkey ever since.'

I groaned. 'What is going to happen now that it's gone then?' I asked.

'Ach, stop frettin'. He thinks it's run all the way back to England and he's quite certain you'll get it for him when next you go,' she returned placidly.

Though it was difficult to believe such a hoax could have been carried through as successfully as the perpetrators claimed, I must admit that Euan seemed to be in no way disappointed with the performance of his counterfeit donkey. On the contrary, he continued to regard me with an embarrassing devotion which showed not the least sign of diminishing.

12. *The Wedding*

As the great wedding day drew near, the Bruachites bent themselves to the task of writing congratulatory telegrams.

'What are you goin' to put in your own message?' asked my land-lady one evening, and when I replied that, as I had every intention of being present at the ceremony, it seemed unnecessary to send a tele-gram, she was genuinely surprised, and insisted that it was the custom for telegrams to be sent whether or not one would be there in person. It was also the custom, she told me, for some of the self-styled bards of the village to compose congratulatory messages in verse, and sug-gested that one Peter would 'make a verse' for me if I so wished. I shook my head; my acquaintance so far with local compositions had forced me to the conclusion that, provided rhyming, metre and grammar could be discounted entirely, their work might be tolerably good—certainly not otherwise. My landlady's cousin, a master in a Glasgow secondary school, had, she confided, supplied 'a grand verse' for her own telegram. 'My, but he's right good at them. Just wait till you hear it,' she exalted with a girlish gleam in her eyes, and added coyly: 'I shan't tell you now though for fear of spoilin' it.'

I murmured something about contenting myself with the prosaic 'congratulations and best wishes', whereupon Morag stared at me with the stricken expression of a child who has been punished for a sin it is not aware of having committed; and abruptly changed the subject. She did not mention the telegrams again.

A belated dawn heralded the wedding morning itself and after rubbing a clear patch on my window I saw that it promised to be a dull, depressing, typical December day. Downstairs my landlady was humming Gaelic airs to herself as she scuttled about her morning chores, for she was intending to leave early, having promised to lend her assistance in the kitchen for the major part of the day. The cows were to be left in the byre instead of being turned out on the hill as usual, and I had promised to give them their evening feed before setting out for the church after lunch. When Morag had gone, I spent the morning in polishing 'Joanna' who, in spite of her age, was in remarkably good condition. At lunch-time I cooked and ate a rather frugal meal—the frugality being in anticipation of the menu for the wedding feast proving somewhat onerous. I was on my way, in gumboots and mackintosh, to give the cows their feed before changing into my wedding finery, when the vehement blasting of a horn made me look round, and I beheld the taxi-driver in an opulent new taxi signalling furiously in my direction. I crossed the park to the road.

'Isn't that fellow the biggest fool in the Island!' he burst out passionately, without making even the expected allusion to the weather. I sensed instantly that something was seriously wrong.

'Which man? And what has he done?' I asked, puzzling as to why I had been chosen as confidante.

'Why, Sandy, the bridegroom, of course,' the taxi-driver explained. 'He's gone off in his boat round to Lochnamor this mornin' before they were up, they're tellin' me, and there's no sign of him comin' back yet. I've been waitin' over half an hour on him.'

I looked at my watch. It said ten minutes past two and the wedding was timed to take place at three. Lochnamor was an hour away by boat, but there was a rough track across the glen which, if it proved to be negotiable all the way, should take 'Joanna' there in about twenty minutes. The taxi-driver's expression was eloquent.

'I suppose you want me to take my car through the glen and get him?' I said.

'Well, Miss Peckwitt,' he answered humbly, 'I'm thinkin' it's the only way to get hold of the man, and this thing'—he paused and glared with perfidious disdain at the front wheels of his luxury model —'she's too low in her body for me to think of tryin' it.'

'There's precious little time,' I pointed out, 'and I have yet to feed the cows.'

The taxi-driver alighted quickly from the car. 'I'll feed the cows myself,' he offered obligingly.

I thanked him and started off towards 'Joanna'. 'And you'll have to water them too,' I called as I ran. 'The well is over there.'

'Ach, I'll put them outside for a while and they'll drink their own water,' returned the taxi-driver.

'Oh,' I said unhappily, but shrugging my shoulders I left him to do what he pleased, for there was no time to argue. I was glad that 'Joanna's' engine had already been running that morning so that she responded to the first pull on the starter and I was quickly able to back and turn her into the road. Putting my foot down as hard as I dared, I headed her towards the glen. The track was sinuous and rutty; loose stones flew on all sides of us and rattled with distressing frequency on the car's underparts. The bends were nerve-racking, but she skidded round them contemptuously with the air of a thoroughbred on familiar ground, and we eventually reached the spot where the track widened into the shore of a tiny, sheltered bay. The tide was well out, and high and dry above the line of surf was a fishing-boat on 'legs', beneath which two dungaree-clad figures crouched industriously scraping barnacles off the keel. They were far too engrossed in their task to notice my arrival and doubtless the noise of the sea had muffled the sound of 'Joanna's' engine. I turned the car back towards the way we had come and then raced down to the beach.

'Hey, Sandy!' I addressed the bridegroom, gasping as I inhaled the strong smell of fish, seaweed and tar which hung around the boat. 'You're going to be terribly late for your wedding.'

'Good God!' burst out one of the figures as it squirmed from beneath the boat. 'It's surely not today, is it?'

Sandy, a slim, brown-haired fellow, sporting a moustache that made him look as though he had just taken a bite out of a hedgehog, stared incredulously first at me and then at the other dungareed figure who had emerged from under the boat's stern. It was obvious from their expressions that both had completely forgotten the wedding.

'I did want to bottom her today,' mourned Sandy, staring sadly at the half-scraped hull of his boat.

'You'll be bottomed yourself if you don't turn up for your wedding,' I threatened him with a smile.

'I'll have to go.' Despairingly he turned to his confederate. 'You'll have to stay and bottom her by yourself,' he told him.

'But I'll need to come. I'm your best man,' expostulated the other.

'Wedding or no wedding, we canna' leave the boat like this for the tide to come up,' objected Sandy.

'We could rush back in time for the tide maybe?' suggested his partner hopefully.

Sandy appeared to reflect for some moments on the propriety of rushing away from his own wedding in order to attend to a boat.

'No, I might not be able to manage it,' he said, his tones betraying the degree of temptation he had been subjected to. 'You'd best stay and see to it yourself.'

Reluctantly the best man resigned himself to his martyrdom and I set about coercing the vacillating tar-spattered bridegroom into 'Joanna'. Once again I drove at reckless speed through the glen and at ten minutes to three Sandy, impatient enough by now, tumbled out of the car into the arms of his family who were waiting on the doorstep. His mother was holding his wedding trousers; his aunt was holding his shirt and his grandmother his jacket; his father, an old man almost crippled with rheumatism, hovered in the background meekly offering a collar and tie and a pair of shoes. Outside on the road the taxi-driver, his hair and shirt front decorated with stray wisps of hay, fretted uneasily beside the luxury model. How the family accomplished the feat of inserting Sandy into his wedding attire I have no idea, being intent on manœuvring 'Joanna' round and past the taxi; but as I drove away home I caught a glimpse of the bridegroom rushing down to the burn, both hands clutching at his trousers, followed by the taxi-driver-cum-cowman brandishing a pair of braces and a towel. I had pulled up outside Morag's house and was scrambling out of my seat when the taxi, with engine revving and horn blasting merrily, surged past. A man's white handkerchief fluttering from one lowered window of the car acknowledged my small part in the proceedings.

There remained still the task of making myself presentable and it was plain that, even if the wedding were delayed by the late arrival of the bridegroom, I should still be lucky not to miss the ceremony. With fumbling fingers I changed into my suit and, after a quick glance around the kitchen to ensure that everything was in order, hastened once more to 'Joanna'. Just as I was settling into my seat a voice hailed from a distance and, fuming with impatience, I craned my neck round the door to see the rheumaticky figure of the bridegroom's father toiling gallantly up the hill towards me. Breathlessly and with the sweat pouring from his furrowed brow, he attained the car and collapsed against it with a plaintive bleat.

'Are you coming to the wedding?' I asked.

'No,' he panted sorrowfully. 'Somebody has to stay and see to the cows.'

'Don't tell me then that Sandy has forgotten the ring,' I prompted, pulling at the starter.

'No indeed. It's worse than that.'

'Worse?'

'Aye, he's forgotten this,' announced the old man gravely, and produced from his pocket a small bundle wrapped in a white handkerchief.

'What is that?' I asked suspiciously.

'It's his teeths,' he replied, 'and he canna' get marrit without them.'

'Oh, they won't really make any difference,' I consoled, but the old man drew himself erect and spat with unexpected vigour.

'It will to her,' he said. 'She's always at him, at him, like a mouse at a taty, for not wearin' his teeths, and if he turns up for the weddin' without them, sure the bitch will turn on him even in the church itself.' He spat again. 'You'll take them for him will you?' he cajoled, and there was both distress and urgency in his voice. 'You'll haste, won't you?'

I took the handkerchief-wrapped bundle and laid it on the seat beside me and then, bidding the old man goodbye, I let in the clutch. 'Joanna' screamed her way up the hill. By the time I had covered a few miles the humour of the situation had begun to strike me, but, even before I could raise a smile, a wildly gesticulating figure appeared in the middle of the road. 'Someone's been left behind,' I grumbled to myself as I braked to a stop. An old man, whose attire was in no way suitable for a wedding, rammed at the window with fingers that must have been about as sensitive as skittles.

'Ach, but it's cold, cold, cold,' he began conversationally as I lowered the window.

'It is,' I agreed shortly. 'But I'm in a tearing hurry. What is it you want?'

He looked mildly hurt at my brusqueness. 'Are you goin' through the village?' he enquired, leaning his elbows on the door of the car.

'I am. Please tell me what you want,' I repeated testily.

Shocked by my reply, his manner developed a certain hauteur.

'She's wantin' to know will you take a chicken to the post for her?' He nodded condescendingly towards the house where presumably 'she' was.

'I can't wait one second more,' I told him, one foot already on the accelerator and the other on the clutch. 'If it's quite ready I'll take it.'

'She's just after finishin' pluckin' it now,' he said languidly. 'Will you no be comin' in for a wee moment?'

'Look here,' I replied exasperatedly, 'I'm on my way to the wedding and I've simply got to get there in time because there'—I pointed—'in that bundle are the bridegroom's false teeth and he cannot get married without them.'

'Can he no?' queried the old man.

'No he can't,' I replied tersely.

His countenance assumed an expression of mingled pity and curiosity. 'Why can he no get marrit without his teeths?' he enquired, and then giving me an immoral wink went on: 'Sure, he'll no be marryin' her just to bite her, will he?'

Fiercely I let in the clutch and 'Joanna', leaping forward like an outraged debutante, left him gurgling contentedly at his own witticism. The halt, though it had entailed only a few seconds' delay, made me despair of ever reaching the church on time and I drove as I had seldom driven before. The minute hand of the clock on the dashboard seemed to race almost as madly as the car and it was pointing to nearly half past three when I at last arrived outside the church. Debating as to how I was to get the precious bundle to Sandy, I hurried into the porch where, pausing to take stock of the situation, I heard the minister intoning the marriage service in a voice that was suggestive of the spell-casting demons of pantomime. Hope sank, but rose again as I realized that the service had only just begun and that there were still some few minutes before the fatal moment arrived. Stealthily I tiptoed up a side aisle to the front pew, before which were grouped the young couple, the two bridesmaids, the sponsor and the taxi-driver who, having already acted as valet, driver and cowman, had now been pressed into service as groomsman. Taking a deep breath which served as an aromatic reminder that Sandy's toilet had indeed been a sketchy one—the church reeked with the mingled odours of fish, seaweed and tar—and ignoring the faintly hostile glances of the occupants of the pew, I urged them to make room for me. The slight disturbance made the minister look up from his prayer book and direct upon me a frankly enquiring stare. I gazed with the utmost reverence at the hassock by my feet. Cautiously I nudged my neighbour. 'Here are Sandy's teeth,' I hissed. 'Pass them on; don't drop them whatever you do.' With bated breath I watched over the progress of the white bundle along the pew until a plainly audible 'Hi!' told me that it had nearly reached its objective. The taxi-driver stepped back a pace, reached behind him surreptitiously, stepped forward again and a moment later, after a barely perceptible movement of his arm, the teeth were safely deposited in Sandy's pocket. It was just in time.

'Wilt thou take this woman . . .' the minister began. Sandy's hand went into his pocket and then to his mouth. He appeared to be stifling a prolonged yawn. '. . . so long as you both shall live?' concluded the minister. The bridegroom's 'Adam's apple' rose and fell twice.

'I will,' he responded thickly.

The minister turned to the bride and repeated the question. Sandy took the opportunity to bestow upon her a devastating smile.

'. . . so long as you both shall live?' The minister's voice ceased and the congregation waited in hushed expectancy. The bride flicked her husband-to-be with a brief, speculative glance.

'I will,' she replied firmly.

The tension over, I relaxed as well as I could into the small portion of pew allotted to me by the well-cushioned relatives. The minister closed his book and the organist, a diminutive woman with a round, rosy face and tight coils of hair, which supported a blue straw hat heavily overladen with cherries, suddenly began to writhe like a hooked mackerel as her short legs laboured at the pedals. Almost before the hymn was announced the organ whinnied forth into the opening bars of 'The Voice that breathed o'er Eden', in which the congregation joined half-heartedly. At the end of the service the principals disappeared into the vestry and as soon as the door closed upon them the organist snatched off her high-heeled shoes and began to massage her feet tenderly. The congregation broke into a buzz of conversation which included a good deal of awed comment on my late arrival and the reason for it. My explanation attracted so much interest that in no time at all quite a number of people had gathered round me asking for more details. Even the little organist tiptoed from her stool to stand, in stockinged feet, listening to my story. I had just reached the point where the old man had wanted me to wait for the hen, when, without warning, the vestry door swung open and the happy couple emerged, both grinning toothily. The guests melted back to their places and the organist, after one horrified glance at the vestry, flew back to the organ and strove vainly to reach the pedals. The bride, who was expecting to hear the triumphal strains of the Wedding March—having paid for it—looked questioningly towards the mute organ beneath which a dishevelled little figure was now searching desperately for her shoes. The blushing bridegroom, with arms stiff and fists clenched, studied his feet intently, while in the background the minister could be seen furtively wiping his mouth with the back of his sleeve.

I slipped outside to get my camera from 'Joanna' and found that the threat of rain had now resolved itself into a fitful shower. I had no sooner taken up my position than the bridal couple and their retinue appeared at the door of the church, belatedly accompanied by a crashing discord on the organ which matched in harmony the cerise and orange of the well-washed, but quite un-ironed, bridesmaids' dresses. The music came to an abrupt conclusion, and almost simultaneously the determined but rather rumpled little organist came charging through the church door, still in stockinged feet, and clutching in one hand an outsize bag of what I took to be confetti; in the other, the cherry-laden hat. I checked my camera, besought the guests to stand out of the way of the group, clicked a few times and nodded that I had finished. I was wishing that rice or confetti had been obtainable, but the grocer had run out of the first and had never stocked the second. I found old Murdoch beside me.

'I've been savin' up all my eggshells for weeks. There's no better confetti than crushed eggshells,' he told me as he hurled a fistful at the newlyweds. The organist began pouring generous quantities from her bag into the eager palms of those not so fortunately equipped. I saw that it was not confetti but semolina, the fact that semolina could be used as a substitute for rice in puddings evidently being sufficient recommendation for its use as a substitute for rice at weddings. The bridal party ploughed their way to the waiting taxi through a mixture of pudding ingredients and good wishes, their footsteps crunching as though they were walking on fresh cinders. As the door of the taxi slammed upon them a shrill yell rent the clamour of greetings and we turned to see Lachy, already in a state of mild inebriation, lurch towards it. With a merry toot of the horn the taxi drew away from the kerb, the bride and bridegroom waving gaily from inside. On the edge of the kerb teetered Lachy, pointing jubilantly to the rear bumper of the taxi, from which dangled a pair of easily identifiable high-heeled shoes. The crowd roared in approval and like frolicking children the main body of it surged after the taxi and turned the corner to vanish in the direction of the hotel. From the scattering of people left behind the organist detached herself, and advancing vengefully upon Lachy she proceeded to bespatter him with a stream of formidable Gaelic which the uncontrite recipient acknowledged with fatuous grins. Somehow or other Lachy must have managed to placate her, for as I bent to crank 'Joanna' I heard a series of whoops and yelps and beheld the lady herself undergoing a 'piggy-back' from the shoe thief. With one hand pressing her hat securely on to her disarranged coiffure and with the other clutching resolutely at the 'piggy's' goitre, she looked far from happy about the performance of her steed. She was touchingly grateful for the lift I offered and, during the short journey to the hotel, was loud in her condemnation of Lachy's trickery.

At the hotel, Morag, flushed with pleasure and the heat of the kitchen, but very much in her best attire, greeted me volubly.

'Why, there's ninety people catered for and over a hundred and thirty turned up, so the housekeeper was sayin',' she told me. Fortunately it had been taken for granted that there would be gate-crashers and the easy-going hotel staff were more pleased than perturbed at having a couple of score extra mouths to feed. It is on occasions like this that one thanks God for the Gael.

'It's them men that was loadin' sheeps,' continued Morag by way of explanation. 'They said they wouldna' be able to get, but I doubt they meant to come all the time. Here they are anyway, and here they'll be stayin' till they think better of it.'

Here they were indeed, and certainly here they appeared to have every intention of staying; men who had been lifting sheep on to lorries all day; men whose clothes were covered with grease and sheep dung; men whose hands looked as though they had been playing with greasy coal. Here they were, their hobnailed boots planted firmly on the carpeted floor of the hotel lounge, their tired bodies leaning on rough crooks while their dogs, bewildered by the strangeness of the surroundings—they would have been quite at home in the bar— threaded their way warily among the legs of the assembled guests and paused every now and then to look at their masters with mute enquiry.

'Of course,' Morag's voice began again in my ear, 'with there bein' so many of us we'll need to take our meal in layers.'

'Relays,' I corrected automatically, but her attention had already wandered elsewhere.

The guests had now begun to file past the newlyweds and, after a handshake, each man pressed a slim envelope into the groom's hand. (I heard later that Sandy made forty pounds profit on his reception—ten pounds more than he had reckoned on making.) Next, the wedding cake, under the careful supervision of the minister, was cut by the simpering bride and handed round along with glasses of port wine and sherry. The guests congregated into hilarious little groups, sipping their wine self-consciously and endeavouring to swallow their cake without chewing it—they are taught at school that this is the essence of refinement. The sheeploaders, mingling freely with those more suitably attired, clutched their glasses in strong calloused hands and tautened chapped dry lips to sip daintily at the wine. They shuffled constantly from one foot to the other, a habit which I have noticed to be prevalent among hill-reared people.

Almost everyone I had ever met in Bruach was present at the reception even to the most decrepit of the old folk. The Gaffer, looking strangely unfamiliar without the string which usually adorned the knees of his trousers, leaned an arm on the shoulder of old Farquhar who was clad in a greeny-black suit, the pockets of which bulged so suspiciously that I wondered if he had brought his rats with him. ('No,' said Morag, 'that'll just be a couple of bags so's he can take home what he canna' eat.') The uncles Hamish and Roderick were peering with thinly veiled contempt into the bottom of their empty glasses. Ruari and old Mac sat in a corner bellowing pleasantries at each other until the vacant chairs about them seemed to shudder with the impact. Adam the gamekeeper slumped in his chair, sniffing contentedly, while the old crones from Rhuna gabbled confidences across his broad, tweed-clad chest. The policeman, hardly recognizable in plain clothes, talked animatedly with Dugan and tried not to notice the intoxicated Lachy, who was crawling around the floor on his hands and knees searching for his lost spectacles. As Lachy had never in his life owned a pair of spectacles to lose, his search looked like being a prolonged one.

A maid appeared and, pointedly ignoring the bride and bride-groom, mumbled a few words in the minister's ear. He nodded under-standingly.

'Come and take your dinner!' he commanded forcefully, and as he took upon himself the task of escorting the bridal couple into the dining-room the guests obediently fell in behind.

The repast itself was by Island standards luxurious, and was par-taken of with a vigour and relish which could undoubtedly have been heard a mile or two away. Plates clattered; knives and forks pinged against plates, glasses and false teeth; tongues wagged, chairs scraped, stomachs rumbled and feet shuffled, while throughout the several courses the dishes were passed and re-passed across and around the table in a manner more reminiscent of a rugby football field than a dining-room. At the end of the meal the minister proposed the health of the couple in a long speech which, if one could judge from the laughter it evoked, was also a vastly amusing one, but as it was in Gaelic there was little of it I could understand. The bridegroom refused point-blank to reply to the toast and so did the bride. The best man also begged to be excused and, as everyone was impatient for the reading of the telegrams, the minister, sensibly refusing to argue with his stubborn protégés, gathered up the sheaf of congratulatory messages and began to read them out in English.

Those telegrams! Never in my life had I heard such pointed ribaldry as I heard then. Never before could I have imagined that a minister of the Church would condone, still less participate in, such vulgarity. Yet there he stood in his clerical collar and black suit, trying vainly to conceal his own enjoyment as he read each message slowly and meaningly. At one time I was conscious of hearing my landlady's name being called as the sender of one of the telegrams, and chancing to catch her eye at that moment I saw her gleeful smile. The bride could hardly tear her shining eyes from the minister's face, except when she wished to prod her abashed husband into a better appreci-ation of the 'humour'. In her white garb of chastity she displayed about as much inhibition as a tom-cat.

When the telegrams came to an end we returned to the lounge, where a white-haired fiddler, nearly as advanced in liquor as he was in years, played a 'Strip the Willow' with exaggerated caution.

'Quicken it up a bit, Peter,' urged the bride, who was partnered by the taxi-driver-cum-cowman-cum-best man, her husband having adjourned to the bar with a few friends. Offended at the criticism of his playing, the fiddler accelerated hard, and the bride, in order to keep the pace, had to leap and bound with a calfish recklessness that traced her movements with a clearly marked pattern of semolina. Her exertions were, however, not wholly successful in dislodging the stray pieces of eggshell which still adhered to the tendrils of her well-frizzed hair.

The dancing continued, with several breaks for refreshments, until about eleven-thirty, and at ten minutes to midnight the husband was rescued from the closed bar and despatched upstairs with his wife.

'In the old days,' said the elder Rhuna crone beside whom I now found myself, 'it used to be the custom hereabouts for the old folk to stay the night with the bride and bridegroom and then the bride would get up in the mornin' and give the old folks their breakfast.' She sighed regretfully.

'How long ago was all that?' I asked.

'Oh, not more than thirty, maybe forty years ago I can mind it happenin'.'

'And did that happen at your wedding?'

'Me, my dear? Why, bless you I've never been marrit in my life,' she replied innocently.

I laughed unrestrainedly. Several times during the evening I had caught glimpses of her and every time there had been a wine glass in her hand. I put her answer down to too much whisky.

'You're not very sober, are you?' I teased. 'Fancy trying to tell me you've had thirteen children without ever being married.' I laughed again.

'Indeed, Miss Peckwitt, but it's as true as I'm here,' she assured me earnestly. 'I've never been marrit in my life, and surely it's glad I am that I havena' a man to be frettin' me in my old age.'

I stared at her stupidly. 'But the children?' I blurted out unthinkingly.

The crone drew herself up and stared with magnificent virtuousness at the ceiling. 'Indeed,' she said with elaborate piety, ' 'twas the Lord Himself put the breath in them.'

'My God!' I breathed, thunderstruck, and turned to gape at the Madonna-like expression on her old face. She showed no trace of shame or embarrassment at my reaction but merely went on to tell me what a blessing her children had been to her. Providentially a waitress approached us at that moment bearing a tray of drinks for the road, carefully pointing out that there was whisky for the men-folk and sherry for the ladies. Ignoring her reproving glance I helped myself to one of the whiskies. I felt very badly in need of it.

In order to avoid further shattering revelations I went in search of my landlady and, having found her, we said our goodbyes and pre-pared to depart. On reaching the door of the hotel we found the way blocked by a jostling, rumbustious throng of wedding guests, servants and bar customers.

'It's what we always do when there's a weddin',' Morag informed me. 'Their bedroom is just above the porch here, and when the bride opens the window and throws out her stocking it'll be time for every-body to take themselves off home.'

As soon as she had finished speaking, there was a tumultuous roar from the crowd and the blind was lifted from a window above and the sash raised. A hand appeared and a moment later a white silk stocking came floating down into the midst of the spectators and landed on the policeman, who flourished it victoriously before rolling it up and thrusting it into his pocket. Immediately the swarm of people began to disperse in different directions, some arm-in-arm and singing happily, others barely capable of holding themselves upright.

The next morning Morag had woeful news to impart. Lachy and Johnny were in gaol! According to her they had started to fight soon after the wedding party had broken up and Lachy had crowned Johnny's head with a whisky bottle. It was terrible news, for the rela-tionship normally existing between Lachy and Johnny was of a David and Jonathan-like quality. It sounded impossible for such a thing to have happened to such good friends, but that it was only too true the policeman himself confirmed when I met him later that day.

'Poor Lachy,' I said. 'I'm sure he didn't mean to hurt Johnny. They were always such good friends.'

'No of course he didn't,' agreed the policeman, who was really very decent. 'And that's just what Johnny himself says when he comes around. My, but Johnny was mad when he found out I'd locked up Lachy. He called me all the bad names in the language and more besides. "He's my best pal," he says. "Your best pal," says I, "and he's just split your head open with a bottle!" "He meant me no harm you b——" says Johnny. "Look here," says I, "if you don't stop cursin' at me I'll lock you up along with him." "I'll come right enough too," says Johnny, and by God! Miss Peckwitt, he came so quick I had all I could do to keep in front of him,' finished the policeman.

I clucked sympathetically.

'And when we got to the police station, did you hear what he did then?'

I shook my head.

'Well, the fool grabbed the fire extinguisher off the wall and he turned it full on me and the sergeant. Of course we had to lock him up then. There was nothin' else to do.'

'Ruined our clothes,' he went on in aggrieved tones, 'and I had my best suit on too.'

I gathered from his further remarks that there was but one cell available on the Island for the lodging of offenders. The reunion, he told me, had been absolutely pathetic.

'What will happen to them?' I asked.

The policeman pursed his lips. 'Depends,' he said. 'A fiver maybe.'

'Lachy must have been terribly drunk to have started it,' I said.

'My, if you'd seen him!' rejoined the policeman. 'He was as wild as a bull.'

'How did you manage to get him to the police station?' I asked, knowing just how unhelpful the villagers would have been in such a situation.

'Well, he was a bit of a job, I can tell you,' he confided. 'He needed handcuffs he was that strong, but I didn't have any on me. When you go to a weddin' you don't expect to have to take handcuffs with you.' He glanced at me as though expecting reassurance. 'Well, I was havin' such a struggle and then I remembered somethin' I had in my pocket.' He smiled, a secret, reminiscent smile. 'So I twisted his two hands behind him and I slipped on this thing. "Now Lachy," I says, "I have the handcuffs on you and you're under arrest!"' Here the police-man laughed outright. 'The trick worked all right and he came quiet as a lamb, his two hands clasped behind him as though he was sayin' his prayers back to front, for he was so blind drunk he couldn't tell the difference between a pair of handcuffs and this.'

With a wry smile he thrust his hand into his tunic pocket and held out the makeshift handcuffs. I recognized it of course. I had discovered a pair of them in a decaying little shop in an insignificant side street; it was speckled with rose-buds, bordered with lace and tufted with swansdown—and the bride had been enchanted with it.

The Sea for Breakfast

LILLIAN BECKWITH

The Sea For

Illustrated by DOUGLAS HALL

Breakfast

Contents

A Place of My Own

ONE hundred and ten; one hundred and eleven, ouch! One hundred and twelve, damn! For the third torrid day in succession I was exasperatedly discovering and extracting nails of every tortured shape and unexpected size from the wooden walls of my cottage kitchen. My tool, which I had previously understood to be a claw-headed hammer, had been bestowed upon me by Ruari, the

imperiously obliging brother of my former landlady. He however
had referred to it more colourfully as a 'cloven-footed' hammer. It
was a typically Hebridean tool with a thick, rough handle and a rusty
head so loose on the shaft that it was a toss-up each time whether the
nail would be prised out of the wall, or whether the 'cloven-foot' would
remain poised vacillatingly on the firmly embedded nail while I reeled
back, brandishing the handle and recovering myself just in time to
receive a blow of acknowledgement from the descending head. For
the umpteenth time I stopped to massage tingling elbows with grazed
fingers and swore as I jammed the head savagely back on to the shaft.
For the umpteenth time I wished, rather half-heartedly, that the little
village of Bruach were not set amidst such glorious isolation and,
most whole-heartedly, that the terrain were less abundantly provided
with handy-sized stones. As it was, even this poor makeshift had
necessitated some diligent seeking. Still, I comforted myself as I
doggedly counted my successes (simply so as to prove just how
many nails one may expect to find in an old croft kitchen), the unpre-
dictability of proceedings did serve to enliven a task that otherwise
might have been as soporific as counting sheep.

Just why any household should have wanted or needed more than
a hundred nails disfiguring their kitchen I could not understand. The
six-inch ones higher up on the walls and the ones in the rafters would
of course have been used for hanging fishing nets. In addition to those
serving as picture hooks and those used for hanging coats and oilskins,
some of the rest would doubtless have been used for strings of salt fish
or rabbit skins. A few dozen nails, even fifty, I would have been prepared to accept as a normal complement, but over a hundred! . . .

'My kitchen walls,' I lamented to Morag after my first impact with
them, 'have more nails to the square foot than a fakir's bed.'

'Aye, but those is Hamish's men's nails,' she replied reverently, and
seeing that I looked blank, continued: 'Ach well, mo ghaoil, d'you
see, Hamish and Mary that lived there had seven sons and all of them
men y'understand? Not like the wee ticks of things we have nowadays,
but big men they was and strong, and every time one of them got back
from the hill or from the sea they'd likely have a rabbit or a few fish
and maybe a skart and they'd be after pickin' up a stone just and
bangin' a nail into the wall so as to hang it away from the cats and the
dogs.'

'It still puzzles me why there should have been such a glut of nails all ready to hand, here in Bruach of all places,' I said.

'But isn't the wood you gather from the shore full of them just, lassie? Have you no seen that for yourself? And Hamish's men wouldn't be the kind to be wastin' them.'

Thus was the plethora of nails explained. Now I should like to explain why I, during three picnic-perfect days of early June when cuckoos were yodelling across the sun-soaked moors and bluebells were pealing wildly into bloom, should be gloomily and resentfully pulling all Hamish's men's nails out again.

When her nephew in Glasgow had been involved in an accident which was supposed to have affected his health generally, Morag, the crofter landlady from whom I had rented half a house since my arrival in Bruach three years previously, had decided that he and his wife, who was herself a semi-invalid, should come to live with her on the croft where she could keep a strict eye on the two of them. She also, she said, intended to keep a strict eye on their precocious little daughter, a design which I suspected privately, having met the child, would result in her having one more subject for her tyranny, for Morag, like all Gaels, loved to have a child about the house to indulge. Naturally the new arrangement meant that Morag and I, to our mutual regret, must part company, and I was faced with the alternative of returning South or looking for other accommodation locally. After three years of crofting life and with ill health only a memory, I found I did not relish the idea of returning to the noisy clutter of life in England where nowadays it seems there is too much prosperity for real happiness; too much hurry for humour. In Bruach there was prosperity enough for most things and time mattered little. My days were pleasant and full and the nights brought unbroken sleep so that even dreams had the continuity of one long novel in contrast to the disjointedness of a book of short stories. And undoubtedly I had grown fond of Bruach and its inhabitants, for the Gaels of the Hebrides are indeed a happy race. Even their language is happy; listening to the Gaelic is like listening to a series of chuckles; there is always a lilt even in harangue; often a smile in a scold. I might be shocked at some of the events of the day, but at night I could chuckle myself to sleep over them. I wanted to stay in Bruach, so I looked for a place of my own.

There were two empty cottages not far from the village. 'Tigh-na-Craig' (House on the Rock), to the north, was situated close to the burial ground, the other, with an unpronounceable name—the nearest I could get to it was 'Tigh-na-Mushroomac'—to the south, adjoined the cleg-infested moor. Faced with a choice between clegs and corpses I chose the clegs and was immensely relieved I had done so when I later heard Erchy, the poacher, telling someone: 'Ach, the grave will no take long to dig. It's no a County Council burial ground so you'll not have to go more than two feet. It's no trouble at all.' The County apparently insisted on four feet.

The cottage of 'Tigh-na-Mushroomac' had been empty when I had first arrived in Bruach but the fact that it might be for sale did not emerge until after I had announced my intention of settling. The Bruachites are averse to putting their property on the open market but like to be wooed into graciously permitting you to buy provided you can convice them of your need and of your bank balance. Calum, one of Hamish's surviving sons and the owner of the cottage, lived in Glasgow, so I lost no time in contacting him and in visiting the local policeman in whose charge the key had been left.

My first meeting with the policeman, soon after my arrival in Bruach, had left a distinctly droll impression on both our minds. I had been on my way back to Morag's one drearily wet evening when I had come upon his car parked plumb in the centre of the road, without lights of any sort. A little farther along the road a lorry too was stopped and beside it the policeman, watched attentively by the lorry driver, was siphoning petrol out of the tank of the lorry into a can. When he had transferred the petrol to the tank of his own car, the policeman generously offered me a lift home. Morag had been away in Glasgow at the time and as the policeman had yet to finish the enquiries about poaching he was engaged on making in the village, I invited him in for a meal. Earlier in the day Erchy had handed me a parcel of fish which he had said offhandedly were mackerel. I cooked one for the policeman. Before the meal he had seemed much dispirited by the results of his day's work, but after the fish and several cups of tea his geniality was restored. Indeed he became quite jovial. He complimented me on my cooking and when he got up to go he impressed upon me that I must be very sure to thank Erchy for him and tell him that he, the policeman, had 'never tasted mackerel like them'. I assured him I would do so.

'He said what?' demanded Erchy when I had innocently kept my promise.

'He asked me to tell you he'd never tasted mackerel so good,' I repeated.

'Damty sure he hasn't,' muttered Erchy, turning a little pale. 'Why the Hell did you want to let him see them?'

'But you told me they were mackerel. Weren't they?'

'Mackerel indeed! D'you mean to say you can't tell the difference between what's a trout and what's a mackerel? And do you not know trout's illegal?'

At that stage of my initiation I was incapable of distinguishing a legal fish from an illegal one, having hitherto relied on my fishmonger to identify my fish for me. Full of contrition, I admitted my defections.

Erchy stared at me with both pity and amazement. 'Sometimes,' he said crushingly, 'I think school teachers is the most ignorantest people out.'

Since that episode one of the policeman's eyes had always drooped into an indubitable wink whenever we had met and now that I approached him with a request for the key of 'Tigh-na-Mushroomac' he appeared to find it excessively funny.

'You're thinkin' of buyin' "Tigh-na-Mushroomac", are you? Well, right enough I did have the key once but I've lost it now. Indeed, when the door was blown in by the storm a year or two back the only way I could keep it shut again was to ram a big stone behind it and tie a good piece of string to it. You'll see the string under the door. You'll pull it towards you when you come out and it rolls and jams the door. Keeps it closed better than the old lock that was on it before, I'm tellin' you.' He was so taken with his contrivance that it seemed a pity to draw his attention to the fact that I must first get into the cottage. 'Ach, you'll give it a good shove just. Mind now, it'll need to be a right good one, for it's a biggish stone. You'd best get one of the lads to do it for you,' he added on second thoughts.

It was a grey day with sneaky little flurries of wind which dashed us sporadically with chilly drops of rain when Morag and I went to pay our first visit of inspection. Morag had enlisted for me the help of Peter, the son of Sheena, who worked the croft adjoining 'Tigh-na-Mushroomac'. Peter was a doughty, chrysanthemum-headed youth whose

shape suggested that his mother had placed a heavy weight on his
head in childhood to make him grow broad rather than long. When
he smiled his wide gummy smile it looked as though someone had cut
his throat. When he laughed he looked as though he was going to
come to pieces. He now strode beside us along the shingle track, his
shoulder hunched as though in eager preparation for the assault on
the door.

'My,' confided Morag with a little shudder, 'I don't like the look of
him at all. He looks that wild.' I glanced surreptitiously at Peter, who
was wearing such a ridiculously tight pair of trousers and such a
constraining jersey that it looked impossible for him to be anything
but extremely well disciplined. 'And he's that lonely,' went on Morag
steadily as she assessed the baby hill and the bare half mile of road that
separated 'Tigh-na-Mushroomac' from the rest of the houses, 'you'll
have none but the sheeps for company.'

I told her, patiently, for I had told her many times, that I did not
mind the solitude.

'But, mo ghaoil,' she argued, 'you could die here and none of us
the wiser till the butcher smelled you out.'

Built of grey stone, 'Tigh-na-Mushroomac' squatted in smug solitude at the extreme tip of Bruach bay, its two lower windows like
dark secrets half buried in the three-foot thick walls. From the sloping
felt roof two tiny dormer windows peeped inquisitively at the sea
which at high tide skirmished no more than twenty yards away.
In fact it would not have needed an unduly exaggerated fishing rod
to have enabled one to lean from one's bedroom window and draw
upon the sea for breakfast each morning.

Behind the cottage was the neglected croft which merged into the
wildness of the moors and they in their turn stretched to prostrate
themselves at the feet of the lonely hills. It would have been cruel to
have insisted to Morag that its distance from the rest of the houses was,
for me, one of 'Tigh-na-Mushroomac's' chief attractions. The Gaels as a
general rule seem to have no desire for privacy, building their houses
as close to one another as croft boundaries will permit. 'Alone-ness'
is a state they cannot endure and 'any company is better than no company' is a maxim that is accepted literally whether the company be
that of an idiot or a corpse. Not desiring it for themselves, they can
neither understand nor really believe in the desire of other people for

privacy and so genuinely anxious are they that you should not be lonely they continually seek you out of your cherished solitude.

Outside the cottage Peter turned on us his cut-throat grin and poised himself ready for action.

'All right now, Peter,' said Morag. 'I'll lift the sneck.' Peter rammed his shoulder fiercely into the door; there was a short, sharp protest from the rusty hinges as they parted company with the wood; the door fell inwards, see-sawed across the big stone so thoughtfully provided by the policeman, and flung Peter into the farthest corner of the porch. Bewilderedly Peter picked himself up, revealing that he now had two long, gaping splits in the seat of his trousers.

'Peter!' upbraided Morag, blushing for his predicament. 'You've broken your trousers!' Peter looked somewhat puzzled and felt each of his limbs in turn but thus reassured he became more concerned with locating a splinter which, he said, had 'come out and lost itself on him'. I diplomatically went upstairs and minutes later heard his exclamations of relief and then his dismissal by Morag. Through a bedroom window I caught sight of his stocky figure fleeing homewards across the moors, presumably minus his splinter and with his rear parts effectively camou-flaged by Morag's best floral silk apron which she had fortunately been wearing beneath her coat. My landlady joined me upstairs.

'Didn't I tell Sheena this mornin' just,' said Morag complacently, 'that Peter was gettin' too tight for his trousers?'

Inside, 'Tigh-na-Mushroomac' was a replica of all the two-storeyed croft cottages I had seen, there being a kitchen leading off one side of the entrance porch and 'the room' off the other. In Bruach this second room was never known as anything but 'the room', presum-ably because no one was really sure of its intended purpose. Morag, in her original letter to me had described hers as 'the room that wasn't a kitchen'. Usually the anonymous room was necessary as a bedroom and indeed in many of the single-storeyed croft houses these two rooms, with a recessed bed in the kitchen, comprised the whole of the living accommodation. Yet in such limited space large families were reared and a galaxy of scholars produced. It was no unusual sight to see a university student at his books by the light of a candle in a corner of the small kitchen, while all around him the neighbours jostled and gossiped, argued and sang. Neither was it unusual in due course to see that student's name high in the list of honours graduates.

'Tigh-na-Mushroomac' provided ample accommodation for a spinster. It had two rooms upstairs and, though these were of attic proportions with the windows at floor level so that one had to sit down on the floor to look out through them, they were habitable. The cottage needed a certain amount of repair; first on the list was a new front door. But its walls and its roof were sound. I liked what I saw.

It seemed to me that everyone in the village took a hand in the ensuing transaction, and when it came to bargaining they ranged themselves with complete affability either on the side of Calum or myself, or, with true Gaelic adroitness on the side of both parties. With so many cooks the broth should have been irrevocably spoiled but eventually everything was settled to everyone's complete satisfaction and I became the delighted owner of a cottage and croft.

As I could afford only the minimum number of alterations to begin with, I decided that priority must be given to getting larger windows put in the kitchen and 'the room'. I wanted snugness but not permanent twilight in my new home.

'But, mo ghaoil, think how they'll show up the dust,' warned Sheena, who had lived all her life in a dark, thatched cottage and whose only use for a duster was to wipe over a chair whenever a visitor accepted the hospitality of her kitchen; a necessary precaution, considering a hen had most likely been the former occupant.

Erchy, with whom I consulted, startled me by admitting that he 'quite liked a bit of work now and then just as a change when he could spare the time', and by promptly agreeing to undertake the task. True to his word he was soon at work taking out the old frames and enlarging the window space. When he had got thus far there was a lull in his activities.

'What's happened to Erchy these days?' I asked at a ceilidh one night. 'He seems to have gone on strike. There's been no work done on my cottage for days.'

'Oh, he'll not be workin' at anythin' for a week yet,' explained Johnny. 'He's got his girl friend from Glasgow stayin' in the village and they're away every night to the heather.'

'That's not his girl friend,' contradicted Morag indignantly.

'Maybe not,' conceded Johnny easily, 'but he'll make do with her while she's here.'

But the return of Erchy's proxy girl friend to Glasgow did not, unfortunately, result in a resumption of activity by Erchy. A wedding was announced at which he was to act as best man. Erchy got drunk in anticipation, drunk for the solemnization and drunk again in recollection. A week later there was a dance and Erchy got drunk in preparation. He reckoned he'd never have the courage to ask a girl to dance with him if he was sober. A cattle sale followed closely on the heels of the dance and Erchy's beasts made the highest prices; he stayed drunk for nearly a week! By this time winter was upon us and Noachian deluges, lashed by fierce gales, washed the exposed room inside and out. Hailstones pitted the wood-lined walls; spiders' webs were torn from their anchorages; salt spray filmed the floors. It was on a particularly savage day, with a full-blooded gale inverting the waterfalls over the cliffs and sending them billowing skywards, that I went over to the cottage to reassure myself that it was still there. Hungry green breakers were hurling themselves at the shingle shore, flinging spume high over the roof of 'Tigh-na-Mushroomac'. The wind seemed to have chosen the poor little cottage as its main target and I was buffeted towards it. Inside I found Erchy frenziedly prising out the small window from the back of the kitchen.

'My, but it's coarse, coarse weather,' he announced.

'Erchy!' I yelled, ignoring the greeting in the belief that he was still suffering from the effects of his recent orgies. 'I don't want that window out, you idiot!'

'I canna' get it open,' Erchy yelled back. 'I've got to try will I get it out. It can go back when it's needed.'

'It's needed now if ever it was,' I retorted savagely.

'My God, woman!' Erchy shouted at me above the storm. 'Do you not know that where the wind gets in it's got to get out again? If you don't let it out here you'll lose your roof. Wind's the same in a house as it is in a stomach; you've got to let it blow its way out once it's in. You canna trap wind.'

I watched him dubiously, slowly becoming aware that not only was the floor pulsing as though there were an engine beneath my feet, but that interspersed with the noise of the storm were strained creakings and groanings from the timbers of the ceiling.

'This floor's quaking,' I said tensely.

'You are yourself too, I dare say,' retorted Erchy unrelentingly.

'And if you had this amount of wind under your beams you'd be quaking a lot worse.' I subsided into the most sheltered corner of the kitchen. 'Hear that now?' Erchy continued as an ominous thudding became audible from somewhere above. I listened; it sounded as though the ceiling joists were stamping against the walls in their impatience to be gone. 'That should stop when I get this clear.' He wrenched the window free and lowered it to the comparative shelter of the ground outside. 'Now listen!' he commanded, but though I listened obediently I was not much the wiser. The whole cottage seemed to be threatening to take wing at any moment. 'Aye, you'd have lost your roof all right tonight, I doubt,' said Erchy with great satisfaction.

Through interminable weeks 'Tigh-na-Mushroomac' waited, naked and exposed, for the new door and windows to arrive. Glass, I was told, was scarce and when at last it was obtainable the mid-winter gales followed, one after another, so that the carrier complained it was impossible for him to get across to the mainland. A brief respite from the gales brought the snow, which blocked the road. Blessedly came the thaw—which washed the road away. A day of calm dawned; there was no snow and the road had been repaired. With bated breath I telephoned the carrier.

'Oh, indeed I'm sorry but the tide's not just in the right state for loadin' at the pier,' he said with practised apology. 'Not till next week it won't be.'

Next week brought a repetition of the previous delays but when the tide had crept round again to a suitable state and miraculously it coincided with a period of calm I again 'phoned the carrier.

'Did you no hear, Miss Peckwitt?' he answered plaintively. 'My lorry broke on Monday and I've no managed to get it sorted yet. I canna' say when I'll be out now.'

Every time I visited my refrigerated little cottage I became a little more despondent. Every night I prayed the Almighty for patience. But the day did come when the elements acted in unison and nothing 'broke' and the carrier's lorry came romping along the track to the cottage to deliver two beautiful new windows and one front door. The front door was not new. There was a little note from the merchant explaining that he had not been able to procure a new door of the right size so he had taken the liberty of sending this one which had been removed from the local police station. He hoped I wouldn't mind! The carrier had also brought cans of paint, rolls of paper and turps, so whilst Erchy set to work installing the windows, I began to paper 'the room'. The original colour of the walls of 'the room' was really indescribable and the nearest I came to identifying it was in the recollection of a time when Morag, suspecting her calf was sick, was debating with me whether or not she should send for the vet.

'What makes you think there's something wrong with him?' I had asked as we watched the beast skipping around on his tether. 'He looks healthy enough to me.'

'Aye,' Morag had agreed reluctantly, 'he looks all right in himself but see now,' she had explained, indicating his smeared rump, 'his dung is such an unhappy colour.'

Once the windows had been put in I installed a camp bed and a couple of borrowed chairs and one or two other essentials and moved into the cottage. A few nights afterwards four of the girls from the village turned up to inspect progress. My spirits sank a little, for where the girls went soon the men would follow and then there would be a ceilidh and I would have to stop work and provide tea. I told them I was just planning to start papering upstairs. 'We'll give you a hand,' they volunteered. My spirits sank lower. As I expected, it was not long before some of the lads were bursting in, completely sure of their welcome and, giving up any thought of doing more work, I prepared to settle down for an evening's ceilidh, hoping the girls would forget their offer of help. The prospect of a wasted evening was not nearly so discomposing as the prospect of having to accept their help with the decorating.

'Come on,' said Dollac, the village beauty, inexorably. 'We're all goin' to help Miss Peckwitt paint and paper upstairs so she can have it all ready for a good ceilidh. Get the paint, you Ally. Is the paper cut? Those that can't do paintin' or paperin' can do some scrapin'.' Feebly I tried to dissuade them. 'Now just you get on with finishing the room,' they told me. I submitted to the juggernaut of their enthusiasm and when I had put the last few touches to 'the room', I carried water from the well and coaxed the stove into heating it. I found biscuits and collected odd cups and mugs, since my own crockery had not yet arrived. As I worked there came from above bursts of song, the banging of doors, clanging of paint cans, uninhibited shrieks, yells of tension, thudding of feet and generally such a hullabaloo that

I doubted if ever I should be able to clean up their mess in anything short of a decade.

'Tea!' I called up the stairs and there was such an immediate scatteration that I fully expected a brace of paint cans to come hurtling down the stairs too. My helpers had enjoyed themselves immensely; that at least was obvious. Each one of them had a swipe of paint across a cheek, a decoration which Dollac dismissed as being the result of a game of 'paint-brush tag'—to see who would get the most paint on him. When they had finished their tea and biscuits they rampaged back upstairs to 'finish things off'. I felt that the phrase would turn out to be most appropriate. I heated more water and washed the cups, envisaging myself having to take time off from cleaning up the farrago in order to go to the post office to 'phone for a large supply of paint remover and a repeat order for paint and wallpaper. It was the early hours of the morning before my helpers came trooping down the stairs again. They had cleaned the paint off their faces and I wondered vaguely how and where. They had finished both bedrooms, they said, and they were 'beautiful just', but they must have my promise not to go upstairs and look at them until after breakfast. They wouldn't look so good until then, they explained, because there were still some wet patches; I must wait to inspect it until it was all properly dry. The promise was an easy one to make for I felt much too debilitated then to climb the stairs and face up to the chaos which I was certain would confront me. Yet, after breakfast, when I felt strong enough to bear the sight of it all, I went upstairs and found there was no chaos at all; I could not have hoped to have done the job nearly so well myself. The unused materials were stacked tidily in a corner, and paint splashes had been cleaned away. It was, as they had said, beautiful— beautiful just. But only Gaels, I believe, could have accomplished such a splendid job and yet have derived so much fun and frolic from doing it.

The following night the volunteers turned up again but now there remained only the kitchen to be decorated and as I insisted that all the nails should come out first and as no more tools were procurable the evening's work degenerated into a cosy ceilidh. And that is why on this hot June day I came to be pulling out my one hundred and twenty-third nail when I heard the voice of Sheena, Peter's mother, hailing me from the door.

'My, but you're a hardy!'

I gathered up my harvest of nails from a chair and pushed on the kettle. In Bruach no work was ever considered too pressing to neglect hospitality and the arrival of the most casual visitor automatically ensured the popping on of the kettle.

'I've taken a hundred and twenty-three nails out of this kitchen so far,' I told Sheena, 'and I believe there are still one or two left.'

'Oh aye,' she replied. 'But Hamish was always such a handy man. Mary had never but to ask for a nail and he'd have it in for her. Aye, a right handy man he was.'

'I'm not nearly so handy at pulling them out,' I said ruefully.

'No, but why go to the trouble mo ghaoil? You'll surely want to hang things yourself and you'll be glad of a nail here and there.'

'Not a hundred and twenty-three times,' I said.

'No, maybe,' she admitted. 'But there's pictures.' (I should mention that the kitchen was about twelve feet by ten feet and no more than seven feet high.) 'And will you no need a nail for your girdle?' In Bruach a girdle is something a woman bakes on – not something she steps into. 'And then you never know but what you might want to dry a rabbit skin or two, and a few fish maybe.' I hoped I never should. 'You'll need some for towels some place and a corkscrew . . .' she was enumerating enthusiastically now; 'and a holder for your kettle and a couple of calendars and a wee bunch of feathers for the hearth. You have no man,' she giggled, 'so you'll no be needin' nails for him. Men needs an awful lot of nails in a house,' she told me. 'You must see and keep some mo ghaoil surely.'

I surveyed my rusty harvest. I'd be dammed if any of them were going back in again, I decided, and between sips of tea Sheena sighed for my improvidence.

'My, but your new windows are beautiful just,' she enthused, slewing round her chair so that she could stare out at the sea. The windows had made an enormous difference to the cottage, giving a wide view of the bay which today was full of sunshine and silver-flecked water. On the shore, sandpipers scurried busily in the shingle and serenaded the quiescent ripples while thrift danced to the music of the sea. Above the outer islands comically shaped clouds, like assorted carnival hats, were strewn haphazardly across the sky. The black hills lay in a drugged haze, Garbh Bienn looking like an old man who has fallen peacefully asleep in his chair; the wisp of white cloud across its middle like the newspaper fallen from his face.

'You know,' said Sheena, whose appreciation of nature was purely gastronomical, 'this weather ought to bring the mackerel in.'

She finished her tea and as she got up to go she remembered she had a telegram for me in her pocket. 'I was passin' the post office and NellyElly said would I bring it. It's only to tell you your furniture's comin' next Tuesday.'

Sheena had only been gone a few minutes when Morag arrived and we were soon joined by Erchy who had been painting his dinghy down on the shore. The kettle had to go on again. I begrudged no one tea and I had grown tolerant of time-wasting, but I was plagued by the fact that water for every purpose had to be carried from a well over a hundred yards away down on the shore, which meant that I had to struggle uphill with the full pails. It was aggravating to have to squelch about the croft in gumboots even during a prolonged drought and to realize that though there was an excess of water everywhere it was too undisciplined to be of use to me. I was ironically reminded of my own mother's injunction, 'Don't leave the kettle boiling, wasting gas'; here I had to remind myself, 'Don't leave the kettle boiling, wasting water'. With so much cleaning to do the carrying of water was proving a strength-sapping business and I was very anxious to get the guttering of the cottage replaced so that I could have rainwater for household purposes. The guttering, along with a rainwater tank, had been on order for many weeks and Morag brought news of it now.

'She's on her way,' Morag announced triumphantly. 'You'll not want for water when she comes.'

'You're not telling me that my rainwater tank is on its way at last, are you?' I asked hopefully.

'Yes, indeed. I saw the carrier yesterday just and he told me to tell you that if the Lord spares him he'll be out with her tomorrow for certain.'

'That will be a blessing,' I said. However, as I pointed out, the new tank would not overcome the drinking water problem because I had discovered that when there was a combination of high tide and a strong wind the sea came into my well so that the water was decidedly brackish sometimes.

'So it will be, mo ghaoil,' Morag agreed. 'But you know the old doctor who was here always used to tell us that if everybody took a good drink of plain sea-water once a week there'd not be so many sore stomachs goin' around.'

'That may be true, but I don't like salty tea,' I demurred. 'I rather wish I could get hold of one of those water diviners to come and find me a nice convenient well here on the croft.'

'Them fellows,' said Morag contemptuously; 'they had one here-abouts a long time back to try would he find a corpse in the hills and a few folks was sayin' we ought to let him try would he find more wells for us here in Bruach.'

'What happened?'

'Oh, they let him try all right, and he said there was water here and there was water there, and my fine fellow took ten shillings from each of us for sayin' so, but when folks started digging they found it was drier underneath than it was up at the top. They'd lost their money and they'd found no water.'

'They didn't go deep enough,' put in Erchy, with a wink at me.

'Indeed they did. He said there was water on our own Ruari's croft at twenty feet and Ruari dug down until we could see only the cap of him just, sticking out of the top of the hole he'd made and still there was no water. Ach, I'm no believin' in them fellows at all. Maybe they can find corpses but I doubt they canna' find water.' It struck me then as strange that the Bruachites, who genuinely believe in and often claim to be gifted with the second sight, should yet be so sceptical of water divining. I recollected that I had never heard of a Hebridean water diviner.

'What you'll have to do, my dear,' went on Morag, 'is to drink the wild water.'

'The wild water?' I echoed.

'Aye, what you catch from your roof.'

'For drinking?' I grimaced, thinking of all the dear little birds I heard scratching and sliding on my roof every morning; of the starlings fumigating themselves around the chimney and the gulls daily parading the length of the ridging. Morag laughed.

'You'll soon get used to that, lassie,' she predicted firmly. And she was right.

She watched me take out the last half-score or so of nails, giving a grunt of 'there now!' at each success.

'Anybody would think it was you doin' the work,' Erchy told her.

'If you was half as good as the men who put in the nails you'd be after takin' them out for Miss Peckwitt instead of sittin' watchin' her,' she rebuked him.

Erchy drained his cup. When Morag was on the defensive her tongue could become caustic and he was ready to flee from it.

'D'you know you're wearin' odd shoes,' he taunted her.

'Ach, Erchy, but you know me. I just puts my feets into the first things that I pull from under the bed.'

'That could be damty awkward sometimes, I doubt,' he said as he disappeared homeward.

Morag watched me fill a pail with hot water and pour in some disinfectant.

'My,' she commented with an appreciative sniff, 'I do like this disinfectant you use. It has such a lovely flavour.'

While I washed down the walls she told me of the prowess of Hamish and his sons. They had, it seemed, all possessed Herculean strength though, according to Morag, the sons had been no match for their father. She told me of the prodigious loads he could carry; of how he alone could lift to shoulder height the three stones at the entrance to the village by which every man coming home from the sales was accustomed, in days gone by, to test his strength; of how he could lift a boat that taxed the strength of four lesser men. She related with pride the stories of his skill in breaking horses; of how he used to walk all the way from Glasgow once every five years and, when he reached home, to show he was not tired, he used to leap over the garden gate. (I was less impressed with this latter feat, for if I had left Glasgow two hundred miles behind me I have no doubt I too should have felt like leaping a gate.)

'What are you goin' to name your cottage now that you have it ready?' she asked, draining her fourth cup of tea.

'Oh, I shan't bother to change it from "Tigh-na-Mushroomac",' I said. 'I must get the correct Gaelic spelling.'

'Here, but you mustn't call it that. Not on letters, anyway,' Morag said with a gasp.

'Why not?' I asked. 'What does it mean?'

'It doesn't suit it just. And it's no rightly a name at all. It's just what it's always been called since I can remember.'

'But, Morag, what does it mean?'

'Indeed I don't know,' she lied firmly. 'Erchy's mother says to tell you she has a wee poc of fish put by for you when you're passin' that way,' she continued hastily and made for the door.

It was of little use pressing Morag further, that I knew, and I walked with her as far as Erchy's, pondering on the meaning of 'Tigh-na-Mushroomac' and why it should be considered an unsuitable name to be put on letters. I recalled the excessive amusement of the policeman when he had learned I was thinking of buying the house and wondered if it had been caused in some measure by the unsuitability of the name. I knew that in the Gaelic 'Tigh' means 'house', but never having seen the spelling of the name I could not identify the rest as being any Gaelic words I knew.

'Erchy,' I demanded, 'what does "Tigh-na-Mushroomac" mean?'

Erchy looked a long, long way out to sea, and his lips tightened to repress a smile. 'Don't you get feedin' any of that fish to the pollis,' he warned me, 'and if you meet him with it, run for your life.'

'How do you spell "Tigh-na-Mushroomac?"' I persisted, after a hasty glance at the fish which I could now recognize as being nothing more illicit than mackerel.

'Indeed, I don't know,' he replied with simulated apology.

His evasion strengthened my determination to find out so I put the question to an old scholar who loved his language and who was patient with those who might wish to learn it.

'Oh well, now, you mustn't call the house that,' he answered me smoothly. 'No, no, that wouldn't do at all. It's not really a name but just a description the village has always had for it. Go and tell Morag she must tell you the story of it. She's the best one to tell you, and you must tell her that from me.'

I thanked him and went again to Morag. She was washing dishes and when I told her why I had come she began scrutinizing each dish lingeringly to avoid meeting my eye.

'Well, mo ghaoil,' she began, with an embarrassed chuckle. 'It was Hamish's lads when they was younger. They wouldn't come out once they were in . . . y'understand?' She managed to give me an insinuating glance, and then plunged on with her story. It appeared that one or two of Hamish's less tractable sons had developed a dislike for work and so evaded it by disappearing into the 'wee hoosie' in the back garden where, immune to the threats and cajolery of their parents, they had stayed for long periods reading books or papers. Hamish had at last become so incensed that he had one day taken the saw and sawn the traditional round hole into a rough square one. The simplicity of his strategy was rivalled only by its effectiveness and, after enforced experience, I have no hesitation in recommending this form of torture to anyone who is barbaric enough to be interested in such practices. Inevitably, Hamish's family had come to be known in Bruach and beyond as the 'square bums' and their house as 'the house of square bums'.

Once acquainted with the story I lost no time in choosing for my cottage a name that I could unashamedly put on my letters. For the seat in the 'wee hoosie' I had already substituted one of more conventional shape.

Settling In

WITH MY cottage brightly redecorated so that even the unhappy walls of 'the room', now my bedroom, were laughing with warmth and colour, I was ready to receive my furniture which, as the telegram had said, was due to arrive the following Tuesday. I very much wanted to pay a visit to the mainland to buy one or two last-minute necessities and as 'Joanna', the little second-hand car I had bought in England, was undergoing repairs, I planned to catch the bus on Monday morning, do my shopping, stay the night and get a lift back with the furniture lorry the following day. Everything worked according to plan except for one tense half-hour when, with only a few minutes to spare before I was due to meet the lorry, I darted into a telephone kiosk on the station and was imprisoned as the result of a careless lorry driver backing his lorry against the kiosk door and going off for a cup of tea. It was an embarrassing and vexatious experience. People hurried by to the train, heedless of my gesticulations; they heard neither my calls nor my hammerings. When I did eventually manage to attract the attention of a couple of station loiterers they stared at me with mingled curiosity and trepidation before they would come near. When they realized what had happened they bolted off in search of the driver, believing no doubt that I was intending to catch the train which was due to leave in a few minutes' time; fortunately another loiterer waited long enough to listen to my plea for someone to go down to the pier and hold up the furniture lorry.

At the pier, where I arrived harassed and apologetic, the driver was as glad to see me as I was to see him. He had never been to the Island before, he told me, and he hadn't any idea of the road anyhow and he might have been driving around all day looking for the place. The two itinerant labourers, who had already been recruited to help with the unloading, tore themselves away from a knot of arguing fishermen and installed themselves in the back of the lorry and we set off. Weightily the lorry rumbled along the rutty roads with every now and then explosive comments from the driver on their condition and their sinuousness. Shepherds called in their dogs to heel while they stood and watched us impassively. Women, carrying water or moving tethered cows, stopped their work to wave and smile. At one isolated cottage which had a long view of the road, an old woman came hurrying out holding aloft a large jug of milk and some cups. The driver pulled up and taking a slopping cup of milk which she urged upon him, handed it to me. I drank obediently, and allowed the driver to drink his too, stifling the knowledge that conditions in the interior of the woman's home much belied its white-washed appearance and that of her batch of children several were patients in the mainland sanatorium. She would accept no payment. It gratified her to offer refreshment to passing strangers and our enjoyment of it was her reward. When we handed back the empty jug and the cups her maze of happy wrinkles deepened delightedly and her kind old face flushed with pleasure. She still stood there as we drove away, smiling, nodding her head and waving until we were out of sight.

The road now wound picturesquely around the head of the loch so that we had the full-skirted hills jostling us on one side and water lapping at our wheels on the other. The driver said, not inaptly, that he felt as though he was between the Devil and the deep blue sea though the day was grey and the loch not blue but darkly reflective. The hill peaks loomed sinister through swirling clouds of mist which polished their craggy faces. Scenically it was awe-inspiring. The driver said it gave him the willies. He would have liked to accelerate and get away from it but the road made that impossible. He became noticeably less talkative.

I was preoccupied with the problem of how to arrange my various possessions in the cottage and was already experiencing the thrill of once again handling some of the dear, familiar things which I knew were stored in the back of the lorry: the silver model of 'The Old Curiosity Shoppe'; the white Grecian urn that would be the perfect setting for the large sprays of rowanberries in their season; my set of Cézanne prints. . . . The lorry came to an abrupt stop. I looked at the driver questioningly. He was staring aghast at the little wooden bridge spanning the burn which surged and rumbled over the green grey rocks into the loch.

'I'm not taking this lorry over that thing,' he said flatly.

I was appalled. I had to admit the fragile appearance of the bridge and recalled that when I had first travelled the Bruach road I had had serious doubts about its suitability for anything but the lightest of vehicular traffic. Since then I had seen loaded lorries, buses and even a steam roller negotiate it with absolute safety. There was a thumping from the back of the lorry and in a moment the two recruits appeared beside the cab. They looked at the bridge suspiciously and agreed with the driver that it didn't look safe.

'The bus goes over it regularly,' I said brightly. 'And coal lorries with a couple of tons of coal.'

The driver shook his head.

I visualized myself and my furniture being abandoned beside the loch miles from Bruach. I wondered what on earth I should do.

'Well,' volunteered one of the men, 'you canna' turn round and go back, there's nowhere to turn.'

Thank God for that, I thought.

The driver looked momentarily panic-stricken. The two men walked along to the bridge and tried jumping up and down on it, cautiously at first and then with growing confidence. The driver decided to go and inspect it for himself and soon all three of them were trotting up and down the bridge with serious concentration.

'It takes a lot of heavy traffic,' I called out.

'Aye?'

'Aye!' I confirmed.

The driver came back. 'I can try it,' he said timorously.

'Wait now,' commanded one of the men, pointing to one of the smaller struts of the bridge. 'This piece is broken.' He pulled a piece of parcel string out of his pocket and painstakingly tied the two halves of the strut together. When that was accomplished he waved the waiting lorry forward.

'We'll walk across,' they offered magnanimously, 'that'll lighten the load.'

'Aye?' agreed the driver dubiously.

Their apprehension had its effect on me and I too climbed down from the lorry.

'Every little helps,' I comforted treacherously.

With stiff-faced pessimism the driver inched the quaking lorry across the bridge, his relief on reaching the other side showing itself in a little burst of speed that sent an exultant spatter of gravel and dust up from its tyres. He waited for us to get back in, but first I ran back to the bridge. I had a camera with me and under the pretext of taking a photograph of the burn I focused it on the string-tied strut. I still have that photograph. It shows plainly the two halves of the strut bound firmly together—the string is tied in a lover's knot!

There was a covey of Bruachites at the cottage to unload the van and after a couple of hours of heavings, pushings, questionings and teasings the furniture was installed and we were waving good-bye to the driver and his men who, much impressed by the repeated assurances of the villagers as to the enormous loads carried over the little wooden bridge and fortified by a tip and a couple of drams of whisky apiece, seemed not at all dismayed by the prospect of the return journey.

It was some days later that Morag, who had devoted much of her time to helping me straighten things out, sat with me in the kitchen drinking tea. 'Everywhere looks beautiful just,' she murmured happily, 'and so tastily furnished,' she added, looking as though she might at any moment take a bite out of the settee. I was really quite taken with the way things were looking myself. 'Now that you're near settled and you've got your gramophone, you'll have to give a party,' she said.

'I'd already thought of that,' I said. 'I'll have to ask the grocer if he can get me some drinks. I used up the last of mine on the removal men.'

'Oh, you'll not get whisky from him, mo ghaoil,' she informed me flatly. 'He hasn't got an explosives licence.'

Though there was still a certain amount of renovation needed inside the cottage I had to abandon work on it temporarily so that I could start cutting a supply of peats for the winter. Peat was still the main fuel used in Bruach though all but a few diehards were beginning to use coal in addition to the peats which their deep old-fashioned grates consumed ravenously. Coal supplies, however, were erratic and depended very much upon the caprice and commitments of the undertaker who ran the business of coal merchant as a sideline and who seemed to think it would be as indelicate to offer a ton of coal before it was needed as it would be to offer a coffin. Any order for less than a ton per household he would decline arrogantly, even when rationing elsewhere was at its strictest, and not until he had collected firm orders for the minimum number of tons needed to coax a coal boat from the safety of a Glasgow wharf would he dispatch the order. Weeks later, when a sufficiently derelict puffer, looking as though the only reason it had managed to make the trip was because it was trying to run away from itself, came chugging and wallowing its laden way to the Island pier, the undertaker would hastily enlist volunteers and croft work would be neglected while the men went off to unload. The coal was tipped in half-ton scoopfuls straight from the boat into lorries which then took it to the consumers, the different tons being separated by odd bits of cardboard or sacking which would of course be blown away or shaken down among the coal before the lorry had gone more than a mile or two. The unloading of a 'puffer' was always a merry affair with Gaelic oaths and jests flying about as thickly as the coal dust itself. It was a regular practice of the men to try to fling one another's caps into the lorry just at the moment the coal was being tipped in and there was much mirth both at the dispatching and receiving ends when this was successfully accomplished. But the trophies one might discover in one's coal were not confined to caps: as the same pier was used for unloading coal as for unloading fish, it was not at all unusual to find fish hooks, fish heads, bits of seaweed and crab claws on one's shovel; though the fact that after some stoking one's kitchen became redolent of a guano factory was more often the result of the loaded lorries having to pass through a passageway locally termed 'bomb alley', where hundreds of gorged seagulls wheeled in ecstasy and extruded indiscriminately. When unloading was completed the volunteers, black all over, would return home to clean themselves up and to have their clothes well sprinkled with the louse powder they used for the cattle. The Bruachites maintained that coal was full of fleas and houses close to the pier were said to become infested whenever a coal boat was unloading.

Thus was one's supply of fuel obtained and the disadvantage was that if one had ordered a couple of tons or so and it turned out to be of poor quality then one was stuck with it. I discovered this for myself the very first time I took a delivery of coal—two tons of it—at the cottage. My suspicions were aroused at first sight. Good coal usually looks bright and brittle; this stuff slid off the lorry in flat shaley-looking slabs that made almost a metallic noise. When I put some on the fire it lay there sluggishly, defying heat or flame to ignite it; the chimney blew down smoke, no doubt in protest at the filthy stuff going up it. It was easily the least combustible fuel I had ever seen. Somewhat exasperated I got on the 'phone to the undertaker. He was not at home, I was told, but a voice I had never heard before and most emphatically never wish to hear again asked me in rich Highland accents if it could be of any help.

'I wanted to know if there was a chance of getting hold of some coal,' I said.

'More coal? Surely, Miss Peckwitt, you took two tons of coal last week just. What have you done with that?'

'I'm building a castle with it,' I retorted acridly. 'I want to talk about coal, not this rubbish.'

'Indeed, and isn't it terrible stuff? My own mother was saying herself just last night that she might as well carry dung from the byre and try will it burn.'

'Well, that's an idea anyway,' I conceded. 'I suppose if this was India we might be able to do that.'

'Do what? Use cow dung? For fuel, you say?'

'So I believe.'

'Indeed then, they must have very inflammable cows out there. I don't think it would work here at all. Supposing you tried mixing a little peat with the coal.'

'I have tried,' I said. 'It helps, certainly, but even so there's very little heat from it.'

'Ach, but you English,' the voice chided patiently, 'you're always complaining of feeling the cold.'

'It's no good sending me stones to keep me warm,' I retorted.

'No, indeed.' From the mouthpiece came the faintest of sighs. 'Well then, Miss Peckwitt,' the voice suggested blandly, 'will I come out myself tonight and have a damn good try?'

The months of April and May are regarded as being the best time for peat cutting so that the peats will have a chance to become thoroughly dry before the wet spell which can be relied upon to reach the Hebrides by the end of June or early July. This year a faltering spring had delayed all the croft work and the hiccoughing cuckoos were already warning us that 'June was nearly away with the calender' before a spell of fine weather was confidently predicted and Morag and I were able to set out together for the area of moor reserved for the village peat cutting. We followed first the track through the glen which, after years of agitation, the County Council had been persuaded to widen so that vans and lorries could reach some of the more isolated crofts where hitherto supplies had had to be carried by the women. Work on the project was slow and to all appearances involved the men in nothing more strenuous than chipping caves in rocky outcrops so as to provide shelter for them when at their card games.

'My, but you're busy,' Morag called as we passed a couple of them absorbed in scratching noughts and crosses on a face of rock.

'Aye.' They spared us a glance of tepid interest and then returned to their game.

'Indeed, I don't know why the County bothers to give them picks and shovels,' said Morag. 'I think it must be more for company than use.'

'They don't seem to do much work,' I agreed.

'Their main work is dodgin' the Gaffer. They wake him up in a mornin' to report for work and once they've done that then every time his back's turned they're out with their cards or else away up the hill with Donald's ferret. I canna' count the number of rabbits he's puttin' on the bus every mornin' since he's been working on the road.'

I glanced up towards the top of the hill and sure enough saw a straggling bunch of figures who looked as though they might be roadmen.

'You'd think,' I said, 'that they'd want to do some work occasionally, if only as a change from doing nothing.'

'That's just what Erchy told them now,' replied Morag warmly. 'Says he, "I'm sick of cards, cards, cards, I'm off to do some work," he says, and nobody stopped him!'

Bruach's peat glen was a sad, desolate-looking place, scarred by peat hags, some long neglected, and pocked with dark pools. The crofters, though they may not have cut peats for years, jealously guarded their rights to hags used by their forbears, their claims frequently encompassing quite large areas. Those who did rely on peat for fuel were continually forced to take out new hags further afield as the old ones became exhausted, and as a consequence it was usually the poorest and least accessible hags that were regularly worked while the best hags, close to the track for easy transport, were reserved for people who would never cut peat again, either because they were in the money or in their graves.

The only hag available for me was naturally one of the inaccessible ones. We turned off the track in its direction, the sodden moor squeaking protest at our every step. The previous day rain had fallen heavily and the hills, marble black against a paling blue sky, were still veined with white rushing burns whose muted thunder pressed at our ears. Now, the fresh-laundered sun was kindling the torches of asphodel into golden flame and coaxing the limp bog cotton to dry its plumage in the frisky breeze that sent contingents of ripples scurrying across the moorland pools.

' 'Tis a right day for the peats,' said Morag, 'but if this wind drops the clegs will eat us.'

'I wish there was a better path to my peats,' I said as we jumped dark drains and wallowed in spongy moss.

'Right enough,' replied Morag, 'but a few years ago you might have been glad of it.'

'How?' I asked.

'Indeed, but it's only a few years just since the scholars had each to take a peat with them to school every day for the fire and it's no the hags back here they'd be taking the peats from. No, it was always the easy ones nearest the road they took instead of their own. There was plenty of miscallings and skelpings about it in those days, but they never stopped them. My own bairns was as bad as the rest.'

My peats had already been 'stripped' for me by Erchy, which means that he had taken off the thick matted top layer of heather roots and turf, exposing the soft black peat. Stripping is traditionally a man's job and I was heartily glad it was so, for the widow Mary, who had given me the use of the hag, had confided that she believed its toughness had helped her husband into his grave. ('Ach, if you'd seen the man she had,' said Morag, who would have liked to cull the substandard of any species, when I told her; 'nothing but a long drink of gruel and his trousers near fallin' off the backside of him for want of somethin' to hold them up.') In Bruach, the fact that a job is heavy or strenuous did not necessarily mean that it was classed as a 'man's job'. It was, as I soon found out, mostly the women who did the heavy work of carrying and lifting, no matter what their age, shape or condition, and they seemed to pride themselves on their ability. The first time I saw an able-bodied crofter watching indifferently while his wife laboured under the burden of a boll of meal (140 lb.) I was provoked to the point of remonstrance. When, a few days later, I saw the same crofter meeting his dressed-up wife off the bus after a day's shopping on the mainland and chivalrously carrying her shopping basket, I was speechless. But gradually I grew to accept such things, so much so that I was only amused when I heard that Alistair Beag, a lazy man even by Bruach standards, had been taken to hospital after rupturing himself when trying to lift a load on to his wife's back. And then came a day when an old gallant, seeing me carrying home a sack of peat, said admiringly, 'My, my, but you have a good back for carrying,' and I was startled to find I had accepted it as a compliment.

Morag and I took turns at the cutting and throwing out of the peat, as we had done when I had shared her cottage and she was teaching me the essentials of a crofting life. I could of course have cut peats by myself, but it would have been a slow business. One cannot hurry peat cutting, but two people can establish a rhythm that more

than halves the time and the work. I unashamedly enjoy working at
the peats and not only because of a certain squirrel-like tendency which
even in town was sometimes difficult to repress. It is satisfying to be
mining for oneself; to be one's own coal merchant; to know that the
harder one worked in the spring—always provided the weather played
its part—the bigger fires one could indulge in when winter came. I see
the glow of the fire in each peat as it is cut and tell myself: so many
to keep my feet warm; so many to keep my back warm; now we
have cut enough to burn for an hour; now for a day.

Peat cutting is one of the most companionable and one of the
messiest jobs in the world. The cutter cuts; the soggy, chocolate-brown
slices tilt into the waiting hands of the thrower out; there is a dull
thud as the peat hits the heathery ground, releasing the scent of crushed
bog-myrtle, or, if the aim is not particularly good, there is a resounding
smack, succulent as a Louis Armstrong kiss, as it lands on its predecessor. The mud spreads up your arms—over your ankles; the sun beats
on your back or your face depending on whether you cut or throw;
the wind blows comfortable coolth. As you work, you and your
companion discuss tranquilly the problems of your neighbours, of the
country, of the world and, as the heather becomes progressively patterned with peat, you drift deeper into philosophy. So engrossed do
you become that you do not notice that the wind has subsided briefly
until the vicious clegs fasten on your bare limbs and you forget philosophy and filth and slap at the beastly things until you are a pattern of
chocolate-brown yourself.

We stopped for lunch. In books on crofting life I have seen delightful photographs and descriptions of tablecloths being spread on the
moor for the crofter families' alfresco meal while at the peats. I look
upon them with the utmost scepticism. Perhaps it was the custom years
ago; perhaps it was by arrangement with the photographer. Certainly,
I have never seen it happen in Bruach, nor have I ever met anyone who
recollected it happening. Why a crofter wife who normally sees no
necessity to set a table for a meal in the house, let alone use a tablecloth, should make work for herself by taking a tablecloth to spread on
the moor when such a dirty job as peat cutting is involved I cannot
understand. Morag and I pulled bundles of moss and wiped our hands
to a uniform brown and ate oatcakes and crowdie and peat. We
cupped our hands and drank water from the well where a family of

robbers were said to have disposed of the bodies of their victims. It was very good water. And then we started cutting again. A normal supply of peats for a household not using coal is nine good stacks, which means some thousands of peats. We reckoned we cut at the rate of about ten a minute—six hundred an hour—and we carried on until the breeze dropped away completely, the sun was threatening to dehydrate us and we could no longer stand the onslaught of the clegs.

'I'm badly needin' a cup of tea,' said Morag. We straightened our backs, shouldered our tools and retraced our path to the road.

Work on the road had made no noticeable progress during the day. Some of the men, under the eye of the now alert Gaffer, were chipping languidly at the rock while others were loading the chippings into a lorry with a deliberation which suggested that they were rationing the number of pieces on their shovels before attempting to raise them from the ground.

'Hear the Gaffer gettin' right mad with them,' said Morag with evident relish, 'and isn't my fine fellows enjoyin' themselves. Tormentin' him till they have him hoppin' about like a hen on a hot girdle.'

The Gaffer was an ex-seaman and his vocabulary when provoked was reputed to make the hills blush. We coughed and talked louder than was necessary as we approached and the abruptness with which his stream of abuse ceased was equalled by the alacrity with which the men ceased their work. He was a short, leathery old man who walked about with his hands tucked into his waistcoat and with the air of someone looking for a place to spit. It was rumoured in Bruach that he was a secret admirer of Morag's and as he turned to greet us his thick lips were stretched in a fatuous smile.

'Wass you at the peats?' he asked superfluously.

'We was till this minute,' replied Morag. 'But the clegs was murderin' us once the wind dropped and we could stand it no longer.'

'Aye, right enough,' agreed the Gaffer, 'they'd be bad at the peats. And yet can you believe it they can come all round me and I've never been bitten yet. It's funny that now, isn't it?'

'It's no funny at all,' interpolated the driver of the lorry. 'Clegs is teetotal. One sup of your blood and they'd die of alcoholic poisoning.'

The Gaffer's capacity for drink was phenomenol and always a source of awed comment and speculation in Bruach. It was said that when he had been ill the previous year the hospital had found it

necessary to allocate to him a special blood group—White Horse. It
was said that the doctors had found it necessary to wear gas masks
when taking a blood sample for fear they would get drunk on the
fumes. But, despite his addiction, it was rare for the Gaffer to make an
exhibition of himself. He imbibed in the seclusion of his hut and only
the men who, with true Gaelic warm-heartedness, hovered around to
see he did himself no harm, witnessed and reported the state he drank
himself into. The only time I was aware of his being even moderately
inebriated was when I had been a passenger on the bus one evening
and we had got stuck in a snowdrift. Spades were invariably carried
in the back of the bus for just such a contingency and the male passengers each took one and set to work to dig us out. All day a blizzard
had been blowing but now, though the wind had dropped, the snow
was still falling with steady menace. It was bitterly cold and the men
were too wrapped up mentally and physically to notice the Gaffer,
whose reaction to having a spade thrust into his hands was to shovel
and lift, shovel and lift. This he did, loading snow enthusiastically into
the mails compartment of the bus through the open rear door and
inappropriately accompanying his exertions with a quaintly original
version of 'Fire Down Below' which he rendered with trumpet-tongued
disharmony.

The Gaffer's smile broadened reluctantly as the men chuckled over
the driver's badinage.

'Gaffer, go and brew up a cup of tea for the ladies, they'll be needin'
one,' Erchy suggested gallantly. 'And I believe I'll take a cup myself
while you're at it.'

'Tea!' The word burst from the Gaffer's throat like a gas jet
extinguishing itself with its own ferocity.

'Aye, tea,' the voice repeated. 'Aren't you always tellin' us what a
great one you used to be for entertainin' the ladies? Well then, see
and go and brew up a cup of tea for them now while you've the
chance. An' don't forget us lot. We're damty dry with all the work we're
after doin', aren't we, boys?'

The Gaffer looked as though he was about to spit but catching
Morag's eye he swallowed and admitted cautiously: 'The kettle's
boilin' for my own tea. Will you take a cup if I made it?'

'In my hand,' consented Morag, whom I had never known refuse a
cup of tea no matter what the situation or circumstance.

He disappeared inside his hut as with startled winks and delighted chortles the men opened up their haversacks and produced a variety of sturdy mugs which they set out on an upturned wheelbarrow. We all made ourselves comfortable on boulders and on other upturned wheelbarrows. Cigarettes were handed round; pipes were lit. After a few minutes the truckling Gaffer reappeared carrying a steaming kettle and a tin of condensed milk; at the sight of his audacious henchmen placidly enjoying the interlude a certain lugubriousness was restored to his features but again he swallowed and forbore to comment.

'Careful with that stuff, Gaffer,' quipped one of the men as he proceeded to pour out black tea from the kettle. 'It's that strong I'm thinkin' it will be crackin' the cups.' As I accepted a cup my stomach quailed at the thought of drinking it. Under the pretext of waiting for it to cool I lazily transposed the mosaic of gravel caught in a cleft of rock beside me and watched everyone else alternately gulping tea and extracting suicidal clegs from sticky cups. The pleasantries between Gaffer and men continued unceasingly, and I was able to take advantage of a particularly amusing volley to tilt my cup surreptitiously into a convenient hillock of moss.

'It's queer to me,' said Morag, as she finished her tea and stood up, 'why you folks don't use gelatine for blowin' up all this rock, save havin' to chip at it day after day like you're after doin'.'

'My God,' breathed the Gaffer piously, 'I'd have no head left to think with and no legs left to run away with if you put gelignite in reach of these buggers. Why, that man, there,' the Gaffer went on, pointing an accusing finger at Neilac, 'he came near to killin' me with his pick yesterday, never mind gelignite.'

'It was an accident,' retorted Neilac complacently; 'and anyway, what's it matter if I did kill you; you'd still keep wrigglin' like an eel, there's that much of the Devil in you.'

'If you killed me first and then stripped the skin off me, my bones would keep on movin',' retorted the Gaffer, who seemed to accept that his body was just a collection of bones laced together with whisky.

Murdoch, an indomitable old man who could always be found where there was money to be made no matter how trivial or how hazardous the effort involved, was perched on a section of up-ended culvert pipe looking at his watch which he took from a tin in his pocket.

'Yes, what is the time?' Morag asked him.

'Wait and I'll tell you,' muttered Murdoch, still studying his watch.

'How that man knows the time with a watch that has the minute hand so short you can't tell it from the hour hand I don't know,' said the Gaffer.

'Indeed, if I watch it long enough I can see one of them move,' replied Murdoch.

'That's not what you're here for,' expostulated the Gaffer, jumping up and giving Murdoch a push in the chest that sent the old man buttocks down into the culvert pipe. 'Get that lorry finished loadin'.'

'Here, here, man,' remonstrated Murdoch indignantly, 'I canna' load a lorry with my arse tight in a drainpipe. Have sense, man.'

Laughingly the men pulled Murdoch out of his predicament and sauntered back to their work.

' 'Tis five o'clock then,' announced Murdoch as he returned his watch to his pocket.

The men froze animatedly and awaited the Gaffer's corroboration.

' 'Tis no more than five to,' he said firmly. 'Get on with it.' Watch in hand, he urged them on to fill the lorry and as the minute finger touched the hour he took a whistle from his pocket and blew. The men with picks arrested their strokes mid-way; the men loading tilted their shovels so that the chippings slid back on to the road and then they threw down their implements, collected their jackets and bags and hoisted themselves on to the lorry.

'Look at that,' called the Gaffer caustically. 'In a big enough hurry to knock off at night they are, but never one of them here on time this mornin'.'

'That's a lie!' Tom-Tom, an excitable muddle-headed little man, squeaked in protest.

'That's as true as I'm here,' asseverated the Gaffer.

'It's a lie, I'm tellin' you,' spluttered Tom-Tom, jumping down from the lorry and confronting the Gaffer with all his five foot nothing of bristling indignation. 'I was here in good time. I know because I jumped straight out of my bed when I heard the wireless time and indeed I came out in such a rush I left the door in bed and my wife wide open.'

The faces of the men remained impassive and the Gaffer checked a wheeze of laughter before setting his face into a scowl which he bestowed upon the driver who, with one hand in his pocket, was trying nonchalantly to crank his lorry.

'What like of a man is that?' asked the Gaffer contemptuously. 'Tryin' will he start a lorry with one of his hands stuck in his pocket.'

The driver put both hands into his pockets and regarded the Gaffer coolly.

'Who's grumblin' about my hands bein' in my pockets?'

'I am,' exploded the Gaffer.

'Well, at least my hand's in my own pocket,' retaliated the driver, the grin plucking at his lips belying the testiness of his voice. 'You keep your grumblin' till you find them in your own pockets.' He stepped up into the cab and gave a long pull on the self-starter which coaxed the engine into a clatter of activity. The men lifted their hands in farewell gestures that ranged from the sickly to the regal as the lorry jogged away round the bend.

'Look at them,' commented Morag acidly; 'wouldn't you think it was to a convalescent home the lorry was takin' them.'

Just Hector

'Tsere is a tsing,' said Hector appealingly. 'A tsing in tse shed at tse back of tse house, will mend it. Callum said I would get it if I wanted it.'

I took a deep breath and the key of the shed from the drawer and accompanied Hector to ferret out his 'tsing'.

Within a few months of having bought the cottage from Callum I was getting thoroughly tired of having his name quoted in exoneration of their actions by those who descended upon me with predatory intent. Callum, it transpired, had hurriedly disposed of everything movable in and around the cottage as soon as I had popped up as a prospective buyer. There had been a useful store of peat in one of the sheds which I had thought would help me through the winter but a week or so after I had settled in when, I suppose, the unmistakable blue of peat smoke had been seen eddying from my chimney, visitors had come in the night with sacks and appropriated the lot. Had I been a Gael I should either have nursed my grievance until there was a chance to retaliate or I should have referred to it obliquely, perhaps blaming the fairies. I did neither.

'Why did you come in the night and take peats from my shed?' I taxed the offenders.

'Indeed they were no your peats at all,' they retorted loftily. 'Callum said we could have them a while ago, but we left them till we would get a chance to move them.'

'Then why couldn't you have told me and taken them in the day-light instead of coming at night?'

'Why? Did we frighten you? Ach, we're awful sorry. If we'd known you were going to be frightened we would have come some other time right enough. We just thought we wouldn't disturb you.'

Similar appropriations happened every other month or so to begin with. A pair of wheels and an axle which I had annexed for making into some sort of a box cart were claimed immediately I made known my intention and I had to endure being thanked effusively for having looked after them so long. A boat-hook and a pair of oars were spirited away when it was discovered I was looking around for a dinghy; a sack of fleece which I had envisaged having spun into knit-ting wool likewise vanished. Always the excuse was 'Callum said . . .'. I padlocked the shed eventually and though admittedly the claims decreased they have not ceased altogether during the years, and I am still apprehensive that the massive lump of oak which was once an engine bearer in a boat and is now my mantelpiece will some day be recognized and desired by someone with an irrefutable claim to it, or that I shall wake up one morning to find the cattle breakfasting in my garden because the shafts of a cart which make the gate to keep them out have been requisitioned for their original purpose.

By far the most persistent claimant was Morag's nephew, Hector, who had now returned to Bruach with his wife and child to settle on his aunt's croft. Before his return Hector had been rather a shadowy character, rarely alluded to by Morag or anyone else until he had met with the accident, the alleged effects of which were bringing him back to Bruach. Once it was known he was coming his name was soon on everyone's lips. His transgressions were remembered and related with glee. Hector was the son of Morag's sister who, according to Morag, had married a real bad man, English of course, who had soon left her to bring up their son as best she could. She had brought the boy to the home of her parents and there let him run wild. Morag strongly disapproved of Hector's upbringing.

'My sister didn't believe in skelpin',' she lamented to me. 'She used to say you can't knock sense into a lad's head by thrashin' his backside, but I was always after tellin' her that sense can work its way up from the bottom to the top same as everythin' else in this world.'

It seemed however that Hector had not entirely escaped thrashing.

'Always takin' the day off from school to go fishin' he was,' Erchy told me. 'One mornin' he went fishin' off the Black rock and he fell into the sea. He was near drowned but for Big Willie bein' out in his boat and pickin' him up in time. He was brought into school. Ach, we thought he was dead right enough, but the teacher turned him over and squeezed a lot of water out of him. By God! The teacher was that mad with him as soon as he came to he lay him across the desk and thrashed him till his pants steamed. That cured Hector of drownin' and of playin' truant from school, I can tell you.'

Hector's main claim to notoriety though, as everyone admitted, was his success with women.

'Hell, what a man he was,' Erchy told me reverently. 'Used to carve his initials on every rock he'd taken a women behind, and when we go after the deer in the hills we keep comin' across these "H.M.Ss" chipped all over the place. Makes you feel hot to see them there's that many. Honest, he's as bad as the stags themselves, that man.'

'Perhaps marriage has changed him,' ventured someone, but from the way the suggestion was received it was obvious that no one really believed Hector could change appreciably.

I naturally expected to meet an Adonis, but when Morag brought him to my cottage I was confronted by a middle-aged man, with thinning black hair and with a pale, marrow-shaped face, carelessly shaven and deeply lined between nose and mouth. He was tall and well made but he drooped despondently over his stomach and jumbled his arms and legs about when he walked. He had, however, a pair of very beguiling blue eyes, a charmingly shy smile and a unique gift for making every woman he paid even the scantest attention to feel that she was someone very, very special. He exerted a little of his charm on me that day and I succumbed immediately, despite all the warnings I had been given. I was soon deluding myself that never again should I have to wait for someone to do for me the little jobs that were beyond my capabilities; that Hector's strong arm would always be ready with help whenever I needed it; that I should always be a welcome guest aboard his boat; that a fish would be procured for me, one way or another, whenever I might express a fancy for one. For hours after he had gone I glowed with satisfaction.

The very next day Hector came and enlisted my help to haul up his boat for repairs. *Wayfarer* was a thirty-two foot motor-boat, heavily built and deeply keeled, and I felt rather as though I were taking part in an ill-matched tug-o'-war when I was harnessed, along with most of the able-bodies in the village, male and female, to a thick rope and exhorted repeatedly to heave. We strained and sweated, our feet shifting and skidding on the shingle, while all the time Hector, who had to keep an eye on a 'tsing', appeared to do nothing more strenuous than caress the boat's stern.

A few days after the boat hauling I started clearing out my sheds and Hector, who had proffered help, stepped in only to assert his claim whenever I discovered anything useful and to magnanimously bestow on me anything that was not. I soon found that most of what I thought I had paid for had been previously disposed of to him by Callum – even an old log basket which had been woven for me by a friend, but which he confidently asserted was one of his grandfather's unorthodox creels. I found too that while he was not averse to sitting in the kitchen drinking innumerable cups of tea, his capacity for which was even more impressive than his Aunt's, he melted away like the mist when I gave the slightest hint that I should like some help. He would sometimes go fishing if I agreed to row him about while he dangled a line, but it was in Hector's company that I was able to prove that the old fisherman's belief: 'If a red-haired woman crosses your

path when you are going out fishing you may as well go home because
you will not catch a fish', is no idle superstition. A red-haired woman
once crossed our path and Hector promptly abandoned me and any
ideas of fishing and took off in pursuit.

There were undoubtedly times when Hector's behaviour was
infuriating, yet I could no more have vented my spleen on him than I
could have thrown a stone at a blackbird stealing the strawberries in
my garden. He was weak, but he was lovable, gentle, philosophical,
and so kind-hearted that the word 'no' simply did not come into his
vocabulary. Sooner than make someone momentarily unhappy by a
refusal he would promise faithfully anything at all, without having the
slightest intention of keeping his promise. If anyone reproached him
he assumed an utterly dejected air, his blue eyes would open wide and
he would start to explain haltingly how some 'tsing' had prevented
him from keeping his word.

Hector could be in turn gallantly attentive, shy and gangling and
guilelessly candid. In a moment of confidence one day he whipped up
his shirt and showed me the operation scar on his stomach and seemed
disappointed when I did not whip up my skirts and show him mine.
Though he came to regard my cottage much as a second home and to
feel that he knew me too well to address me as 'Miss Peckwitt', he
could never permit himself the familiarity of using my name (Gaelicized
as 'Lilac') or the diminutive 'Becky' by which I am known to my friends.
In conversation he referred to me as 'she' with a nod in the direction
of my cottage or my presence. If he wished to attract my attention
for any reason, he would sidle up to me and give me a companionable
slap on the behind. This aversion to using my Christian name persisted even when he adopted the disturbing habit of kissing me good-
bye. He would lumber across the kitchen towards me, fling his arms
around me and, because I dodged expertly, land a kiss somewhere
on the back of my neck. It was the utterly simple, warm-hearted kiss
of a child, or of a brother or sister, grateful for understanding. At first
I had wondered if I should permit it but it was gradually borne in upon
me that every time he kissed me good-bye some tool or other useful
article disappeared from the cottage on loan. Once it was my nail
brush and when it was surreptitiously returned I realized from the
smell in the bathroom that it had been used for scrubbing the 'berries' off
'berried' lobsters which are not allowed by law to be marketed. Once

it was my toothbrush which came back reeking of oil and petrol, no doubt after having been used to clean a 'tsing' in his engine. Another time it was my paraffin drum because his own had developed a leak. Dusters he collected and stowed away in his boat much as a park attendant collects waste paper and I grew accustomed to seeing my cast-off under and outer clothing wrapping greasy tools or used for swabbing down decks. Though eventually I came to accept this good-bye kiss as pure camouflage, at first there were times when I rebelled at his perfidy and avoided his embrace. Then he would slouch away and not return for several days or even weeks. The last time I had practised such an evasion Behag, Hector's wife, had come to see me the next day. Behag was a fat, pallid voiced, sagging little woman whose only interests in life seemed to be her child, her retinue of cats and the knitting of colourful pullovers for her husband. She was curiously placid and remained completely indifferent to her husband's affairs unless they were right under her nose and even then she evinced only tolerant amusement. I liked her tremendously and thought she deserved so much better than she had got but she was content with the way things were. As she got up to go, which is the time all Gaels reserve for the offhand disclosure of the real reason for their visit, she had asked anxiously: 'Were you cross with Hector last night, Miss Peckwitt?'

'Yes, a little,' I had admitted briefly.

'And last Thursday week, no it wasn't Thursday but Friday. You were cross with him then too, were you not?'

'Perhaps. I can't remember.'

'I can,' she had said sorrowfully. 'I can always tell.'

'Can you? But how?' I had asked.

'Because if you won't let him kiss you good-bye, he comes home and he kicks the cats,' she had told me with infinite pathos.

Today, Hector wanted a 'tsing' for his engine. It was time his boat was launched for the summer tourist trade, he said, and though he had scraped and 'bottomed' her and patched any leaks with tingles he was now having trouble with the engine. My shed was by now reasonably tidy. If only Hector had shifted the boxes of ancient engine parts he so much cherished I might have been able to whitewash it and fit it out for its eventual use as a dairy. He tipped up one of the boxes, cascaded wheels, nuts, washers and unidentifiable lumps of rust on to the floor and scrabbled through them. I watched him unhelpfully.

'I wonder at you, Hector,' I said. 'You've had such a lot of work to do on this boat and yet you told me you spent quite a long time looking for a good one when you were in Glasgow.'

Hector sat back on his heels and clasped his chin with rusty fingers. 'Well, you know how it is,' he explained slowly. 'You go lookin' for a boat like you go lookin' for a wife. You wander from place to place having a good look first at one and tsen at another. If you find exactly what you want and tse price is right, tsen you say, "Ach, she's too cheap, tsere must be somsing wrong with her," and like as not you end up with gettin' the worst.' He bent again over the scatter of things on the floor and extracted an object which seemed to give him some satisfaction.

'I'll just try will tsis do,' he said. 'I'll need to come back and clear up tsese tsings for you.'

That was the last I saw of him for about a week.

When he came again I was at the far end of the croft from the house, trying my skill at building up a collapsed drystone wall. Hector must have seen me but he sprackled across the croft with the deceptive aimlessness of a hen on her way to a secret nest.

'You're busy,' he greeted me.

'Yes. Are you any good at building up walls, Hector?'

'No indeed, I was never any good at it, tsough I remember my grandfather always used to say to keep my middle well filled.' He teetered one or two of the stones I thought I had wedged in position but he was too polite to comment.

'She looks as tsough she'll make a nice day yet,' he murmured.

'You think so?'

'Aye. Too nice for a funeral, anyway.'

'Whose funeral?'

'Well, you see, an uncle of Behag's has died and he's bein' buried today and Behag tsinks I should go. What do you tsink yourself?'

'If Behag thinks you should go she's probably right,' I replied. 'But how will you get there if the funeral's today. The bus has gone long ago.'

'Well,' he admitted, 'tsat's tse way of it.'

I realized that I was going to have to insist on taking him in 'Joanna'.

'Ach, it's no right. I'm givin' you too much trouble,' he said as I expected him to.

'Not at all,' I replied, as he expected me to. 'How soon do you want to go?'

'I was wonderin'. You see I have a box of mackerel I got tsis mornin' just and I tsought maybe if we could put it in tse back I could sell it to one or two of tse hotels on tse way. If we could start out early enough, say in about an hour's time.'

I left my stone-building and went to get myself and 'Joanna' ready, not really sorry to be taken away from my work for a day out even if it were for a funeral. The service was to take place at the hospital where the old man had died and I should not be expected to attend it. It was just a matter of taking Hector up, collecting him after an hour or so and then bringing him back. At least, that is what I thought in my innocence.

All dressed up in his best blue suit and cap, Hector was waiting by the gate of Morag's cottage when I stopped 'Joanna'. He lifted the box of fish into the boot and came and got in beside me. Morag and Behag, colourful figures in the silvery morning sunshine, waved to us from their work on the croft.

'Tse cailleach tsinks it's goin' to rain,' said Hector as he settled himself. 'She's wantin' to get all the tatties cleaned before she comes.' I wondered fleetingly if it really was at Behag's insistence that Hector was dashing away to her uncle's funeral.

Our run was extremely pleasant. The sun spent long periods in moody retirement but the rain disported itself only across the out-lying islands, and left us alone. Hector pointed out a hotel and asked me to drive round to the back door. He disappeared inside and ten minutes later came out again followed by two very capable-looking ladies, one carrying a white pail and a cloth. They went round to the boot, some discussion went on and they all three went back into the hotel. I stayed in 'Joanna'. Hector soon came out, wiping the back of his hand across his mouth, and rejoined me and we drove on to another hotel where much the same thing happened. Hector finally emerged, once more wiping his mouth and growing noticeably more benign. At the third hotel, once the transaction was over, I was invited by the housekeeper into the kitchen for a cup of tea, an

invitation which by this time I was very glad to accept. The kitchen of
the hotel was large and cool and refreshingly clean. A long white
wood table, scoured to perfection, ran down the centre; at one end
was a tempting-looking tea-tray laid for two and at the opposite end
there was a scale and a large dish of silvery trout. The grateful smile
and the words of thanks I was uttering died away as I stared first at
the trout and then at Hector.

'Hector!' I ejaculated hoarsely. But Hector sat with his knees locked
girlishly together, rubbing the palms of his hands slowly up and down
his thighs, and except for a couple of furtive glances in my direction,
concentrated his attention on the decorative fly-catcher which hung
from the ceiling. I was appalled. Here I had been driving round with a
box of illicit fish in the boot of my car and everyone who had seen
me and the friends and relations of everyone who had seen me would
be quite certain that I was in this poaching business up to my neck. I
was so shocked at his treachery that I drank little and ate less of the
'strupak' that was offered me and even that gave me indigestion.

'Hector,' I upbraided when we were outside again, 'I can't forgive
you for this. You've really gone too far.'

'Ach, but nobody worries about a bit of poachin' nowadays,' he
soothed. 'So long as it's not too much. And someone else would
have tsem if I didn't take tsem myself.'

'You could have been honest with me,' I said. 'You could have
told me they were trout, not mackerel.'

'Ach, well now, surely you'd know tse hotels wouldn't want to be
buyin' mackerel from me?'

'Are there any more left?' I demanded, abashed at my own stupidity.

'Just about four, maybe the half dozen. Ach, we'll not worry about
tsem. You can take tsem for your dinner.'

'You know perfectly well I wouldn't dream of taking them, but I
do want them out of my car,' I told him.

'Aye, tsen, I'll take tsem in a wee minute, but see and just come
with me to the shop now before tsey close. I'd like you to help me
choose a tsing for Behag,' he wheedled.

I yielded sufficiently to choose a lovely fair-isle jersey for Behag
and to help him buy some sweets for Fiona and Morag. We were on
our way back to the car when Hector muttered suddenly: 'Oh, my
God!'

'What is it?' I asked. He was staring across the road at a policeman who was standing near the kerb. My knees started to feel a little weak. I recalled hearing of poaching penalties which included the confiscation of the offender's car.

'He'll see me in a minute,' muttered Hector. 'Here, take tsese.' He thrust the parcels at me.

'What's the matter?' I asked agitatedly.

'He'll want to shake hands with me,' Hector replied. 'I used to know him well and I haven't seen him for years,' and then added by way of explanation, 'I should have asked to wash my hands at that hotel, tsese bloody trout scales stick like glue. Are tsere any on my cuffs?' He displayed his right hand liberally dotted with unmistakeable trout scales and then rubbed it vigorously on the seat of his trousers. We were approaching the policeman who, turning, caught sight of Hector. His face split into a grin as he came across the road to greet him. Hector's hand rubbed even more vigorously behind him. 'God!' I heard him mutter desperately.

The policeman put out his hand, grasped Hector's and shook it firmly. As soon as it was released Hector plunged both hands deep into his jacket pockets and kept them there.

'Tsat's a nice fellow,' he told me when everything had passed off serenely, 'but all tse same, if I'd known he was in tsis part of tse world I wouldn't have wanted him to see me.' I made no comment. 'I'd best go to tse service now,' he said when we were putting the parcels in the car and after I had discovered that it was early-closing day so that my shopping would not get done.

'You'll get rid of those trout before you do anything else, Hector,' I insisted firmly.

'Oh yes, aye, aye.' He heaved a big sigh. 'I wonder what will I do with tsem?'

'I was expecting you to to say you'd present them to the policeman,' I said with bitter sarcasm.

Hector looked at me with surprised approval. 'I could do tsat too,' he rejoined. 'I'll see will I get a wee bitty paper to wrap tsem in.'

'Hector,' I called despairingly, but he was hurrying away. I cringed behind the wheel of 'Joanna' and shut my eyes as he bowled confidently through the open door of the police station opposite. I opened them again when I heard him at the boot. He came round to the door of the car with a box tucked under his arm.

'I won't be more tsan a minute,' he assured me happily. I could not bring myself to ask him what had happened, but before very long he was back at the car again, whistling discordantly. 'I'm away to tse service now,' he said.

'What did you do with the trout?' I managed to ask weakly.

'Ach well, I went into tse pollis station and asked for him but tsey said he was takin' his dinner, so I went round to see his wife, and told her I wanted a wee bitty paper or a box to put somesing tasty in for her man's dinner. She gave me a box and so tsat's got rid of tsat lot.' He sighed. 'Well, I'd best be away,' he repeated, but he had reckoned without the grateful attention of the policeman who now came hurrying towards the car. Hector beamed complacently as once again his hand was grasped and shaken. But this time it was the policeman's hands that were covered in fish scales.

When Hector returned from the service he asked me if I would mind very much following the hearse back to the burial ground instead of returning straight to Bruach, as we had originally intended. Behag's uncle, he explained, had been something of a reprobate and had cut himself off from the family. As a consequence Hector had been the only mourner and he thought Behag would not like it if he left the old man to go alone to his final resting place. Though I suspected in this arrangement a design to await the evening opening of the pubs before returning home I fell in with it because it meant that I should be able to see part of the Island I had never seen before. While Hector supervised the actual interment, I thought, I could wander over the moors looking for wild flowers of which there might be some species not found in Bruach.

When we arrived at the burial ground we were met by a trio of indignant grave diggers who roused themselves from their perches on listing tombstones to inform us that they had not received a word about preparing a grave until an hour ago. They had the cows to milk and other chores to do tonight and they couldn't get the grave finished until morning.

'What'll we do with him for tse night tsen?' asked Hector

'We could put him in the church,' suggested one of the trio. The grave diggers and the driver of the hearse carried the coffin into the church. Hector watched them impassively.

'You know,' he said when we were seated again in 'Joanna' and heading for Bruach, 'I tsink tsat's likely tse first time tse old man has ever been in church in his life.'

I dropped Hector at Morag's cottage and because I was still feeling aggrieved over the business of the trout I made an excuse not to go in for a 'strupak'. I supposed both Morag and Behag knew that it was a box of poached trout Hector had loaded into my car that morning but as no Bruachite really believes poaching in moderation to be a crime they would have assumed that I also knew and approved.

I had barely finished feeding my poultry and having my own tea when Hector sparked in through the gate in a new electric blue and viridian pullover. He came with a saucer of fresh-made butter from Morag and really sincere offers to help me with one or two jobs which he knew perfectly well I had already done for myself. He sat on the bench watching me as I cleared the table and washed the dishes, too ashamed and embarrassed to keep up a conversation but humming every now and then to show me how much at ease he felt. I had some letters to write and I wished he would go but I could not bring myself to say 'I mustn't keep you back', which is the accepted Gaelic way of telling anyone 'For goodness's sake, go!' My expression must have been a little forbidding because he tried several times to draw a smile from me by telling me feeble jokes. At last he could bear it no longer.

'I wish I hadn't made you cross with tse fish,' he said miserably.

'Oh, I suppose it's all right,' I conceded stiffly.

He got up and lumbered towards me, his arms outstretched. I remembered the cats, and capitulated.

Beachcombing

ONE of the chief delights of living in Bruach was that there was always an excuse to go rambling along the seashore in search of drift-wood for kindling. To negotiate much of the tide line one needed to be fairly agile. It was a matter of leaping from one slippery rock to another whilst wearing equally slippery gumboots; of wallowing ankle-deep in sodden tangle; of wading through shell-strewn pools,

and sometimes climbing up steep barnacle-encrusted rocks to skirt
the incoming tide. To me it was all sheer glory. With the sharp clean
smell of the sea filling my nostrils, the roaring of the breakers in
my ears and the astringent caress of fine spray on my cheeks I was
content to wander for hours. The dominant motive was always to gather
driftwood, but it was difficult to resist the fascination of collecting a
few limpets or winkles to smash and feed to the waving tendrils of
the anemones in the colourful pools, or turning over a stone to watch
the green crabs scuttling to fresh hiding places. There was always
plenty of driftwood and one began by collecting every piece and making
little piles along the shore to be collected on the return journey, but
always, a little farther along, there were choicer pieces of driftwood
than those one had already gathered and so one continued acquisitively
until there were far too many piles to be carried home and one had to
select the most desirable pieces and leave the rest, hoping it would be
there another day.

Apart from driftwood, the assortment of objects washed ashore was
limitless. Tins of American shaving cream (which Morag reckoned
was splendid for washing Hector's sweaty socks); plastic cups; letters
in bottles (very unromantic ones); oars; brooms; deck shoes; cans of
paint. It was doubtless due to the finding of half-full tins of paint that
the walls of my cottage had been such a peculiar colour. Once I found
an undamaged vacuum flask which I use to this day. Once a necklace,
and once, very fortuitously, a full tin of dripping. My bread-board is
the door of a ship's locker; my door-stopper is the vertebra of a whale
which visiting small dogs frequently linger to gnaw and visiting large
dogs determinedly try to appropriate. My most treasured find to date
is merely a piece of driftwood, part of the branch of a tree, but beautifully sculptured by nature into a classic representation of a female
figure.

Many of my neighbours were dedicated beachcombers, sometimes
spending stormy nights in convenient caves so as to be the first to
pounce on any trophy the sea might bestow – no doubt kept warm by
the unflagging hope that it might be a cask of whisky. I can recall someone
finding a sack of flour which he claimed as quite fit for use because
the flour on the outside formed into a paste which had kept the inside dry.
Another found a box of candles which were certainly useful. From
washed-up crates I have been given onions that were so impregnated

with salt they needed none in the cooking, and grapefruit that were un-
eatable for the same reason. Such things as bales of rubber were at one
time considered lucrative finds because in addition to the pound or two
reward from the Receiver of Wrecks quite high freight charges could
be claimed for rowing them to a convenient spot for collection. So
long as these charges were paid undemurringly the Bruachites continued to increase them until they reaped the reward of their own
avarice, the authorities deciding that the recovery of the rubber was
no longer economical. So the bales were left to rot on the shore along
with the pit props, trawl bobbins, net floats, old coconut husks and fish
baskets, which are the inevitable adornments of the tangle-woven
shingle.

In the autumn, after the hay and corn had been stacked for the winter
and all the peats had been carried home from the moor, the Bruachites
would go winkle picking for the Billingsgate market. Often when
beachcombing I met groups of them working their way along the
shore, filling pails with the shiny blue-black shells; carrying the full
pails to tip into the waiting sacks, and carrying the full sacks up the
brae to the lorry. There was supposed to be good money in winkle
picking and as my budget was a tight one I thought I would like to
try my hand at it. Wearing about three pullovers and with scarves
round my middle, round my neck and over my head, and oilskins
topping everything, I took my pail and followed the outgoing tide.
Crouching low, my back towards the sea, I turned over rocks, seeing
the sparks fly and smelling the sulphurous smell as they crashed against
one another and exposed the writhing cat-fish, the spotted gunnels,
the myriads of sandlice and the pathetically few winkles beneath them.
Working my way up again, with the incoming tide chasing me inexorably, I discovered colonies of winkles, but before I could get more
than a couple of handfuls of them into my pail the tide was swirling
around my boots and over the winkles so that I could no longer see
them to pick. A good picker can pick a bag or more in a single tide,
that is two hours before and two hours after low tide. After a few days'
practise I found I could manage about a pailful and there are five
pailfuls to the sack. To get even that sad quantity I had to concentrate
so much that when I shut my eyes at night I saw only troves of black
glistening winkles and in my dreams reached out to gather them. I
did, much to the astonishment of the other pickers, achieve a full

sack eventually, but only by waiting another ten days or so for the next daylight low tide. In due course I received a cheque from a Billingsgate firm but the amount, after payment of the crippling freight charged by the railway was no reward for my worn nails and sore chapped hands and the ache in my back caused by wrestling with stubborn boulders. Yet the Bruachites looked forward eagerly to the beginning of the winkling season and I came to understand their eagerness. The work could be squeezed in between the other chores and the money earned was always welcome. For some of the younger folk who could not go to the mainland for employment because of having to look after the old folks it was often their only chance to make some pocket money. They winkled, as they did so many things, in happy, chattering groups, never wandering out of earshot of one another; but though the sea stays comparatively warm until after the New Year, to crouch down for four long hours on an exposed shore, drenched with spray and with a bitterly cold wind hurling its icy daggers between your shoulder blades is a desperate way of earning money. Particularly when you have not even the comfort of a hot bath to look forward to, but only a couple of kettles of hot water—if you first go to the well and fill a pail.

The most inveterate beachcomber and by far the speediest winkle picker in the village was 'Euan, the son of Euan, the son of Euan', the Gaelic pronunciation of whose name approximated to a long drawn-out yawn. He was a bright-eyed old man, always picturesquely dressed in an old peaked cap and a seaman's jersey—relics of his days on a yacht as a steward—and his legs bound round from the top of his tackety boots to above the knee with thick rope so that they resembled the legs of the Michelin Tyre man. He flatly refused to have anything to do with gumboots, saying that they 'cooked his feets', and stoutly maintaining that his strong hill-boots and rope puttees were more effective in keeping out the wet because it did not get a chance to leak over the top. Yawn had made some of the most envied finds on the shore. It was rumoured that he really had found a large cask of whisky and that he had secreted it somewhere in the hills.

'He's never without a dram in the house,' Postie assured everyone earnestly. 'And his pension doesn't give that to him.' As everyone was sure that Postie was bound to know exactly what Yawn's pension gave him they accepted the story of the secret cask and whenever Bruachites did not know what to do with themselves, as on Sunday afternoons, they were inclined to form into little bands of searchers for Yawn's treasure. As they always came back sober they obviously never found it.

Yawn lived with his two sisters on the croft next but one to my own. Brother and sisters were all over seventy and of the three only Yawn himself could read or write or tell the time. His two sisters were utterly unlike. Sarah, the younger one (seventy-four), was a delightfully bobbish little lady doing all the housework and most of the croft work with never a word of complaint except that she was tormented by her corns. The elder sister, Flora, had once been a lady's maid and could not bear to forget it. She sat stiffly all day long in a chair, commenting disparagingly on everything Sarah did and doing absolutely nothing else. She could neither read nor write. She did not knit, sew or darn. She would not move from her chair to cook or even to lift a boiling kettle from the fire. What little food she ate she took on a plate on her lap. She was not ill, nor paralysed in any way, but she had sat so still for so long that the chair seemed to have merged itself into her body and her body into the musty black skirts that clung to the floor as raggedly as old wainscoting so that one would not have been at all surprised to see mice darting in and out of them. On her head she wore the most impressive tea cosy of hair it is possible to imagine. It completely overbalanced her face and marvelling at the edifice I sometimes wondered if the weight of it was responsible for the apparent fixation of her body and mind. It was said in Bruach, and I can well believe it, that she had not touched her hair with comb or brush, soap or water, for over forty years; that if it was investigated thoroughly the remains of at least half a dozen hair nets and several hundred hairpins would be discovered, all completely enjungled. Some recalled with awe that before her hair grew quite so matted she had been seen to reach for the toasting fork that used to hang beside the fire and scratch her head with it, but now either her head had ceased to itch or she had mislaid the toasting fork.

Flora spoke in a flat voice, her remarks being addressed invariably to the fire.

'You have cut your hay.'

'Aye.'

'You have stooked it.'

'Aye.'

'Your wife and your daughter helped you.'

'Not my daughter.'

'Your daughter was away on the bus.'

'No, she was out fishing.'

'She caught fish.'

'Aye.'

'You will bring me a fish for my dinner tomorrow.'

'Aye.'

'Sarah, you will cook the fish the way I like it.'

'Aye, sister.'

And so it would go on. She never asked a question and never answered one. She was waited on hand and foot and there appeared to be not a thing organically wrong with her. She was the most uncannily idle and least endearing personality I have met in my life.

Because of Flora, I think, the household was not much visited by the Bruachites, and so until after I had gone to live in my cottage I had not come much into contact with either Sarah or her brother. One dark autumn morning however, when the mists were soaking into the hill tops and the hooded crows were croaking their 'grace before meat', I looked out of my window to see a big strong calf grazing on my croft and trailing behind him what looked like a tangled clothes line. I went out to investigate and the calf, seeing me, started to run away, dragging the clothes line after him. I was horrified to hear a groan. I started forward again cautiously, but again the calf bounded away from me. Sarah's voice from the bundle of clothes came tremulous but clear.

'If I keep a hold of the chain perhaps you could cut the wee bitty rope with a knife.'

I rushed back into the house and got the sharpest knife I could find and as Sarah hauled on the chain I managed to grasp the beast's head rope and slash it quickly. The calf bounded away and I ran to Sarah.

'He pulled up his stake,' she explained. 'And then he got it round my foot and came galloping away down here dragging me after him.' She was half lying on the wet ground, her face chalk white. 'I think the beast has broken my leg for me,' she murmured lucidly and then fainted clean away.

I ran for Yawn and told him what had happened.

'She's broken her leg, you say?' he asked with patent disbelief. Yawn had always regarded me with suspicion; I think he was afraid that I too lurked in caves in stormy weather and might some time beat him to the choicest finds. 'I think so. But do hurry and come and get her.'

'Ach, I suppose I'd best take the wheelbarrow,' he said ungraciously, leaving his half-finished cup of tea. Flora made some derogatory remark in the direction of the fire. I paused for a moment thinking that if I explained Sarah's predicament to her carefully it might rouse her into action and wondered vaguely if she did attempt to rise whether the chair would cling to her back, like the shell of a snail. Her vacant immobility quelled the impulse and I hastened back to Sarah.

'Could we get her to my cottage?' I suggested to Yawn.

He bestowed upon me and my cottage a look that should have annihilated the two of us.

'No,' he replied, 'I'll take her to my own house. I don't suppose there's much wrong with her.'

I hated to see Sarah bundled into a wheelbarrow and trundled over the rough ground, but I realized that under the circumstances it was the best thing we could do. She obviously must not be left there until neighbours could be recruited to find a stretcher. Had we decided on that course I felt that some tactless souls would have been certain to turn up with the bier from the burial ground. So Yawn struggled and swore his way home while I hovered meekly behind. A scholar on his way to school came running up to us enquiringly and I sent him with a message intentionally to Morag and unintentionally to everyone else in the village. I 'phoned for the doctor, who came and affirmed that Sarah had indeed broken her leg.

Sarah, quite conscious again, sighed with a certain amount of relief at the news. 'It's thankful I am he didn't have the leg right off me,' she said, displaying her left hand minus its thumb which as a young girl she had lost in a similar accident.

'In that case you would have to have a beautiful new wooden one,' I soothed jovially.

'Ach, like that man with the fire brigade,' she rejoined. 'I believe he keeps a wooden leg some place.' She looked up at the doctor anxiously. 'I will be able to walk again, doctor, will I?'

'Of course you will,' he assured her. 'You'll have to rest it for a while but you'll be as good as new in a few weeks' time.'

'I wish you'd cure my corns for me as quickly while you're about it, doctor,' she said wistfully.

'What are you doing with corns, Sarah?' demanded the doctor.

'It's they big boots I have to wear. Yawn won't let me have gumboots, and they're after puttin' terrible corns on my feets.'

'Very well, I'll send you over something for them,' promised the doctor, who was new to Bruach and did not yet know that Sarah's corns were almost as old as her feet.

'I wonder was he just sayin' that about my leg to comfort me?' she asked us dubiously, when he had gone.

'Now, Sarah!' admonished Morag, who had by this time arrived on the scene full of bracing sympathy and competence. 'Why would he say that if he didn't mean it? Sure, she's been a good leg to you all these years and there's no reason for thinkin' she won't be a good leg to you again.'

Sarah nodded slow acquiesence and stroked the broken leg with tender pride.

Despite her age, Sarah's leg did heal in a remarkably short time. While she was incapacitated I visited her often, taking her whenever I could pictures and photographs of the royal family, to whom she was touchingly devoted. So eager was she to hear of royal activities that whenever she could she stationed herself close to the timid-toned old wireless at news bulletin times simply to hear the Queen mentioned. Under her bed she kept several ribbon-tied boxes full to bursting with photographs she had cut from magazines and newspapers for over half a century, and whenever she had the excuse or the opportunity these were brought out and examined lovingly. The Queen Mother and her two daughters she particularly adored. 'Ach, the bonnie wee Scots lassie,' she would croon as she studied a photograph of the Queen Mother, and 'They sweet little darlings,' as she pored over photographs of the Queen and Princess Margaret as children.

When she was not gloating over photographs of royalty Sarah spent her evenings sewing, using, because her eyes were weak and she would not wear glasses, an outsize darning needle which her brother jocularly referred to as a 'boat-hook'. Flora's former mistress had left her trunks of ravishing evening gowns and it was strangely affecting to see Sarah's white head bent over lengths of pink taffeta or blue satin, her stiff, rough fingers stabbing the large needle in and out as she transformed the gowns into what she considered to be suitable day dresses for herself. I have seen her mucking out the cow-byre arrayed in sequin-spangled pink taffeta. I have met her on the hill, her swirling skirt of gold satin pulled high above her thin wool-encased legs which stuck out from her black tackety boots like sticks from a glue-pot. I have watched her winkle-picking attired in silver lamé and velvets, reinforced by old meal sacks.

By the time she was on her feet again Sarah and I were close friends. I had taken on the task of writing her letters for her, much to the relief of her brother who disliked letter-writing and considered he had quite enough to do to write his own. I sympathized with Yawn; living in isolated places demands an enormous amount of letter-writing, ranging from ordering a pound of sausages from the butcher to a new dress from the store. Yawn, who I suspected was really very fond of his younger sister though he never allowed his affection to show, had come by this time to accept me as not quite such a menace to his fortunes as he had at first believed. Soon he took to calling in at my cottage and presenting me with some of his trophies: a sisal doormat, which I was very glad to have; tortured lumps of paraffin wax which helped fire-lighting considerably; a life-jacket, and more than once a lump of venison which I had to believe was from a freshly washed-up stag.

'Yawn,' I asked him one day, voicing a fear of my own; 'have you ever come across a body on the shore?'

'Indeed I did once,' he admitted, 'and I was wonderin' to myself what sort of a beast it was till I saw it was wearin' socks.'

'I found a baby seal washed up the other day and that was horrid enough,' I said with a shudder. 'It very nearly cured me of beach-combing. I don't know what I'd do if I found a human body.'

'Ach, there's no need to do anythin' but let the tide take it away again,' he told me. 'We used to get four pounds for them but there's nothin' in it now.'

He watched me as I nailed an old piece of linoleum to the top of a tea-chest which I hoped to use as a coop for a broody hen.

'She'll no keep chicks warm enough in that,' Yawn pronounced, 'But I have in my shed what will do for you to cover it over. I'll bring some of it with me next time I'm passin'.' A few days later he brought me some suitable lengths of heavy felted material which I draped over the tea-chest.

'What do you call that stuff?' I asked him. 'It seems to be the ideal thing for the job.'

'Indeed I don't know,' he replied. 'It was just some stuff I got on the shore. In a big sort of tank it was, lots of it. I had Sarah make me a mattress of it and I can tell you I've never laid on a more comfortable bed.' I was dubious of its attractions as a mattress, but thought it possible that Yawn preferred his bed to be as tough and unyielding as himself.

'I doubt you'll have to nail it on for the storms,' he called as he shut the gate behind him.

'I shall probably do that in any case,' I assured him, but lazily left it for another time.

Some days later when Sarah came to have her letters written she brought the news that Yawn was in bed with lumbago. The doctor had sent him some pills but he was to rest in bed for a while.

'And there's the corn half-cut, and the hay still in cocks,' Sarah moaned. 'We'll be gatherin' in the corn at New Year. I can no understand it,' she went on, 'he used to have terrible rheumatics right enough but when once he'd started sleepin' on that new mattress I made him of that stuff he found on the shore he's never felt hardly a twinge.'

Hector and Erchy were persuaded to give a hand with scything corn while Sarah and I gathered and tied it into sheaves, and when it had spent the required three Sundays in the field we stacked it. Yawn was still confined to his bed.

My broody hen had hatched her chicks—three cockerels and two pullets, five out of a setting of a dozen eggs. The rest of the eggs were infertile.

'You'd best get yourself a cockerel that isn't so particular,' said Morag when I told her.

Autumn was bullied out of existence in a single night and when I went the next morning to feed my chickens, which had been growing strongly, I found the felt covering their tea-chest had been blown off and the tea-chest itself turned over. The valiant mother brooded the two remaining chicks in its shelter. I resolved to go to the mainland that day for some nails to secure the felt.

The following morning was bright and, as I now knew, treacherously calm, and after breakfast I collected my nails and a hammer and went off to make for the broody hen the home she deserved. As I went out through the door the policeman, his peaked cap catching the sunlight, was opening the gate.

'You haven't a dog, have you?' he asked.

'No,' I said. 'Why?'

'There's been complaints of sheep worryin' and I'm wantin' to see all the dog licences,' he told me.

He saw my hammer and nails. 'What are you going to do? Building yourself a new house, is it?'

I took him and showed him the tea-chest and the cheeping chicks and the indomitable old mother. His eye lit on the strips of felt that lay in readiness.

'Good God!' he gasped in horror. 'Where did you get that stuff?'

'On the shore,' I replied, a trifle bewildered.

He picked up a piece and examined it very gingerly. He passed his tongue over dry lips.

'What are you thinkin' of doin' with it?'

'Oh, I'm going to nail it to the top of the tea-chest to keep it warm and dry. It's good heavy stuff too, it will add a bit of weight.'

'Like hell you are,' said the policeman. I noticed he had gone pale.

'How much of this stuff have you got?' he demanded.

'Oh, just that you see there.'

'Has anybody else got any?'

'I don't know,' I replied evasively. Yawn would never forgive me if I betrayed the fact that he was sleeping on a mattress of it.

The policeman became authoritative. 'You'll not touch that stuff at all,' he ordered. 'You'll leave it there till I get my instructions what to do with it. I'll go away and 'phone now. Don't you touch it on any account. It's highly dangerous. A find of this kind should have been reported right away.'

'Dangerous?' I echoed incredulously; the stuff looked harmless enough to me. 'Why, what is it?'

'Gun-cotton,' returned the policeman abruptly.

'Good God!' I gasped, even more horror stricken than he had been.

He loped off to where his car was parked and as soon as he was out of sight I flew to Yawn's house in mounting panic. I rushed into the kitchen. Sarah was out and for the only time in my life I had reason to be grateful for the impassivity of the figure beside the fire. It recalled me to my senses.

'Is Yawn in bed?' I asked with enforced calm.

'In bed he is.'

I raised my voice. 'Yawn!' I called. 'May I come in?'

'Come in.' I went through into the bedroom. Yawn was propped up with pillows, placidly smoking his pipe. I was not wholly conversant with the properties of gun-cotton but my stomach nevertheless turned over at the sight of him.

'Yawn,' I began, 'can you get up without help?'

'Ach, no indeed. My back's that bad I canna' even turn myself over. The pain's terrible. Terrible just.'

'Then you'll have to be got up,' I insisted urgently. 'That mattress you're sleeping on . . . .'

'Indeed it's a grand mattress right enough,' he interpolated. 'An' I believe it's helpin' a lot to cure me of this lumbago the doctor says I've got. It's doin' more than his pills is doin' for me anyway. I was helpless at first; helpless like a child, but just lying' here in my bed I'm feelin' myself gettin' better every day, though the pain is still awful bad when I move.'

I took a deep breath. 'Yawn,' I enunciated carefully, 'the policeman has just seen some of that stuff your mattress is made of and he tells me it's explosive!'

'Never!' protested Yawn.

'Yes, he's certain it's gun-cotton and highly explosive.'

Yawn's body stiffened and his eyes fixed themselves unwaveringly on my own. He must have seen my panic.

'Get out of the room, woman!' he directed me sternly. I stood blinking at his tone of voice. 'Get out of the room while I put on my trousers,' he shouted at me. I fled.

Now if any doctor reading this is sceptical about the efficacy of gun-cotton for curing rheumatism and lumbago I should like to assert here and now that within five minutes of acquainting him with the news I saw Yawn outdoing the man of Bethesda; he not only took up his bed but he ran and ran and ran to where his croft ended in a cliff that overhung the sea. He flung the mattress over the edge and then went back to the house where he finished dressing himself. Then he went out to feed the cows. He has never suffered from lumbago or rheumatism since.

Sarah came hurrying back into the kitchen, full of consternation.

'My brother, my brother!' she gasped out. 'What has happened to him?'

I told her.

'Well, well, and wasn't he always after sayin' it was wonderful stuff,' she said.

Flora looked at the fire. 'He is himself again.'

'Aye, sister.'

'He has thrown away his bed.'

'Aye, he has so.' A bawl from a calf took Sarah scurrying outside. Flora wanted to be told why Yawn had thrown away his bed so she repeated her statement.

'He has thrown away his bed.'

'Yes.' The old 'cailleach' was getting no indulgence from me.

Her empty eyes slid from the fire to my face and back again.

'It was damp.'

'No, not damp.'

'It was no longer comfortable,' she vouchsafed.

'It had become very uncomfortable indeed,' I agreed, and wished I could ask the policeman to leave me a sample of the gun-cotton to offer her as a cushion.

Work on the Croft

THE sky was effervescing with lark song, the rocky outcrops of the croft were starred with wide-eyed primroses and every convenient wall or hedge near each house was draped with blankets out for their annual sun bath. I sat in my garden trying, very inadequately, to put the tints and demi-tints of the dry-stone byre with its thatched roof, its blue door and its hem of tiring daffodils on to paper, when I heard the

voice of Yawn calling to me from the garden gate on which he was
leaning with contorted self-possession.

'I was wonderin' would I get a hand to plant the potatoes,' he asked.
'The tractor says he'll be here at ten o'clock in the mornin'.'

I told him I would certainly help plant his potatoes and carried on
with my painting. Yawn, gaining confidence, came into the garden and
looked over my shoulder. 'My, but it's mighty like,' he exclaimed with
unflattering surprise.

I murmured non-committally, being well aware that my artistic
skill is negligible. I venture to paint only when I feel compelled to
preserve, strictly for my own enjoyment, some scene that I fear I may
never see again. In this case I knew that the thatched roof of the byre
was rapidly disintegrating and that it must soon be replaced with
corrugated iron. I knew too, from shivering experience, that in
winter the dry-stone walls merely acted as funnels for arctic draughts
and fine snow and that if Bonny were ever to have reasonably comfortable quarters they would have to be mortared and cemented. From
the point of picturesqueness I regretted having to replace the thatch,
but the prospect of the walls being mortared and thus denying access
to all the little birds which nightly shared Bonny's steading was indeed
a gloomy one. Admittedly, I rarely glimpsed the birds but, each
morning, the stall was so liberally betokened that I knew there must
have been at least a dozen of them snug in their secret roosts above
Bonny's warm breath. I liked to imagine the night noisy with their
cheeped 'gardyloos'.

'You know,' went on Yawn, 'there's some of these painters comes
here and sits around for days with their paints and when they show you
what they've done you'd not be knowin' whether it was the hills
themselves or some cocks of old hay that's been left out in the wet
you're lookin' at. Indeed, I've seen my cow paint better pictures with
his tail on the back of his stall than some of them. But that,' he made
an indulgent gesture towards my pad, 'that's like, right enough.' He
watched me for a few moments longer. 'You'll be after wantin' a nice
frame for it when you've done,' he suggested.

'Oh no,' I said, and firmly resisting further compliments I put the
finished painting inside an old blotter along with several others and
dismissed it from my mind.

The following morning again dawned sunlit and light-hearted with a brisk wind that coaxed the ripples of the bay into new-toothed baby smiles and as soon as I heard the noise of the tractor in the distance I pulled on a pair of gumboots and went to join the coterie of people who were already assembled on Yawn's croft. The cultivation of the land in Bruach could not begin until the cattle, which were allowed to graze the crofts from the end of November until the spring, had been driven back again to the hills, and so it was always well into April or even early May before spades were probing into the hoof-pitted ground and 'pliachs' were thrusting through the newly turned soil. There were no tractors in Bruach. Only one man still used the 'cas chrom', the old hand plough. Those who were lucky enough to possess a horse and considerate enough to feed it oats in the winter might be able to use it for the spring ploughing but generally the horses, left to roam the moors wild and unfed throughout the severe winters, were too weak to pull a plough by the time spring came round. For most of the crofters, the only alternative to digging was to await with that peculiar brand of patience inherent in the Gael the arrival of the itinerant Department of Agriculture tractor and, as the tractor's schedule, never a very strict one, was likely to be upset by weather and by mechanical breakdowns so that it might be late in the season before it reached the village, the noise of its approaching engine was always a very welcome sound indeed.

It was the custom for all the would-be hirers of the tractor to band together and help one another with their planting, not only because the tractor was charged by the hour or because of the ever-present fear that the weather might break but because in Bruach potato planting was, curiously enough, traditionally a co-operative task and it was entered into with something like a festival spirit. A string of women and girls, all with bright floral aprons covering their tweed skirts and all gumbooted like myself, were stationed along the plot when I arrived. Others were filling pails and bowls from the sacks of potatoes and fertilizers, their unrestrained chuckling and chattering adding yet more geniality to the day. The men, sombre in comparison yet equally loquacious, were carrying on their backs the last creelfuls of dung to the heaps dotted along the length of the plot. The manipulation of heavy creels of dung requires a certain amount of skill as well as strength. The men first removed their caps to save them from falling off and being buried in the dung and then, as they bent well

forward, they jerked up the bottom of the creel from behind so that
the contents spilled out over their heads. As every one of the men
showed a round, bald patch on his head when he removed his cap I was
forced to the conclusion that hair and potatoes do not respond to the
same fertilizers. When the tractor was ready to start ploughing, the
men, except for Yawn, took forks and plunged them into the heaps
of dung and, as the furrow was turned, they threw the dung into it.
Yawn followed, placing potatoes at regular intervals on the dung,
demonstrating with unspoken authority to the women who followed
him how far apart he wished the plants spacing. Those of us who were
not planting filled and carried pails of artificial fertilizer and, straggling
in the wake of the tractor like dilatory gulls, we circled each potato
with a handful of fertilizer. Sarah, who was supposed to be in the
kitchen preparing a 'strupak' for everyone, kept scurrying anxiously
from the house to inspect progress and to plunge her bare hands deep
into a pile of dung to add a couple of handfuls when she feared a potato
might suffer from lack of nourishment. She wore a sacking apron over
a plum-coloured velvet dress, the deep-hanging sleeves of which
were lavishly trimmed with flounces. The flounces were soon showing
signs of overnourishment.

When the last sod had been turned and the empty sacks had been
shaken out in the breeze, we sat on the grass waiting for the tractor-
man and those who had accepted the invitation to a 'strupak' before
moving on to a neighbour's planting.

'I could do with a cup of tea myself,' said Erchy, 'but I'm damty sure
I'm no goin' to have to talk to old Flora just so as to get it.'

'Nor me either,' panted Anna Vic who, despite her stoutness and
the shortness of her breath, was one of the nimblest workers in the
village.

'That old cailleach,' went on Erchy with strong disapproval, 'I
believe she'd still stay fixed if you snatched the chair from under
her.'

'Indeed yes,' echoed Anna Vic, with a giggle. 'Sarah was around at
our own house the other night askin' would she get a broody hen so
she could hatch out some chicks. I hadn't one, so I told her she should
try puttin' a clutch of eggs under Flora to see what would happen.'
She laughed apologetically.

'I believe they would have hatched too,' said Erchy, 'but I doubt you'd never be able to find the chicks supposin' they did. Not till they was grown hens anyway.'

'Aye, but, poor soul, it must be awful sittin' there with nothin' to look foward to from one year to another.'

'Nothin' but gettin' the flu' every winter,' corrected Erchy.

When the village potato planting was finished the tractor started to plough for corn. I was fortunately able to grow enough potatoes in my garden for my own requirements and also to provide Bonny with her evening mash of boiled potatoes dried off with oatmeal, which is the nightly fare of a cosseted Hebridean cow, but I yearned to see some of the matted turf of my croft turned into black earth to match the crofts of my neighbours and so I resolved to try growing a patch of oats. I had already learned how to tie and stook corn from helping Morag and I was fairly certain that I should be able to get someone to come and cut it for me when it was ready. So the tractor came and ploughed and Peter, always fiercely eager to oblige, came and broke down the sods by harnessing himself to some home-made harrows and dragging them over and over the plot. To the casual observer the sowing of oats looks ridiculously easy and when I used to hear Morag importuning various male relatives to come and sow corn for her I used to wonder why such an independent old woman did not undertake the task herself. Whenever there was an opportunity I watched the sowers at work. They appeared to do nothing more strenuous or scientific than to walk steadily up and down the plot scattering hand-fuls of seed from the pouch full of grain which they wore as a sling over one shoulder. I evaded acceptance of Yawn's offer without com-mitting myself to a definite refusal and, tying an old sheet over my shoulder and filling the pouch of it with grain, I went forth sowing. It was not long before I began to suspect that there was a good deal more to sowing corn than there had always looked to be. I paused to survey my work. In some parts of the plot the grain lay almost as thick as it lay in my pouch: in others it was as scant as if I had aimed each seed singly, like a dart at a dartboard. I gave up when I had covered a few more square yards without noticeable improvement in my aim and as soon as dusk came I surreptitiously forked earth over my efforts and humbly approached Yawn, who came the following day.

'I see you've been after tryin' to do it for yourself,' he rebuked me, for the birds had traitorously uncovered my attempts at concealment.

'Yes, I did, as a matter of fact,' I admitted with limp gaity. 'It always looks so simple when other people do it.'

Yawn grunted and started to sow, the grain scattering from each effortless swing of his arm with the conscientious regularity of spray from a watering can.

'I wish you'd tell me the secret of getting the seed to fall so regularly,' I said.

Yawn retorted with another grunt.

'Is there a special way of sowing so that the seed falls so regularly?' I persisted, for in spite of having tried and failed, it still looked remarkably easy.

'Yes, there is,' said Yawn reluctantly, not lifting his eyes from the ground. 'You must always see that you throw it five grains to the horse's hoof-mark,' an instruction which, considering the ground had been ploughed by tractor and harrowed by Peter, wearing gumboots, was only faintly enlightening. I stood watching him perplexedly while the shadows of gulls' wings passed unconcernedly over the plot. In the early morning the gulls would be stuffing themselves on the grain, abortively it seemed, for the locals maintained that the birds could not digest the grain and vomited it shortly after eating it. Still baffled by Yawn's technique I left him absorbed in his task while I went to put on the kettle for his 'strupak'. When I returned he had finished sowing and was himself watching Peter who had brought his graipe and was forking over the seed.

'You could get a sub-side-y on this ploughin',' Yawn told me. 'There's not been a plough on this croft for years and there's a good grant for it.'

'Oh, I hardly think it worth while,' I said. 'It's such a small plot.'

'Indeed, it's no small at all. I believe it's the same size near enough to my own piece and that's near an acre.'

'An acre? Not that plot we were planting the other day with potatoes behind the tractor?'

'Aye, that one.'

'That was never an acre, Yawn, or anything like it,' I contradicted flatly, after a swift mental rehearsal of the table of square measure.

Yawn turned on me a withering look that gradually grew less withering as he realized I might possibly know what I was talking about. 'Well,' he conceded with lofty defiance, 'it was an acre long anyway.' He stalked away crossly, not waiting for his cup of tea, but a day or two later when he had forgiven me for being right and wished to make amends he was back again at my door with a parcel under his arm.

'I have but what'll do a nice frame for the picture you were paintin',' he said. 'I got it washed up on the shore a day or two back just. It's lost its picture and I've had to put a wee bit board on the back and this bit chain I had by me to hang it. See and get your picture now and we'll try will it fit.'

Feeling rather touched by his thoughtfulness I went into the bedroom and got my painting and when I came back into the kitchen Yawn had unwrapped the parcel and was proudly holding up a very distinctive horseshoe-shaped frame enamelled in turquoise blue. I stifled an incredulous gasp and watched his face intently as he carefully inserted the picture between the backing and the frame. I swear there was no trace of guile in his expression. 'There now,' he said, holding it up for my inspection. 'Do you not think that looks fine now?'

With a tremulousness that he fortunately took to be modesty I agreed that it did indeed.

'It makes all the difference to a picture to put it in a nice frame,' he told me. 'Now, where would you like it hangin' and I'll put a nail in for you while I'm here?' I indicated a spot in the darkest corner of the room. 'Ach, but it'll no catch the light there at all. Folks will not see it there.'

'It's not a very good painting,' I demurred.

'Ach, it's no bad. No bad at all. What about havin' it here?' He held it up on the wall above the cooker. 'See now, there's a nail here all ready for it.' Silently I cursed the obstinacy of that one nail. Yawn stepped back to admire the effect. 'Beautiful just,' he commented. I echoed his admiration. 'I knew as soon as I saw the frame lyin' there on the shore that it was just the proper frame for your picture,' he assured me with solemn affability as he hurriedly took his leave, no doubt to escape the profuseness of my gratitude. Dear Yawn. How shocked he would have been had he suspected the double entendre of his last remark. But if anyone between here and America happens to have lost a turquoise blue enamelled lavatory seat they might be interested to know that it hangs in my kitchen above the cooker framing an amateurish representation of an old stone byre with a decaying thatched roof and a hem of tired daffodils. It looks beautiful just!

As spring advanced and the days lengthened to accommodate all the extra work it brought, peats were cut and dried and stacked; cows calved. Normally Bruach cows were left out on the hill to calve where they chose, the calves being left to run with their mothers until the rounding up for the autumn sales but, when the date for Bonny's calving drew close, Morag, who had never ceased to be as watchful over my interests as her own, advised me to bring her into the croft so that I should be able to keep an eye on her.

'You mind yon trouble our own Ruari had with his bought in heifer,' she cautioned.

I remembered the trouble very well. One evening whilst I was still living with Morag, Bella, Ruari's shy and untranquil wife, had rushed round calling distractedly for Morag to come and help because their new heifer was 'stuck up with his calf'. I was implored to go and 'phone for the vet. Some hours later, when I was sitting in my own room with my knitting and my nightcap of cider, I heard a knock on the door and one of the young village boys put his head round and said, with perfect seriousness: 'Morag's wantin' a clean sheet for the calf's bed.'

I could only echo his request uncomprehendingly.

'Aye, she's sayin' you will get one from the drawer up in the wee room.'

For a few moments I stared at the boy, trying to reconcile my knowledge of Bruach calf pens with the likelihood of a calf being put to bed in clean sheets in one of them. Deciding that the boy was probably playing some game of 'dare and do' and I was the chosen dupe, I grinned and relaxed into my chair.

'She's wantin' it right away if you'll give it to me.' The boy's voice was edged with intolerance.

'Are you sure it has to be a clean sheet?' I mocked, fully expecting to hear a burst of giggling from his cronies who I felt sure were bolstering him with their presence out there in the dark.

'Yes indeed.' His expression grew tense as I still made no attempt to go upstairs. 'Must I go back and tell her you'll no give me a sheet then?' he demanded testily. 'Will I tell her she must come and get it for herself?'

Against my better judgement I went up to the wee room and taking a fresh-laundered sheet from the drawer I thrust it into his waiting hands, resigning myself to the fact that if it was a hoax it would be all over the village by morning. I could, of course, have gone over to Ruari's and made discreet enquiries but as my presence would doubtless have added to the complexities of the situation it seemed unfair to pester them with my doubts. Morag had still not returned when I went to bed that night and the next morning when she brought in my breakfast she was looking as dishevelled as if she had spent the night outdoors in a gale of wind.

'Well, Ruari has a fine bull calf for himself after all the trouble,' was her greeting. I murmured suitably, waiting for the teasing which I was sure would soon begin. 'An' fancy Bella never havin' a clean sheet that would do the calf's bed,' she exclaimed disgustedly.

I answered her with a look of easily simulated amazement.

'Wasn't all she could find an old cover that the colours leaked out of when it got wet,' she enlarged. 'It would never have done for the beast. I would have been ashamed of myself.' She shook her head sadly over her sister-in-law's shortcomings.

'I thought the boy was playing a hoax on me when he came and asked for a clean sheet for the calf's bed,' I confessed ruefully.

'You did? Right enough he told me you didn't seem as if you wanted to give it to him. Why was that now?'

'I just couldn't imagine a calf being put to bed between sheets,' I told her. 'I still can't. It sounds so utterly unlikely.'

Morag suppressed a snigger. 'But, mo ghaoil, a calf's bed is what the beast lies in before he's born. What would be the English for it now?'

'The womb, you mean?'

'Aye, right enough, the womb. Well, that came away with the calf last night and we had to try would we push it back in again with a sheet. Some folk use a bag of straw but Ruari, he would have none of it. A clean sheet, he said, and nothin' else it had to be.' As she went into more gruesome details I realized that my appetite for breakfast – haggis and egg – was wilting rapidly.

'And you say everything's all right now?' I cut in desperately.

'Ach, aye. The vet had to do a wee operation on the calf but this mornin' when I sees him he was skippin' around on his legs as though there'd never been a thing wrong with him.' She poured herself a cup of tea and sat down. 'My, but that vet was tired before he was finished and that was at the back of four this mornin'.'

'It was a bitterly cold night too for this time of year,' I said, mentally experiencing the discomforts of the average Bruach byre.

'Aye, we was all complainin' of the cold though the vet was sayin' he was warm enough where he was.' She ended in a little hiccough of laughter.

'Why, where was that?' I asked innocently.

'Half-way inside the cow for the best part of the time, mo ghaoil,' she informed me with great relish.

So Bonny awaited her confinement on the comparative lushness of the croft, becoming more of a household pet daily. She was the nearest thing to the real old Highlander it had been possible for me to buy: shaggy, red-haired, with a black-ringed snout. Her horns were crooked.

'One of her horns points to Heaven and the other to Hell,' my neighbours said when they saw her. 'You'll find she's half angel and half devil.' But she was mostly angel. I could perhaps have regularized her appearance if I had taken Morag's advice which was to bake a large turnip in the hot peat ashes and clap it quickly on to the crooked horn, gradually coaxing it into position as it softened. I doubted if Bonny would take kindly to the treatment and secretly I was glad of her cock-eyed appearance because it made her more easily distinguishable from the scores of other Highland cattle out on the hill. I had embarrassed memories of volunteering to feed Morag's cows and of standing calling forlornly in the gathering dusk unable to tell one cow from another, until one of them had had the good sense to recognize me.

When Bonny did calve she accomplished it uneventfully. I went to pay her my usual morning visit and found she had a tiny replica of herself snuggling into her flank. Her eyes were dark and dilated with love and she lowed softly as I approached, but though she shook her wide horns at me in a cautionary way when I started to fondle the calf she was careful to ensure that they did not touch me. The first thrill of having a croft of my own had come when I held in my hand the first warm egg from my hens. Then had come the acquisition of Bonny; the first turned earth, and now Bonny's calf which was a sturdy little thing with a tightly curled light brown coat that reminded me of aerated chocolate.

Once all the village cows had calved, milk, which was always scarce in winter, became super-abundant. Crowdie was offered with every strupak and cream was not only served at every meal but was smoothed on the skin as an emollient for sunburn. As the days grew warmer and we discarded winter coverings, the clegs became aggressively familiar; weeds seemed to appear in full stature overnight, imperilling the young potato plants; the grass on the crofts grew long enough to ripple in the wind; the midges which outrival Glasgow bread and lavish Public Assistance as the curse of the Highlands, came in their hordes, vanquishing the clegs no doubt in the manner of 'greater fleas,' and tormented us as we hoed and earthed up our potatoes. The rainy spell of July came and went leaving behind it a lush carpet of growth that effectively camouflaged the stony soil and when, just about the time in English churches the harvest festival hymns were being rehearsed, scythes were brought out and sharpened: the hay harvest had begun.

All hay in Bruach was cut with scythes by the men. The spreading and cocking being left to the women and children until the hay was cured and ready to be built into winter stacks when the men again took charge. I had learned to scythe inexpertly but I could not keep up the steady swing hour after hour which is necessary to cut an appreciable amount of hay. If I were not to have to buy in for Bonny's winter feeding I had to have help. Erchy, on whom I could always rely for croft work, cut most of the hay aided by oft-promised, perfunctory and Morag-goaded assistance from Hector, but even so I began to find the spreading, raking, turning, cocking and re-spreading every fine morning rather more than I could manage alone. I discovered to my dismay that I was lagging behind my neighbours and though everyone assured me periodically that there was no hurry because haymaking could go on until the New Year if necessary, I went to see Peter's mother, Sheena, to ask if she could spare him to help me sometimes.

Sheena and Peter, though they worked the croft adjoining my own, lived at the farther end of the village. Sheena was old, totteringly agile, but thoroughly indomitable and she managed to keep Peter who, despite his simple-mindedness was possessed of exuberant strength and way-

ward fancies, in complete subjection. Her home with its heavy-lidded
thatched roof was one of the oldest in the village and her dim kitchen
exuded friendliness as uninterruptedly as its sagging stove exuded
smoke. The door was open, letting the blue peat smoke, tinged with
the smell of newly scorched flour, breathe out into the serenity of
the evening air and I waited for a few moments before making my
presence known, listening to Sheena reading aloud to Peter from the
newspaper in a halting baritone. She jumped up as she heard my voice,
dragged me inside and bustled around in her stockinged feet making a
'strupak', pausing every now and then to clap me on the shoulder to
tell me how hardy I was and to ask Peter if she had not been saying
to him just that day how she loved me like a sister. She began rooting
under the recess bed in the corner of the room and disinterred a brown
paper parcel tied with string. I realized with despair that I was once
again going to have to swallow a piece of special presentation shortbread which Sheena had once been sent from Edinburgh and which
she had since hoarded for honoured guests. The firm claimed on their
tins to have been making the shortbread for over a century and when,
on the occasion of my very first visit to Sheena, I had unsuspectingly
accepted a piece, I was immediately convinced that Sheena's tin was
one of the original ones. Since then, despite repeated invitations and a
genuine affection on my part for the old lady, I had purposely made
my visits rare ones, always in the hope that enough honoured guests
had called on her meantime to ensure my never being offered the shortbread again. It appeared, however, that the supply was inexhaustible
and I wondered how many more tins reposed in the scarcely explored
territory beneath the bed. Sheena's eyesight was poor and I could
easily have secreted the shortbread in my pocket had it not been for
Peter, whose gaze followed my every movement like that of a mes-
merized sparrow.

'Peter, take your stare off Miss Peckwitt this minute!' Sheena admonished him and thrusting the newspaper into his hands with a
gesture that made him wince she bade him look at the pictures. Peter
obliged with goggling eagerness until his mother, suddenly suspicious,
looked over his shoulder and snatched a double page of bathing beauty
photographs from him and substituted a veterinary catalogue. Above
its staid pages Peter's gaze fastened despairingly on my feet. Peter's
habit of staring fixedly at me was one of the most disconcerting things

I had to endure. Though I had lived in Bruach for some years I was acutely aware that my activities were still a source of unflagging interest to the inhabitants but they at least watched me covertly. Peter had not the wit to conceal his curiosity and whenever I appeared in sight he became so obsessed with watching me that he completely forgot whatever he was doing until his mother reminded him of it by boxing his ears. Though his attention was embarrassing the inevitable result was that watching Sheena and Peter trying to work together whenever I was at all visible was as entertaining as the antics of a couple of members of the Crazy Gang. Only that afternoon I had gone out to turn my hay and Peter, who had until then been steadily raking hay while his mother gathered it, suddenly caught sight of me. Immediately his raking had become so wildly abandoned that he had raked poor Sheena's tottery legs from under her and tumbled her into the hay before her shouts had penetrated his excitement and he had stopped long enough to allow her to pick herself up and rush at him to box his ears. The previous day they had been building a cock in a rising wind and Sheena had been running here and there gathering up bundles of hay in her arms and bringing them into the lee of the cock. So tired was she and so intent on getting the job finished that not for some time had she noticed that Peter, whose eyes of course were fixed undeviatingly on me engaged on a similar task, was grabbing each bundle of hay as she brought it and was flinging it ecstatically to the top of the cock so that the wind caught it and scattered it again for Sheena to gather afresh.

After the necessary preliminaries had been gone through I made known to Sheena the purpose of my visit.

'An' indeed Peter shall come and help you, mo ghaoil. Indeed he shall. He's a good boy though he is what you say in the English, "softly up the stairs". But you shall have him with pleasure, Miss Peckwitt. Just as soon as he can be spared from our own hay.' She did not consult Peter. 'An' he loves you, Miss Peckwitt,' she continued ardently. 'Is that not true, Peter? Are you not after tellin' me near every day how much you love Miss Peckwitt?' Peter nodded startled but vigorous acquiescence and under cover of their protestations I thankfully transferred the piece of shortbread to my pocket and embarked upon a fresh-baked girdle-scone, the appetizing smell of which had been filling the kitchen when I had first arrived. I cut short what seemed to be developing into a panegyric on my attractions and Peter's abilities by complimenting Sheena on her scones.

'Ach, mo ghaoil, but I threw them together just when I came in from the hay for the bread had grown such a beard with the mould that was on it. Indeed, I was sayin' to Peter it looked just like myself after yon hot spell we was havin'.' She struck her mouth with her hand. 'Ach, but I wish I had the right words and I could tell you. I could make you laugh if I had more English,' she said regretfully.

'But you are always making me laugh, Sheena,' I answered with perfect truthfulness.

'Well, glad I am to hear it, mo ghaoil, for laughter is as good for folks as a plate of porridge, and just like porridge everybody should have some every day.' She squeezed my shoulder emphatically. 'Well, I was tellin' you, my face got that sore with the sun and the wind that I just splathered the cream I'd been savin' for the butter on it and I sat out at the front of the house in the shade for I was gaspin' like the birds with the heat. I must have fallen asleep for mercy!, when I woke up and put a hand to my face it was covered with hair like a goat's. "Here," says I to myself, "what in the world has happened to me?" But then I see the hairs has come off in my hand.' She laughed noiselessly. 'What did I find with it all that my fine fellow Peter here was after tryin' would he cut his hairs and he'd had to come and sit out beside myself to do it, and the wind had blown his hairs all over my face so that the cream had stickled them.' She had been squeezing and patting my shoulder repeatedly while she was relating the incident and when she had finished she bent herself double with spasms of laughter that had worn themselves to shreds before they reached her throat. I laughed delightedly at her story but Peter, no doubt remembering the punishment he had received on that occasion, only watched his mother warily. 'Ach, mo ghaoil, but if only you had more of the Gaelic, I could tell you better the sight I looked,' she lamented again. So I laughed immoderately to please her.

The kitchen darkened as the sky composed itself for rain and stray drops came down the chimney to sizzle on the warm stove.

'That old chimbley never did keep out the piss properly at all,' Sheena explained pleasantly.

'Well,' I said, getting up from my chair, 'I suppose we really need the rain.'

'Right enough we do,' she replied. 'Indeed, did you ever feel weather as hot as it was this last week or two back?' she demanded hoarsely.

'It certainly was hot,' I admitted.

'My, but poor Peter's that burned through his shirt workin' in the hay that he's after goin' every few minutes to rub himself on the dyke the same as the cattles with the itchin' it's givin' him.' I caught a look of desperate appeal from Peter in time to stifle the sceptical comment I was about to make on the possibility of the sun burning through the thick flannel shirts which Peter wore perennially and recalled having seen him basking shirtless on a secluded part of the shore the previous Sunday when no doubt his mother had believed him to be in church.

I said I must go before the rain became heavy and Sheena, leaving Peter sitting in the deep gloom of the unlit kitchen, escorted me part way along the road, asseverating earnestly that 'the first fine day after the next,' I would get Peter for my hay if the Lord spared us all. She had not put on a jacket to accompany me and I pressed her to return home before she got too wet.

'Ach, a little rain will never wet me, mo ghaoil,' she asserted airily, but nevertheless she allowed me to go on alone. It was not until she turned away that I noticed she was still in her stockinged feet!

The rain continued all night, making it impossible to work in the hay the next morning, and I resolved to try to catch up on some of my house cleaning which had been neglected for the urgency of hay-making. I had just started to polish the floor when Sarah came to tell me that Bonny was bulling. She advised me strongly to take her to the bull straight away. I quailed at the thought of taking Bonny within a mile of any bull.

'Would Yawn take her for me?' I asked hopefully.

'Yawn would take her right enough but he's away on the bus this mornin'. His brother's havin' a funeral to himself today,' she explained.

Erchy and Hector would, I knew, be too busy with tourists and even if there had been no tourists Hector would have been too busy with all the pretty girl relatives who were staying in the village. I could not go to Sheena and ask for Peter because she had never permitted him officially to know the facts of life. I had to reconcile myself to the fact that if I was to have milk next summer I must take Bonny to the bull myself.

Long ago, when I had first come to Bruach, I had once encountered a large, shaggy, Highland bull standing in the middle of the high road with 'Monarch of the Glen' impassivity and I had, some time later, been an astonished witness to the spectacle of a young girl coming up behind the bull, slapping its rump with her bare hand and commanding it to 'get on there!' The bull had trotted off obediently! When I had come out of my petrified trance and the telephone kiosk in which I had taken refuge at first sight of the bull, I had determined that someday I myself would do, or try to do, exactly as that young girl had done. It was a resolution which seemed destined to remain unfulfilled, perhaps because it has subsequently been my misfortune always to meet my bulls face to face, a situation which is intimidating enough to wilt far less feeble spirits than mine. Now, on Bonny's behalf, I must go and scrape acquaintance with one. I led the docile Bonny on a short length of rope, experiencing increasingly the sensation that my torso was trying to disclaim kinship with my legs. At Morag's I called in, partly for a brief respite, partly to enquire whether she could tell me the bull's whereabouts.

'Surely, mo ghaoil, but it's lucky you are. He's away tomorrow in the float and Angus has him in on the croft till the lorry will come and get him. You'll only need to take the beast there.'

Fiona, Hector and Behag's little daughter, started to pull on her gumboots busily.

'Where do you think you're goin', Fiona?' asked Behag, with motherly indulgence.

'I'm away to take Miss Peckwitt to the bull,' announced Fiona firmly and neither Morag nor Behag appeared to find her intention at all extraordinary. Behag was always content to have Fiona in my company because apparently I was the only guardian the child did not try to elude. Fiona was a born roamer and tended to disappear for hours even when a strict eye was being kept on her. She was also the most intractable, unquenchable little bundle of independence I have ever come across and I most emphatically did not want her company today.

'No, Fiona,' I said. 'You can't come today.'

Fiona ignored my refusal and struggled with childish maladroitness into a cardigan.

'You heard Miss Peckwitt say you were not to go,' said Behag, with a helpless look at me and Morag.

'I'm away with her,' said the child imperturbably.

'Fiona!' interjected Morag sternly.

The only sign Fiona gave of having heard was to tighten her lips.

'You must stay with Aunty and Mummy today,' I told her, infusing decision into my voice. 'I'll take you for a walk tomorrow.'

Fiona's grey eyes regarded me implacably. 'I'm comin' with you,' she announced. 'Hurry now!'

Morag gave me an apple as consolation. Fiona demanded one also and she had eaten hers almost before we were back on the road again.

'I'll put your apple in my pocket for you,' she offered insistently as she threw away her own core; 'you can tell me when you don't want it.'

The sun had broken through the cloud to disperse the dampness of the morning and it grew hot on our backs as we climbed the stony track; flies buzzed around my head incessantly, pestering me only a little more than Fiona's unceasing questions. I was thankful for the temporary distraction of Angus's dogs racing to meet us as we reached the house where Angus's wife apologized for the absence of her husband and also for being unable to accompany us. She was leaning heavily on a stick, having, she said, cut her knee that badly she couldn't put her leg under her. The bull, she told us, was away down in the far park, a fact which, judging from her sudden interest, Bonny had already discovered for herself. She bawled and tugged at her head rope, dragging me after her. There came an answering bawl from the bull and when we reached the gate of the park I let go her rope and drove her speedily through, closing the gate firmly after her. Bonny stood coquettishly; the bull came cantering towards her. I lay on my stomach on a stony hillock at a safe distance outside the fence and waited, content to study all the secret things among the heather that only the lazy know. The clouds had finally yielded to the sun and the air was full of summery noises: the drawled comments of leisured gulls; the preoccupied hum of insects; the sibilance of the sea. My attention was concentrated on a brilliant green caterpillar ingesting a leaf when suddenly Fiona's voice broke into my absorption with shattering scorn.

'That's the silliest bull I ever see in my life,' she said.

Her interest in the proceedings was slightly embarrassing.

'Fiona,' I cooed, 'come and see the way this caterpillar is eating his dinner.' The lure was quite ineffective.

'That bull is a silly bull,' she repeated scathingly. 'That's not what he's supposed to do. Take a look will you?' She pulled impatiently at my shoulder.

I turned round. Bonny was standing happily chewing her cud while the bull, with his tail thrashing ecstatically, was down on his forelegs like a calf sucking contentedly at her udder. I stood up and Bonny turned on me a look that was eloquent of bewilderment and pleading.

'What will you do?' demanded Fiona.

'Wait and see,' I said crossly, and stepping over the fence I gave the bull a series of slaps on his rump. 'Get on with you!' I yelled at him, but not waiting to test his obedience I climbed nimbly back over the fence where, shaken by my own audacity, I clung panting to a fence post.

'That's shown him,' shrilled Fiona with untrammelled approbation. She turned to the bull. 'Why did you no do that before, you silly old thing!' she screamed at him derisively.

There was still a long afternoon left for working in the hay when I returned with Bonny so, after a hasty lunch, I went out and began shaking some of the dry hay from the smaller cocks into bigger ones. Peter, at work with his mother on their own croft, was picking the 'stickybuds' (burdocks) out of the hay and, catching sight of me, he flourished a large bunch of them in rapturous greeting. Sheena, who had been bending beside him, straightened herself just as his arm was descending from the greeting. The bunch of burdocks fastened themselves tenaciously to the old grey head. Peter's hands went to his mouth as he saw what he had accomplished. Sheena stood stupefied for a moment and then her hands went slowly up to her own head to assess the damage and then swiftly to Peter's head to administer a flurry of sharp slaps. So much achieved, the two retired to the dyke while Peter did his trembling best to extract the burdocks. For a long and clamorous time the operation continued until finally all the burdocks were removed. Poor Sheena remained seated dejectedly on the dyke but Peter, recovering from the strain of his ministrations, started to re-gather the offending burdocks. I wanted to persuade Sheena to come and have a quiet cup of tea with me to restore her spirits and with this intention I crossed the croft towards the dyke. Peter, whose attention had been temporarily torn from me, became aware of my approach and in a spasm of delight he flung the burdocks he had re-gathered over his shoulder. I gasped. Sheena screamed huskily. Peter turned round and his mouth dropped open as he saw what he had again accomplished. He took to his heels. Sheena, jumping up, tried to totter after him, calling his name savagely but, fearful of her wrath, he kept on running, with only an occasional backward glance. Sheena's hands went up to her twice-tortured head.

'God and Miss Peckwitt forgive me,' she said with both tears and anger shaking her voice, 'but I'm goin' to make a swear.'

And she did.

The Tinkers

'SURE with the spring they'll be here like the spiders,' said Morag emphatically.

She was speaking of the tinkers, those good-humoured, garrulous itinerants of the Hebrides who annually invaded the village, if not with the first breath of spring then very soon after its first pant, arriving about the same time as the young divinity students who spent their vacations peddling bibles and religious books to the crofting communities—an occupation which made sense of carrying coals to Newcastle—and taking the opportunity to do a little door-to-door evangelism. The crofters placated both by their patronage but for sheer entertainment value, the divinity students were simply not in the same class as the tinkers.

The attitude of the crofters to the tinkers, or 'tinks' as they are more often known, was both interesting and amusing. They despised them, they feared them, yet they welcomed them. They despised them because of the impermanence of their homes which ranged from sod huts to the backs of lorries; I sometimes thought that if Lord Nuffield had turned up in Bruach in a caravan he would have been labelled a 'tink'! They feared them because of a lingering belief in their supernatural powers; they welcomed them because, after the isolation of the winter, any visitors were preferable to no visitors, and the tinks with their gossip and their jokes leavened many a dreary hour. In addition to pots and pans, their multifarious bundles offered for many the only chance of personal shopping, so the crofters were prepared to open wide their doors and watch indulgently while their kitchen tables were transformed into miniature bargain counters and the ragamuffins of the road became high-pressure salesmen.

I wanted to buy a milk pail, hence my interest in the coming of the tinkers. Before Bonny had calved, I had equipped myself with all the paraphernalia necessary for providing a supply of milk, butter and crowdie, i.e. setting bowls, milk sieve, butter pats, etc., but some aberration had made me omit to buy a milk pail. There was no way of remedying the omission until I could get to the mainland and I was reduced meantime to milking into a shallow pudding basin which necessitated either my holding the basin in one hand while I milked with the other—a hand-cramping procedure—or else putting the basin on the ground and risking Bonny's using it as a foot-bath—a mishap which occurred all too frequently.

It was after just such a mishap one day when I was carrying a foot-bath of dung-mottled milk to the half-dozen hens, who now queued with disheartening expectancy whenever I went to milk, that Morag, who never used a gate or a path if she could insinuate herself into the garden any other way, emerged from round the back of the byre.

'Look at that,' I said, showing her the bowl. 'It's the third time this week this has happened. I do wish I could get hold of a proper milk pail.'

It was then that she had told me of the imminent arrival of the tinkers.

'I was hearin' of tinks in Neabost last week,' she reported a few days later. I said I must look out for them.

'You mind,' she said, 'yon collapsible lookin' tink that's always comin' from together in the middle?' I nodded, instantly recognizing the man from her description.

'Well, it's himself has the best milk pails, but see now and don't let him charge you more than half a crown for it. I doubt he'll try and get more from you seeing you're a stranger to him, but don't give it to him. Half a crown's what I always pay for them myself.'

Though I had often eavesdropped on my landlady's bargaining with the tinkers I had always been too mistrustful to buy anything from them myself, but when a few days after my conversation with Morag the collapsible tink came gangling happily up my garden path with his shirt gaping out of his trousers, his arms encrusted with shining new milk pails, I greeted him with a welcoming smile and a proffered half-crown.

'I'll take one of your milk pails,' I offered.

Courteously he removed his woebegone felt hat, the band of which was decorated with freshly picked briar roses and bluebells. 'It is a glorious day, madam,' he reproved me gently.

I recollected myself. Even with tinks the politenesses must be first observed. I agreed that it was a glorious day.

'Indeed, but you're badly needin' some rain hereabouts all the same,' he went on conversationally.

'We certainly do,' I said with mounting impatience. I wanted to get back to my goulash which was exasperatedly sizzling its need for attention. Perhaps he too heard the sizzling for he suddenly changed his manner.

'You'd like one of my pails, madam, did you say?'

'Yes, please.' I again held out the half-crown.

'The price is five shillings,' he said smoothly.

I remembered my instructions. 'I'll give you half a crown and no more,' I said.

'I'm sorry, madam, these pails are five shillings. I cannot sell them for half a crown.'

'Half a crown,' I repeated firmly, knowing that if once I gave the tinkers the impression that I was easy game they would never cease their pestering.

Spurning further argument temporarily, he turned his attention to the garden where the young shrubs I had planted were pregnant with blossom and the daffodils had already tired themselves out with the exuberance of their blooming.

'I mind you planting these when I was passin' this way last year,' he observed affably. I have never discovered if tinkers really do have phenomenal memories or if their assertions are just an astute combination of guesswork and glibness. But they seem to remember everything—always.

' 'Tis wonderful,' he mused on, 'how things grow in a year just.'

I agreed rather shortly. The goulash was definitely singeing but I was reluctant to take my eyes off the tinker for one moment. I wanted my milk pail and to be rid of him.

'And your cow?' he asked as he caught sight of Bonny grazing placidly amidst the blue smoky drifts of bluebells. 'My, my, but that beast has grown too—in just a year now. Can you believe it?' He shook his head wonderingly.

'I didn't have her a year ago,' I pointed out.

'Oh, no, you didn't, but I saw her last spring at the place you got her from and she's grown just,' he retaliated nimbly. 'Does she give plenty milk?'

'Over a gallon, morning and evening,' I told him, 'and I've only a shallow bowl to milk into.'

'In that case you're badly needin' one of my pails, madam.' He lifted his eyes contemplatively to the rumpled peaks of the hills showing above the roof of the byre.

Oh Lord, I thought, now we begin all over again. 'That's right,' I conceded.

Slipping a pail from the bunch on his arm he handed it to me. I examined it perfunctorily and with a smirk of triumph handed him the money. He smiled too. Indeed, I do not think he had ceased to smile during the length of our bargaining, but now there was an added glint in his eye. Giving me a whimsical little nod he pushed the half-crown back into my hand. 'Keep that, madam,' he said chummily. 'Keep it till next year, see will it grow any bigger.'

'Here, no!' I expostulated, but he was already on his way to the gate.

'It's all right, madam.' He paused to pull himself together in the middle. 'I'll be callin' on you again next spring and it's wonderful just what a year can do to make things grow. You'd scarce believe it.'

I was too discomfited to do anything but stand and watch him sauntering his tuneful way back along the road. When I returned to my goulash it was nearly charcoal.

That same evening I called on Morag. There was a shining new milk pail decorating her dresser.

'How much did you pay for this?' I asked.

'Only five shillings,' she said.

'Only five shillings! But you insisted that I mustn't pay more than half a crown, Morag,' I protested fretfully.

'Oh, right enough, mo ghaoil, so I did, but you see these pails is twice the size of the one's he usually brings. I wouldn't have the cheek to expect one of these for half a crown. It would be cheating the man.'

After enduring twelve months of self-torture I opened the door one spring day to 'collapsible'. He still gaped distressingly amidships, his hat was again decorated with flowers, but this time he carried only two milk pails on his arm. Evidently trade had been brisk. He greeted me like an old and valued friend, and began complimenting me on the growth of my garden . . . on the growth of my cow . . . I rushed indoors for my purse and of course found that I had nothing less than a ten-shilling note. I thrust it at him. He was sorry, he said, he had no change; he was more than sorry, he said, he couldn't offer me either of his pails instead of change because they were already ordered. He was sorry. . . . Oh, well! It was worth it really.

Once the tink season had started we had no alternative but to submit to their importuning, for rarely indeed did a week go by without a bevy of tinks descending upon us.

'Indeed what did I find when I got back home from my holiday but five shiny new kettles on the mantelpiece,' complained lame Annie to me as we walked up to the post office together, she to draw her

National Assistance. 'And because five different tinks called and them havin' nothin' but kettles to sell just. Jonathon's that soft he couldn't say no to one of them.'

I perforce had to harden my heart even to the extent of resisting 'Aberdeen Angus', the pathetic little Indian whose spotless white turban was always protected from the rain by a plastic bag. Each spring he tottered to our doors, so weighed down on either side by heavy suitcases that he looked to be in imminent danger of splitting down the middle. Mainly because of his skill in reading tea-leaves he was enormously popular despite the exorbitant prices he asked, yet when one saw him leaving the village he still tottered under the weight of his much depleted suitcases.

'Aberdeen Angus' was easily dismissed; he bestowed the same adoring smile on everyone whether or not they refused to purchase. It was not so easy to repulse the elderly female tinks who swung their unconstrained way up to my cottage to extol with soft spoken persistency the quality of men's shirts, combinations, towels, ladies' dresses and underwear which spilled on to the step from their tablecloth-wrapped bundles. When at last they could bring themselves to accept the fact that I was not going to buy they would cease their importuning and look at me for a long moment as though assessing my possible reactions to a different kind of approach—their tongues are reputed to be intimidating on occasion—and then they would flounce away with no more than an indignant rustle of petticoats—or it may have been pound notes.

The only tinkers on whom I came to bestow my custom were 'Tinkerloo' and 'Jinty'. Tinkerloo was a rollicking, robust character who came by ramshackle car to plead with us to buy bootlaces and polish, hair grips and hand cream and to give us devastating insights into the lives of itinerants generally. His appearances were infrequent and, in the hope of encouraging him to come regularly, I bought from him each time he came though his hair grips nearly always showed signs of rust and his hand cream was redolent of bad silage. I asked one of the tinkers once why Tinkerloo did not visit the village as habitually as the rest.

'Ach, him, mam! He's a terrible bad man for the drink, that one,' he told me, with perfidious unction. 'Three times last year and this year already he's been in hospital to be cured of his elephants.'

I was surprised. Tinkerloo had never struck me as being an alcoholic, but the last time I saw him he confirmed it himself, blinking the tears from his eyes.

'Aye, mam, it's true. And now they're after havin' me in jail for three months. Three months, mam, and that for doin' the right and proper thing.'

'How was that?' I asked him.

'Well y'see, mam. Whenever I see them pink elephants that you do see, comin' up at you out of the heather, or trees maybe where there's no trees, as I dare say you've heard, mam. Well then, I says to myself, I says, "It's time you done somethin', Joe," I says. So I gets into my car and I just drives myself off to hospital. It's what I've always done, mam, for years now, ever since the curse struck me as a lad.' His body sagged miserably. 'An' now they've stopped me from doin' it by sendin' me to jail for it. What am I to do now?' he demanded sorrowfully.

'You could get someone else to drive you to hospital,' I told him.

He stared at me stupidly. 'You don't understand, mam,' he explained patiently. 'I couldn't get nobody to come in a car with me when I'm in that state. Why, I believe I'm as wild as a bull.' The tears came afresh to his eyes and I had to buy half a dozen tubes of hand cream and hundreds of rusty hair grips before he was even moderately comforted.

Jinty, the other tinker who was certain of my patronage was a wiry little woman of unbounded optimism. She had a wide gap-toothed smile and a nose that peeled so lavishly from sunburn that I swear it became a visible fraction of an inch smaller each year. I observed as much to her once.

'Ach, no, it's not the sun that's my trouble with my nose. No, no, it's my man.'

'Your man?'

'Yes, indeed. He's a bacon and eggs man y'see and travellin' as we are all the time I canna always get it for him. If he doesn't get his bacon and eggs in a mornin' then I gets my nose punched.' She sighed. 'It's the same with the tea. Tea, tea, tea, it is for him every few minutes of the day and if there's no tea in the pot then its a bang on the nose for me again.'

I pressed upon her a packet of tea which she accepted with gummy gratefulness. I had no bacon and it was too early for the hens to have laid but I suggested she should call back later. I made a pot of tea and we sat in the sunshine drinking it. For the sake of Jinty's poor nose I suppose we ought to have gone inside but the chimney had been smoking so badly that the kitchen was barely habitable. I apologized to Jinty telling her that I had been trying to get someone for weeks to come and sweep the chimney but that so far everyone had proved to be very elusive.

'Sure my man will do that for you this evenin',' she offered briskly.

I simulated interest in the offer, not believing for an instant that anything would come of it. The tinkers are notoriously averse to manual work and anyway I doubted if people living most of their lives in tents or in lorries would know the mechanics of sweeping a chimney. It was quite a surprise therefore about four o'clock in the afternoon to be confronted by a fat, panting but very inoffensive-looking little man who wore a bright plaid shirt and who was already sweating in gorgeous Technicolor. He was accompanied by a youth whose figure looked as though some would-be boy scout had been practising knots with it. They had come, they announced, to 'sweep my chimperly' and they were in a hurry. Evidently it was to be swept in the traditional Bruach way, for the youth was carrying a large bouquet of heather and the man was clutching a boulder of suitable size. Fortunately, I had let the fire go out; I showed them the ladder and the rope which had been in readiness for weeks. They tied the boulder and the heather to the rope and then Jinty's man climbed apprehensively on to the roof. I rushed inside and hurriedly threw dust sheets over the furniture, watched by the youth, who had followed me in and who now stood so still that in the confusion I nearly draped him in a dust sheet too.

'What are you going to do?' I asked him.

'I'll be after catchin' the soot,' he replied lethargically.

'What in?'

He looked blank. 'A pail?' he mumbled.

I had only one pail and I didn't want it used for soot. The youth took off his cap and gazed inside it uncertainly. I ran to get a sack but I was too late. There was a rumbling, grating noise from the chimney as the stone was lowered down and simultaneously a great plump of soot fell into the stove and overflowed on to the floor.

'That'll be the better of that,' gloated the youth on whom the sight of the soot seemed to have an electrifying effect. He jerked himself outside and repeated the words to his confederate on the roof. There were some more rumbles and still more soot. The youth returned, paddled his way through the soot to the fireplace and pushed his head up the chimney. The voice, in miniature, of Jinty's man came down.

'He's sayin' the stone's after stickin' in the chimperly and I'll need to go up beside him on the roof to try will it come out,' he translated, and jerked away again outside. There were a few moments of silence before the stone again began banging ominously in the chimney, though there were now only occasional spatters of soot. I got a shovel and a cardboard box and prepared to clear up the mess, but I tripped over some obstacle among the soot, doubtless the tinker's cap, and sat down unexpectedly in the midst of it, banging my funny-bone on the door of the oven. I was still sitting there rubbing it when the voices began. Now although I have often heard the expression 'swear like a tinker', not until that moment had I the remotest conception of what it could mean. I thought I was inured to malediction but the language that came down my chimney as those two tinkers struggled with the stone was indeed a revelation. I could only wonder that it did not pulverize the stone. It was blistering! It was excoriating! I could have sat and listened to it for hours.

Eventually the stone was dislodged and when the two performers came down from the roof and presented themselves for payment I was glad to know that my blushes were masked by soot.

'That chimperly,' Jinty's man said confidentially, 'she's that coarse inside, mam, she'd be the better of a bit of blasting.'

I drew a deep and tremulous breath. 'Well,' I said reverently, 'you've done your best, haven't you?'

I put some eggs into a bag and handed them to him. 'Will you give these to your wife?' I asked.

'My wife?' he looked startled. 'Who would that be?'

'Why, Jinty, of course,' I said. 'You are Jinty's man, aren't you?'

'Is that so?' He turned and spat reflectively. 'Indeed I got a good son from her right enough.' He waddled away contentedly, the youth dragging behind.

Sheena dropped in to see how I was getting on.

'I hear you had the tinks sweeping your chimbley,' she said. 'Did they make a good job of it?'

'I've yet to see,' I replied as I put a match to the paper and sticks. The stove had always been a depressingly sluggish burner. In the mornings when I got up I would light it and it would go out. I would light it again; it would show a little promise and then peter out. Oh, well, I would think to myself, third time lucky—and sometimes it was, but daily it had grown more temperamental so that lighting it had become more like the ritual of plucking petals from a daisy and saying 'he loves me, he loves me not'. This time the paper caught quickly; the sticks were soon crackling and the flames curling round the peats and spearing up the chimney. It was wonderful.

'I don't believe I've ever seen that fire burn so well as that before, even when Hamish and Mary had it,' exclaimed Sheena. 'My, but they must have given it a good cleanin'.'

'I think they very nearly cauterized it,' I murmured with a faint smile.

Sheena had come to tell me that she was due to attend the local hospital the following morning for an ear examination and she wanted me to look out for a tinker called 'Buggy Duck' from whom she was in the habit of buying most of Peter's clothing. He was expected to be in the village the next day and I was to buy socks, shirts, overalls and handkerchiefs for Peter. There was no bargaining to be done, she assured me, Buggy Duck always named a fair price.

Next morning when a huge, savage-looking man with great tussocky eyebrows and broken black teeth bared in a wide grin presented himself at my cottage I recognized him as 'Buggy Duck'. His great arms, bare to the elbow, were shaggy as autumn grass; the skin of his face resembled crusty brown bread. When I had first encountered Buggy Duck a year or so previously his appearance had terrified me—until he spoke. Like so many vast men his voice came out of his body like the squeak from a stuffed toy and every bit of his energy seemed to be concentrated on producing even that ludicrous falsetto. Today he had a little girl trotting beside him—his daughter possibly, but after my recent blunder I decided it was better to refrain from enquiring into tinker relationships, for it seems that some of them cannot endure the stigma of marriage. I led them into the kitchen and while Buggy Duck untied the brightly coloured cloth of his bundle the little girl sat munching concurrently cake and apple and sweets which she had collected from child-loving Bruachites. I picked up a pair of men's socks from the top of the pile and examined them. In a second Buggy Duck had whipped off his battered shoe and, balancing on one leg, was holding up his foot for my inspection.

'Goot, goot socks, these, mam. The same as I have on myself. A fortnight now I've been wearin' these and they chust dhrinks up the shweat.' His squeak was emphatically Highland. My nose corroborated his statement; I put aside half a dozen pairs.

'Those shirts,' I mused. 'I'm not at all sure of the size. . . . ' Mentally I was trying to compare the width of Peter's shoulders to those of Buggy Duck. I gasped as, with a swift convulsive movement of his body, Buggy Duck divested himself of his thick pullover and stood before me in shirt-sleeves.

'Same as I have on myself, mam. Try him across my shoulders for size,' he invited.

I measured hastily and put aside two shirts.

'Vests or combinations, mam?'

'No,' I said emphatically, and hurriedly pulled two pairs of overalls from his bundle, adding them to the shirts and socks.

'Handkerchiefs?'

I breathed again. He displayed his stock of handkerchiefs—a frenzy of polka-dotted pinks, fungus greens and passionate purples. I chose some of the least offensive, and asked him the prices of everything.

'That comes to an awful lot of money for those few things,' I said when he told me.

'Indeed, but the price of things these days makes one shiver,' he agreed passionately. With a gusty sigh he collapsed into a chair, taking the tea I proffered and sucking it into his mouth noisily.

I turned my attention to the child. She was wet-nosed, sticky-lipped and carelessly dressed, but her hair was the colour of sun on corn stubble and her eyes had been put in with an inky finger. Her name, Buggy Duck told me, was Euphemia, 'Phimmy' for short. Normally tinker children are too reticent to speak to anyone, but this child answered me pertly when I asked how old she was.

'Five.' She stared around the room, missing nothing it seemed. 'You have six elephants, so you have,' she accused as her eye lighted on the parade of ebony elephants strung out along the mantelpiece.

'So I have.'

'You have seventeen books on that shelf, so you have.'

'That's right.'

'I think you must like elephants and books, so you must.'

'I think,' I said, 'that you are a very clever little girl, Phimmy, to be able to count up to seventeeen when you're only five years old.'

'So I am,' she agreed complacently.

Buggy Duck reached for my cup and tilted it critically. 'Oh, to be sure, mam, there's happiness in store for you.' The purchase of socks, shirts, overalls and handkerchiefs, I felt, ought certainly to have ensured an auspicious future.

'Go on,' I encouraged.

'You're goin' to come into some money,' he predicted with shrill earnestness.

'I'll need to if I'm going to buy from you,' I countered.

He snorted: a magnificent sound which embodied all the resonance his voice lacked. He stood up and began tying his bundle.

'Well, mam, my thanks to you and good luck till next year.' (Just like a tinker to wish good luck by instalments.)

I walked down the path beside them. Phimmy rushed ahead through the gate. The child interested me and I wanted to impress upon Buggy Duck that she was an exceedingly bright child, and to plead that her education should not be the haphazard thing it is with most tinker children.

'Phimmy,' I began seriously, 'is an exceptionally intelligent little girl.'

'Oh, so she should be, mam,' he agreed eagerly; 'it was a doctor himself who fathered her.'

Phimmy ran back to us. 'There's a bag with his pipes coming up the road,' she burst out excitedly.

I was on the point of correcting her when I saw the shape of the piper and decided it was not really necessary.

'He's getting the wind up now,' she announced. 'He's going to play.'

The piper turned in at the gate. I like the bagpies moderately, though I think the fitting of suppressors should be made compulsory. At a reasonable distance they provide the ideal music for the country of hill and glen, surging and wailing as it does. The trouble is that their devotees seem to think that six feet from one's ears is a reasonable

distance and more than once I have had to suffer the torment of
being entertained by a piper blowing at full blast within the confined
space of a bus.

Phimmy danced and jigged. Buggy Duck tapped his foot and nodded
his head. I fixed a perfidious smile on my face and endured. My spirits
rose as a black cloud, no bigger than a child could hold in its fist,
brought a swift sharp shower, but we only shuffled back to the shelter
of the cottage and the piper did not cease for the space of a breath.
Indoors the noise was shattering and I recalled Jinty's man's advice
regarding the chimney. It was getting a blast now all right.

At last the performance droned away to silence and Buggy Duck
and Phimmy departed; the piper waited expectantly until I pressed a
coin into his hand when a smile that was as thick and dirty as a swipe
of tar parted his lips. 'My thanks, mam,' he muttered sepulchrally.

With the onset of autumn the tinkers gradually deserted us, leaving
behind them the traces of their fires by the roadside and discarded
shoes, garments and broken utensils littering the heather.

'I believe we're seein' tse last of tsem for tsis year,' said Hector, as
we watched a number of them climbing wearily on to their lorry one
rainy day.

'Good riddance too,' said Erchy feelingly. 'You remember that last
lot was here a week ago? Got their lorry stuck in the ditch they did
and they sent word for some of us to go and try would we get it out.
A few of us went right enough, me and Hector was two of them, and
by God! we'd no sooner got their lorry back on to the road than
they was pulling out their bundles and trying to sell us shirts and
socks and things, right, left and centre. Out there, mind you, beside
the road! Indeed I believe they put their lorry in the ditch on purpose
just to get us there.'

I was startled the next morning when I drew back my curtains to
see a perambulator at the bottom of my garden. I stared at it, unable
to believe my eyes. I was sure there had never been a perambulator in
Bruach. No baby would have survived being pushed over roads like
ours. I went to investigate, circling it as a suspicious animal circles
bait. It was certainly a perambulator—not a new one but in quite good
condition. I simply could not account for its presence there and the
only thing to do was to wait and see what happened. Nothing did
happen, so I went to see Morag.

'Morag,' I said, feeling very, very foolish indeed. 'There's a perambulator at the bottom of my garden.'

'Is there now?' she asked with indulgent surprise.

'Who put it there?' I demanded.

'Was it not yourself put it there?'

'Of course not,' I repudiated indignantly. 'How could I?'

'Indeed I don't know then. You'd best ask Erchy.'

I found Erchy mucking out his cow byre.

'Erchy,' I said, 'there's a perambulator at the bottom of my garden. Can you tell me why?'

'Nothin' to do with me,' he disclaimed with virtuous alacrity.

'Has anyone put it there for a joke?' I persisted.

'There's never been a perambulator in the village that I've ever seen so how could they?' he asked.

'I can't understand it,' I said.

Erchy thought for a moment. 'It must have been them tinks left it,' he suggested.

We could think of no reason why the tinkers should bestow a permabulator on a middle-aged spinster.

'Oh, I mind now,' Erchy recalled. 'That last lot that was here when it was rainin'—they had a perambulator on the lorry and then they bought them old tanks from Murdoch. I dare say they hadn't room for everything so they'd just throw off the perambulator and your garden was as handy a place to leave it as anywhere. It's a wonder, though,' he added thoughtfully, 'that they didn't try to sell it to you.'

We decided that is what must have happened and no other explanation ever came to light.

'My, but you're lucky,' observed Erchy when someone referred to the subject a few days later.

'Lucky?' I echoed. 'Why?'

'You're lucky they only left you the perambulator. They might have left the baby in it too. You can never trust them tinks.'

Happy Band of Pilgrims?

BRUACH suffered from the misfortune of having no public hall and, though the education authorites were not averse to its use, some local demigod was always sure to raise objections if the school were suggested for any social function.

'We canna' even have that W.R.I. here,' Morag told me and Behag indignantly, 'just because some folks thinks it's too sexular.'

As a consequence the only communal relaxations for the crofters within the village were the church services on Sundays; the biannual communions; an election meeting once in five years and an even less frequent lecture by the poultry adviser, more familiarly known as the 'henwife'. During the winter months our evenings were sometimes enlivened by the visits of young lay preachers, locally termed 'pilgrims', who, with varying degrees of fanaticism, would exhort us poor sinners —who listened with varying degrees of perplexity—to forsake our evil ways and return to the paths of righteousness. Some of the pilgrims stayed for as long as a week amongst us and every night we would endure the hard benches of the church while they, with white strained faces, tear-filled eyes and voices that not only grated with emotion but also implied chronic deafness of the congregation if not of the Almighty, besought for us forgiveness and salvation. Mouthing the name of the Diety with expletive violence they would adjure us to give up our pipe-smoking, our church socials and our concubines. (Curiously enough I never heard alcoholism specifically mentioned as a sin but I suppose even the most zealous of pilgrims must recognize the hopelessness of some tasks.)

'What's a concubine?' Erchy asked, after one such meeting.

'It's a woman a man takes to live with him but who isn't his wife,' I explained.

'A mistress, like?'

'Yes.'

'Indeed we don't do that sort of thing hereabouts,' refuted Erchy. 'Why would we take them to live with us when they have homes of their own already?'

But, at a ceilidh a few weeks later at Morag's house, Erchy referred again to the subject of concubinage.

'I didn't think when those pilgrims was here that I knew of anybody hereabouts that was livin' with a woman who wasn't his wife, but I remembered afterwards about Dodo.'

'He's no from Bruach,' someone contradicted.

'No, I know fine he's not, but he was livin' with a woman, right enough. And what's more he's had three children by her.'

'That fellow!' ejaculated Morag with righteous scorn.

Dodo was a shiftless, happy-go-lucky, slow-witted character who lived in a nearby village. His house was patchily cement-washed and

his croft work was never quite finished because he ~   ~or ever neglec-
ting it to start on some new job which in its turn was dropped before
completion because some other project had taken his fancy.

'Well,' went on Erchy, 'when the pilgrims left here they went on to
Dodo's place and they must have got a good hold of Dodo for I'm
hearin' now that he and that woman slipped off quietly to Glasgow
and he's married her.'

'Married her? After all these years?' we all echoed incredulously.

'Aye, that's what I'm hearin' and I believe it's the truth.'

There was a moment of silence as everyone digested the news and
then Morag said, philosophically: 'Well, if he has, it's the first time
I've ever known that man finish a job once he'd begun it.'

Because of the attention of the pilgrims it must not be supposed that
the inhabitants of Bruach were any more godly or ungodly than any
other community either in the Islands or elsewhere. It was certainly
not to Bruach that a certain missionary was referring when he complained from the pulpit: 'The birds and the beasts and the roots of the
the earth have their season, but the women of this place are always
in season.' The village had never aspired to a church social—there
was nowhere to hold such a function; the practice of concubinage
was, as Erchy had pointed out, rare enough to be discounted entirely;
admittedly the pipe-smokers unregenerately smoked their pipes with
as much pleasure when the pilgrims had departed as they had before
they arrived. Nevertheless every pilgrim visiting Bruach could be sure
of a full and ostensibly receptive congregation, for the innate courtesy
of the Bruachites compelled them to attend the meetings. The pilgrims
they reasoned, like the henwife, had taken the trouble to come to the
village in order to help them. They might be no more interested in
the destiny of their souls than they were in the destiny of their poultry
but they flocked to the services with dispassionate regularity and listened with evident piety. After the service the women would murmur
sanctimoniously to one another, 'My, but wasn't he a good preacher,'
or, 'What a splendid sermon that was,' for they are easily carried away
by the tritest of dramatic performances; but once away from the
church one could discern that little glint of hope behind the eyes that
one of them would venture some comically outrageous aside and so
allow them to untense themselves with a little burst of laughter. After
long residence among them I do not believe that Gaels are essentially

religious. They have been constrained by Calvinism, but their readiness
to shed the constraint when circumstances appear to offer an excuse is,
for me, sufficient proof that they have not absorbed it. They can be
insufferably pious; they can also be sickeningly blasphemous. I recall
once pausing on the threshold of a house I was about to enter while a
devout old man read with slow reverence the nightly passage from
the Bible to his wife. The lamplit ritual of the scene was most impressive until the old man, coming to the end of the reading, shut the Bible
with a snap and, slinging it across the table towards his wife, commanded her to 'Put that bloody thing away now.' I remember too
an irrepressible old bachelor living alone, who would no more have
considered taking a bite of food without first asking the blessing on it
than of paying his rates without first receiving the final demand note;
after a stormy night which had stripped part of his roof so that the
ensuing rain squalls sent dismal trickles down into his kitchen, he
was sitting before a bowl of breakfast porridge, asking for the customary blessing. As he came to the end of his prayer a steady jet of water
descended from the roof directly into his bowl. Unhurriedly he said
the 'Amen' and then without noticeable pause or alteration of tone
he went on, 'But beggin' your pardon, Lord, I'd thank you not to go
pissin' in my porridge.'

So, with negligible effect on the community, the various religious
representatives, all indifferently referred to as 'pilgrims', came and went.
Once Bruach had been startled to find a black-robed priest in its midst;
a kindly, jovial man who was every day to be seen striding the rough
moors or climbing the hills, his black robes fluttering around him.
'Puttin' all the hens off their layin', that's all he does,' Morag grumbled
to me.

Since I had come to live in Bruach a second church had been built
so that it was no longer necessary for the two sects to hold joint
services.* The new church was about half a mile farther along the
road than the old one and was similarly constructed of plain corrugated
iron. It was to this new church that Morag, Behag, Kate and myself
set out one Wednesday in October to hear the last of a series of services
conducted by two earnest young men who were making an evan-
gelistic tour of the Hebrides which, they hoped, would arrest if not
recall the great number of people who had back-slidden since their
previous visit. The opening of their campaign in Bruach had been

* See 'The Hills is lonely.'

accompanied by the onslaught of a fierce gale which had raged almost without respite throughout the first four or five days, buffeting the walls of the church and driving rain and leaden hail against the roof with machine-gun force. During the last day or two, however, the storm had moderated, first into busy squalls with flurries of hail-stones that stung one's cheeks like hot sparks, then into frisky breezes that brought tinsel-like rain, and finally this evening into a dramatic calm that was intensified by the steady sibilance of the sea outside the bay. Above the décor of hill peaks the stars flicked on haphazardly and the immature moon peeped out from a stage-wing of cloud, like a too-impetuous performer.

A tall figure leading a cow on a rope loomed up before us as we approached the church.

'Surely you're no bringin' the cow to the service, Ruari?' shouted Morag.

'Service?' bawled deaf Ruari.

'Aye, at the church tonight,' replied Morag patiently.

'What are they after havin' the bull at the church for?' demanded Ruari. 'No wonder I canna' find him. Here's me been leadin' this beast round since twelve o'clock this mornin' and no a sign did I see of him yet. I was thinkin' he must have gone over a cliff. At the church indeed!' His tirade rumbled into disgusted expectoration.

Morag took hold of his ear and explained firmly. 'It's they privileges. They're holdin' a service again tonight. There's no bull at the church.'

'Here, here, but the bull was down in the Glen yesterday. I saw him myself. He can no be far away,' volunteered Kate.

'He could be far enough,' muttered Ruari, sitting down by the road and wiping his hand over his face. 'I'm tired out lookin' for him.'

'Then come and sit in the church and listen to the privileges,' suggested Morag. 'It's no use sittin' there on the wet grass where you'll get your death of cold.'

'It's too late to take her to the bull tonight,' said Kate. 'D'ye think she'll hold till mornin'?'

'She might,' admitted Ruari half-heartedly.

'Ach then, see and tie her to the post just and come to the service,' instructed Morag, taking the rope from the unresisting Ruari and tying it round a telegraph pole.

Obediently Ruari followed us into the church whither we were pursued by reproachful bawls from the cow. We were late, so we had to sit in the front row, the church having filled from the back. The pilgrims, with resolutely happy faces, were ready to start.

Several times during the week I had encountered the pilgrims on my daily walks and always it was difficult to reconcile the pleasant-spoken, normally intelligent young men with whom I conversed with the two who from the pulpit stridently harangued the congregation each evening. Tonight they seemed to be even more emotionally tense than hitherto. Taking their text from the Acts of the Apostles they warned us, contradicted by frustrated bawls from Ruari's cow, not to emulate Felix and 'await our more convenient season'. They illustrated the text by relating to us the story of a young man who had elected to postpone his decision on conversion until after he had attended a social function in the church hall. At this function the young man had caught a cold which had rapidly progressed to pneumonia and when at last he lay dying he had charged the evangelists to ensure that when his coffin was carried past the church hall they should stop and give the people this message: 'I am in everlasting damnation and all because of a social and dance in the church hall.' The pilgrim, the muscles of his face and throat working, paused for a full threatening minute to allow the congregation to reflect upon the tragedy. Ruari's cow did not pause for an instant, but bellowed despairingly. No one appeared to be much affected by either performance. 'Ah, my friends,' continued the pilgrim, battling manfully against an obvious desire to weep; 'that young man waited his more convenient season and it was too late.' At this juncture he was so overcome by emotion that he had to sit down hurriedly in the pulpit and cover his face with a handkerchief while his partner took over the rest of the service. We sang a hymn and after being adjured once again to get rid of any 'Drusillas in our midst' we paid our fee at the door and filed out.

'Well done!' was Morag's first remark and I, thinking she was commenting on the sermon, was about to agree spinelessly, when I saw her eyes were on the moonlit road in front of us.

Kate's guess that the bull could not be far away had apparently not been very wide of the mark and the bellowed invitations of the cow had brought him to her. 'She wasn't goin' to wait her more convenient season,' whispered Kate wickedly.

I was not at all surprised to hear the following morning that after the service the bus, packed with members of the congregation, had left Bruach for a dance in the next village. In the wee small hours, long after the exultant pilgrims had retired to their beds, they were blissfully unaware that the noise of engines that penetrated their celestial dreams announced the return of last night's congregation, or a significant part of it, exhausted after a fervid dancing session and not a little the worse for whisky. It was still later that Angus and Hector arrived home. They had taken their rifles with them in the bus and dropped off on the return journey so as to go poaching venison at first light.

The two male pilgrims were soon followed by two middle-aged lady pilgrims who, no doubt feeling that the Bruachites were in need of constant rather than intermittent ministration, moved into the empty house adjoining the burial ground and prepared for a lengthy stay. One was a spinster, tiny, shiny, plump and gushing, with small blue eyes which glistened with tears whenever she was emotionally aroused, as perhaps by an observation on the weather or by the receipt of a compliment on a pretty dress. The other was a widow who had been married briefly to a jockey. She was dark and morose, with curiously mottled cheeks which looked as though they might have been used for stubbing out cigarettes, and her long, thin face constantly wore such an outraged expression that it reminded me of an emphatic exclamation mark. Also she had a pronounced stammer and in no time at all the village had dubbed them 'Flutter and Stutter'. They did not, I think, belong to any particular denomination and from Stutter's faintly servile attitude one got the impression that her religion was a very neutral affair, whipped into fervour only when necessary to appease her more ecstatic companion and so ensure a continuance of her favours. Flutter's religion was, I am convinced, mainly glandular.

When she was not occupied with religious meetings or in visiting, Flutter knitted prolifically and was distressed because she could find no market for her work. Stutter's quaint hobby was the making of finger-stalls from odd scraps of material; checked ginghams, pyjama cloth, tartan, all were neatly sewn and finished with white tape. I ordered one of Flutter's jerseys, which made her so happy the tears spilled over. I could have cried too when I got the jersey home and found it would have amply made a loose cover for my armchair.

Fortunately, Stutter did not try to sell her finger-stalls but she generously left me a bundle of them whenever she visited me. After she had gone I used to exmaine my fingers critically, counting them to make sure I really had only ten, and then I would count again the rising stock of finger-stalls in my first-aid tin which at its peak totalled a hundred and six.

Because they were female 'privileges' and because they preached happiness instead of hell-fire, the men did not feel it incumbent on them to attend the weekly meetings which the two pilgrims held in their cottage, but the women, with their more pliable conscience and glad of any diversion, turned up regularly to sing hymns and be read to by Flutter. Sometimes the readings were from the Bible but just as often they were stories from missionary magazines or, on particularly exciting evenings, from *The Man-Eaters of Kumaan* or even *King Solomon's Mines*. For the reading Miss Flutter invariably took up her position directly in front of a mirror above the fireplace into which she glanced frequently for reassurance. When it was time for prayers, regardless of the work-a-day attire of her congregation, she would take her hat from the dresser and carefully arrange it on her head before announcing 'We will now try to put up a little prayer,' much in the same way as a poacher might confide that he was going to 'try to put up a little grouse'. I must admit there were times when the 'Go-back, go-back' cry of the disturbed grouse would have seemed an appropriate response. These meetings were repeated on Sundays for the children of those parents prepared to endure the jeremiad tongues and lashing sarcasm of their Calvinistic elders to whom Sunday school was frivolous to the point of profanity. At the Sunday meetings and to a semblance of the tune of 'Hear the Pennies Dropping' extracted from a tortured violin by Miss Stutter, the children were invited to drop their pennies into a 'Present from Blackpool' teapot. In return they received a gaily coloured tract card; when the pilgrims ran out of tract cards they substituted cigarette cards. The children thought little of Flutter's reading; they thought even less of Stutter's violin ('It's as wicked as the bagpipes on a Sunday but it's no half as good a noise,' one little boy confided to me); some of them reckoned a coloured card a very poor return for their penny, yet, because it was somewhere to go to escape the smothering Sabbath piety of their own homes, the children attended with a regularity that both flattered and astonished the pilgrims. So much so that they decided to give a party as a reward, some of the money they had collected being used to provide the refreshments. Now although many of the crofters had been broad-minded enough to join in the services at the cottage the association of parties with religion was to them completely unacceptable and though it was only obliquely expressed the pilgrims would not have needed undue powers of perception to have become aware of the general disapproval of their project but, happily insulated by their own egotism, they sailed along with the arrangements. Miss Flutter resolutely learned poetry to recite. Miss Stutter practised her violin, while both made the rounds of the village extracting so many faithful promises of attendance that I wondered what the outcome of it all would be.

On the day and at the time stated I set out for 'Pilgrim Cottage' expecting to meet up with others along the road. Sarah called to me from the door of her own cottage.

'Aren't you coming to the party?' I asked, seeing that she was still wearing gumboots and old clothes.

'Indeed no, my dear. The cow's just near calvin' and I canna' leave him now.'

'I can see to him myself,' interpolated her brother, who was carrying a pail of water into the house. 'You can go to the party, right enough.'

'Ach well, d'you see, I canna' find one of my stockings,' Sarah went on glibly. 'I had it for church last Sunday, and I dare say I threw it under the bed the same as I always do, but where it is now nobody can say.'

I could offer no help as Sarah wore only thick black woollen stock-ings. Not long after I had said good-bye to her with the promise that I would convey her apologies to the pilgrims, the bus pulled up along-side me.

'Are you comin' to the fillums?' Johnny, the driver, asked.

'No, I'm going to the party,' I replied. 'Aren't you coming?'

'Well we were thinkin' of it right enough.' He turned for confirma-tion to the dozen or so passengers he was carrying. 'But you see it's *Whisky Galore* they're showin' and we might never get a chance to see it if we don't go tonight.'

'I'll have to go to the party,' I said. 'I did promise faithfully I'd go.'

'Didn't we all,' said Johnny lightly and everyone laughed as the bus started off again.

The Bruach road was busy. Hector, whom I had heard swear to cut his throat and wish to die if he didn't attend the party, was now coming towards me, pushing a bicycle. I asked him whether he was coming.

'Ach no, my cycle's broke and I'm away to Padruig's to see has he got a tsing will mend it.'

It looked as though attendance at the party was going to be sparse indeed. Morag had butter to churn and the cream would not keep until morning and Fiona had been sick all day, so neither she nor Behag could, come.

When I reached the cottage I was greeted by the flustered and delighted pilgrims. Miss Flutter was dabbing continually at her brimming eyes; Miss Stutter was wearing exotic finger-stalls on two fingers of her left hand. Inside, I was confronted by a large table bearing innumerable plates each piled high with sandwiches of a variety of pallid-looking fillings. Miss Flutter began to introduce me to each plateful; egg and cheese; cheese and egg; cheese; egg; meat paste; fish. When she was unsure of a filling she lifted the lid of a sandwich and peered.

We sat down to await the rest of the guests, I with steadily increasing dismay. When the kettles on the side of the stove had been sighing for nearly two hours and the tops of the sandwiches were beginning to curl querulously, Miss Stutter decided that she had better make the tea.

'I've made it nice and strong, so that we can add plenty of water to it when they come,' she said with tenacious optimism as she poured me a cup that was the colour of faded sun-tan. Miss Flutter, by now completely dry-eyed, invited me to try a sandwich. I chose a salmon filling; she looked puzzled.

'We haven't any salmon,' she said.

'Oh, I beg your pardon,' I apolgized. 'I heard you say fish and as it looked pink I took it to be salmon.'

'Oh, no, this is cod,' she corrected me with an earnest smile and handed me the plate. 'It's a recipe we invented ourselves to use up some that was left over.' She took a closer look at the plate. 'But they've turned pink!' She stared accusingly at Miss Stutter, who looked guiltily down at her two finger-stalls and then surreptitiously put her hand behind her back. I changed my mind and had cheese.

When ten o'clock came round and still no one but myself had arrived for the party, the despondent pilgrims packed away the sandwiches into tins. I hoped that this might mean I could escape but they felt that as I had taken the trouble to come I must be entertained, and so I sat submissively while Miss Flutter rendered *The Lady of Shallott*, *The Forsaken Merman* and *Abou Ben Adhem*, and Miss Stutter chafed her violin with its bow and elicited from it jig-like noises that were no more musical than a two-stroke engine.

The following day the Bruachites were abject in their excuses and apologies to the pilgrims and made such asseverations of their disappointment at missing the party that the pilgrims were ready to believe the fiasco had been largely due to their own mismanagement.

'You know,' said Erchy, when he strolled into my kitchen some days later; 'Hamish had to take a gas cylinder to those pilgrims yesterday and he says they're still eatin' their way through piles of stale sandwiches. They asked him to stay for tea, but he knew fine what he was in for, so he said he had to go to the hill. They've asked quite a few in to tea since the party, but everybody's too wise to go.'

'It really was too bad,' I told him. 'They did ask everyone first and nearly everyone said they would go.'

'What else can you say when people asks you straight out like that?' he demanded. 'You can't just tell them you won't go.'

'Why not?'

'They'll want to know then why you won't go, and if you give them a reason like as not it will turn out to be a lie. It's easier to tell them yes.' He sat down by the window and lit a cigarette.

'How did you like *Whisky Galore*?' I asked him.

'It was grand,' he replied. 'My but they got drunk there, I'm tellin' you.'

'Drunker than people get here?' I asked doubtfully.

He pondered my question for a moment. 'Well,' he conceded, 'it looked to me as if they was pretty drunk, but what I couldn't understand is, they was in their ordinary working clothes. Ach, I don't think they can have been drunk at all or they would have had on their best clothes. I think they was only acting.'

Erchy had dropped in on me on his way back from gathering hazels for a lobster creel he was making for me. I had bought a small, light dinghy, one that I could launch and pull up the beach unaided, and Erchy, knowing my fondness for lobsters, had suggested that I put out a creel and try catching them for myself. It was now my ambition to sit down to a meal of fish I had caught; bread and butter I had made; vegetables and fruit I had grown; so the prospect of a lobster creel pleased me as much as the prospect of a bottle of French perfume would have a few years before.

'What are you makin' now?' Erchy asked, as he watched me breaking eggs—from my own hens—into a bowl.

'Lemon curd,' I replied.

'Now that's stuff I like,' he enthused. 'There's only one thing I like better and that's blackcurrant jam.'

'I like blackcurrant jam too,' I admitted sorrowfully. The garden of the cottage had been a tatter of blackcurrant bushes when I took over and I had cut them all down to ground level. Since then they had yielded seven blackcurrants.

'I'll get you plenty blackcurrants if you'll make them into jam,' Erchy offered.

'I'll make them into jam quickly enough,' I agreed. 'But where are you going to get blackcurrants?'

'Never you mind,' said Erchy. 'You provide the sugar and I'll provide the blackcurrants and we'll split fifty-fifty.'

Though Erchy's mother was an excellent baker of girdle scones and bannocks she had never tried her hand at making jam and was completely confident that she could never achieve a 'jell'. Indeed, few of the crofters made any attempt at jam-making despite the abundance of blackberries and brambles in their season. Those with families had no storage space; and the women complained that if they did make half a dozen jars of jam then each member of the family would take a jar and a spoon and eat the whole lot at one sitting. So I agreed to Erchy's proposal.

The following Thursday evening I went along to 'Pilgrim Cottage' for the weekly meeting. It seemed as though the villagers, ashamed of their absence from the pilgrim's party, were trying to make up for it by their attendance tonight. The women and children crowded the little cottage and we had to have the door open so that the menfolk standing outside could join in. Erchy, Johnny, Hector, Alistair, Angus, all were there. Miss Flutter was ecstatic; she lost her place when reading several times, and put her hat on back to front for the prayers. The hymns were sung so lustily that Miss Stutter's violin could be heard only for a bar or two when it managed to get away ahead of the rest of the starters. When the meeting closed the two radiant pilgrims waved blessings and good-byes from the doorstep until we were out of hearing. My own feelings of vexation at the behaviour of the Bruachites towards the pilgrims the previous week melted. It seemed that they felt genuine compunction for their neglect, and when, the following morning, Erchy brought the promised blackcurrants—two milk pails full—I mentioned to him how much pleasure it had given the pilgrims to see such a good turn-out. He agreed with me abruptly and left.

There were about ten pounds of blackcurrants and I had eight full jars on the table ready for labelling and another panful of jam boiling on the stove when Miss Flutter called.

'Oh, you're making jam,' she observed. 'Blackcurrant too,' she sniffed appreciatively. 'You know, we thought we'd make blackcurrant jam today too. We had such a lovely lot of blackcurrants on our bushes only yesterday afternoon, but we decided to leave them until today.' She sighed. 'Now we're wishing we'd picked them because when we went out to get them this morning there wasn't one to be seen. Could the birds have stripped them so quickly, do you think?'

I was quite certain they couldn't have. I was ready for Erchy when he called to collect his jam later that evening.

'Erchy, where did you get those blackcurrants?'

'From the pilgrims' cottage. Where else?'

'When?'

'When we was at the meeting last night. Why else do you think we went there? All us boys had to go, some to do the pickin' and some to do the singin'. When they sang very loud it was to warn us that one of the pilgrims was near the door and we'd need to dodge back to the service. Ach, what are you worryin' about? They would have been wasted if we hadn't got them.'

'They were going to make jam themselves today,' I told him. 'Miss Flutter was here this afternoon and told me that when they came to pick the blackcurrants they'd all gone.'

'She only wants things after she can't have them,' Erchy retorted.

'I feel terrible about it,' I said miserably.

'Ach, just you give her a pot of jam and shut her up,' he soothed. 'Aye, and give her one from me too. That'll be more jam than ever she would have got from her blackcurrants.'

Miss Flutter and Miss Stutter were very very grateful for the two jars of jam. They no doubt used it to help down the last of the sandwiches.

Back to School

THE great tit in the rowan tree behind the house had been calling
'tea-cher, tea-cher' since early morning. I little thought at the time
that he was being prophetic but, later in the afternoon when I was
gathering an armful of washing from the line, I turned to see the head
teacher of the school striding towards me. When I had first come to
Bruach with its scattered houses and discovered its preponderance of

spinsters, bachelors and old-age pensioners, I had been a little surprised to find that there was a village school.

'But are there any children to attend it?' I had asked artlessly.

'Surely, we can make children here the same as they do everywhere else, you know,' Erchy had retorted with ruthless indelicacy.

The heavy figure of the head teacher leaned over me as she spoke with pious sibilance. It seemed that Elspeth, the junior teacher, had been taken ill suddenly and would not be able to carry out her duties for a few days. The head herself was suffering from a severe cold and was finding the strain of double duty a little too much. Would I, she pleaded, step into the breach temporarily? I liked the idea, particularly as Mary, my friend from England, was due to arrive the following day to stay with me and I knew she would be delighted to have Bonny and the chickens to minister to for a little while.

The Bruach school consisted of one classroom divided by a green baize curtain with about ten double desks on either side. When I entered the first morning the head teacher was already there. She introduced me briefly to the work in hand and gave me instructions, and while we awaited the arrival of the children we conversed together with the taut heartiness of two women who have little in common.

'I hope you don't object to my washing,' she hissed, indicating a pan of sheets that was bubbling away on the side of the fire; 'but with not being so well lately I've got behind myself with everything.'

At ten o'clock the children filed in, their eyes fixed on me with passionate interest. Johnny, who had given me my first lesson in fishing from the rocks, was there among the bigger boys, and the twins, whom I had long ago christened 'Giggle and Sniggle', each a complete replica of the other, were huddled into a desk together, bringing with them a lingering atmosphere of the ceilidhs. When the children were settled the head read the morning prayer and the whole school recited the Lord's Prayer in measured tones, their rich Highland voices lingering on the r's and softening the consonants. I noticed they rendered the third line of the prayer as 'Thou will be done on earth' and thought irreverently that from what I had seen of the behaviour of some of the little scamps out of school hours the substitution of the personal pronoun for the possessive was not inapt.

I took out the register.

Once in Bruach I had been approached by a stranger and asked if I could direct him to the house of a Mr. McAnon. Out of a total population of a little over two hundred, it had been necessary to explain to him, there were fifteen Mr. McAnons. It was Mr. Lachlan McAnon he wanted. The information made identification only a little easier, there being five Lachlan McAnons. I probed for other details. Was the Mr. McAnon married? Yes, in his letter he had referred to a wife. The number of possibilities was cut to three. Was he dark or red-haired? He didn't know, but if it would be of any help he could show me a sample of handwriting. I doubted it; I had been struck by the fact that all Bruachites seemed to have similar handwriting. Some might be more literate than the rest but they all wrote with the same painstaking legibility and added identical flourishes. A graphologist would probably have judged them to be of uniform character. However, by a process of elimination we did at last manage to select a suitable Mr. McAnon for him to call upon and it transpired that it was the right one.

The calling of the register was much like my experience with the stranger, the majority of the children bearing the same clan surname and, because the custom of naming children after relatives was followed slavishly, there being much duplication of Christian names. In my small class I found I had two Alistairs; two Angus's; three Floras; and two Morags. Two of the Floras were sisters, the elder being named for her mother and known as 'Flora Vor' (Big Flora) and the younger being named for her grandmother and known as 'Flora Vic' (Little Flora). It was fortunate that I knew them all by sight.

My class struggled over their arithmetic, muttering, coughing, scratching their heads, jabbing pens into inkwells and doing all the other things that children do in a classroom. Fiona lifted her head and stared at me coolly. She disliked school and tended to be rebellious in class. Giggle and Sniggle, their hair-styles making them look as though they were going to take wing at any moment, chewed pens and whispered to each other. Both twins were backward, hence their presence in the junior class. A series of sniffs, resonant with satisfaction, claimed my attention and I traced them to a little boy with an exceedingly turned-up nose whom I knew only as 'Beag a Mor' (Big and Small). Apparently he had been given the same name as an elder brother and when the brother had died the younger one, for some implausible reason, had inherited both adjectives. I went over and asked him quietly if he had a handkerchief. He delved into a pocket and after much rummaging produced a filthy tatter that led me to suspect that his nose might have turned up at the sight of it. Seeing my look of revulsion he explained engagingly that his handkerchief was not dirty. It was just that it had been tucked under a black jersey he had been wearing and when the jersey had got wet it had leaked.

As the children worked, there arose a strong tang of seaweed that competed with the smell of soapy washing to fill the classroom. Most of them were chewing and when they thought my attention was elsewhere they would furtively pull from under their desks sections of the peeled stalks of tangle-wrack, which they called 'staff', and from which they took large bites.

From the other side of the curtain came the sibilant voice of the head teacher who was putting her class through the agonies of mental arithmetic.

'If one egg costs twopence halfpenny, how much does twelve eggs cost?' and without waiting for an answer she carried on conversationally, 'Did your mother's hens lay yet, Jessac?'

'No, they didn't yet.'

'Fancy that! I got eight from my fifteen yesterday. Did yours lay, Johnny?' Johnny's reply was inaudible. 'See and tell your mother to put in some spice with their food. The van sells it and it makes a great difference, I find. Now where were we?'

After a few more questions asked and answered her voice again penetrated my consciousness.

'If ten pounds of sultanas . . . Annac, did I not hear your mother askin' at the van for sultanas last week?'

'I believe she did.'

'Well, mind and tell her when you get home that Ian the shop has some lovely ones, but she'll need to hurry because everybody was buying them to make dumplings when I was there.'

And again: 'Pomegranates are threepence halfpenny. . . . Has anyone here seen a pomegranate?' No one had apparently because she went on to explain ingenuously: 'It's a fruit like a cucumber. Anyone who's seen a cucumber has very nearly seen a pomegranate.'

When written arithmetic was substituted for mental she set them the old faithful one of the taps and the water cistern but adroitly she rendered it, 'If your boat was leaking and the sea was comin' into it. . . .'

Thus companionably lessons progressed. Was it perhaps, I mused, partly because of homely observations such as these that Highland education is second to none? My musings were interrupted by a knock on the door of the classroom and the teacher, answering it, stayed talking to someone in the porch for a few minutes.

'It's the shepherd,' she came through the curtain and whispered to me hoarsely. 'He's after leavin' his job here and he's wantin' me to write him a reference.'

When morning break came the head took her pan of sheets and prevailed upon the canteen cook to give her a hand with the wringing and before the end of break they were billowing on the line across the school garden. At lunch time the children trooped into the tiny canteen shed at the back of the school where Giggle and Sniggle were deputed to act as waitresses. There were so many eager hands ready to grasp the plates as they appeared, however, that serving was accomplished with astonishing rapidity, as indeed was everything else. The meal began with Scotch broth and uproar.

'Anyone want my vegetables?' shouted the teacher as she ladled up her soup and pushed the vegetables to the side of her plate. 'Big and Small' came over and claimed the barley but he did not want the vegetables. She repeated the question, standing up and offering her plate like a market woman offers a bargain: there were no takers. The speed with which the children shovelled down all their food was phenomenal. With grubby fingers they crammed the utensils into their mouths and gulped, spilled, gurgled and sucked like starved puppies. I watched them, spellbound, reflecting upon all the sore stomachs in Bruach and remembering that a tin of bicarbonate of soda was as much of a necessity on the table at mealtimes as sugar or salt and as familiar an ornament on a mantelpiece as a tea caddy.

'It's no wonder the canteen's full of rats,' said the teacher through a mouthful of mince; 'they spill that much of their food. I've had to get some rat poison and I'm goin' to put it down when school's over.' I offered to stay and help.

Giggle, leaning over me, whispered something that seemed to imply I was a 'cursed tart' but which I knew was merely an offer of custard with my prunes. The meal was cleared away while the cheeks of the children were still bulging with their last mouthfuls and we stood up and thanked God for what we had received, though I considered a more appropriate grace would have been 'Thank God we didn't choke'.

Outside the sun was brilliant, raining silver darts on the blue water and gilding the steep cliffs of the cove that sheltered the school. I sat on the steps watching the children, and the teacher brought out a basket of darning and joined me. There were few games the children could play in Bruach. It was nearly always too windy to skip; it was too steep for ball games; too rough for playing hop-scotch. The younger ones strolled now in groups along the shore, poking into rock pools or playing a clumsy game of 'tag' over the boulders. One child walked alone playing with a chopped-off hen's leg of which he pulled the exposed sinews so that the toes opened and closed with horrid agility. Some of the older boys had found a washed-up pit-prop and began a game of 'tossing the caber' while others played at 'finger-stones', a most peculiar game resembling rubbing one's tummy with one hand and patting one's head with the other. The first and second fingers of the left hand are slid to and fro over a boulder whilst the boulder is hit rhythmically with a stone held in the right hand. It is a savage method of I.Q. assessment, the less alert boys frequently hitting their fingers; it was considered a great joke locally to get the village idiot playing 'fingerstones'.

'You wouldn't like to go back to teaching?' asked the head suddenly.

'No, not at all.'

'Fancy! I wouldn't be without it. There's always somebody to talk to when you're teaching. Don't you ever get lonely?'

'How many of the children can swim?' I asked, deflecting her attention from myself.

'Why none of them, I don't believe.'

'It seems a pity, with the sea so close,' I said.

'More than a pity,' she agreed. 'Indeed the risks they take climbing about the rocks sometimes, I'd be a lot happier if they could swim.'

I said nothing but I thought I would talk over the matter with Mary, who was not only a splendid swimmer but was also a part-time swimming instructor.

When lessons began again the sun had moved round full on the schoolhouse windows. The fire had been left to go out but the class-room became increasingly torrid. The discarded chunks of staff under

the desks became decidedly odiferous and the classroom began to give
off the musty, sour smell of sweating children mingled with that of
sunlight on dust-impregnated wood and cloth. The children were taking
it in turns to read aloud from a book of fairy stories I had taken because
there were none in the school library. I had to remind myself constantly that they were naturally Gaelic speakers with English only as an
acquired language. Giggle's turn came at the end of the story and she
faltered along, stabbing at the odd words she knew with expressionless
indifference and shaping her mouth experimentally over the syllables
of the rest. 'And . . . the . . . prin . . . cess . . . mar . . . married . . . the
. . . d . . . duck. . . .' There was a burst of tittering from the class which
I quelled with a look. I told her to read it through again but she still
persisted on pronouncing 'duke' as 'duck'. Suppressed titters came
again, this time not only from my own pupils but from the other side
of the curtain where the class, with india rubbers audibly in evidence,
were engaged in drawing a map of North Africa.

'Flora,' I reasoned with her, 'a princess wouldn't marry a duck,
would she?' Flora stared at me with unblinking stupidity. I insisted
she try again, telling her to use her common sense. It was of no avail.
She was still determined to marry the princess to a duck.

Impatiently I turned to Sniggle, whose eyes were bright with contempt for her sister. 'Murdina,' I said, 'can you tell your sister what a
princess would be likely to marry?'

Murdina's hand shot up eagerly. 'Yes, Miss. Please, Miss, it would
have to be a drake.' The whole room dissolved into laughter and the
teacher bustled from the other side of the curtain to add her ridicule
before she called us firmly to attention for evening prayers.

I stayed behind when the children had gone, so that I could lend a
hand with the rat poison and the teacher took the opportunity to show
me the reference she had written out for the shepherd.

'Is he as good as this?' I asked doubtfully. It was an enconium. I
doubt if there has ever been a better shepherd.

'You'll know him, of course?' she asked. 'He lives outside the village
but he goes to my own church regularly.'

'I know that Netta had a baby by him a little while ago,' I
admitted.

'Oh yes, indeed. But he's done the right thing by her. He's made
sure the baby was registered under his own name.'

'But if he admits he's the father and wants the baby in his own name, why on earth didn't he marry the girl?'

The teacher looked at me in shocked surprise. 'Oh, Miss Peckwitt,' she hissed reproachfully, 'he's a good-living man and he's hoping to be a missionary some day. He could never marry a girl like that.'

We adjourned to the canteen and spread slices of bread with rat poison.

'They're supposed to become thirsty with this stuff and leave the premises in search of water and when they drink they die, isn't that the way it works?' I asked.

'Yes, but I think we'll make sure they can get at water here,' she said as she thoughtfully placed saucers of water in the cupboards.

'Have you used it before?' I asked her. 'Do you know how effective it is?'

'Well, I don't really, but Sandy Beag says it's good right enough.' She sniggered. 'Me and my husband were watching Sandy Beag put some rat poison down a few weeks ago round his sheds. I don't know if it was this stuff he was using then, but there he was carefully putting down pieces of baited bread and there at his heels was his dog following faithfully and eating every piece as it was laid down. Every now and then Sandy would catch him and swear at him and start laying the trail again, but he couldn't stop the dog. At last he shut the animal in the house, but it wasn't many minutes before it was out again and eating it. It was a good thing it wasn't harmful to domestic animals or Sandy would have lost the dog right enough, and he was fond of it.' She sniggered again. 'Indeed, I think he just decided he must put up with the rats after all.'

'He should try Erchy and Johnny's remedy,' I said, with a reminiscent smile. The story of how Erchy and Johnny had once been given the job of ridding an hotel outbuilding of rats had often been related in the village. The two rat catchers had stipulated that they be given a bottle of whisky apiece, their professed plan being to soak pieces of bread in the whisky and to wait until the rats got drunk on it. They would then pounce on the rats before they could dodge back to their holes and hit them on their heads. They swore that rats were attracted by whisky and that their method had proved effective several times previously. Armed with stout clubs the two of them reported for work one night and the hotel proprietor, sceptical but desperate, provided the whisky. But early the next morning, so the story goes, when he went to find out how the men had got on, he found Erchy and Johnny and several rats lying drunk on the floor—some of the rats being cradled in the crook of Erchy's arm. At his shout of rage the rats had sprung up and bolted unerringly for their holes, but the two apostates had managed to struggle to their feet only to collapse again under the full blast of his wrathful sarcasm. The most curious outcome of the night's affair was that, inexplicably, the rats thereafter deserted the outbuilding.

'Seein' the state those two were in was enough to drive any self-respectin' rat away,' the hotel proprietor explained sardonically.

'It was your damty bad whisky that got rid of them,' retorted Erchy. 'And your damty bad language,' added Johnny morosely.

That evening I discussed with Mary the possibility of swimming lessons for the children. She fell in with the idea at once, and I sent a message to the mothers saying that any of the children who could bring a bathing suit and towel could stay after school if they wished to be given lessons—provided the weather remained calm and sunny. After break two or three of the scholars came to assure me that it was surely going to 'make a fine day'. They shook their cupped hands and opened them to show me horrid woodlice struggling on their backs. If the woodlice had rolled up into a ball it would have been a sure sign of rain.

The sun continued to shine, the wind stayed muzzled by the heat, and when school was over for the day every child was waiting on the shore.

'All right, go and get into your bathing suits,' I told them as Mary appeared. The girls flocked into the porch and the boys dove behind the playground walls and all emerged wearing their bathing suits— their ordinary wool vests with a large safety-pin between the legs. With Mary and me in attendance, they splashed through the strokes in the shallow water, the more promising ones being taken out individually and tutored in deeper water. When it was decided that they had had enough for the time being, they asked for a demonstration of swimming and Mary, who is as adept as a seal in the water, performed for her entranced audience willingly. Then she and I went into the schoolhouse for a 'strupak'. We were standing on the step taking our leave of the teacher when Seumas Beag, the father of the twins, came shuffling diffidently up to us.

'What are you wanting, Seumas?' the teacher teased him. 'Have you come to learn how to swim?'

'Not me indeed. I'll never learn to swim,' he replied.

'Why not? You're always out in boats. Wouldn't you feel better if you could swim?' I asked him.

'I would not. I was talkin' to a man who was drowned once and he warned me never to learn to swim. No, what I came for was the cailleach wanted me to tell you the twins is gettin' their tongues awful cut on the knives at the canteen. She's sayin' they're too sharp altogether.'

'It's their own fault entirely,' retorted the teacher loftily. 'They shouldn't push them so far into their mouths.'

'How do you manage to tell the twins apart?' I asked Seumas. 'I find it very difficult.'

'Indeed, some times I'm not knowin' that myself,' he admitted sadly. 'I was thinkin' I'd get the subsidy man to clip their ears for me the next time he comes, same as he does with the calves.' A smile fumbled longingly at his lips.

'Why was Hamish not in school today, Seumas?' the teacher taxed him.

'Ach, he's no well in himself,' replied Seumas shiftily.

'He was out on the hill last evening, I saw him myself. Was there anything wrong with him then?' she asked dryly.

'No, indeed. It was this mornin' just, after he'd taken taken his breakfast, he felt bad with a pain in his stomach.' Seumas started to shuffle hastily away.

'He'd probably eaten too much breakfast,' retorted the teacher.

'No more than two raw eggs boiled hard did he have,' contradicted Seumas indignantly as he hurried away.

'He's away to warn Hamish not to show himself,' commented the teacher knowingly. 'Indeed, the lice that man gives me is terrible.'

I knew from the puzzled expression on Mary's face that I should have to explain that the teacher was referring to Seumas's plausibility and not his parasites.

We decided that as the tide was low we would pick our way leisurely homeward along the beach and had not gone more than a few hundred yards when we came upon Sandy Beag himself with his gun and his dog, ensconced upon a rock looking out for likely 'skarts'. Sandy complimented Mary on her swimming, and then remarked that he thought we would soon have thunder.

'I was wonderin' if you'd teach my own dog here to swim,' he went on hopefully. 'Here's me after shootin' skarts day after day and the tide takin' them away on me because my dog cannot swim.'

'But all dogs can swim,' responded Mary, valiantly suppressing a smile.

'No this one, indeed,' argued Sandy Beag. 'I've thrown him in a couple of times and he's near drowned for fear of movin' his legs. I thought maybe if I took him out in my boat and threw him overboard and you'd be waitin' just by to grab him and wriggle his legs for him to see will he swim. If he knew that he should wriggle he'd maybe be all right after that.'

Mary laughingly refused to 'wriggle'. 'He's a nice dog,' she said, stroking the animal's head.

'Ach, he's nice enough, but he's no use to me at all. It's chasin' the hills myself I have to be while he just sits there watchin' me and scratchin' himself. Aye, but my wife is fond of him y'see so I canna' get rid of him.' Thus he excused his own attachment to the dog.

Just at that moment Sandy jumped up, flung his cap in the air and flapped his sides with his arms. It is a contention of Bruach 'skart' shooters that if a 'skart' is swimming out of shooting range it will come close to investigate a cap thrown into the air, presumably believing it to be another 'skart'. The lure does appear to be effective.

'If I get this one I'll bring it round to you,' promised Sandy Beag.

Some people say that 'skarts' are not worth eating; that they taste fishy. In Bruach we buried them for three days and then we skinned them. There was not the slightest trace of fishiness about them after this treatment and the amount of meat on their breast and legs has to be seen to be believed. One boarding-house proprietor I know used to serve them up as 'sea turkey' and was often congratulated on the dish. Mary and I made a couple of very sleek and expensive-looking feather toques from their skins, simply by stretching them over a piece of pit-prop and then having them cured and lined.

After the heavy heat of the day I, at any rate, was tired and we sat long over tea watching a spider's web outside the window gradually filling with midges so that it began to resemble a faint pencil sketch being drawn over heavily with charcoal. The web had been there for some time for it was too perfect a thing to destroy. Each morning it had been cleaned of its catch and the spider grew perceptibly bigger and fatter. We wished him long life. I roused myself at last. It was the night for my fortnightly writing of Sarah's letters and Mary intended to stroll along with me and then go on up to the post office with her letters. Usually Sarah came over to the cottage with her writing materials but the hot weather had been very trying for her feet and I had promised tonight that I would go to her. Veiled against the midges we set out, Mary threatening to collect me on the way back so as to meet the fabulous Flora, who, though I had often described her in my letters, Mary maintained was too incredible for her to accept. To the south the sky was strangely lit and screened by still, dark clouds with deckled silver edges. The thunder Sandy had predicted murmured faintly behind the hills and the sea, sullen and shadowed, seemed to be growing chill with apprehension. The crofters we saw at work were rubbing the midges off their faces and necks.

Sarah had paper and envelopes already waiting for me and she appeared to be unusually flushed and excited.

'I want you to write to the Queen for me,' she blurted out as soon as I sat down at the table.

'The Queen,' I echoed, startled. 'What do you want to write to the Queen about, Sarah?'

'I want to write and ask her what she uses for her husband's corns,' she elucidated.

'But has the Duke of Edinburgh got corns?' I asked, vainly trying to recall some news item that might throw light on her resolve.

By way of explanation Sarah produced a recent photograph of the Duke of Edinburgh in polo kit. 'He must have corns,' she replied, pointing at his footwear. 'Wearin' they big boots would put corns on anybody's feets. You do as I say and write and ask her, mo ghaoil. She won't mind tellin' an old lady like myself who works hard and has such terrible feets, and she's bound to get the very best for him, you know.'

I have regretted ever since that I dissuaded Sarah from sending off that letter.

Mary called my name through the open door and came in to be staggered briefly by the impact of Flora, but there came a long drawn-out roll of thunder and big splodgy rain drops hit the stone steps so we cut short our visit and ran through the early dusk, now mercifully midge free, to the cottage. Mary sat by the window a little awestruck by the sheer quantity of water that was sheeting down on to the sea and cascading from the shed roof to flay the full water-butts. I lit the lamp and started to mark the history books I had brought home from school. The class had been doing the battle of Mons Graupius and, perhaps because Elspeth would be returning to her duties in a day or two, I had taken special pains to ensure that they had a good grasp of the subject. They had written on the battle for homework and the first few books seemed to indicate that my toil had not been fruitless. I marked away happily. And then I opened Giggle's exercise book. My head flopped forward on to my hands as I stared in dismay at the solitary line of writing across the otherwise empty page: 'Mons Graupius was a big, fat man.' I read it again and again, puzzled by a vague consonance, and I groaned histrionically.

'What is it?' asked Mary, looking round. 'Goodness!' she went on, half rising from her seat, 'there's someone coming here, Becky. In this weather!'

'Anyone you know?' I asked indifferently.

'No, I don't think so, but I can't tell, he's all done up in oilskins. It's a man though. A big, fat man.'

'That,' I said heavily as I got up to go to the door, 'will certainly be Mons Graupius.'

The 'Tour'

'Now that I have Hector and Behag at home will we go for our little tour?' asked Morag, to whom any sort of outing, even a day's shopping, was a 'tour'.

'That's a good idea,' I agreed, 'but while we're about it let's be ambitious. Let's go as far as Inverness and see some shops.'

Morag and I had often talked of going away together for a few days' holiday but always before she had pleaded that her animals and poultry prevented her from leaving the croft for more than a day. I was prepared for excuses now.

'Aye,' she agreed surprisingly; 'and we might even get farther. I'd like to go to Edinburgh and see them little penny-goin'-ins I seen when I was there a few years back.'

'You mean those slot machines you put a coin in and get chocolate or something in return?' I asked.

'No, no, mo ghaoil. I mean them black and white birds they feed fish to at the zoo.'

Our tour was soon arranged. To save us the usual early morning bus ride and to make our journey scenically more interesting, Hector volunteered to take us to the mainland in his boat. He reckoned he could count on getting together a party of tourists who could be persuaded into thinking that the trip was exactly what they wanted and thus make it a financial success.

The day arranged for our tour broke unpromisingly grey and damp with frayed clouds working their way sluggishly over the hill tops and a rumpled line of sea stretching across the mouth of the bay. Only one or two tourists were waiting at the shore when Morag and I arrived there.

'What sort of a trip are we going to have?' I asked Erchy, who was acting as temporary crew for Hector.

'It'll be choppy enough out there when we get,' he replied, 'but we'll no be sayin' anythin' about that until we get the tourists aboard. It's calm enough here on the shore.'

Familiarity with the sea since I had come to the Hebrides had completely overcome my former terror: the prospect of a choppy passage I now found exhilarating. Erchy rowed us out in the dinghy to the *Wayfarer* where Hector had mugs of tea waiting for us in the tiny fo'c'sle.

'Best fill up tse kettle again and we'll give tse rest tea when tsey come aboard,' said Hector. Erchy filled up the kettle from a rusty water-can and put it back on the Primus stove.

'How many people are you expecting to come today?' I asked.

'About twenty altogeszer, I believe,' Hector replied.

'As many as that? I thought you weren't allowed to carry more than twelve fare-paying passengers without a Board of Trade licence?'

'I'm not allowed to drown more tsan twelve fare-paying passengers,' Hector corrected me gravely. I chuckled, but his expression remained perfectly serious. It appears to be a curious legal anomaly that in this country any greenhorn can take up to twelve fare-paying passengers in any boat, be it held together by nothing more than paint and prayer, and so long as he does not drown more than the twelve he is not committing an offence in law; it is a very serious matter if he drowns thirteen. That, at any rate, is how the Hebridean boatmen interpret the law.

Hector finished his tea and popped his head up out of the fo'c'sle. 'Tsere's quite a few folks waiting on tse shore now,' he announced. He collected the cups and washed them in the kettle. 'Tsat'll put a bit of strength in tseirs for tsem,' he remarked happily.

Erchy hauled the dinghy alongside and jumped down into it. 'There's more than twenty there now,' he remarked as he pulled at the oars. 'I wonder will they all want to come?'

'If tsere's more tsan we can take tsen see and pick tse young ones, tsey's easier to get aboard if she turns bad on us,' called Hector.

The dinghy's stem crashed into the bow of *Wayfarer*.

'She's tsere when she bumps,' commented Hector sarcastically.

'Erchy's sometimes no very good at manuring the boat alongside,' Morag murmured to me.

Half a dozen people came aboard, four sparsely haired though youngish men and two girls. One of the girls was a curvaceous blonde whom Hector's eyes appropriated as soon as he saw her.

'Here, Hector,' called Erchy, 'd'you know who's on the shore wantin' with us?'

'No, who?' demanded Hector.

'The pilgrims — Miss Flutter and Stutter. Will I get them?'

'God!' said Hector expressively. 'Are tsey goin' away?'

'They're goin' some place,' said Erchy, and added warningly: 'Pilgrims is as bad as ministers for making the weather blow up.'

'Aye,' Hector agreed, massaging his unshaven jaw perplexedly. He brightened. 'See if you can get tsem by tsemselves and tell tsem it's goin' to be awful wild,' he said.

'I've done that already,' said Erchy. 'They just told me it's a good forecast.'

Hector groaned. 'Maybe it was a good forecast for tse Bay of Biscay tsey heard,' he said. 'Ach, well, if you canna' leave tsem behind you'll just have to bring tsem, tsat's all.'

Miss Flutter and Miss Stutter came out with the next boatload. Miss Flutter greeted us effusively. She simply must, she insisted, sit outside in the breeze to stop her from feeling sick; she had brought her knitting for the same purpose.

'I find I simply must keep my mind occupied,' she said, pulling a half-knitted sleeve out of her bag and commencing work on it immediately. Miss Stutter managed a taut smile and twined her gloved fingers together ceaselessly.

By the time we had taken aboard the third boatload the sea outside had infected the bay with its restlessness and *Wayfarer* was beginning to rock tentatively at her moorings.

'I'm sure to be sick,' asserted a great cart-horse of a girl who sported a frugal pony-tail, and in preparation she draped herself into a suitable position. More boatloads of tourists were harvested from the shore, always with young women predominant, and not until we had more than thirty people squatting along either deck and littering the forepeak did Hector call at halt.

'There's seven more still wantin',' said Erchy. 'They think I'm goin' back for them.'

Hector looked speculatively at his packed boat and then yearningly at the seven extra fares. 'Best go for tsem,' he said.

'No damty fear I'm not,' said Erchy relentlessly. 'They're all old or fat or lame so we'll be the better without them.' He clambered aboard and went forward to cast off the mooring as the engine throbbed into activity. *Wayfarer*'s bow commenced to dip a series of smug farewells to the disappointed tourists on the shore and then headed out of the bay.

'You can give her the gutty now,' Erchy shouted as he finished coiling ropes and picked his way carefully among the bodies back to the wheelhouse.

'You'd best make tse tea,' Hector said, 'before we get out of tse bay.'

'Here, here,' remonstrated Erchy, 'how am I goin' to serve tea round this lot. It'll all be spilled and wasted.'

'We've said tea was included in tse fare so we must offer it to tsem,' insisted Hector. 'Be quick now and let tsem have it before we get outside. It's no our fault tsen if tsey canna' drink it.'

Erchy grumbled a little more and then dived down below. I wedged myself in a corner of the wheelhouse and watched with mounting satisfaction the seas growing shaggier and shaggier as we approached the open water. Morag had found an old newspaper and was engrossed in reading the obituary notices. Hector leaned against the wheel, apparently steering with his backside, and riveted his eyes on the luxuriant tresses of the blonde. Erchy soon reappeared from the fo'c'sle with slopping mugs of milky tea which he thrust sulkily at the startled passengers. His arm also described a semi-circle with a tin of biscuits but the gesture was so repressive that no one had the courage to do anything but refuse. Some of the biscuits looked to me as though they had been refused for a long time.

Before we reached the black rocks, crenellated with shags, which flanked the entrance to the bay, *Wayfarer* had begun that confident surging and swinging motion with which a sturdy boat meets the challenge of the waves. It was not a savage sea but a snarling and defiant one and our course lay directly into the wind. The bow was soon lifting to each breaker, sagging down into the troughs and flinging lacy scarves of spray up over the half-decks. The passengers, amply clad in anaraks and waterproof trousers, appeared so far to be enjoying the cavorting of the boat. Right up on the foredeck a muscly young giant sat with his arms tightly encircling his emaciated girl friend. Each time the bow dipped his arm tightened; it was debateable sometimes whether the noise we heard was the crackling of water under the stem head or the scrunching of the poor lassie's bones. The girl cart-horse leaned resolutely over the gunwale and waited for something to come up. Miss Flutter knitted industriously.

Suddenly a peculiar bumping sound became apparent. The two boatmen looked at each other questioningly.

'Tsat's tsat light anchor come loose,' said Hector. 'Best go and fix it.' Erchy started forward along the side deck, which was now wet and slippery.

Once aboard the *Wayfarer* the sexes seemed to have mutually agreed to separate and the starboard deck was lined with huddled girls while the smaller number of men spread themselves out in comparative comfort along the port deck. Erchy picked his way gingerly through the mass of girls, secured the anchor and came back the same way. We had not progressed very much farther when the bumping began again.

'You couldn't have done it properly, Erchy, it's loose again,' said Hector.

Erchy muttered imprecations under his breath and prepared to go forward.

'Erchy,' I suggested, 'wouldn't it be better, with the boat tossing about like this, if you went along the port deck. It's not so crowded.'

'No damty fear!' he replied. 'Those decks are slippery for me in gumboots.'

'That's why I suggested you should go along where the men are,' I said; 'after all, if you did happen to slip. . . .'

Erchy stared at me in serious surprise.

'What's the use to me of a lot of bald heads or crew-cuts if I lose my footing?' he demanded scathingly. 'I'm goin' where the women are so I'll have some hair to grab hold of.'

I dwindled back into my corner of the wheelhouse.

After about half an hour the Islands retired behind blinds of rain and the sea became perceptibly friskier. *Wayfarer*'s motion began to have its inevitable effect. The cart-horse squandered herself upon the deck and when several of the others had laid listless heads on the shoulders of their companions Erchy, with great jubilation, was able to point out to Hector that the making of tea had indeed been a waste. I felt dreadfully sorry for poor Miss Stutter, who sat rigid beside her companion, staring with glazed eyes at the sea. Miss Flutter knitted on in desperation. The length of the sleeve had increased considerably during the half hour but whether it was due to her industry or whether it was sagging with the wet it was impossible to tell.

Hector was obviously anxious to get into conversation with his blonde so he left the wheel to Erchy and in a few moments was luring the blonde into the fo'c'sle. Erchy raised his eyebrows at me meaningly. Morag, who had appropriated the only seat in the wheelhouse, affected not to notice her nephew's disappearance.

'Here, see that rock we're just passin',' Erchy said to me through the side of his mouth after a swift glance at Morag. 'Take a good look at it.'

I stared obediently at an apparently isolated black rock rearing up out of the water a few yards offshore.

'Yes, but what about it?' I asked.

'You'd wonder at it now, wouldn't you?' asked Erchy.

I looked again but saw nothing curious about the rock which was black and jutty and sea-washed like so many other rocks and which had a small flat area of green moss, no more than two or three feet across, capping it.

'There doesn't appear to be anything unusual about it,' I said.

'Well, I daren't go closer in to let you look, but surely you can see the letters that's on it?'

'Good Lord!' I ejaculated. Inconceivably, on the dark face of the rock the tell-tale letters 'H.S.M.' had been painstakingly chipped.

'That's what I was meanin',' said Erchy, his voice betraying awe and admiration. 'You'd wonder at it bein' possible.'

I began to find it difficult to stay still for though I was wedged into a corner of the wheelhouse there was nothing for me to hold on to. Morag's eyes were closed as she rocked to the movement of the boat. Erchy clung to the wheel and as *Wayfarer* began leaping I was thrown repeatedly against him.

'Here,' expostulated Erchy, when a particularly violent lurch of the boat flung me against him so hard that his hand was wrenched from the wheel and *Wayfarer* swung beam to sea. 'Get you up on that shelf and stay there out of my way.' He indicated a shelf across the corner of the wheelhouse about half-way up the sides. I had to be helped up into it, and when I was deposited my legs would not reach the floor and I found there was absolutely nothing I might cling to.

'I shall fall,' I objected, and screamed, flinging out my arms to save myself as the wheelhouse canted treacherously to port. Erchy rammed the palm of his large hand into my diaphragm and fended me off as indifferently as if I had been a sack of meal. He seemed to find this position very stabilizing for himself and thus ignominiously I completed the journey.

When we arrived at the mainland pier Erchy and Hector abandoned us to rush off and sell their lobsters and to meet a party of campers they were expecting to take back to Bruach.

'See and remind Miss Peckwitt's fire to keep in,' were Morag's parting words to her nephew. Behag had the key of my cottage and so that I should not return to a cold, damp house, she had promised to send Hector to light the fire for me each day.

The pier was full of activity. Lobsters and crabs were being landed and sorted; baskets of fish were being dumped on the scale; the bell that indicated to buyers that fish was ready for auction was being rung imperiously; gulls swooped low and squealed their frustration as lorries were loaded high with dripping fish boxes; boats were being refuelled; trollies were being pushed hither and thither by apathetic porters; fish-box squirters were dreamily playing their hoses on stacks of empty boxes, recollecting themselves only to apologize to passers-by who might be absent-mindedly squirted, or to swear at the unquench-able dogs who were determined to help. Sundry urchins darted among the fishermen rescuing moribund crabs to fling triumphantly at the jettisoned loaves of Glasgow bread, still in their waxed wrappings, which floated in the harbour. I could think of no more suitable fate for Glasgow bread.

A trio of labourers were having some difficulty pushing a large barrel along the pier which, at the point they had reached, was slimy with oil and fish offal. The first of the men crouched down and gave a hefty push but his feet slid from under him and he lay flat on his stomach. It was a very rotund stomach. He picked himself up and swore colourfully at the pier. The second man obligingly thrust his weight behind the barrel but his feet too slid treacherously. His stomach was less rotund and perhaps as a consequence his abuse was even more colourful than that of his predecessor. The third man tried his strength and again exactly the same thing occurred. The trio stood surveying the obstinate barrel and abusing the pier in increasingly picturesque language, much to the amusement of a fry of young fishermen who had gathered to watch the spectacle.

'Here, you'd best be careful with your language,' shouted one of them facetiously. 'Likely the pier will be gettin' up and swearin' back at you.'

With an hour to spare before our train was due to leave, Morag could think of nothing but getting herself a cup of tea and left to weave her way through the bustle of the pier to the nearest tea-room. I turned into the butcher's first with a message from Peggy. One of the disadvant-ages of living in isolation is that when one does manage to get away, much of one's time is spent in transacting business for oneself and others in an effort to make the isolation more endurable. The butcher's shop was low-ceilinged, cool and dim, its floor heavily carpeted with fresh sawdust. A fat, slovenly woman was leaning torpidly on the scrubbed wooden counter, a shopping bag hanging limply from her arm.

'What'll I give you today, Mary?' asked the butcher.

'Ach, somethin' for their dinner.'

'What? Chops, steaming, roasting?'

'Ach, I don't know at all.'

'What did you have for your dinner yesterday?'

'Ach, stew.'

'Well, I'll give you a bit of mince today then, will I?'

He weighed out the meat and put it into the woman's bag, and watched her slouch out of the shop.

'There's some of the men heareabouts would get no dinner at all if I didn't see to it,' he hissed at me.

The butcher was an exceedingly devout man, speaking invariably on indrawn breaths that kept his mouth constantly prim, and no one but myself appeared to think the large picture of the Crucifixion which hung above the gory joints so tastefully arranged on the slab behind him at all incongruous.

I translated Peggy's complaint of 'Neilly says he's not goin' to put his teeth in just to eat the stuff we've been gettin' lately' into suitable cuts and joints, and went on to the chandler's shop which by contrast was cosy as a cabin. It was full of the rugged smells of tar and oil and twine and paint. The chandler, one of the finest characters I have ever encountered, was wearing a grubby white coat which to us who knew him proclaimed the season of the year just as accurately as the weather or the calendar. At the beginning of the tourist season his coat was new-starched and spotless; the chandler himself was correspondingly constrained. As the season advanced the coat became progressively limper and grubbier and its wearer daily more relaxed. At the end of the season the coat was abandoned for the winter and the chandler reverted to his normal happy self. He greeted me now with a genial smile and made a careful note of my order and then he leaned on the counter talking of the things that mattered: of the goings on of Bruach and the neighbourhood with which he was well acquainted; of the merits of different lamp oils; of the construction of a creel; of the fastidiousness of crabs which need fresh bait to lure them into a creel and yet which will pull off their own claws and eat them; of the less fastidious lobsters which are more easily tempted by salted or slightly smelly bait but have less cannibalistic tendencies. There were frequent interruptions to our conversation while he attended to the children, little girls mostly, who came in with their pennies to buy fish hooks for their boy friends to fish with off the pier.

'I'll bet,' the chandler said with a smile, 'they're for that young Jimsey. Looks like a little angel with his golden curls and blue eyes and all the girls want him for their boy friend. The wee tartar just exploits the lot of them. He's that clumsy with the hooks anyway he's always losing them and some of the lassies haven't a penny left of their pocket money to buy sweeties for themselves.'

We chuckled together over the ways of love and it followed naturally that he should go on to speak of Hector.

· 'My, but I got the surprise of my life when I saw him walk in here today,' he said.

'Didn't you know he had come back to live in Bruach then?' I asked.

'That I didn't. In fact, I doubted if I'd ever see him again.'

I waited with raised eyebrows.

'Well, it's like this,' he told me. 'Hector, as perhaps you've heard, was never very quick at payin' his bills but I just let him go on for a while without botherin' him. They never amounted to much at a time, but when it came up to eighteen pounds I sent him a bill at last. Next time he was wantin' somethin' he came in here and promised to pay but he said he hadn't the money on him then, though I know fine he must have had or he'd never have been able to get as drunk as he did. The next time was just the same, he promisin' to pay, and the next time again and so it went on for five or six years till he went away. I sent him the bill a few times more but when it got to twelve years and never a word I gave it up as a bad job. Well then, today he walks in here, only a few minutes since. "Sandy," he says, "I'm owing you eighteen pounds and I've come to pay it." You could have knocked me down I was so surprised, but he put three five-pound notes and three one-pound notes down on the counter and asked for a receipt. I gave him a receipt quick enough but I was so happy to have got the eighteen pounds after all these years that I wanted to do something to make him happy too, so I took up the three fivers and I gave him back the three one-pound notes. It was worth it to see his face light up.' The chandler grinned benevolently.

Our gossip had lasted rather longer than it should and I had to hurry if I was to deliver a note that Johnny had asked me to give to the joiner. The road from the harbour was steep and I wished I had the same incentive as the fishermen in whose wake I toiled: the public bar was at the top of the hill and the way they were drawn towards it was like the force of gravity in reverse. I found the joiner's shed but the door was tight shut and there was little to indicate that any sort of business was carried on there except for a notice-board which bore the esoteric announcement:

NEW BOTTOMS.. .... 1/6d each
ditto, TARRED.................. 2/3d each

I knocked at the door of a neighbouring cottage, from the garden of which two ragged-looking geese eyed me apprehensively, and enquired after the joiner. He had gone, I was told, with his family on a Sunday School picnic.

I rushed back down the hill to find Morag.

'Did you give the joiner Johnny's message?' she asked, as we hurried to the station.

'No,' I told her. 'He's gone off on a Sunday School picnic.'

'What like of man is that then, goin' off on a Sunday School picnic on a Saturday,' she scoffed.

The guana spattered train with its assemblage of covetous gulls was already in the station and we dived hastily for the shelter of the corridor. We found an empty compartment and barely had we seated ourselves when the train gave a jolt and started to move resolutely away from the platform. I held my watch to my ear, thinking it must have stopped, but there was too much noise to hear anyway. Then the train stopped, vacillated for a while between jostlings and bumps and groaned slowly back into the station.

'What is all this shunting for?' I enquired of a flaccid porter who appeared to be rooted to the platform outside our compartment. He blinked, looked pallidly about him and then with an obvious shock of recollection informed me solemnly:

' 'Tis all for the sake of the fish, madam. Just for the sake of the fish.'

'I expect they've had to put us on to an extra fish van,' Morag interpolated. 'I was talkin' to a woman in the tea-room and she told me there'd been heavy landings today.' She produced a bag of pepper-mints and sat back, sucking contentedly.

'You mind,' she said reminiscently when the driver had let the engine have its head, 'that woman I was talkin' to in the tea-room? Well, her man's a fisherman and he was in today with a good catch, but do you know what that man is gettin' for his tea tonight?'

'Boiled fish,' I guessed.

'No, but fish fingers—them artificial fish out of deep freezers. And he loves them, she says, and so does the rest of the fishermen.'

'Good gracious!'

'Aye,' agreed Morag indignantly. 'Them things! For a man! And not a bit of taste to them at all, until they come back.'

I have an unfortunate habit of falling asleep on trains and so I was soon startled by Morag's shaking me and telling me to get ready to alight. We were breaking our journey so that I could visit a dentist and so that Morag could seek out a builder's yard where there might be second-hand sinks and basins for sale, for now that Hector was home she clung to the hope that he would put in piped water for her.

The delightful lady with whom we had arranged to spend the night heaped our beds with eiderdowns as though the temperature were several degrees below zero, although it was but mid-September, and heaped our plates with food as though we had been starved. 'Oh my, I wish I had two stomachs,' sighed Morag greedily when she had eaten.

The dentist obligingly fitted me in without a previous appointment. He was a charming man and when his receptionist showed me into his homely surgery he was sitting on the floor playing happily with an adorable little puppy. He was wearing a starched white jacket, bedroom slippers and no socks. I sat in the chair and waited timidly while he gathered up the puppy and carried it over to its basket. He put it in, patted it and told it to stay there and then came and stood over me. Taking an instrument from an array on a nearby shelf he told me to open wide and began to probe. 'Ah, yes . . . perfect, perfect . . . now puppy . . . naughty puppy! Stay there puppy . . . nice puppy. . . .' Even rolling my eyes to their extremities I could not see what the puppy was up to but my attention was caught by a shelf above that on which the instruments were arrayed. It looked to be a species of museum shelf and reposing on it was a collection of awe-inspiring relics of previous clients. The dentist continued with his inspection. 'Good teeth you have . . . yes. . . .' He jerked away suddenly. 'Puppy! Naughty puppy!' He turned and shook the instrument at it admonishingly. 'When he wants me to play with him he has a habit of nipping my ankles and his teeth are terribly sharp,' he vouchsafed by way of explanation. He bent over me again but, changing his mind, he picked up the puppy and stowed it again in its basket.

'Now stay there, puppy,' he bade it firmly. 'My wife usually looks after it but she's gone off to hospital to visit her mother,' he said companionably. 'And my secretary's away home now.' The puppy sat in his basket looking appealingly vague. The dentist resumed his inspection. 'Aye, yes, now there's a wee holey there . . . no more I think. Ouch!' He jerked away again.

'Puppy!' He sounded really cross and looked about him helplessly for a moment as though wondering whether to put down the instruments and chastise the offender. His eye suddenly lighted on the museum shelf. Surreptitiously he flicked off one of the relics, which rattled across the surgery with the puppy gambolling happily after it. The dentist breathed a sigh of relief and concentrated his attention on stopping my tooth. As a retriever the puppy was not a conspicuous success and there were only one or two relics remaining on the shelf when I took my leave.

In Edinburgh we spent our days and nights being entertained by past residents of Bruach, by relatives of present residents of Bruach and by Morag's own innumerable friends and relations, so much so that I saw hardly anything of the city and Morag did not find time to renew her acquaintance with the penguins. On our return journey we touched Inverness briefly on a hot, busy day with the buses grinding heavily along and ice cream trodden over the pavements. Inverness suffers too much from the cult of the laird to be popular with Islanders and when they go away they prefer the indiscriminate affability of Edinburgh and Glasgow. At Morag's suggestion we carried on to Dingwall, which is a delightfully scatterbrained little town wavering between East-coast industry and West-coast indolence. Coming out of the station we were confronted with what looked like the preparations for a Guy Fawkes bonfire but which we found was the Seaforth memorial to the battle of Cambrai. But Dingwall is really dominated by the church tower with its four clocks of which, during the time we were there, no two were in agreement and not one was correct. Our landlady was no generous Highlander; she did not smother us with eiderdowns nor overtax our stomachs, but she was the only landlady I have ever come across who had the courage to put a supply of the day's newspapers in the lavatory in addition to an ample supply of toilet paper. I like Dingwall for its individuality and for its decorous bustle but mostly it will linger in my memory as the place where at night the men stand so still on the street corners that even the dogs get confused.

The train journey from Dingwall to the West is beautiful indeed and the halts frequent enough to allow it to be fully assimilated. I slept most of the way and roused myself for lunch to find that our compartment was now shared by a corpulent old Highlander and a heavily built, masculine-looking woman. The man was dressed in black suit, black hat, black shiny boots and with a snowy Woolworth's handkerchief in his breast pocket. I know it was a Woolworth's handkerchief because I had just bought a dozen for Erchy. When he was not conversing with Morag in the Gaelic he sat self-consciously in his corner staring at the pictures of Morecambe and Bognor Regis which decorated the compartment. He looked as though he had left his croft and his bible only for a few hours and was already wearying to return to them. I discovered he had been travelling the world for the past eighteen months visiting his scattered children and was only now on his way home. The woman was wearing an amorphous raincoat and a deer-stalker and she was so engrossed in a novelette with a lurid love scene backing that she appeared to be oblivious of our presence and even of the attractions of Morecambe and Bognor Regis.

We were back to contentious seagulls; back to 'Tea-rooms' (instead of restaurants) with their stale cakes that looked as though they had been kept on a shelf for six months and taken down and dusted only occasionally. The drizzly rain was full of salt; boats bumped against the slip; ropes were flung; the men's oilskins flapped and crackled. We squelched over seaweed to the ferry. I saw Morag aboard and then asked the ferryman if he could wait while I nipped into the shop on the pier. I had bought a large vacuum jar and I thought it would be a good idea to get it filled with ice cream for the children of Bruach who rarely got the chance to taste it. The youth in the shop considered the capacity of the jar and finally decided that two family bricks would compress suitably. The boy took the bricks and the jar to the back of the shop. He was gone for rather a long time and I could see the ferrymen were becoming restless.

'Please hurry,' I called; 'the ferry is waiting.'

He appeared hastily, rather red in the face, and handed me the jar.

'I had no idea it was going to take so long,' I said testily as I handed him the money.

'Ach, but d'you see, I had to melt them first to get them to go in,' he consoled me fatuously.

I hurried down to the ferry.

'Miss Peckwitt! Miss Peckwitt! Mattam!' I stopped. A cadaverous oilskinned figure was lumbering towards me.

'Miss Peckwitt, am I spekink to?' He was very, very Highland.

'Yes,' I admitted. 'Do you want something?'

'Would you be goin' back to Bruach now, mattam?'

I admitted I would.

'In that case would you be takink a wee message to Willy John MacRae? The phone iss not workink.'

I said I would.

'You will tell him then that there iss a corp to come over for him tomorrow on the boat.'

'A what did you say?'

'A corp, mattam, to come over. . . .'

The ferrymen were revving the engine impatiently.

'Yes,' I cut in, 'I know, but what is it you said was to come over in the boat?'

'A corp, mattam.'

'A corp?'

'Indeed yes.' He could not conceal that he thought me very unintelligent. 'Willy John's uncle has died in Glasgow and his corp is to come over tomorrow,' he explained patiently.

'Oh!' I exclaimed. 'You mean a corpse!'

He looked at me pityingly.

'Mattam,' he rebuked me gently. 'I was spekink in the sinkular.'

The 'Herring Fish'

'THE trouble with this place,' complained the local vet exasperatedly, 'is that every single soul in it is a fierce individualist. Other townships manage to work together for their own good, but Bruach, never!'

The veterinary surgeons of the Hebrides are splendid men doing gruelling work over a vast area for long hours, often with little consideration or co-operation, yet they are unfailingly helpful, good-humoured and appear to be completely tireless. Our Island vet was no exception, but his exasperation was occasioned by the fact that he had spent a long day under appalling weather conditions chasing over mile upon mile of moor and bog trying to get within 'stabbing' distance of cattle that were as wild as the hills that bred them. He had out-manœuvred aggressive mothers with calves at foot; stalked refractory two-year-olds that had never before submitted to human touch; thrown himself upon young calves that fled on nimble legs from anything that had not horns and shaggy hair. In all this he had been hampered by a pack of vociferous Bruachites who, unable to agree as to the best way to catch a beast, had each gone about it in his own way; and by a pack of equally vociferous dogs which, frantic with excitement, had streaked in and out among the distraught beasts taking surreptitious nips at their heels.

'It's one thing to hold a beast when it's half-mad, but it's another when there's a dog chewing at his tail,' was another complaint the vet made; a complaint well justified by the number of rolls of coarse hair from the tips of tails that were later to be seen strewing the moors.

For such a round-up of cattle other villagers, as the vet pointed out, had combined to fence off cattle 'parks'. Bruach had never aspired to anywhere other than the school playground but, to everyone's indignation, the present teacher had protested against its use for penning cattle, maintaining that the uproar distracted the pupils and that the language they could not help overhearing, particularly when one of the more recalcitrant beasts managed repeatedly to evade its captors, was altogether unsuitable.

Another way in which Bruach lagged behind other townships was in its reluctance to run a joint sheep stock. This arrangement whereby each crofter has an equal share in a common stock on the hill, one member of the community being employed as shepherd, appeared to work harmoniously in other places. Bruach preferred to carry on as their fathers and grandfathers before them, each man having a few sheep on the hill and shepherding them whenever he felt the need or the urge to do so. It was a method which meant the flock was being constantly separated and harried from place to place, for however unco-operative their owners may have been the Bruach sheep still retained the instinct to flock together. Half-hearted proposals to merge stocks had been put forward from time to time but they were always resisted for a variety of reasons. They had felt their resistance to be amply justified when they heard of a stranger who, having taken over a croft in a neighbouring village and with it the share of the sheep stock, had ingenuously declared his annual profit from the stock on his income tax returns, much to the interest of the Inland Revenue Authorities and much to the consternation of the rest of the holders.

If the Bruachites had shown more spirit of co-operation they might have achieved a Public Hall of some sort. They might even have managed a piped water supply instead of one house in three having an abundance of water while the rest depended on moody springs. Though the inability to work together appeared to be congenital with the majority of the villagers yet it rarely developed into anything more serious than peevish wrangling. The two main causes of perceptible friction in Bruach were centred on the boats in the tourist season and in the herring fishing season, though if there was a glut of either tourists or of herring the crews managed to work together with the utmost cordiality, the idea being that it did not matter much which boat netted them so long as they were not allowed to get away. It was when there was a scarcity of either that any trouble flared up.

Between *Wayfarer*, Hector's boat, and *Seagull*, the boat of which Erchy and deaf Ruari, Morag's brother, each had a half share, there was at times bitter rivalry. They each took tourists for trips in the season. They each fished herring when it came into the loch. Their battles over tourists not only provided much entertainment for the rest of the village but more than once resulted in neither boat getting a trip because the passengers were afraid to risk going on the water with such fierce-sounding men. Deaf Ruari was mainly responsible for their apprehension for though he was an extremely forbearing old man normally, the power of his lungs undoubtedly increased in proportion as his wrath and the sparse white hairs on his face could bristle most aggressively. At such times one could not wonder at the tourists preferring to admire the scenery from the safety of the shore.

As the tourist season came to an end so the boat crews gradually became more amicable, helping to haul up each other's dinghies, respecting each other's lobster ground and frequently reporting where good catches were to be obtained. Then the herring would come in and the antagonism would spring up again.

Herring appear to be creatures of habit and they usually shoaled into Bruach waters some time in April for a couple of weeks and then disappeared until the autumn. The Bruachites took little interest in April herring. They wanted their fish for salting and the autumn herring, being less oily, took the salt better. Round about September the previous year's supply would be finished, or, if it were not completely finished, the fish that were left would be thrown out on to the croft for the cows, so that one became accumstomed to the sight of a cow standing chewing at a herring as a man chews at a cigar. The empty barrels would then be placed under a convenient waterfall to get thoroughly clean. (In an Island where the hills are full of streams there is never any difficulty in finding at least a cascade of water for each family's barrel.) The herring nets would then be taken down from the rafters where they had been stored since their 'mothproofing' at the end of their last season. The Bruachites mothproofed their nets by the simple method of leaving them in sacks or boxes for a time at the back of the house where the men could urinate on them. This very effective method of mothproofing is not, it seems, confined to herring nets; I know of one lady who gave away her hand-woven tweed suit after spending a winter holiday in a small weaving village and deducing the reason for the weaver's daily collection of pails of urine from their neighbours.

On calm, cool, moonlit nights with the sea lisping on the shingle shore, the noise of herring playing in the lòch is a beautiful and exciting sound. A sound to be evoked on hot, parcel-burdened days in town or when enduring the stuffy torture of a long train journey. It is as though the shoal tickles the surface of the sea and makes it bubble with laughter. On just such a night of calm I was returning home from a ceilidh with Morag when Erchy's voice hailed me.

'We'll be thinkin' of ceilidhin' with you tomorrow night,' he said.

'Good,' I replied with polite warmth. 'Who's we?'

'Me, and Johnny and maybe one or two others,' he enlightened me generously. 'The loch's teemin' with herrin' and we'll need to get after them before it's away for the winter.'

'The herring's in already?' I exclaimed.

'Surely! Are you no hearin' it?' I had to admit that until he had mentioned it I had not heard any unusual sound. 'Aye, but the noise of herrin' is like that,' said Erchy. 'Unless your ears is tuned in to it you can miss it altogether.' I paused now, and listened rapturously.

The following morning when I rowed out to lift my lobster creel two groups of men were busy preparing their nets for shooting in the evening. Erchy, Angus and deaf Ruari comprised one group and Hector and Duncan, the son of the postmistress, the other. The distance between them emphasized that the period of camaraderie was already beginning to wane. I went over to talk to Hector.

'No lobster, I see,' he greeted me.

'None today.'

'Nor yesterday, I'm tsinkin'.'

'No, not yesterday.'

'No indeed, when tse herrin's in tse loch it drives everytsin' away. I've seen whales in here, killers at tsat, and a big shoal of herrin' has come in and frightened tsem away out of it for tseir lives. It's as true as I'm here.'

I was pondering this unlikely information when Nelly, the daughter of Elly, and consequently known as 'Nelly-Elly', came hurrying down to the shore. Nelly-Elly ran the post office.

'They're wantin' you to go to the hills with the pollis,' she panted. 'There's been an accident.'

'I'll bet you tsat will mean a corpse,' said Hector glumly.

'It does so. A man's fallen and killed himself.' She paused for a few moments while we reacted to the news and then continued irately: 'I don't know whatever came over that Tom-Tom. Just because he finds a corpse he feels he should be able to tell me how to do my work. He kept ringing me up at the kiosk when I had a long-distance call occupyin' the line and tellin' me I was to cut short the call because he had an urgent message for the pollis. Urgent, he said! I refused to do it. "It's no urgent at all," I told him, "the man's already dead." '

We approved her assessment of the situation by nodding our heads. 'The pollis will be down in half an hour,' she added soberly.

'Is Tom-Tom goin' back with them?' asked Duncan.

'No, he says he's not fit to go.'

'Do tsey know where tse body is, tsen?' demanded Hector, who was still very sulky with the police because he had recently been fined for carrying more than the stipulated twelve passengers in his boat. 'I'm no waitin' about for tsem while tsey go lookin' for it. I'll take tsem tsere and leave tsem, just. Tsey can walk home.'

'You'd best tell them that yourself,' said Nelly-Elly with a toss of her head. 'Or if you don't want the job I can give it to Erchy.'

'To hell with tsat,' responded Hector. A great bone of contention between the two boats was that since the wily Hector had taken Nelly-Elly's son, Duncan, to work with him he had naturally fallen in for all the telephoned boat bookings, there being only one telephone line to Bruach.

'I'd been tsinkin' I'd get home to my dinner and take a wee snooze tsis afternoon,' Hector mumbled lugubriously. 'We'll be up all night at tse herrin' and I didn't get to bed tsis mornin' till tse back of four.'

'Four o'clock isn't all that late for you,' I retorted. 'Behag tells me you're reading until about three every morning.'

'Aye, it was no awful late right enough, but I'm feelin' a wee bitty tired just tse same. I tsink I'll come up to tse cottage with you, seein' we can't get home, will I? And you'll make us a strupak?'

'What about you, Duncan?' I asked. 'Are you coming for a strupak too?' Duncan was large-boned, thin and dark, with a metallic-looking moustache. Whenever I spoke to him he looked at the ground. I got the impression that he thought his eyes so bold and bright that he conscientiously dipped them as one dips the headlights of a car.

The two men accompanied me to the cottage and while they drank tea and munched thick slabs of fruit cake I packed a few sandwiches for them. The way the Bruach men were inclined to go out in their boats for long spells without taking any food distressed me. I could only assume that their tummies had been too maltreated to be sensitive to mealtimes, for they just did not seem to notice hunger. Hector, who was wandering in and out of the kitchen with his half-full cup of tea, suddenly perceived the silver buttons of the policemen and went off, cup in hand, to meet them.

'Tsere tsey are, nice as you like to me today,' he muttered when he came in to deposit his cup and collect his sandwiches. 'Fine you one day and hire your boat tse next day to sweeten you. Tsat's tse pollis all over. But I'm damty sure tsey're no keepin' me away from tse herrin'. Corpse or no corpse, I'll be back for tsat.'

I watched the weather as anxiously as the men. I loathe salt herring, but the crofters consider it not only a necessity but a delicacy. If it blew up there would be no herring fishing and the excitement that had threaded its way through the village with the coming of the shoal would die away. All morning the sun and the rain argued with each other while the wind played a bustling arbiter, but with the afternoon the sun finally triumphed and calmness again spread itself over the loch. As I fed the hens in the evening, *Wayfarer*, seeming downcast by her mission, struggled up the shadowed loch leaving an arrowed wake and, soon after she had moored up, a lorry which had been waiting at the shore juddered past the cottage with its gruesome burden, covered in tarpaulins. Another lorry full of glowing, gaily waving men, presumably members of the rescue party, followed shortly afterwards, and then the car with the policemen. Hector and Duncan called in at the cottage on their way home. Duncan looked a little white and strained, Hector merely looked smug.

'You see all tsat load of men goin' up tse road in tse lorry?' he demanded of me. I nodded. 'Well, every one of tsose men I brought home in my boat in one load, and tsere was over twenty of tsem without tse pollis.'

'How did you get away with that?' I asked him.

'Well, tsey came down to tse shore and tsey had tse body so tsey put tsat on board. Tsat was all right. Tsen came tse sergeant. "All aboard, we've finished for tse night, lads," he told tsem, nice as you like. When eleven was on tse boat I held up my hand. Says I, "I'll have to come back for tse rest of you, I'm no allowed to carry more tsan twelve on tsis boat, I have no licence." "Where's your twelve?" asks tse sergeant, and he looks cross. "Eleven of you and him in tse tarpaulin," says I. "Tsat makes my twelve." Tse sergeant looks at me and he says, "Tsat's a fine big boat you have tsere, Hector, and tsough tse law says twelve it's a daft law." "It was no so daft a few weeks back," I told him. "Why, tsat boat's safe enough with fifty aboard," he says. "On you get with you, boys." "It's your responsibility," I says. "My responsibility entirely," he agrees, so off we go, happy as you like. Ach, but tsey'd been trampin' the hills and climbin' around all day lookin' for tse body and they didn't want to be left tsere in tse dark. Tsey knew I'd take my time before I'd go back for tsem.'

'The sergeant was quite friendly, then,' I said with a smile.

'Friendly!' echoed Hector. 'He was tsat friendly when I offered him a sandwich he near bit tse hand off me. Aye, but I know what I'll do if tsey catch me with more tsan twelve again. I'll say all tse rest over twelve is corpses.'

I mentioned to Hector before he left that Erchy and his friends were expecting to ceilidh at the cottage that evening.

'We'll maybe be tsere ourselves too,' he promised. I was perfectly well aware that it was not my company that was being sought but only the convenient shelter of my cottage. The Bruach herring fishing was done from dinghies and the net was set and reset every hour or so, the crew coming ashore between settings. My cottage, so close to the shore and to their nets was ideally situated for them, and I resolved that as soon as Morag and Behag, who were also coming to ceilidh with me that evening, had left for their own home I would retire to bed and leave the herring fishermen in possession to brew themselves tea and make themselves comfortable as they wished.

While Morag and Behag were still with me the first lot of fishermen trooped in and flopped down on the available chairs and on the floor. There were Erchy and Johnny and Angus, nearly always an inseperable trio in any evening ploy; there were Tom-Tom and a cousin from Glasgow. Their eyes were shining and they all looked drunk, but they were drunk only with the excitement of the occasion.

'The loch's stiff with fish of some sort,' pronounced Erchy.

'If Hector catches herrin' tonight I'll no get him to bed for a week,' mourned Behag.

'No man needs to sleep when he's catchin' herrin',' Erchy told her. 'I've stuck at the herrin' for a week near enough without gettin' a wink of sleep and never felt tired. So long as you're catchin' them it's all right. It's when you're not you get tired.'

I noticed the absence of deaf Ruari whom I had expected to be there as skipper of the *Seagull*. 'Doesn't Ruari go herring fishing at all?' I asked.

'Ach, he cannot come because Bella's afraid to sleep by herself. Honest, the way that man looks after his wife you'd think there was a subsidy on her.'

'How come you to be here then, Angus?' asked Morag. 'Isn't Ishbel on her own and in no fit state to be left?'

'I got my brother to stay beside her tonight,' Angus excused himself.

There were noises outside and soon Hector, Duncan and Sandy

Beag were adding their voices to the general teasing and argument which inevitably accompanies an impromptu ceilidh like this.

'You'd best see to your nets,' said Morag as she tied a scarf over her head in readiness to go home. 'You've been in here over an hour, Erchy. You'll no catch herrin' in Miss Peckwitt's kitchen.'

'The way you women talk about the fish it's a wonder we ever catch a single one,' cut in Sandy Beag irascibly.

'Oh, stop frettin' yourself, Sandy,' Morag told him. 'Erchy himself has been speakin' of the herrin' by name, have you not, Erchy?'

'I believe I did,' admitted Erchy.

'Then he'll no catch any the night,' predicted Sandy earnestly.

'There are quite a lot of superstitions connected with herring fishing, aren't there?' I began, and stopped as I met a glare from Sandy.

'Aye, there's a few right enough,' Erchy said. 'One is that you mustn't go fishin' for them on Fridays. Another that you mustn't let a woman cross your path when you're on your way.'

'I thought it was only a red-haired woman?' I interpolated.

'A red-haired woman's all right for ordinary fish, but herrin' are more particular. Any woman will put off herrin' so they say. Then, you mustn't point at them when you hear them playin'. You've got to show where they are without pointin'. And you must never turn the boat against the clock when you're goin' out to the net. That's the only one I take any notice of myself.'

'You mark what I say, Erchy, you'll no get the fish you're wantin' tonight the way you're after speakin' of them,' Sandy reiterated.

After Morag and Behag had gone, I went to bed and heard vaguely throughout the night the heavy clumping of sea-boots in the kitchen and at times the disturbing sound of raised voices. When I got up there was a lovely fire burning in the grate, the kettle was hissing on the hob and the cups they had used had been washed and put away. News came later that the night's fishing had yielded one herring.

The following night I was in bed when they arrived, but I had told them to make use of the kitchen. I slept soundly and the dawn was only a paler shadow over the sea when there came a thumping on the door of my room.

'What is it?' I called sleepily.

'Were you not sayin' you were wantin' to get a lift to the mainland if you could, so as to get your car?' Erchy's voice shouted.

I grunted that I had indeed said so. The repairs to 'Joanna' were now completed, the garage had said, and she was ready for collection.

'Well, now's your chance. We've 'phoned for a lorry to take our fish and it'll be here in half an hour. I'm away now.'

I got up quickly and went into the kitchen. The table was strewn with dirty cups—no saucers—and the floor was littered with cigarette stubs. There were only elusive red cinders under a mound of warm peat ash in the grate. An abandoned cap hung on a chair, glistening with herring scales in the lamplight. I pushed the dishes into the sink and brewed coffee. The air of the kitchen was still thick with tobacco fumes and my mouth felt as though I too had been smoking all night. I finished my coffee as I heard the noise of an engine, and threw on my coat. The hens and Bonny would have to wait until I got back.

Hector loomed up in the open doorway. He looked in surprise at my attire. 'Are you comin' with us?' he asked, his eyes signifying immense pleasure at the prospect.

'I thought it was Erchy who told me to hurry,' I said. 'Are you sharing a lorry between you?'

'No, indeed,' he replied. 'We're havin' a lorry each.'

'You must have got a lot of herring,' I complimented him.

'Well, we got a few cran.'

'And how many did Erchy get?'

'Ach, he got very few herrin'. Mostly mackerel it was in tseir net, tsough I don't know why. Tsey didn't set tseir nets much different to our own.'

'Sandy will be more superstitious than ever,' I said. 'But Erchy will be disappointed.'

'Aye, he was disappointed right enough,' he said with spurious sympathy, and then added brightly, 'God! I could hear him swearin' away tsere all night. I believe he made a swear for every mackerel he took out of tse net.' He chuckled. 'You may as well come on our lorry,' he went on. 'It'll be tsere before Erchy's.'

Erchy bounded in at this juncture, looking a little cross.

'Are you ready?'

'Yes, I'm ready, but Hector says his lorry will be there before yours, and I must try to get back here as soon as possible.'

'Damty sure it won't be there before my lorry,' Erchy said combatively.

'Damty sure it will,' responded Hector.

'I'm going on the one that's in front at this moment,' I said firmly, and went out and got into the cab, leaving the two still arguing in the kitchen.

The foremost lorry was loaded with herring and ready to start. The mackerel lorry was only now coming up from the shore. Duncan and Sandy, the latter looking very self-satisfied, hoisted themselves to the back of the lorry with the fish. Hector jumped in beside me. 'Come on! Give her tse gutty,' he urged the driver. 'Tsere's a good dram in it for you if we beat tsem to it.'

'Why are you so bothered about beating Erchy's lorry?' I asked as the driver roared the engine full ahead. 'Surely if he has mackerel his catch won't affect the price you'll get for your herring, or the other way round.'

'Indeed it will so!' Both the driver and Hector turned on me indignantly. 'If he gets tsere first with his mackerel tsey won't be nearly so keen to pay high prices for our herrin'. Oh, tsey'll buy tsem, right enough, but tsey're no big buyers and tsey cannot take a lot of fish. We could very easily lose by it. Y'see, Erchy has some herrin' himself. He'll sort tsem on tse way in and if tse buyers tsinks tsere's only a few tsey'll pay him top price. Tsen when tsey see us come in with our lot tsey'll tsink tsere must be plenty more so tse price will drop.' He turned to the driver. 'Make every bit of speed you can, Neilly,' he exhorted him. The driver nodded understandingly.

Whilst we were on the narrow road we had no difficulty in keeping our lead. The horn of the following lorry was sounded repeatedly but whenever we came to a passing place our driver took the middle of the road and frustrated any attempt on the part of the other driver to get ahead. I wondered if Erchy was in the cab of the lorry similarly exhorting its driver and promising a similar reward. As we careered along at furious speed my hair began to stand on end. I knew the tortuous Bruach road and treated it with respect. The lorry driver must have been equally familiar with it but this morning he treated it with contempt. The lorry was senile and unbuoyant and through the gaps between the floorboards I glimpsed the rough road planed by our speed. When we reached the narrow strip of road with the sea a sheer drop of eighty feet below I cowered into my seat and had I not

been firmly wedged between Hector and the driver I believe I would
have essayed a jump from the offside door. When we came out on the
high road I felt a certain amount of relief though our speed was still
perilous.

Hector glanced behind him. 'He's comin' alongside,' he told the
driver. 'Head him off!' But the driver, to whom I hoped sanity had
perhaps returned with the constraint of a main road, refused to swerve
more than a foot or two. The cab of the second lorry drew inexorably
up on us, its grim-faced driver visible crouched over his wheel. Our
own driver increased his speed so that the two lorries kept their bon-
nets dead level. I was surprised to see that Erchy was not in the cab
of the other lorry, but by turning to look out of the rear window
I could see him and his cronies standing up among the piled mackerel,
looking desperately streamlined with their caps back to front and their
clothes flat against their bodies. They were all fiercely gesticulating
and mouthing what I knew would probably be wild insults at the
men on the back of our own lorry. I saw Erchy pick up a mackerel
and hurl it vengefully towards us. I saw his cronies instantly pick up
fish and hurl them likewise, and almost immediately I saw the herring
raining down on them from our own lorry. I glanced at Hector but
he was intent on chewing his fingers, his eyes glued to the road.
It was fortunate that it was so early in the morning and there was no
traffic; if there had been I doubted if our drivers, in the mood they
were in, would have got out of the way. I looked round again as we
passed a tinker encampment beside the road. Two of the tinkers stood
outside and I saw their expressions change rapidly from outrage to
delight as they too were pelted with fish.

'Two loads of mixed herring and mackerel,' announced the fish
buyers' assistant when the lorries finally halted at the pier.

'Here, no!' protested Hector, hurrying to the back of the lorry.
His mouth dropped open as he saw his confederates standing shamefaced among the herring and mackerel. He went closer. 'How in hell did
tsis happen?' he asked, dazedly.

'Ach, we just had a bit of an argument,' Erchy told him. 'It's settled
now.'

'God!' ejaculated Hector when he had heard the full story. 'Tsat's
a joke right enough. I wish I'd seen tse faces of tsose tinks when tse
fish hit tsem.'

'Indeed, we near fell off the lorry ourselves laughin' at them,' chuckled Johnny.

The fish dealer paid them their money and they all went off happily together to wait in some congenial place for the pubs to open so that they could spend it. Only the two drivers were left and they stayed in their lorries glaring at each other lugubriously until they were gestured away by impatient fish porters.

'Ach, them Bruach men,' said the fish buyer in my ear, 'there's no sense in them at all. I believe they're as mad as I don't know what.'

I went to collect 'Joanna' and allowed my body to untense itself slowly as I drove homeward. The morning mist was rising from the hill corries and from the tumbling, bracken-fringed burns. Above the mountains to the east the sunlit clouds had the metallic look of crumpled tinfoil. At the tinker encampment the family were gathered round a fire and a big fat woman was flourishing a frypan. A most delectable smell of fried herring was wafted across the road.

Bread and Uisge-Beatha

'The Hebrideans,' declaimed the holidaymaker from Glasgow, 'are very pure, you know.'

I didn't know, so I waited for her to explain. She had been coming to Bruach for a holiday every winter for the last ten years, long before I had known of its existence, so she really should have known what she was talking about. I wondered if she would next trot out the myth that crofters are hard working. She did. 'Bruach in my opinion,' she summed up, 'is an ideally happy, healthy, moral and law-abiding community.' Janet, her landlady, slid me a wary glance from the corners of her eyes.

'Indeed, and isn't it nice to hear someone say that?' she asked me.

'Oh, but I mean every word of it,' enthused the visitor. 'I should simply love to live in Bruach.'

It is curious that the people who express a longing to live in the Hebrides usually avoid doing so. So far as I knew, the only people who had made any real effort to find a home in Bruach had been middle-aged spinsters like myself, and for this the fact that the village had more than its share of middle-aged bachelors may have been largely responsible.

It was a chilly evening in November; an evening of chastened calm after a day and night of such storm and fury that when I had looked out of my cottage that morning I had been faintly surprised to see the outer islands still occupying their normal positions. Janet, the visitor and myself were comfortably ensconced in the visitors' sitting-room awaiting the arrival of the grocery van which visited the village each week. Though there was a small general shop in Bruach, the owner of which claimed to sell everything from 'fish to chemistry', many of the crofters preferred to go to the van for the bulk of their purchases. The main reason for this, I believe, was that it came on specified days at more or less specified times so that everyone could congregate round it when it stopped and indulge in a 'good crack', as they called a gossip. To wander up to the shop when the chances were that you would meet no one but the grocer or his family was not considered nearly such good entertainment. Wild weather on van days gave the excuse to drop in at the houses of friends who lived near the road and to chat over a cup of tea while listening for the long-drawn-out blast of the horn by which the driver always announced his arrival.

'My, but the van's very late,' observed Janet, getting up to put more peats on the fire.

The outer door opened and a man's voice shouted.

'Is that you, Murdoch? Come away in,' called Janet.

Old Murdoch opened the door and put his head inside. He obviously had not shaved for days and his face looked as though it had been planted by the Forestry Commission. His nose reared through the growth like the beginning of a forest fire.

'What's that you're sayin'?' enquired Janet.

'I'm sayin' it's no good you waitin' here,' he told us. 'The van's away back home. You'll no be seein' him tonight.'

'Why ever's that?' asked Janet.

'Indeed, he gave no explanation at all,' said the old man. 'He stopped once just at the top of the village and then he turned the van and went off home without a word to anybody.'

'Well, well,' murmured Janet. 'I wonder whatever has happened.'

'They're sayin' there's a dance on at Sheehan and he's wantin' to get back in time for it,' said Murdoch.

There was a gasp of disapproval from the visitor.

'That's no good enough,' observed Janet indignantly. 'Leaving us all without supplies just to go to a dance.'

'Aye, there's some of them awful wild about it,' agreed Murdoch. 'Nelly-Elly's sayin' she hasn't a bitty sugar in the house to take with their tea. And Anna-Vic's sayin' she hasn't a biscuit left though she's bought nine pounds this week already.'

'Nine pounds of biscuits! In a week!' repeated the visitor incredulously.

'Aye, but she has a big family,' Janet said defensively.

'Her own mother had a big family too,' exclaimed Murdoch. 'And I never saw her buy a biscuit in her life. She baked everythin' herself on the girdle.' Murdoch took his pipe from his pocket, brandished it compellingly and settled himself on a chair. 'Never a shop biscuit nor a shop loaf went into that house and look at the fine family she reared.'

'No, but the vans didn't come in those days,' argued Janet.

'No, and there wasn't so many pensions to pay for all the stuff, either,' retorted Murdoch.

Janet smiled disapprovingly. 'Murdoch would like to see us all back to the old days when women did nothin' but work all day long,' she said. 'That's why no woman would marry him.'

I said good night, leaving Murdoch reminiscing happily with the visitor. Janet came with me to the door.

'I wonder when the van will come now?' I asked, though aware of the triviality of the question.

'Dear knows,' answered Janet, 'but there'll be some miscallin' of that man if it was nothin' but a dance took him from the village.'

I thanked her automatically for the strupak. 'Don't thank me for that, my dear, it was just thrown at you,' she disclaimed modestly. 'You'll be at Jeannac's weddin' party tomorrow?' she reminded me. I assured her that I would be.

There was now a nip of frost in the air, and across the vastness of the sky shooting stars dodged brilliantly as though hectored by the presumptuous moon. Beyond the bay the scattered lighthouses flashed like jewels against the rustling dark velvet of the water while close at hand the noise of the burn swelled and diminished as it was caught by the fickle breeze. I walked briskly homewards, meditating with some amusement on the visitor's declamation on the purity of the Gael, suspecting that her opinion was based not so much on her own perception as on a superficial acquaintance with the excessive prudery of a Gaelic dictionary (which is so chaste that it gives only the alternate letters of any word that might be thought improper!). The remark had undoubtedly been offered in extenuation of the strange obsession of Janet's sister, Grace, whose story Janet had just been telling to the visitor.

Grace, even as a young girl, had never been particularly bright, and at fifteen she had 'got herself into trouble'. When she was fifty, Grace had suffered a slight stroke which, though not affecting her general health in any way, had left her with a fitful stammer and with an inexplicable aversion to the fly buttons on men's trousers. Her brothers began to find that if they left their trousers in the kitchen to dry overnight, when they came to put them on in the morning the fly buttons would all have been removed and the flies securely sewn up with strong thread. During the summer months when Janet took in boarders Grace's affliction had proved very embarrassing for the family and though they had kept a strict eye on her whenever male boarders came with wet clothes to be dried, she had on more than one occasion successfully eluded their vigilance. When Grace was sixty she had suffered yet another stroke which, though still not affecting her general health, had completely deprived her of the power of speech and, to the dismay of the family, had intensified her passion for correcting male attire. Her brothers now found it necessary to hide their trousers when they retired to bed because she would stealthily enter their rooms whilst they were asleep and appropriate any she could. The moment a male tourist entered the house Grace would fix the offending fly with a fierce stare, her fingers would hover above the scissors on their hook, and she would have to be strenuously dissuaded from following him up the stairs to his room, snapping the scissors anticipatorily. As Janet had confided to me, the only relief the family had was in knowing that she waited until the men had taken off their trousers before she 'Dis-Graced' them. Now Grace was nearing seventy. 'And dear knows what will happen if she has another stroke,' Janet had lamented. 'I can see us havin' to stop takin' in boarders altogether.' I suggested she should take only men who wear the kilt. 'No, no,' Janet had shaken her head dubiously. 'Maybe we'd better not risk that.' Comic as it seemed the problem was certainly a serious one for Janet and she had all my sympathy.

Around mid-day the following day the prolonged bellowing of a horn summoned me from my work. As a general rule I patronized the vans very little, begrudging the time I had to spend awaiting my turn. I could go to the village shop and get what I wanted in a quarter of the time and still be able to linger for a pleasant chat, but for some perishables and some of the more sophisticated items, like fruit juice and cream crackers, I had to rely on the vans.

'Did you hear why the van driver turned back last night?' I asked as I joined up with a group of crofters who, with rolled-up sacks under their arms, were already converging on the van and its inevitable entourage of scavenging gulls.

'Aye, poor man. It wasn't the dance at all he went back for. No, when he got to the top of the village he found he hadn't a dram to see him through the rest of the night, and he had such a thirst on him he just felt he couldn't wait another minute, so he turned straight back. He said he knew we'd all understand. Right enough, some was sayin' last night they'd be after reportin' him to the manager, but then they thought it was the dance he'd gone to. Ach, but you cannot hold a man's thirst against him.'

The wherewithal for a Hebridean to indulge his thirst seems to be always available, no matter how unremunerative his regular occupation may appear to be. I cannot explain why it should be so; I can only accept the fact that it is.

'Next for shavin'!' The gamekeeper's wife stepped down from the van and called out jovially as she stowed loaves and groceries into her sack and heaved it on to her shoulder. Whenever a Bruachite finished buying at a van it was the custom to call out wittily, 'Next for shavin'.' The phrase had been called out by every crofter at every van I had ever waited upon throughout the years and it had never failed to bring a chuckle from the audience; the Bruachites venerated age even in their jokes.

It was Old Murdoch's turn next. Though Murdoch lived with his sisters he did all the shopping because, he maintained, his sisters were too vague about the value of the different coins. Today Murdoch had been selling cattle and when he came to pay for his groceries he opened a purse well stuffed with notes. He was having, as Murdoch was invariably having, some tetchy argument with the van driver about the price of something he had bought and as he had no pipe handy to gesticulate with he used his open purse. A curious gull flew low over the van: in the next moment I realized that the word 'shit' can be onomatopoeic. The waiting crofters shrieked and fell back with laughter and Murdoch stared at his open purse with horror and disgust. It was the first time in my life I had seen a Gael look at money in such a way.

'That bloody gull's spilled into my poc!' he spluttered as though doubting the evidence of his own eyes.

We were all helpless with laughter and Murdoch, seeing himself as the chief entertainer, gallantly played up. He shook his fist at the gull; he danced about with rage. He gave every feather of the bird its full pedigree before he minced away holding his bulging purse at arm's length in front of him as apprehensively as though it had been a shovel full of hot coals. Altogether the scene was one of the funniest I have ever witnessed and when my own turn at the van came I had great difficulty in composing my features ready to make the serious complaint which was my main reason for wishing to see the driver.

In the Hebrides, where in the smaller village shops stocks are inclined to be slow moving, purchases might prove on occasion to be very unappetizing, sometimes inedibly so. In fact I had more than once been enabled to fulfil a life-long ambition to accept the printed invitation enclosed in each box of chocolates to 'return with this slip in case of complaint'. Generally speaking, one could understand and excuse, but the van driver had sold me mouldy bread and for this I could see

no excuse at all. Admittedly mould grew prolifically in Bruach; so much
so that one almost caught oneself pulling up one's sleeve to examine
what was only a dark smudge on one's arm, but the bread I had bought
was supposed to be fresh and it had been wrapped bread. Normally I
baked my own, but a new cooker was in process of being installed in
my kitchen—Hector and Erchy had between them undertaken the task,
but with Hector mislaying 'tsings' and Erchy anticipating Jeannac's
wedding, progress had been slow. The lack of a cooking stove had
necessitated my buying bread temporarily and the first week I had got
it fresh from the van, or so I had thought until I had taken off the
wrapper and found it to be liberally spotted with mould. The following
week when I had attended the van I had complained bitterly to the
driver and threatened to report the matter unless he ensured that he
sold me an uncontaminated loaf.

'How am I to tell whether a loaf's mouldy or not when it's all
sealed up in a wrapper?' he had demanded pettishly. 'I don't make the
damty stuff.'

'Well then, you'll just have to unwrap the loaf and examine it before
you sell it to me,' I had insisted.

Ungraciously he had yielded and I had rejected about half his complement of loaves on the grounds of staleness or their resemblance to
charred rubber before I was satisfied with the one I bought. However,
when I came to cut a slice for my breakfast the next morning there
was mould all the way through it.

Now, full of righteous indignation I stepped up to the van and
glaring coldly at the driver reminded him of my complaint of the
previous week and retailed unsparingly to him how, the very next
morning, the loaf had been cut and found to be full of mould.

The driver made a pretence of listening earnestly and then returned
my glare with an equally irate one.

'I'm damty glad it was mouldy then,' he said astonishingly.

I was thoroughly shaken. 'What did you say?'

'I said I'm damty glad it was mouldy. God! But that's funny,' he
said, bursting into laughter. 'All that trouble you put me up to last
week and all your greetin' and grumblin' and then you go and pick
out a mouldy loaf for yourself.'

The van driver had the most infectious laugh in the world and it was
a very merry shopping expedition for everyone that day.

Morag was waiting her turn when I stepped down. 'You're comin' to Jeannac's weddin' party tonight?' she asked, adding quickly, 'If you're spared.'

'Yes, of course,' I replied.

Jeannac and her husband had been married quietly a day or two previously on the mainland but now they had returned to have a proper wedding celebration at home.

'You mind when we were invited to her sister's weddin' two or three years back?' said Morag. 'It was on a Friday and they were boastin' that their weddin' cake weighed ten pounds, and the very next Friday they were boastin' the same about their baby, and you were that put out about it.'

I remembered it all very well. At the time I had been fairly new to Bruach and when the news of the birth of the baby had come so soon after the wedding I had been shocked indeed. Several months later when Morag and I had been collecting for some charity or other we had called at the house of the newlyweds. The baby had been crawling by then and such a delightful, bonny child was it that I was soon cuddling it and bouncing it on my knee. As we were coming away from the house I had observed to Morag that it was a lovely baby. 'Yes,' she had replied, 'but do you mind when you first heard it had come you said the couple should have been whipped?'

'Oh no!' I had at first protested, but the faint suspicion that I might once have been so intolerant as to have made such a remark grew into a positive recollection. I had felt thoroughly ashamed of myself.

'Yes, you did, mo ghaoil,' Morag had asserted. 'And I've never forgotten the look on your face when you said it.'

I have long since grown accustomed to 'God's wedding presents' being bestowed a little prematurely but there have been times in the wakeful hours of the night when I have wondered just what that wise old woman saw in my face that day

The van's being delayed until the day of the wedding party had given me rather a rush of work. I had left Erchy putting the finishing touches to the new stove and there would, in addition to my ordinary chores, be the cleaning up of the kitchen afterwards. Intent on planning how best to accomplish everything I had to do, I was hurrying home when Peter jumped suddenly over the stone dyke from his croft with a gun under his arm. His appearance gave me a momentary fright but he dropped the gun abruptly, spat on his hand, rubbed it vigorously up and down his jacket, and offered it to me in greeting.

'Any luck with the rabbits, Peter?' I asked with a cautious glance at his abandoned gun which in places was bound with string and pieces of wire and looked as though it might prove more lethal to its handler than to any target.

'Yes, Miss,' he struggled breathlessly to tell me. 'One and a half.' His struggle for words was emphasized by the fact that his cap kept wriggling about on his head as he spoke.

'Jolly good,' I complimented him. 'But what happened to the other half?' (envisaging half a rabbit running back to its hole).

'He's no there when I go get he's, so I leave he's there.'

He lifted his cap, recaptured hastily the two moribund but not completely inert fish which escaped from it, replaced them and pulled his cap down more firmly on his head, leaving their tails hanging over his forehead in an animated fringe.

'Those will make a nice dinner for you and your mother, won't they?' I told him.

'Yes, Miss, I'm away to toast she's,' he said, retrieving his gun.

I was delighted to see smoke coming from the kitchen chimney of my cottage and when I pushed open the door Erchy, looking very glum for Erchy, was standing back speculatively.

'Wonderful!' I remarked with a contented smile.

'Aye, it's no so bad.'

'It's splendid,' I insisted, 'and the chimney seems to be drawing perfectly.' I lit the small gas ring and put on the kettle. 'You'll take a cup of coffee before you go?'

'Aye, thank you.'

'You do sound gloomy,' I told him. 'What's the matter? Disappointed because you didn't get away to the dance last night?'

'No indeed, I'm no disappointed about that at all.'

'Well, you're not like yourself,' I said.

'I don't feel like myself then.'

'You mean you're not feeling well?'

'Ach, I'm fine. I just don't feel like myself.'

I gave him a cup of coffee and put on the table some biscuits and cheese, and waited for the confidence which I knew was on its way.

'It's funny,' said Erchy, after a sip or two of coffee. 'I believe I must have been in love with Jeannac.'

'Jeannac? The Jeannac who got married on Wednesday?'

'Aye. I must have been in love with her, or why else would I feel so bad at her marryin' another man?'

I could only stare at him in speechless sympathy and wonder how much he was suffering.

'It was the same when Marjac got married. I felt just as bad then, so I knew I must have loved her,' he told me.

'But, didn't you realize before either of them married that you were in love with them?' I asked him.

'No, that's my trouble. I always have to wait for them to get married before I can tell. If I feel bad on their weddin' day then I know I was in love with them. If I don't feel bad I know I wasn't,' he said miserably.

His complaint, I thought, constituted the best recipe for remaining a bachelor that I had ever heard but Erchy was much too serious on the subject for me to dare any comment. I tried to take his mind off his sufferings.

'I suppose they've stocked up well with whisky for the party to-night?' I said.

'They stocked up well. They got seven bottles the other night and they thought they'd have a wee drink to start off with and before the night was through they'd finished the seven. I was there myself. Adam's havin' to go in to the pub on his motor bike to get some this evenin'.' He brightened considerably and by the time he had embarked on his second cup of coffee and reinspected the burning of the stove he was practically his normal self again. 'This coffee's good,' he approved. 'I don't rightly care much for coffee, but I like this stuff you make. Those pilgrims gave me a cup of coffee when I was in sortin' a chair for them the other day and it tasted no better than singed water.' He accepted a third cup and then decided he must go home and 'take his potatoes' '(his dinner). I'll see you tonight,' he told me as he went.

'Yes,' I replied meaningly, 'probably in triplicate if past functions are anything to judge by.'

About ten minutes after he had left he was back again. 'Here, come and see a sight,' he commanded.

The afternoon sun was still shining brightly but within the hour it would be snugging itself down for the night behind the humped shapes of Rhuna and the outer islands, and I had a great deal to do before it got properly dark. I demanded to know if the sight were really worth my taking time off to see.

'I doubt you'll never see the like again,' promised Erchy. 'I've never seen it before anyway.'

He led me in the direction of Murdoch's cottage and how I wished when we got there that I had taken my camera with me. Murdoch, who by turns was irascible, obstreperous, rhetorical and benign, was born to be a clown. If there was a situation in which he was involved it would inevitably become a comic one. He sat there now in his garden on an upturned pail watching with morosely unswerving eyes about twenty dripping one-pound and five-pound notes which were pinned with safety pins to his clothes line.

'God!' murmured Erchy appreciatively, 'the old bodach's washed the lot of it.'

When I arrived for the wedding party at Jeannac's house the guests were already overflowing the kitchen and 'the room' and were sitting happily on the stairs right up to the tiny landing. For all I knew there may have been more in the bedrooms. The heat inside hit one like a poultice though cold breaths of frost panted in through the wide-open door. I managed to insinuate myself into a corner of the kitchen where someone handed me a glass of sherry and a piece of crumbled cake. Everyone was talking and laughing happily and strangely enough no one appeared to be more than moderately intoxicated. Sandy Beag called that we ought to be dancing and clutching the reluctant Jeannac he started to jig, kicking his feet behind him but he was made to desist after nearly de-skirting one or two of the black-draped old women who were standing near.

'Here, take her, Ian,' Sandy Beag pushed the bride towards her groom who was leaning pallidly against the dresser.

The announcement of the engagement of Jeannac and Ian had hit the village with startling suddenness and no matter who I met during the intervening weeks before the wedding day the question 'Why is Jeannac marrying Ian?' was always one of the first to be asked. The Bruachites were great diagnosticians. In sickness, whether of animals or humans, the symptoms were discussed profoundly and the ailment diagnosed before the arrival of the vet or the doctor. The symptoms of a forthcoming wedding were discussed in much the same way, for though addicted to romantic fiction the crofters were sceptical of romance in their own lives and they liked to have some incontrovertible reason to offer for any impending marriage. The engagement of the vet brought the comment, 'Well, right enough he's got to have someone to answer the telephone for him,' while another marriage, an obviously incompatible union, was excused because 'since his mother's died his sister's afraid to sleep by herself and they can't afford a girl to share her bed.' However, I had heard no plausible reason advanced for Jeannac's acceptance of Ian. Jeannac was strikingly good looking, intelligent and financially secure, and looking across at her now, glowingly happy beside the sleazy Ian, I wondered more than ever why she had chosen him. I said so out loud to Old Murdoch and Morag, who were standing close beside me.

'Ach, well, Miss Peckwitt,' Old Murdoch began with a slightly apologetic air, 'a woman comes to a certain stage just like a salmon at the back end that will jump at a piece of old rag, and then she'll take anythin' at all.'

'But Jeannac's not old,' I protested, turning to Morag for confirmation. 'Surely you don't think it's a case of last chance with Jeannac?'

'No,' she admitted, 'I dunna believe it's that at all, but I'm hearin' he made a song for her, though what was in it she never told a soul, and then she made a song back for him and the next everybody knew they was plannin' to get married.'

'Did you hear how the wedding went off?' I asked.

'Ach, it was quiet just. Just the two of them and Johnny and Elspeth, though I did hear that Johnny was so keen not to lose the ring he put it on his own little finger and when he came to hand it to the bridegroom it had got stuck. He was after havin' a great struggle with it, Elspeth said, and indeed at one time she thought Ian would be after marryin' Johnny with the way it was.'

More and more people were packing into the house and a good deal of drink was being spilled on dresses and suits and on the floor as we were jostled against one another. I was thinking how much more pleasant it might have been if the party had taken place in the summer so that the guests could perhaps have taken their refreshments outside and conversed or danced without too much discomfort.

'Here,' said Erchy, threading his way towards us with an open bottle of whisky. 'You're lookin' miserable. Fill up your glass, there'll be plenty more when Angus get's back.'

'I'm not miserable,' I denied, lifting my still half-full glass out of reach of the threatening bottle. 'But Erchy,' I asked him. 'Tell me will you why Bruach people always choose the winter time for their weddings?'

Erchy stared me firmly in the eye. 'Because the nights are longer,' he replied with unflinching candour.

'What's happened to Angus?' asked Morag.

'They're wonderin' that themselves,' replied Erchy. He went off on Adam's motor bike to get some more drinks about three hours ago and he said he'd be back within the hour, and he's no back yet.' He wandered away again, still proffering the bottle indiscriminately.

'I didn't know Angus could ride a motor bike,' I murmured to Morag.

'I don't believe he can,' she said, 'but he's gone off on it just the same. Somebody had to go, they said, and Adam's crinkled his back and canna' stand up on his legs.'

'I should jolly well think they would be wondering what has happened to him in that case,' I said with an anxious glance in the direction of Angus's mother. 'He might have had a spill.'

'Ach, if that lad has a spill he'll make sure he chooses a soft spot,' said Morag lightly.

One of the highlights of the evening was to be the reading of the congratulatory telegrams without which no Highland wedding would really be complete. After much hilarious discussion it was decided to wait to read them until Angus had returned so that he should not miss the fun. Since attending my first wedding in Bruach I had become inured to hearing the youth of the village composing bawdy messages to send to their friends when they got married. In the last few years Hebridean post offices have become much less easy-going than they used to be in their attitude to the sending of such messages and there had been bitter complaints this time that two of the verses composed for the congratulatory telegrams had been refused for transmission on the grounds of their being too coarse. Dollac, who was not only beautiful but also as happy a natured girl as I have ever met, was particularly adept at such compositions and when the subject came up she was loud in her condemnation of the post office.

'Oh come,' I pleaded, 'they must have been pretty bad if the post office refused them.'

'Indeed they were no bad at all. I've sent worse. They're gettin' so particular nowadays it won't be worth while spendin' our money on them.'

'Tell Miss Peckwitt what was in yours,' urged Morag, with a sly smile.

'Yes, go on, tell me,' I encouraged.

Dollac giggled. 'May your honeymoon be like our dining-room table—four legs and no drawers,' she quoted unblushingly.

'And the other one?'

'Ach, that was just:

> "Ian, Ian, don't be shy,
>   Put out the light and have a damn good try".'

'What's wrong with those, I'd like to know?' demanded Morag indignantly. 'They must have nasty minds those telegraph fellows.'

'They're no worse than I sent my cousin when he got married,' said Dollac, 'and they took that one all right.'

'What did you have to say then?' I pressed, conscious of a sneaking admiration.

> 'Two little pillows edged with lace,
> Two little people face to face,
> And everything in its proper place',

she recited amidst shrieks of female laughter.

At this moment Angus flung himself sulkily through the door and plonked down some bottles emphatically on the table.

'Why Angus, what on earth has been keepin' you back?' asked his mother.

'Those bloody pollis, that's what,' Angus retorted with seething resentment.

A strained hush fell over the kitchen. 'You mean you're after bein' caught?' his mother whispered.

'Caught? No, but I had a lucky escape.' He labled himself a drink of water and swallowed two or three times before pouring the rest back into the pail. 'What happened was I was just comin' out of the bar when I sees those two pollis passin' in their car. They sees me and they stops. "Where are you away to?" they asks me, quite friendly. "I'm away home," I tells them, "whenever I can get. I've just been gettin' the drinks for my sister's weddin' party." "And how are you gettin' home," they asks me. Well I couldn't tell them I had the motor bike because I have no driving licence and anyway Adam has no insurance for his bike. "There's a fellow goin' that way says he would give me a lift," I says. They asked me who it was so I told them the only name I could think of. "Ach," they says, "you'll wait all night for him, he left over an hour ago. Come on and we'll give you a lift with us." I was swearin' to myself I can tell you. "Are you goin' to Bruach?" I asks them. "Not all the way," they says, "but a good part of it. Come on and jump in." I knew if I didn't go with them then they'd guess somethin' and start lookin' around. So I just didn't look at Adam's motor bike and I got into the car with them and they took me as far as Sheehan. Indeed at one time I thought the buggers were goin' to take me farther. When they stopped, I got out and as soon as they was out of sight I hid the bottles in the ditch and started walkin' back again to the pub for I didn't want the bike to be found there. When I got there the pollis car was still not back from Sheehan. Hell! I thought, what do I do now? So what I did was to get on the bike and start off, for by this time it was dark and every time I saw a pair of headlights comin' towards me I had to jump off and fling myself and the bike into the ditch and lie flat. I'm wet through. I could have murdered those bloody pollis, I can tell you.'

Relief spread over everyone's face at the successful outcome of Angus's escapade and at the sight of the full bottles on the table. The party rapidly became noisier and distinctly less pleasant so far as I was concerned. The male Bruachites firmly believe that they must get drunk before they can enjoy themselves, and the women, who seemed to find the men too inhibited unless they were drunk, encouraged them in their belief.

In 'the room' a gramophone began to contribute to the general cacophony and Morag drew me through there to listen to records of Gaelic songs. They found a record of 'Loch Lomond' which they put on for me because it was in English, though it was little more than a tuneless whisper.

'That record is nearly worn out,' I said to Morag.

'Yes,' she rejoined, 'but it's a very old tune, isn't it?'

Janet, looking very merry and bright, beckoned us into the kitchen where tea was being prepared and we inched our way through, passing Erchy, who was sprawled on a bench beside Sadie, a young girl from a neighbouring village. Sadie was full-bosomed, strong and possessed of gypsy-like good looks and Erchy was proposing marriage to her with sleepy earnestness. 'An' I'll make you a good . . . good husband,' he was saying. '. . . An' I'll work . . . work hard. . . .'

I smiled to myself, recalling the autumn day when I had met Erchy, looking very harassed, making for his home at the double, his scythe over his shoulder. Only a short time previously I had seen him scything the corn on his croft so I called out to him, teasingly, that he was leaving off too early.

'Indeed it's no that at all,' he had replied breathlessly. 'But that Sadie and her friend is down there in the grass shoutin' to me and I'm damty feart they'll have the trousers off me if I stay much longer on my own. I'm away to get my mother to work beside me.'

'An I'll look after all the bairns . . .' he was saying now, as he patted her knee with befuddled repetition.

We reached the relative quiet of the kitchen.

'Janet, what has happened to your visitor?' I asked. 'She should be here tonight, shouldn't she?'

'Indeed, mo ghaoil, she's away to her bed long ago.' Our eyes met and we exchanged a grin of understanding. 'Aye,' Janet added, smiling, 'she's gone to bed with a Gaelic dictionary.'

Johnny, coming in to replenish glasses, overheard the remark. 'That's a damty funny thing for a woman to want to go to bed with,' he commented.

By midnight the house was thick with tobacco fumes and resonant with song and laughter, shrieks and shrill argument. Cups were being hooked and as quickly unhooked from dresser shelves as a chorus of steaming kettles was whisked from the stove to wash dishes or to brew tea and then to be refilled for yet more tea. My head had begun to throb with the heat and I felt I could unobtrusively slip away. Outside, revived by the frosty air, I loitered for a few moments looking through the windows, curtained only by condensation, at the happy throng within. The old men were singing tranquilly, with half-closed eyes, their joined hands lifting and falling to the beat of the tune. The old women chattered animatedly. The young people teased one another and giggled disproportionately. On the bench Erchy was still sprawled, still making the same earnest proposals, still patting a knee—but it was a different girl!

The Christmas Party

LONG after the wavering 'Vs' of geese had passed over on their way south and advertisements in the national newspapers had begun to draw our attention to the ordering of Christmas cards, some of us in Bruach were still making hay, pulling with numb fingers the frosty, wet patches from cocks which had taken in the wet and scattering it to dry on days of intermittent and glacial sunshine. Hallowe'en, which normally sees the end of the harvest, overtook us and still there was hay to be gathered in. Only the children exulted, Hallowe'en being the one day in the year which they could really call their own. From about mid-October they were preparing for it, designing for themselves masks of painted cardboard on which they sewed fearsome quantities of unwashed fleece, and rooting under beds and in lofts for discarded garments so as to further disguise themselves. The clothes they unearthed were almost invariably black and reeking of mildew or manure depending upon where they had been stored and as soon as it was dark on Hallowe'en, the children arrayed in their masks and stumbling about in voluminous skirts or rolled-up trousers and looking more like guys for a bonfire than revellers, banded together to visit each house in turn. There, not speaking or unmasking until their identities had been guessed correctly, they waited in musty groups to receive an apple or a sixpence before rushing off on their rounds. Once all the houses had been visited and perhaps some apple-dunking indulged in at one or two of the more cordial homes, the children threw away their masks, abandoned their old clothes beside the road for collection later and embarked on the really exciting business of the evening.

It was a strictly honoured tradition in Bruach that at Hallowe'en nothing is ever 'stolen'. If spades or forks disappeared from a shed overnight, or a wheelbarrow from a byre, it was just part of the fun. If you were unlucky enough or lazy enough to have potatoes still in the ground and you found them uprooted and scattered over the croft, or if a hay rake disappeared completely because the children could not remember what, in their excitement, they had done with it, then it was 'Ach well, we was all young once'. A wheelbarrow or a cart might suffer damage during its nocturnal journey, but what else could you expect? 'It was too heavy for the children to manage of course.' Bruach did not have child delinquents. They were allowed to get it all out of their system in one glorious Hallowe'en spree.

As a result of the late harvest many implements had not been stored away for the winter and the revellers, sometimes reinforced by their elders, made the most of their opportunities. I awoke next morning to find my garden gate had been replaced by Peter's harrows and that Yawn's barrow was hidden beneath a pile of discarded clothes in my byre. When I set out to locate the gate, which the smiling grocer had discovered at the back of his 'wee hoosie', I was joined by many of the neighbours, all grumbling good-naturedly as they searched out their belongings in all sorts of unexpected places. In company with them I found myself staring stupidly at a colourful array of ladies' underwear pegged out on the clothes-line at the bachelor home of Farquhar until I recognized it as some of my own which I had forgotten to take in the previous night. By midday, everyone seemed to have reclaimed his property and even the most irascible sufferer had been soothed by the laughter of his neighbours. Only Sheena, who had made the mistake of sending the children away without reward or invitation to enter, because the previous year they had managed to secrete a live hedgehog in her bed, still nursed a grievance, for the children had repaid her churlishness by climbing on to the roof of her cottage and placing a sod on top of the chimney.

'Me and Peter was sittin' in the kitchen and I was readin' the paper to him when the smoke started to come down the chimbley as though it was on the funnel of a ship we was,' she told me, her red-rimmed eyes still moist with indignation. 'Of course it's no a right chimbley at the best of times but, "Peter," I says, "we must get some heather up here tomorrow," I says. Mercy!, but the smoke got that thick I can tell you I was takin' bites out of it.' She bit the air demonstratively. ' "Peter," I tells him, "for the dear Lord's sake open up that door for fear we'll be like the kippers with the smoke." Peter goes to open the door. "It's stuck, cailleach," he tells me. "Never!" says I, not believin' what he was sayin', but when I tried would it open it was stuck right enough. "Help!" I shouts, for by this time me and Peter is coughin' our stomachs near into our throats. "Help!" I calls again, though who would be after hearin' me I'd not be knowin'. Then I hears them childrens laughin' outside. "Help! Open the door for us, childrens," I calls to them, but they just laughs and shouts back at me and mocks me and they bide their time till they think we've had enough before they cut the string that's tyin' the door and scramble away. Peter and me, we just fell outside with the coughin' we was doin', and there in the moonlight Peter points up and he says to me, "There's no smoke comin' from the chimbley, cailleach," and I looks and I see what's happened for fine I remember the boys doin' it when I was young. "You get up on that roof right away, Peter," I tells him, "and get that sod off the chimbley." He went up, tremblin' and shiverin', for he has no head for the heights, mo ghaoil, and I was shiverin' myself with the cold before I was able to go back inside again, and this mornin' I see my bed's all yellow with the stain of it.' Sheena sighed noisily and shook her head over the brutal treatment she had received.

After Hallowe'en was over, there was nothing for the children to look forward to except the spectacle of their elders getting drunk at New Year, which they considered vastly amusing. Christmas, as I had soon found, was ignored completely. The only time I can recall feeling lonely was when I had gone for a walk on my first Christmas morning in Bruach and had gaily wished everyone a 'Happy Christmas'. Not one of the people I met had returned my greeting with a trace of enthusiasm, their response being an embarrassed 'Yes, it's a nice day,' as though I had said something out of place. I learned later that though one religious sect did in fact condemn the celebration of Christmas, most of my neighbours had not returned my greeting simply because the unexpectedness of it had left them at a loss for a conventional reply.

It seemed to me that a children's party at Christmas would be a good idea and I set about planning one. My motives, I regret to say, were not entirely unselfish, for I love the tinsel and glitter and the festivities and bustle that go with Christmas, and a children's party would provide the excuse for plenty of it and so do much to enliven the day for me. The cottage was far too small for entertaining more than one or two people at a time but I had now had built a new shed of corrugated iron with a concrete floor. Assessing with Dollac and her friends the suitability of the shed for a party, it emerged that it was a pity there was to be only a celebration for the children.

'We could have a grand dance here,' said Dollac, and began humming as she danced across the floor.

'I don't see why we shouldn't put on a pantomime in this village,' I said without much seriousness.

'A what?'

'A pantomime.'

'What's a pantomime?' They turned to me with faces that were both puzzled and amused.

'Oh, you know what I mean,' I said, thinking there was probably an obscure Gaelic word for pantomime. 'Plays like *Cinderella* and *Mother Goose* and *Aladdin*.'

'Who did you say? Cinderella? Mother of Goose? What are they? What was a lad in?

I found it difficult to accept that they really had never heard of any of them. 'Well,' I began to explain. 'You know the story of Cinderella, don't you? The poor little girl with the two ugly sisters and the fairy godmother. . . .' Their expressions were revealingly blank. So I told them the story, adding that in pantomime the male parts, except for the dastardly villains, were usually played by females and that the comic female parts were usually played by men. They thought it a splendid idea and it was decided there and then that we would celebrate Christmas, first by having a children's party to be followed by a pantomime at which the children could be present and then, after the children had gone home, by a dance for adults. The children were obviously delighted at the prospect: the adolescents greeted the news of the pantomime and dance with restrained enthusiasm and the older people, after praising me for my generosity, predicting great success for each of the entertainments planned and fervidly assuring me of their intention to be present, retired into their cocoons of Calvinism and waited to see what everyone else would do about the whole affair. Remembering the fiasco of the pilgrims' party, I knew that I too must wait and see.

I wrote a pantomime that I thought would amuse the village, which meant that I could unashamedly use all the chestnuts I had ever heard. I also, perhaps a little cruelly, gave one or two members of the caste the opportunity of openly criticizing my early attempts at crofting, which I knew had caused much humorous comment locally. Buttons' haircut was supposed to look 'as though Miss Peckwitt had been at it with a scythe'. A rickety chair was to collapse 'like a Peckwitt hay-cock'. My intention was to try to convey to them that I accepted their criticism ruefully but as well deserved, but the cast defeated me by courteously ignoring such lines, even when the text did not make sense without them. To my surprise rehearsals were not only well attended but were enormous fun and those few weeks leading up to Christmas were, I think, the most hilarious I have ever spent in my life. On three or four nights of every week we assembled at the cottage to read our lines and no one, I think, was serious for a single moment of the time. The roadman and the shepherd capered through the parts of the ugly sisters lustily: Erchy, as the stepfather, was impressive when he could remember not to read out all the stage directions with his speeches; he was an absolute riot when he forgot. The postman, who was playing Buttons, used to come in the middle of his round, sling his half-empty mailbag into a corner of the hall and, with his mobile face creased in anticipation and his eyes shining conspiratorially, read over his part with prickly voiced diffidence. The postman's presence was vital, for he was also providing the melodeon music for the chorus to dance to until we could get suitable records.

'What about the mails?' I asked him one time.

'Ach, they know where I am,' he replied with supreme indifference.

I tried to insist that rehearsals should cease at midnight but the Bruachites, who regard midnight as an hour to begin enjoying oneself, had other ideas. They would put back my clock while I was out of the room or put back their watches and swear my clock was fast so that more often than not it was two or perhaps four o'clock in the morning before I could seek my bed and then only because the pressure lamp had defiantly put an end to proceedings by running out of paraffin. As Christmas bore down upon us excitement mounted visibly, more particularly among the children from whom I had begun to receive adoring looks as soon as the party had been announced. 'Tea-parties' became a new game and Fiona, who had been taken by Behag and Morag for a day out on the mainland and who had, as a matter of course, given them the slip, had excelled herself by being discovered in the comparatively urban graveyard engrossed in a game of 'tea-parties' with a grave for a table for which she had collected a bevy of decorative urns and jars from the surrounding graves.

A great disappointment for me was that a box of decorations which I had ordered failed to arrive and two days before Christmas Eve I was faced with the prospect not only of baking all the fancy cakes needed for the party and for the light refreshments at the dance but also with the decorating of a bare corrugated iron shed to which, by hook or by crook, I was determined to give a festive appearance. The solution came unexpectedly when Behag and Morag, who had not been able to finish their shopping on the mainland because of having to search for Fiona, asked me if I would look after the child for the day whilst they went off on their own. I visualized myself spending Christmas Day in bed recuperating from twelve hours with Fiona, but she had not been in the house for more than half an hour before she was demanding paints. I was so relieved she had chosen such an innocuous way of passing the time that I hastened to indulge her.

'You can paint some Christmas decorations for me,' I said, giving her some sheets of thick paper and a particularly robust brush. I went back to my baking.

'I'm needin' more paper,' Fiona ordered briskly.

I rummaged in the cupboard and found more paper which she had covered with splodges of paint almost before I could return to my bowl. It was her incessant demands for paper that gave me the inspiration. I brought out a toilet roll.

'You can paint the whole length of that,' I told her firmly. 'Use lots of bright colours and don't you dare ask for more paper until you've painted every bit of it.' Even Fiona was momentarily daunted by the task I had set her but determinedly she set to work, singing with pre-occupied tunelessness to herself as she daubed her way along the whole length of the roll. The table top was covered in plastic; Fiona was enveloped in an old overall; there was plenty of paint—and toilet rolls. I carried on blissfully with my cooking and when I could spare a few minutes from it Fiona and I cut up the daubed paper into decorative garlands which we later carried out to the shed. When Hector came to collect his daughter we showed him the results of her artistic skill which the child, as though ashamed of my own rapture, dismissed with adult coolness as being 'no bad at all'. Hector immediately volunteered to come next day and hang them for me and with uncharacteristic fidelity he came, bringing a curious Erchy along with him. They were each carrying big bundles of holly and ivy. I had run out of flour and was getting ready to go over to Sarah's to borrow some when the two men arrived so I left them to their work, telling them that if I was not back by the time they had finished they could make themselves a cup of tea and help themselves to scones. The kitchen was luxuriant with trays of tarts and cakes and buns of every kind but, I warned, they were strictly party fare.

'My, but they make my teeths water,' said Erchy, looking covetously about him. 'I believe I could eat the lot.'

'You must promise not to eat anything but the scones,' I told them, and they promised cheerfully.

Before I closed the door I turned to look back at the kitchen, making sure that everything was safely stacked and that I had not left anything in the oven. The sight gave me a great deal of pleasure. On the dresser, already gay with its poppy and blue china, were three trays of sponge cakes waiting to be crowned with a whirl of cream. Éclair cases ready to be filled and iced were piled on the top of the trolly: cream horns wanting their insides stoked with jam and cream covered the bottom. Beside the stove a large sponge cake, roughly shaped like a boat waited to receive its cargo of children's names in coloured letters. On the kitchen table, with its black and white chequered plastic top, reposed trays of blackcurrant and lemon curd tarts, making a colourful centrepiece. My own teeths began to water and I shut the door firmly.

When I called, Sarah was herself preparing to bake girdle scones, while Flora watched impassively. 'Surely, mo ghaoil, but I've plenty of flour,' Sarah assured me as she swung the girdle to one side and pushed the whispering kettle on to the peats. 'Just sit now and rest a bitty while I make a wee strupak.'

I had hoped that she would be busy about the sheds and that I should escape without having to wait for a strupak, but when I sat down I found I was glad to do so. Having spent the whole of the previous two days baking, I felt I was going to enjoy the sight of someone else doing some. Sarah spread a newspaper over the table and floured it liberally. My neighbours made wonderful girdle scones but despite repeated demonstrations I had never been able to achieve just the lightness and texture in my baking that they unfailingly achieved in theirs. Perhaps it was because I used a well-floured baking board to press out my scones instead of a well-floured newspaper. She reached down a small pudding basin from the dresser—another essential for baking good scones seemed to be the use of a too small bowl so that the flour could spill over when mixing began. She brought out a tin of cream of tartar and a tin of baking soda from the cupboard and then stopped in her tracks to peer with a puzzled frown about the kitchen. Several times I had thought I could hear the plaintive miaow of a cat but I had refrained from mentioning it, suspecting that it was quite possibly entombed beneath Flora's skirts and that if this were the case it would only be a matter of time before it burrowed its way out again. Sarah went into 'the room' and brought out a jug of sour milk which she set on the table.

'I can hear that cat somewhere,' she said, looking all round the kitchen again. She picked up the basin and went over to the large wall-paper-decorated barrel which stood beside the fireplace. As she lifted the lid a startled exclamation burst from her and an albino cat leaped on the rim of the barrel and then down to the floor where it sneezed, shook itself vigorously and revealed itself as tortoise-shell. 'Well,' said Sarah, 'so that's where he's been hidin' all this time; in my flour barrel.' She gave a little self-conscious chuckle, dipped the basin down into the flour barrel and began to mix her scones. The cat continued to miaow and rubbed itself against her boots.

'She seems glad to be out again,' I said.

'I expect the beast's hungry,' said Sarah. 'Dear knows how long he's been in there.'

I hurried home, clutching my bag of flour and salving my conscience by recalling some of the less hygienic practices of my neighbours. I could, I told myself, keep back the cakes baked with Sarah's flour and produce them only if and when everything else had been eaten. There was no sound of hammering or of voices when I reached the cottage and I went to the shed to see what was happening. The decorations were up and, betraying not the slightest sign of their humble origin, looked 'beautiful just'. The holly had been nailed in bunches along the walls: ivy cascaded from the roof. In one corner, a tub (an old salt-herring barrel) already filled with peat waited to receive the Christmas tree which was due to arrive the following evening. With a sigh of relief I closed the door. The silence everywhere coupled with the non-appearance of either Erchy or Hector made me wonder if they had already gone home and as I passed the kitchen window I glanced inside. The two men were sitting at either end of the kitchen table with cups of tea beside them. Their chins were resting on their left hands, their right hands held cigarettes from which they flicked the ash periodically into their gumboots. They were looking down at the checked table top with the dedicated air of keen chess players and neither noticed my presence outside the window. I waited a moment before announcing myself and saw Erchy push something a little along the table towards Hector. To my horror I saw it was a blackcurrant tart! Hector retaliated by pushing a lemon curd tart one square towards Erchy. I peered closer and suddenly divining the reason for their absorption I bounded inside.

'Hector and Erchy!' I upbraided them. 'What do you think you're doing with those tarts?'

They both looked up in pained surprise. 'Only playin' draughts,' said Erchy mildly, as with a triumphant flourish he passed a black-currant tart over a lemon curd and drew the spoils towards him.

'But you promised not to touch them,' I reminded them petulantly as I hurried forward to retrieve my precious baking.

'We promised not to eat tsem and we haven't,' said Hector earnestly. 'Honest, we haven't touched a one.' He disentangled a couple of 'crowns' as he spoke, examining their jammy bottoms. 'Look!' he insisted, 'tsey're as good as new.'

I loaded the tarts back on to the trays, sourly ignoring their pleas to 'let's finish the game out'.

'Ach well, I near had him beat anyway,' said Erchy, getting up. 'My but those scones of yours was so light it was like bitin' into a cloud,' he added with awkward flattery.

'Indeed tsey was beautiful just,' supported Hector fulsomely. 'I was after sayin' to Erchy, if only we could eat our draughts when tse game was over, I wouldn't mind losin'.'

Early in the afternoon of Christmas Eve the tree arrived, a magnificent specimen generously contributed by the estate manager. Morag and Dollac were with me at the time helping me to put the finishing touches to the fancy cakes, and we all left off to go and see the tree installed in its barrel. Erchy, Hector and deaf Ruari who, though he claimed to be too old to be interested in such frivolities, was just as curious over the preparations as were the younger generation, had appointed themselves to escort the tree, and inevitably there was argument as to which branches must be cut off and whether the barrel was suitable and whether it was sufficiently stable, but at last they reached agreement and the tree stood gracefully awaiting our attention, its fresh resiny smell filling the shed.

I sniffed appreciatively and winked at Morag.

'Ruari!' scolded Morag loudly. 'You must send your dog out of here. He's throwin' smells.'

'Aye, I got some new meal for him yesterday an' I don't believe it's agreein' with him right,' Ruari submitted by way of explanation when he had ordered the dog outside.

Morag and Dollac and I returned to the kitchen to finish our preparations there before starting to decorate the tree.

'Did I ever tell you?' asked Morag as she painstakingly halved cherries to top the cream cakes, 'I worked in a bakery once and I used to watch the baker decoratin' the cakes with halves of cherries just like I'm doin' now, but my fine fellow wouldn't bother himself to cut the cherries in half. Oh, no, he just would bite them in half.' I wondered fleetingly if she was suggesting she should do likewise and was immensely relieved when she continued, 'I've never eaten a cake with a cherry on the top since.' I debated whether to mention the cat in the flour barrel, but decided against it. I had already taken a bite of one of the cakes made from the flour and though I had come to the conclusion that the cat had been in the barrel for quite a long time, the cake was, I felt, far more palatable than, for instance, Sheena's shortbread.

Midnight had already chimed before we had finished the tree and the long tables which had been borrowed from the school canteen had been covered with wallpaper that had originally been intended for stage decoration but which, due to the non-arrival of the previously mentioned parcel, was to serve a dual purpose—once the children's tea was finished it would have to be whipped off and used for papering Cinderella's kitchen. There had been so many late nights since the hectic preparations for Christmas had begun and when I had managed to get an early night in the hope of catching up on some sleep it had resulted only in catching up on dreams, so I was utterly weary by the time Morag and Dollac, after repeated 'beautiful justs' as they surveyed the evening's work, departed by the light of a reluctant moon. It was still dark on Christmas morning when I began to lay the tables in the shed. As I carried out the plates of cakes and pastries, Rhuna emerged duskily across the water, its string of lamplit windows dim as tarnished tinsel against the brilliant flashes of the lighthouses. When the sun rose it was smudged and angry and with it wakened an aggressive wind that swept the rain in from the sea. Some of the children lived a good distance away from the village and I had promised to collect them in Joanna if it was a nasty day. Accordingly, about four o'clock in the afternoon, I drove through the slatting rain to collect the first of my guests. Marjac, whose five children were all dodding about just inside the door, greeted me with shrill querulousness.

'What on earth am I to do with Shamus?' she demanded. 'He was out on the hill this mornin' and got his trousers soakin' wet so he had to put on his best ones. Now hasn't he caught himself on John Willy's harrows and torn the seat out of them.' Marjac darted back to her sewing machine and turned the handle savagely. 'I'm after makin' him a pair from one of my old skirts,' she said disgustedly. Shamus, a little shamefaced, went to the solid wood kerb in front of the fire and sat down, carefully arranging an old meal sack over his lower half. The rest of the children were ready and impatient to be off. 'There you are,' his mother flung the trousers at Shamus, and clutching at the sack he hurried away to 'the room' to put them on.

'Ian, did you wash your teeths like the nurse told you?' Marjac arrested another of her brood with the question just as he was about to slip through the door.

'No, I didn't yet,' Ian replied.

'Then if nurse sees you she'll ask you and be vexed with you,' his mother warned. 'She'll be at the party, won't she, Miss Peckwitt?' I nodded. 'Nurse says he's got bad teeths and she's given him a brush and some paste to try will he keep the rest from goin' too,' Marjac explained as Ian reached at the back of the dresser for his toothbrush, moistened it by dipping it into the kettle and proceeded to attack his teeth with as much energy as if he were attacking rusty iron with a file.

'What a good thing you were able to run up a pair of trousers for Shamus,' I complimented Marjac during a lull in the activity.

'Ach, I just threw them together out of my head,' she disclaimed.

Shamus came out from 'the room' looking a little perplexed. One trouser-leg was skin tight; the other hung loosely about his thigh. He looked beseechingly at his mother.

'It'll have to do,' she told him. 'Miss Peckwitt cannot wait here all day while I see to it.'

I might have offered to wait, but I doubted if there was much Marjac could do to the trousers except to cut down the wide leg to match the tight one and thus immobilize the mobile half also. The children packed themselves into the car, Shamus rather stiltedly, and I was soon decanting them into Morag's care and rushing away for the rest. By five o'clock all the children had arrived and were waiting tensely in the cottage for what was going to happen next. It is rare for even very young Gaelic children to betray excitement noisily and so it was a very decorous procession indeed which followed me to the shed. There, they seated themselves at the tables as they were directed, not scrambling for places but scolding one another in loud whispers whenever they detected signs of stupidity or slowness.

When they were settled they regarded the heaped-up plates of delicacies with prim dignity. I insisted that everyone should begin with bread and butter or sandwiches and these they accepted demurely only when Morag and I pressed them to do so. We offered them cakes, for which they reached out cautious hands. Remembering their zest for school meals I found their apathy when confronted with my cooking dispiriting. I began to wonder if, not being accustomed to fancy cookery, they had not developed an appetite for it, but in view of their consumption of sweets, jam and biscuits, it seemed highly improbable. I knew there was nothing wrong with my cooking and every now and then I caught the gleam in their eyes as they stared along the length of the loaded tables. I signalled to Morag to come to the door with me and there I turned.

'Look, children,' I said. 'Morag and I must go and see to things in the kitchen but there's to be a competition and a shilling for the one who eats the most. Keep a check on one another and tell me when I come back and the winner will get a shilling and the next two sixpence each.'

They whispered meekly that they would and we left them sitting like jaded gourmands before the feast. The moment the door closed uproar began, and I heard it with satisfaction. We left them for half an hour and when we returned the tables looked as though they had been swept by a hurricane. Shyness and stiffness were completely gone and everyone was clamouring to tell us who had won the shilling.

'Johnny! Johnny's won,' they yelled. 'He had twenty-four cakes and four sandwiches.'

Johnny smiled angelically as he pocketed his shilling.

Shamus was one of the runners up, and one of the youngest children was the other, though we found that he had eaten only the cream centres out of four of his cakes and disposed of the rest under the table.

By eight o'clock the players were beginning to arrive for the pantomime and the 'stage', which was merely one end of the shed sketchily partitioned off and curtained, had to be set. Various helpers came, bringing old railway sleepers which they had collected from the shore and which they set up on old salt herring barrels to provide seating accommodation for the audience. The children, full, and tired after a series of games, were content to sit and watch preparations from the front stalls. Dollac, who naturally was playing Cinderella, rushed in, still wearing gumboots and an old mac, on her way back from taking the hill cows their evening feed. She had been caught in a hail shower and she looked so ravishing with her glowing cheeks and rippling black hair flecked with hailstones that it seemed ludicrous to attempt to make her more emphatic with stage make-up. The postman bustled in to become Buttons.

'That'll make some nice presents for the audience—when they get them,' he said meaningly, indicating the bulging mail bag behind the Christmas tree. 'See and put the postmistress on the back row all the same.'

The pantomime frolicked along from start to finish. The players forgot their lines but the audience knew the play at least as well as the actors (the script had been passed round the village like a best-selling book), so that there were no embarrassing intervals of silence. The chorus tripped through their dances with earnest efficiency, rigidly following the beat of the music even when the gramophone ran down and was wound up again with the record still playing. During rehearsals I had tried, unavailingly, to persuade them to smile as they danced, but tonight they appeared to have great difficulty in repressing their amusement, the obliging little postman having overcome their impassivity by placing himself on the front row ready to make faces at them whenever they appeared on the stage. The audience were enchanted.

'My, but I believe Dollac was as good as any of them fillum stars,' said Morag admiringly when the pantomime was over and the children had gone home. We were in the kitchen hurriedly cutting up more sandwiches, making more tea and replenishing the dishes of cakes, while everyone who could was throwing out or rearranging the herring barrels and sleepers to clear the floor for dancing.

'She'd make any film star I've ever seen look pretty sick,' I said.

'Indeed, yes,' agreed Behag, who had glamorized herself for the occasion by putting on a new dress which became her, and by powdering her face inexpertly so that she succeeded in looking mildewed. 'I was seein' in the paper a day or two ago that some fillum star had just taken her fifth husband.'

'She needs her bumps reading,' I observed dispassionately.

'She needs what did you say?' asked Morag.

'I said she needs her bumps reading. I mean, her head seeing to,' I explained, seeing that she was not familiar with the expression.

'A good dose of castor oil is what we always give them here, mo ghaoil,' she said simply. 'A girl or two hereabouts has got that way sometimes, but a good dose of castor oil works it out of them quicker than anythin'.'

Hector came into the kitchen, sidled up to me and slapped my behind. 'Tsere's one of tsese hikers outside,' he told me, having thus ensured my attention. 'He's wantin' to know will you find him a bed for tse night?'

Immediately I suspected a joke. A stranded hiker on Christmas Day in Bruach was too unlikely.

'Why did he come here?' I asked.

'He says he couldn't see any lights any place else.'

Erchy shouldered his way in. 'Here, it's startin' to snow,' he said, 'and there's a fellow outside says he's stranded. Come out here and talk to him.'

I pretended to agree and went with him to the door. Outside stood a solitary figure huddled into a waterproof cape. A cap was pulled well down over his eyes and he had an enormous bundle on his back. The voice that addressed me was ripe Glaswegian. Dugan, l knew, was an excellent mimic of the Glaswegian accent. I darted at the figure and, exclaiming contemptuously, snatched off his cap and dragged him forward. 'Come along,' I told him. 'You don't fool me.' He hung back, so laughingly I went behind and prodded him forcibly. Inside the lighted kitchen the figure stood shivering with, I hoped, cold, for I realized that he was a complete stranger. Erchy and Hector looked at me as though I had gone mad. Morag and Behag stopped with their knives poised and waited for an explanation. The situation hardly improved when I began to shake with laughter. 'I'm sorry,' I tried to explain, 'but I thought someone had dressed up for a joke. We're having a party here as I dare say you've guessed, and I just couldn't believe there'd really be anyone hiking to Bruach at this time of year and in such weather.'

The hiker's face thawed into a timid grin and after a plate of hot soup he seemed to accept that he had not fallen into such wild company as he must at first have suspected.

'I must go and see if I can get hold of Janet and ask her if she can give you a bed,' I said.

'Ach, put him in your own bed,' advised Erchy. 'Put a pillow between you and everythin' will be all right.'

The hiker's face resumed its hunted look.

Luckily, Janet had a spare bed and took the hiker off my hands. 'Thank God's my sister's away to her bed with the cold,' she murmured as she departed, 'his trousers are soaked through.' It was singularly unfortunate for the poor hiker that when Janet arrived home she found a party of her friends awaiting her. They had come, well provisioned, to begin celebrating the New Year. The hiker had gone off to bed, Janet told me later, but so noisy and so lengthy had been the ensuing celebration that it was doubtful if he managed a wink of sleep the night through. It was even more unfortunate that Janet had overslept the next morning and had not awakened until disturbed by the shouts of the hiker who was having a battle with Grace in the kitchen as to the ownership of the trousers he had left to dry there overnight.

'Indeed, my dear,' Janet said mournfully, 'I believe that's one man who'll never come within sight of this village again so long as he draws breath.'

Various whoops and bangs, interspersed by exuberant retchings of the melodeon, came from the direction of the shed. The dancing had obviously begun and Behag went to extricate Fiona from the throng so that Morag, who was not staying for the dancing, could take her home. It was already past eleven o'clock but the child showed no sign of fatigue. I pushed the kettles to the side of the fire and went to see how things were progressing. Dollac, who had been my staunchest supporter all through the preparations for the festivities, had hurried home to change into a party dress, promising faithfully to be back in time to help me and Behag serve the refreshments. I looked for her among the milling dancers but as yet she had not put in an appearance. The postman was playing the melodeon with a verve that was in some measure due to the bottle of whisky I had seen him furtively stuffing into the mailbag behind the tree. Some of the girls were teaching their partners to dance a St. Bernard's waltz, the tuition consisting of kicking their partners feet sharply until they were in the required positions. They had pulled sprigs of mistletoe from the bunch Mary had sent me and this they wore in their hair, but the men seemed to be uninterested or unaware of the implied invitation.

When the dancers paused there were complaints of thirst and after consulting with Behag I decided not to wait for Dollac's arrival but to serve the refreshments straight away.

'See and put a good tin of baking soda an' a spoon handy, so folks
can help themselves,' Morag had warned before she left, and so I put
a couple of pounds of it in a jar beside the tree and at frequent intervals
the men resorted to it, swallowing down two or three heaped tea-
spoonfuls at a time. Naturally, they had all brought their bottles and
every few minutes purposeful groups of them disappeared from the
shed and came back each time looking a little livelier or a little sleepier,
according as it affected them. The night rushed on. At one time I
noticed Shamus who apparently considered himself young enough for
children's parties and old enough for adult ones, dancing an alternately
constrained and abandoned version of the Highland Fling which
brought much applause. There was a respite for song and the roadman
gave us one of his own composition. It told the story of a hen who
had taken herself off to a secret nest where she had reared one chick—a
cockerel. It was wholly derogatory and brought screams of laughter.

Two o'clock came and there was still no sign of Dollac and as I
had never known her miss a rehearsal or indeed any chance of entertainment, I started enquiring if anyone knew why she had not returned
to the dance.

'You'd best ask Adam,' said Elspeth, with a little secret smile. 'I
believe he knows why she's not here.'

I collared Adam on his way to an appointment with a bottle. He
was bubbling with fun and voluble with whisky and he was only too
ready to tell me what had happened to Dollac.

'Well it's like this,' he began. 'Dollac promised she'd come to the
dance with Duncan, and Johnny didn't like that at all. He thought she
should come with him. Ach, you know fine yourself how it's been
with Dollac and Johnny these three years back. I believe he's been
wantin' her to marry him for a good while but she won't just say
that she will.' As a matter of fact the relationship between Dollac and
Johnny had never appeared to me to be anything more than platonic,
but it seemed I was mistaken. 'Ach, he's crazy about her right enough,'
went on Adam. 'Indeed I'm hearin' he's after buyin' the ring a twelve
month back and he's been takin' her old man buckets of fish heads for
his creels for longer than that. Anyway, while she was out at the cows
this afternoon what does Johnny do but climb in through her bedroom
window and pinch all her clothes. Not a blessed thing did he leave her
that she could wear for the dance. At least that's what she was tellin'

me when I called in on my way here. You see, I had to nip up and put
my mother to bed after the pantomime was finished,' he explained.
'Aye, but I felt sorry for Dollac, right enough. She's been lookin'
forward to this dance more than anybody, and there she was sittin'
beside the fire in her workin' clothes just like she was when she was
Cinderella in the play,' Adam chuckled.

'Where is Johnny?' I cut in, looking in vain for him among the
dancers. Duncan, seemingly unaffected by Dollac's desertion, was
capering friskily through a 'Dashing White Sergeant'.

'I expect he's at home, keepin' guard over Dollac's clothes,' said
Adam. 'He was here at the pantomime, but he went home when Dollac
did.'

It was past four o'clock in the morning and I was yawning undis-
guisedly, hoping to infect some of my spirited guests with a little of
my own weariness, when the door was suddenly flung back and
Johnny and Dollac stood on the threshold, grinning self-consciously at
us all. Johnny's eyes were glittering and he was brandishing a full bottle
of whisky, inviting everyone to 'come and celebrate', an invitation
to which Duncan responded with even more alacrity than the rest.
Dollac was wearing a sea-green dress that had been depicted on the
front page of the most recent mail-order catalogue and captioned 'For
Allure with a capital A'. The colour endowed her with a naiadic beauty
so that it was not difficult to imagine she had swirled in on a cloud of
spray.

'What are you celebratin',' called Adam. 'Is it just that you've
gathered in the last of your hay today or it is because you've gathered
in Dollac at last?'

'Both,' retorted Johnny, with a flash of assertiveness, and with an
enraptured look at Dollac he seized her left hand and held it up for us
to see the diamond sparkling on the third finger.

We congratulated, we hugged, we cheered and admired. The
melodeon blossomed again into a 'Strip the Willow' for which Dollac
and Johnny led off. Heaven alone knew now what time the party would
end.

'Hell!' came Erchy's muzzy voice in my ear, 'the way I'm feelin' now
I think I must have been a bit in love with Dollac myself.'

The Loud Halo

LILLIAN BECKWITH

The Loud Halo

DECORATIONS by DOUGLAS HALL

To
Ealasaid & Goiridh

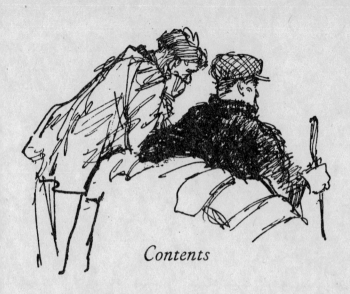

Contents

Johnny Comic

THE storm-force wind was blasting squalls of incredibly wet and heavy
rain across the loch, blotting out the hills and the sky and flaying the
rusty grass of the crofts until it cringed back into the ground from
which it had sprung so ebulliently only a few short months earlier.
All day there had been semi-dusk and when I had returned soaked
and shivering from the moors that morning after a long hunt to give

Bonny her morning hay, I had promised myself I would do nothing but change into dry clothes, put some food on a tray and then sit by the fire with a book. Nothing, that is, until it was time for me to don my sticky oilskins and my coldly damp sou'wester, strain on wet gumboots and go seeking Bonny again with her evening feed.

There was no doubt Bruach cows were hardy creatures, and it took hardy humans to live up to them. Left to roam the treeless, craggy moors for nine months of the year the cattle had to seek shelter where they could from the fierce winds, lashing hail, rain and even snow which beset the Hebrides from about September onwards. The cows, being wise creatures, could be relied upon to find it. The humans, being not so wise, were not nearly so reliable. So, with a milk pail in one hand, a stick in the other, a sack of hay roped to our backs, we plodded the thousands of acres of moor, more often than not in combat with a gale-force wind that hurled stinging rain into our faces. Panting and praying, we climbed up rocks with the intention of gaining a better view; dejected and swearing, we wallowed in bogs with no intention at all.

I use the plural pronoun because on the surface this was what we all appeared to do, but I suspect privately that I, being an acolyte, was the only one who was really exasperated by the weather, by the cantank-erousness of the cows or by the time it all took. The rest of the crofters knew their weather better, they knew their moors better and, in the short days of winter, time to them was only a hiatus between getting up and the evening ceilidh and they had no particular preference as to how they helped it along.

'But why don't you put bells on the cattle like they do in Switzer-land?' asked a woman tourist to whom I once described our sufferings. It was easy to discern that she was dreaming pleasant dreams of 'a little cottage in the Highlands and a cow for milk' when she retired. It was then an evening of summer calm when the protesting cry of a disturbed heron seemed to stab the night with its volume and one could almost hear the whisper of gulls' wings as they dawdled homeward.

'It wouldn't work here,' I told her. 'The wind's far too strong in winter. You wouldn't be able to hear a peal of church bells here in a good gale.'

'But surely if you had a telescope you could just climb the highest hill and then you could see all round.'

She made it sound so easy and I tried to explain to her how impossible it would be for anyone, burdened with hay, to climb the highest hill and then to hold a telescope in the teeth of a gale and that even a telescope won't bend and look down into innumerable secret corries.

I recognized in her remarks the suspicion a stranger is so apt to form on first acquaintance with the Hebrides—that the crofter prefers to make life difficult for himself and that he has a built-in resistance to progress. But experience had taught me there was no other way to keep a self-willed Highland cow in a village where crofts were traditionally unfenced, hay was almost as traditionally scarce and where the cows themselves were as suspicious of a bowl of concentrates as they might be of a bowl of hot cinders. The majority of them tolerated only three additions to their heather and hay diet: a 'potach', which is scalded oatmeal pressed into a ball; a bowl of boiled potatoes dried off with oatmeal; or a bowl of boiled seaweed mashed up with salt herring and dried off with oatmeal. As you could always smell out the kitchen of a crofter who fed his cows on this last delicacy Bonny never got the chance to try it. I had once tried to ingratiate myself with her by buying a bag of turnips and offering them to her at first whole, then chopped up in a bowl and sprinkled with oatmeal, and then, desperately, piece by piece in my fingers. She merely blew her nose over them and me and I formed the opinion then that there can be few creatures in the world that can express disdain so sublimely as a Highland cow. I offered the remaining turnips round the village but neither the cows nor the humans evinced any interest whatever.

'Not even that queer beastie of Kirsty's will so much as look at them,' reported Morag, 'an' yon's the one will eat chocolate cake and jam sandwiches and oranges if she'll get the chance.'

Morag and I shared the rest of the turnips between us and ate them ourselves.

I was thinking of all these things as I put on dry clothes, poured out a plate of soup, drew my chair close to the fire and put my book in readiness on the table. As I turned to sit down my eye caught an unexpected flicker of movement through the salt-encrusted window, and dreading that it was part of the byre roof or hen house blowing away I hurried to peer out.

'Oh blast!' I exclaimed as the movement resolved itself into the wind-flapped edge of a man's overcoat. I had lulled myself into thinking that the malevolence of the day would have ensured for me an afternoon of complete privacy but I had forgotten that there was one man who was completely undeterred from his ramblings whatever the weather. 'Oh well,' I thought resignedly, 'better him than to see the byre roof taking off, I suppose.'

Johnny Comic came in through the gate and turned to shut it, patting it tenderly as though telling it, as he would a dog, to stay there quietly until he returned. This curious tenderness for everything, animate or inanimate, was typical of Johnny and he would no more have dreamed of hurting the feelings of a gate by rushing through it and slamming it after him than he would have of hurting the feelings of a friend by refusing to acknowledge a greeting. He was a strange-looking man, so oddly shaped it looked as if his mother might have made him herself from a 'do-it-yourself' kit and that he had then blundered rather than grown into manhood. He was slightly built, his legs being disproportionately long and hampered with large feet like road shovels; one leg was longer than the other so that it dragged as he walked. His arms were short, while great hands with thick fingers hung from them like bunches of bananas. His eyes were the guileless blue of childhood; his skin pale and smooth as a woman's, and the grey curls around his head were soft and fine as the seed-head of a dandelion. Indeed, one felt one needed only to puff once, twice, perhaps three times, to disperse them all.

I opened the door to him and he stood on the threshold smiling broadly, confident of his welcome, while the kitchen door slammed with a vehemence that juddered all the china on the dresser.

'My, but it's coarse, coarse weather,' he paused to say politely before he stepped inside, despite the fact that the rain was sluicing in through the open door and the wind had whipped the hall pictures into a frenzy of swinging and was now wrapping the wet doormat around my legs.

'Go into the fire quickly, Johnny,' I urged, smothering my exasperation as I leaned hard on the door to shut it against the bullying rush of the wind.

He writhed out of his top layer of clothing, which comprised various pieces of oilskin of assorted shapes, and threw them down on the stairs. Still murmuring faint comments on the weather he wandered into the kitchen, pulled my chair away from the fire where I had placed it and sat himself down.

'I'll make a wee strupak as soon as I've had my soup,' I told him, and sat down opposite him. It was no use offering Johnny soup, that I knew, for his diet was restricted to a plate of porridge and three hardboiled eggs. For each one of his three meals, every day, it was the same, varying only when he took a 'wee strupak' with neighbours, when he would permit himself a piece of girdle scone with jam. He ate neither meat nor vegetables, nor even bread and butter. I was staggered when he had first told me and had sought confirmation from others who knew him.

'Aye, and it's right enough,' they told me. 'Ever since he was old enough to take it that's all he's lived on.' Which made me suspect that death for Johnny, like Peter Pan, 'Would be an awfully great adventure.'

As I ate my soup I watched Johnny, who had extracted a piece of wood from deep in his pocket and was whittling away at it inexpertly with a knife that I knew from experience was as blunt as a stick of rhubarb, and pondered on why he, specifically, had been dubbed 'Comic', a label which I felt could have been much more aptly bestowed on so many other inhabitants of the village. No one seemed to know how he had come by it. Old men, drawing the 'pension', recalled that even in his schooldays he had been 'Johnny Comic' to schoolmaster and scholars alike.

'He was always the clown, was Johnny,' they invariably added, 'and he took in no learning save what the schoolmaster leathered in through the seat of his breeks.'

I had first met Johnny the day I moved into my own cottage in
Bruach when, as soon as the furniture had been carried in and the
willing helpers had left to attend to their cattle, he had suddenly
appeared outside the window, where he had settled himself, elbows
resting comfortably on the sill, and had subjected me to an embarrassing mute scrutiny as I wrestled with a reluctant stove and endeavoured in the midst of chaos to cook myself a meal. When I
appeared to be looking for something he would peer anxiously into
the room, pressing his face against the glass. When I seemed to have
found whatever I was looking for he would grin and nod with satisfaction. He did not live in the village and I had never seen him before
but eventually for both our sakes I called him to come inside; for a
moment his expression was one of horror and then he almost fell in
his anxiety to get away from the window. By the time I had reached
the door he was hurrying across the moor as fast as he could go.

'Ach, but mo ghaoil, he'll not be knowin' you and he'd be frightened
likely that you'd seduct him. The lads tease him, the wretches,' Morag
explained when I told her of the incident.

Once I was settled in my cottage Johnny, apparently having no
more fear of or less aversion to losing his pudicity, got over his mis-
trust of me and became a regular visitor. Every couple of weeks he
would walk to Bruach over the moor, his awkward shambling gait
seeming to carry him rapidly across country in all kinds of weather
without any sign of distress. He came, as he explained, because he
thought I'd like a ceilidh, but his real reason for visiting me, though
it was never allowed to emerge until towards the end of his stay, was
to sell me some small article he had made and thereby earn a few
coppers for 'wootpines', for he loved a clandestine smoke and his
sister Kirsty, with whom he lived, appropriated all his pension. Sometimes it would be a small model boat made from driftwood, sometimes
a glass netfloat in a piece of herring net, but more often than not it
would be a heather besom. The frequency with which he offered me
these indeed suggested that he himself had little faith in the lasting
quality of his handiwork; if he ever noticed the ingenious windbreak
I contrived of upended besoms he never commented on it.

I brewed tea, spread some pieces of scone with jam and put them beside him on the table. Then I made some excuse to go upstairs. My first attempts to entertain Johnny had been embarrassing for both of us. I had poured out a cup of tea and placed it beside him along with a plate of scones. He had sugared the tea and stirred it, wiping the spoon carefully on his coat sleeve before replacing it in the basin. All the time I was drinking my own tea he had talked politely, never so much as glancing at his own cup so that it had got quite cold. I had offered to empty his cup and refill it with hot tea and he had accepted with alacrity. Once again he had repeated the ritual of sugaring it and wiping the spoon, but despite my urgings he had again left it to go cold, and still had not touched the scones. Feeling a little piqued I had filled his cup yet again with hot tea and then quite without design I had gone to get something from the shed. When I returned after only a very brief interval the tea had disappeared and so had all the scones. The next time he came much the same thing had happened but by the time he paid his third visit I knew what was expected of me and obliged accordingly.

When I came downstairs after a discreetly judged interval Johnny had finished his strupak and was leaning back in the chair.

'More tea or scone, Johnny?' I offered.

'No, thank you, I've done lovely,' he replied, lifting one of his large hands in a gesture of repression. He waited expectantly until from the dresser I reached down a jar of baking-soda and a spoon which I kept especially for Johnny. Avidly he dug in the spoon and with obvious relish swallowed three or four heaped spoonfuls of the powder, spilling it down his jersey in his eagerness to get the spoon into his mouth. Then he replaced the jar on the table, dusted down the front of his jersey and leaned back in his chair to stare tranquilly at the ceiling and to remain splendidly indifferent to his own loud and fulsome belchings which when I had first heard them had filled me with consternation but which now I accepted with only slight un-easiness. Once, thinking I was doing Johnny a good turn, I had refused the baking-soda, but when I had returned to the kitchen the trail of white powder from the dresser to Johnny's chair had told its own tale and I was so ashamed of myself for causing the look of guilt on Johnny's normally ingenuous face that I never had the heart to refuse again.

The belchings diminished in volume and I started to move about the kitchen, wishing that Johnny would realize that it would soon be dusk and that I had yet to go and milk my cow. It was unthinkable that the solicitous 'Ach, but I'm keeping you back', which is the polite Bruach way of telling a stranger it is high time he went, should be used by an English woman to a Gael. I groped for an alternative. On the dresser was a bowl of peanuts still in their shells which had been sent to me from England. Taking a good handful I put them into a bag and offered them to Johnny.

'Take these home to Kirsty,' I said.

Johnny turned them over suspiciously. 'Which is these?' he asked me.

'They're peanuts,' I told him. 'Very good to eat.'

He still continued to turn them between his large fingers.

'I'm taking some with me to chew while I'm looking for the cow.'

'Aye?' he agreed uncertainly. He put them in his pocket and went through into the hall where I heard him struggling into his jigsaw of oilskins. I rushed out of the back door to get meal for Bonny's potach and to collect the milk pail. When I came back into the kitchen Johnny met me with an approving smile.

'Them things is good, good,' he asserted.

'What things?' I asked stupidly, my mind on the task ahead.

'Them nuts, you say. They're good I'm tellin' you.'

'Oh, have you eaten some? I thought you'd like them,' I said. 'Here take some more to eat on your way home.' I took another handful from the bowl. 'Give me your bag and I'll fill it up,' I said, anxious to hurry him on his way so that I might look for Bonny without the dubious assistance of a torch. He proffered me an empty bag. 'Have you eaten them all, Johnny?' I asked, mildly astonished.

'Aye, an' they was good I'm sayin'.'

I dribbled more nuts into his bag. 'You'd better give me the shells and I'll throw them into the fire,' I said. 'Otherwise Kirsty will be complaining that I encourage you to fill your pockets with rubbish.'

'Shells?' he repeated vaguely.

'Yes, the shells off the peanuts. Have you thrown them away, then?' I glanced down at the floor hoping he had not scattered them at random as he did his wood chippings.

'These has shells?' he demanded, taking one from the bag and holding it up.

'Why, yes, of course,' I began to explain. 'Look,' and then I broke off to stare at him with mounting concern. 'Johnny, you didn't eat the shells too,' I accused.

'I eat them,' retorted Johnny proudly. 'I eat all of them an' they're good, I'm tellin' you.' With great bravado he popped a couple of nuts into his mouth and chewed them noisily.

'But, Johnny,' I remonstrated, 'you mustn't eat the shells. They'll give you terrible indigestion!'

Completely unperturbed he continued to pop nuts into his mouth, still chewing with gusto. 'Never have indigestion in my life,' he assured me happily.

'Never had indigestion!' I exclaimed. 'Then why on earth do you take all that baking-soda?'

For a moment he looked vaguely perplexed, and then, wagging a finger at me, he recommended: 'Take plenty bakin'-sody and never no indigestion. Just plenty sody.'

I opened the door and the wind charged in. Johnny met it with a magnificent belch which had such a repelling effect that in the brief respite I managed to slam the door behind him.

'Thank you for that, Johnny,' I murmured with a smile and went to the task of getting into my gumboots and oilskins once again.

Matters Marine

HECTOR had decided to sell his boat *Wayfarer* so that he could buy a bigger one with more accommodation for passengers, for Bruach was being discovered by a steadily increasing number of campers and coach tourists and the crofters were confidently predicting that the coming season would be a bumper one. Some days after his advertisement had appeared in a Highland paper

Hector turned up at my cottage with a sheaf of letters he had received in reply.

'It's a grand day,' he proffered with beguilement in his blue eyes and a diffidence in his voice that was no doubt induced by the fact that it was at least six weeks since our last meeting and that I had, on that occasion, soundly upbraided him for daring to borrow my one and only toothbrush. He had been bewildered and hurt by my attack and had been quick to assure me that he had put the brush back most carefully in its tumbler beside the water bucket where it was always kept. What he hadn't been able to reassure me about was why, when I came to use the toothbrush, its bristles should have been fuzzy with black hair that was exactly the same shade and texture as his own.

'Why, Hector!' I greeted him now with genuine cordiality, for no one could help loving him whatever he did, 'where on earth have you been all this time? I don't seem to have seen you for ages.'

'Ach, I'm just where the tide left me when last you saw me,' he said with a gloomy smile. I told him to sit down but he remained standing, shuffling from one foot to another and gnawing along the length of a grubby forefinger.

'Behag was tellin' me,' he began, and then pushing up his peaked cap he rubbed an exploratory hand among the sparse hair it constrained. 'I was wonderin',' he started again, this time pulling at his ear, 'maybe would you do me a few wee letters on tsat machine you have? I'm tsinkin' it would be quicker.'

I looked up from the sewing machine on which I was running up a pair of gay new curtains. 'Of course I'll do them,' I agreed. 'Do you want them right away?'

'Ach, no.' With renewed confidence he drew up a chair and sat down beside me. 'You can finish what you're doin' first,' he told me magnanimously.

I turned back to the machine.

'Will I work the handle for you,' he offered when he had watched me long enough to be sure the task required very little exertion. I said that I would prefer to do it myself and while I put on a new reel of cotton and re-threaded the needle he toyed delightedly with the

material, rubbing it between his stained fingers and examining the
bright red peonies with which it was patterned. 'Tsese is nice flowers,'
he confided. 'I mind they used to call tsem "chrissie-annies" in
Glasgow when I was tsere.'

When I commenced sewing again Hector bent over me anxiously.
Now despite the fact that I need to wear spectacles for close work I
flatter myself that I can run up a straight seam as neatly as anyone,
but Hector, who admittedly had perfect eyesight, was so dubious of
my skill that every few inches if he considered there was the slightest
deviation he would give an audible 'tech' of concern and an enthusiastic twitch at the material, which resulted in the sewing of a pronounced
'V'. I must confess I was too amused to curb his enthusiasm though
by the time I had reached the end of the seam the stitching resembled
a wavering flight of birds. I thought it might be more satisfactory if I
finished the curtains when I was alone but he was insistent that the
work should not be put aside just for his 'few wee letters'. I suspected
that he was thoroughly enjoying guiding what he no doubt believed
to be my very erratic hand, and he seemed greatly disappointed when
we had finished and I announced that I must press the curtains before
they were hung so that he would have to wait until his next visit
before he could admire the full effect of his collaboration.

I put away the sewing machine and brought out the typewriter.
'Now,' I invited, when there was a sheet of paper in the machine, 'tell
me what you want to say.'

He began to chew his finger again. 'Well, what will I tell tsem?' he
demanded perplexedly.

'What do you want to tell them?' I retaliated.

He put the letters down on the table beside me. 'Well, tsat one
wants to know is tse engine forrard or aft. You could tell him it's
aft.' He brought up one of his knees and attempted to rub his chin
on it. 'Tsere's anusser wants to know where is tse wheelhouse. You
can tell tsem it's aft too.' He sat back limp and exhausted.

I glanced quickly through the letters. 'They all want to know the
price you're asking. You'll need to give them an idea of that,' I told
him.

Hector looked momentarily discomfited. He did not want me or anyone else in the village to know the price he had set on *Wayfarer*. 'Well, now, I'll not be knowin' what to ask for her,' he prevaricated. 'Behag's sayin' one tsing and tse cailleach's sayin' anusser.'

'We'll leave that blank then, and you can fill it in when you and Behag have decided,' I suggested.

'Aye, aye. Tsat'll be tse way of it.' He cheered up instantly.

I drew up a list of questions and asked Hector for the answers. 'Now,' I told him. 'We'll just set down all this information in each letter and then they'll know as much about the boat as you can tell them. Is that all right?'

'Tsat's fine,' said Hector.

'Shall I just begin, "Dear Sir, In reply to your letter of such and such a date, here is the information you ask for. . . ."?'

'We cannot say "Dear Sir",' cut in Hector with shocked disapproval. 'Not when you're writin' to folks about a boat.'

'Why not?' I asked with surprise. 'You don't know these people, so you should begin with "Dear Sir".'

'It's no' friendly,' he argued.

'It's perfectly correct,' I insisted.

'Ach, no,' he said, fidgeting with embarrassment at having to argue with me. 'As like as not tsey won't even read it if you say tsat.'

'Why ever shouldn't they, Hector?' I demanded, my voice edged with asperity.

Hector frowned. 'Well, if ever I get a letter and it begins with "Dear Sir" then I throw it straightway into the fire because I know it'll be a nasty one,' he explained.

Together we pondered the assortment of letters, deciphering names and addressing them in as friendly a manner as Hector wished and also, at his insistence, we informed the prospective buyers chattily that in Bruach it had been a very coarse winter; that the potatoes would surely be very late going into the ground this year and that the Department of Agriculture bull had arrived earlier than expected. Hector then professed himself completely satisfied. 'I'll put a P.S. at tse end tellin' tsem tse price,' he said with true Gaelic finesse.

A month went by; a month of exhilarating dawns which heralded days that stretched themselves to hold more and more hours of gentle sunshine. The seared wintry grass of the crofts took on a more comely appearance and wherever one's glance rested there were bursting buds and courting birds and all the lovely lilting things of spring. Old men in creased dark clothes came out of their winter hiding places and leaned against the walls of the houses, sampling the quality of the sunlight and pronouncing upon the condition of the cattle, upon the prospects of the fishing, or, if encouraged, upon the fate of the world. The children left off their tackety boots and thick hand-knit socks and skipped to school barefooted with the same friskiness as the young lambs bleating on the hills, while on the dry, heathery moors the local incendiarists, with whom every village in the Islands seems to be afflicted, wantonly satisfied their urges so that there was rarely a day when one did not see the spreading blue tendrils of heather smoke creeping steadily or tillering and racing menacingly according to the whim of the wind.

For all of us the days were full of the outdoors: cutting peats, turning them, lifting and finally stacking them; burning the unruly patches of sedge that no scythe could master; gathering up the stones which always seemed to stray on to the crofts during the winter of neglect; teaching new calves to drink from a pail while one stroked the sun-warmed curls of its back and endured the caress of a milky tongue. For the women there was in addition the annual blanket washing, perhaps in a zinc bath of water carried laboriously pailful by pailful from the well, perhaps in a cauldron over a wood fire beside the burn. We worked dedicatedly, cramming the days with toil, and when dusk approached and we could feel we had earned a respite we walked to our homes with the clean cool wind from the hill fanning our glowing faces and our bodies heavy with that good weariness that comes from physical labour in the open air.

It was after just such a day that I went out to do my last chore of the evening. The sun had not long set in a splendour of vermilion and turquoise and the sky was still streaked as though it had been clawed by gory fingernails. Busy ripples flecked with silver, raced across the loch and tumbled with Dresden tinkles on to the pebbles of the shore. The hills looked smug and withdrawn behind a faint veil of mist while across the water the brightest of the lighthouses was already beginning to show as a dim spark on the horizon. My line of newly washed blankets, now dry and wind softened, stirred lazily and as I unpegged each one I did it lingeringly and with a feeling of ecstasy as though I might be dipping a flag in salute to the glory of the night.

'Here! Come an' get me a drink of water. My hands is all sticky!' Erchy's voice, uneasy with authority, came from the direction of the house. Obediently, I gathered up the blankets and went indoors. Erchy was holding a large brush in front of him, its bristles sticky with glistening tar. His hands too were liberally coated. 'I'm that thirsty I'm like to faint,' he told me.

I dumped the blankets on the table well out of his way and poured out a large mug of water. He drank it with audible relish but when I offered to make tea for him he declined it.

'I didn't take my dinner yet,' he explained. (In Bruach one always 'took' one's meals.)

'Then you must be hungry. Let me give you a scone or something.'

'I daren't wait,' he insisted. 'See, I promised the cailleach I'd see to the cow for her tonight as she's goin' ceilidhin' over with Katy. She'll be makin' a swear at me already for bein' as late as I am.' He leaned his elbow on the dresser. 'She wasn't for lettin' me come down here today at all but I told her I'd get the boat tarred while she was good and dry.'

'Tar!' I repeated with a grimace of disgust. 'Why is it you always put so much tar on your boats? Why don't you paint them in nice bright colours instead of just slathering them with dirty black tar?'

Erchy appeared slightly outraged. 'Tar keeps out the water better than paint,' he defended. 'Any splits in the planks or any places where she might be takin' in the water, once they're filled with tar they'll keep out the sea for as long as the season lasts,' he explained.

'I'd like to think there was something more than a gob of tar between me and the sea,' I murmured.

'Ach!' snorted Erchy.

'Anyway it doesn't alter the fact that it's unsightly stuff,' I told him.

'Damty sure it is,' agreed Erchy amiably. 'Here,' he demanded. 'D'you mind Tarry Ruari?'

I shook my head. 'No,' I replied. 'I've seen the house where he lived but he was dead when I came here.'

'You've seen his house? Then you'll know the way it's tarred all over—the roof and the walls—all black?'

I remembered Ruari's house as a stained hovel of a place near a boggy slope of the burn and recalled Morag describing it as being 'very delaborated'.

'Yes,' I admitted, 'it did look as if it might have been tarred.'

'Now that's a man went mad with tar,' said Erchy with complete seriousness. 'He tarred his wee boat inside and out over and over again until she was that heavy he could hardly pull her up the beach. Then he started tarring his house—outside at first and then on the inside. He even tarred the furniture. By God! but you never saw such a place in your life. Folks here just used to laugh at him at first but then the nurse went there one day and found he'd tarred the blankets on his bed. They came and took him away then.'

'Good gracious!' I ejaculated. 'Was he married?'

'Oh, no,' explained Erchy simply. 'Just daft.'

He moved vaguely towards the door. 'I'd best be goin',' he said. 'Thanks for the drink. I was badly needin' it.'

'I'm sorry it wasn't something more sustaining,' I told him with spurious apology.

Erchy turned quickly. 'Indeed but I wouldn't have thanked you for it just now, then.'

'No?' I mocked.

'Damty sure I wouldn't. If you'd handed me a bottle of whisky I would have given it back to you without a thought for it.'

'I'd like to see you refuse whisky,' I said.

'Well, you will someday at that '

I smiled disbelievingly.

'You know,' he went on, 'I reckon that's the reason folks like me don't go bad with the drink like they do in Glasgow and them places. You see what I mean?'

I waited, not at all sure that I did.

'What I'm sayin' is, take me at the cattle sale. I've plenty of money on me so I get drunk as hell on it for maybe two or three days. Well, then I come to the end of it and I don' want anything but to get out on to the hill. I make an excuse to go after the sheep and I'm away first light without my breakfast and only a wee potach in my pocket. When I get thirsty I put my head down into one of the burns—the colder the better—and I can tell you it's sweet! When I've had one drink I'm lookin' forward to tastin' the water in the next place and the next. By the time I come back again I feel as though I never want to take a drop of whisky again in my life.'

'But it doesn't last?' I queried.

'No, thank God,' said Erchy fervently. He appeared to muse for a few moments before he spoke again. 'Did I tell you I'm a big sheep man now?' he asked, changing the subject completely.

'No,' I said. 'Since when?'

'I found them up on the hill one time when I was away like I've been tellin' you.'

'Found them?' I echoed.

'Aye, as true as I'm here.'

'How long have they been lost?'

'Well, it was about five years ago now that I was takin' some old ewes that I had to the sale and one of them went lame on the way so I drove her off to the side of the road and left her there. There was no sign of her by the time I got back so I never gave her another thought except that she'd probably go off somewhere quiet and die. The beasts was only worth a few bob then, anyway. Well, like I was sayin', I was up there on the hill and in a wee corrie all by themselves I came on an old ewe and a ram, two sheep and three young lambs. I caught the ewe first an' there was my markings on her. I had the dog with me so I caught the rest of them an' they had no markings on them at all so I knew they must be mine. She would have been in lamb when I left her,' he explained, 'an' it must have been a ram lamb.'

'It's strange no one has noticed them before,' I said.

'Ach, no, not where they was,' he told me. 'Nobody goes much round the back of the Beinn there, an' the corrie they was in you wouldn't see from the path. That old ewe's a hardy, though,' he muttered appreciatively, 'she hadn't as much fleece left on her as you'd need to bait a hook.' He made another vague move towards the door but in his reminiscent mood I knew he would linger for another half-hour at least before he finally detached himself from the cottage, so I began preparing my evening meal.

'It must be very pleasant to come across a flock of sheep you didn't know you had,' I remarked as I grated cheese into a basin.

Erchy watched me curiously. 'Aye,' he admitted. He came back to the table. 'What's that you're makin'?'

'Oh, just a cheese sauce,' I told him.

'I mind fine when my sister was at home—she's a cook in Edinburgh, you know, and she has to make these fancy things there—she found some cheese in the cupboard that had gone dry. Ach, I can eat the stuff in the winter all right but not in the summer when there's plenty of crowdie,' he explained hurriedly. 'She handed me one of those grater things and told me to get on and grate it for her. Hell, by the time I'd finished all my fingernails had gone into the basin, too. When I showed her she was mad at me so I told her she wasn't to make me do it for her again,' he finished with remembered triumph. I opened a bottle and poured a little of its contents into the pan. Erchy sniffed.

'That's beer!' he accused. 'I thought you didn't like it?'

'I don't like to drink it,' I said. 'But I do sometimes use it in sauces.'

'I wouldn't fancy beer like that,' he said, shaking his head. 'Now if it was whisky. . . .'

'There you go again,' I taunted. 'You're obsessed with whisky.'

'No, not me,' he denied. 'I like to have a good drink when I have one but that's only when I have the money. I'm not like these folks from Rudha that has a bottle sent out on the bus two or three times every week.'

'Tell me, Erchy,' I asked, for he had touched on a subject that had been puzzling me for a long time, 'how do they manage to afford bottles of whisky two or three times a week? They're only crofters and some of them even draw Public Assistance, yet they seem to be able to buy drink and cigarettes as much as ever they want to. They don't seem to go short of anything.'

'No, an' I'm damty sure they never will,' said Erchy, looking mysterious.

'What's their secret?' I cajoled.

'Well, it was durin' the war,' Erchy began. 'There must have been a big wreck some place out here an' there was lots of stuff came ashore one night. The Rudha folks got word of it an' they was all waitin' to grab it. Trunks packed with money, folks say there was, an' they hid it all away. There was plenty of corpses too, scattered all over the shore, so when they'd taken as much stuff as they wanted for them-selves the Rudha people told us an' then they told the pollis. Ach, it was a dirty trick,' said Erchy with disgust creeping into his tones. 'Anyway, the pollis didn't come out straight away so as soon as it got dark me an' Tearlach went over there to see would we find any-thin'. All we found was bolls of flour, plenty of them, and corpses, dozens of them too, all over the shore. An' the moon was shinin' on them so that they gleamed an' the tide was washin' round some of them makin' their limbs move so that you'd think they were tryin' to get up. God! We got that scared we just lifted a boll of flour on to each other's back an' we ran home with it as fast as we could go. Indeed I don't believe we stopped for breath until we got to within sight of Anna's house, an' we never went back there again neither.'

The path to Rudha was four miles of narrow sheep track along the shoulder of the hill, below which the land slid steeply to the jagged rocks of the shore. Even in broad daylight the uninitiated take one look and either turn back or tackle it quakingly on all fours.

'An' then the pollis came,' continued Erchy, 'an' they took away the corpses but they left the bolls of flour. The rest of the folks here just went then and helped themselves.' He sighed. 'That's all Bruach ever got out of it—a few bolls of flour, except for Tearlach's dog that got a good feed off one of the legs of the corpses,' he added reflectively.

I put on the tablecloth. 'Your mother will be giving you up for lost,' I reminded him.

'Aye,' he said, without much interest and, still havering in the doorway, he turned to look out into the night. 'Did Hector tell you he has a buyer for his boat?' he asked over his shoulder.

'No,' I replied with some surprise. 'Has he really? Who?'

'Ach, some fellow down Oban way, I believe,' answered Erchy, turning round again and leaning against the edge of the door. 'He's asked me will I sail it down there with him on Friday if the weather stays this way.'

'And are you going?'

'Aye. I might just as well. Seein' we're goin' we're takin' Johnny Comic to the dentist. The poor man's near crazy with the toothache.'

'That's rather a job to tackle, isn't it?' I asked. 'Johnny's never been away from here before, has he?'

'No, an' he's that scared of comin' with us I believe we'll have to put a rope on him first.'

'You'll never get him into the dentist's chair,' I warned, suspecting that Johnny's one idea would be to play hide-and-seek with his companions until they could delay their return no longer.

'Ach, Tom-Tom's comin' to hold him,' said Erchy. 'An' there'll be the two of us if we're needed.' I stared at him in surprise. 'Aye, you can look like that,' he told me, 'but gentle as Johnny is he's a strong man when it comes to strugglin' an' he'll struggle well enough if he thinks he's goin' to have somethin' done to him.' He edged half of himself outside the door and started to pull it to behind him. 'Is there anythin' you'll be wantin' us to bring back for you? We'll likely be doin' some shoppin'.'

There was always at the back of my mind a list of things which I intended to ask people to get for me should there be some prospect of their visiting the mainland. Now, confronted with Erchy's sudden question, I could recall only the relatively unimportant fact that when the previous autumn I had wanted to make use of some small green tomatoes—the grudging produce of a dozen troublesomely acquired and carefully nurtured plants—I had no vinegar to make them into chutney. It was no use even asking the grocer if he stocked it, for the crofters though lavish in their use of salt were as yet not conditioned to, or perhaps aware of, the other condiments. One never saw a bottle of sauce on a Bruach table.

'Would you bring me a bottle of vinegar?' I asked, still vainly struggling to recall some more needful item on my mental list.

'Vinegar?' repeated Erchy in a puzzled voice, and then, as enlightenment slowly dawned, he went on: 'Aye, I mind now what you mean. Vinegar's the stuff they put on chips in Glasgow, isn't it?'

He was outside the door by now and letting in a gently chill breeze that was bringing up the gooseflesh on my sun-tanned arms.

'Hector's supposed to be bringin' back a few chickens for Morag,' he informed me. 'You'll not be wantin' any yourself, will you?'

'That is a good idea,' I responded with enthusiasm. The only chickens one could get in Bruach were the hardy progeny of the inveterate fowls that scratched around every house and cornstack, flaunting their mongrel feathers with the aplomb of peasants attired in their national costume. I had once tried to get pure-bred chickens sent up to me simply to find out if they laid better, but the length of the train journey coupled with the capriciousness of the local carrier had ensured that none of the chickens had survived. I asked Erchy to bring me a dozen day-old chicks—Black Leghorns if they were available.

'I'll do that,' he promised, and then perhaps because he remembered he was going in a leaky old boat on an unpredictable sea, or perhaps because he recalled a previous experience of high life in Oban, he added a cautionary, 'If the Lord spares me.' He sounded a trifle embarrassed. 'I'm away. Good night,' he called, and shut the door.

'Good night!' I rejoined and sat down at last to eat my supper.

There was a clouding over of the sky in the late afternoon of the following day and the next morning the sun, which had shone unrestrainedly for so long, only cocked a sleepy eye before retiring beneath a canopy of grey cloud. It looked as if the spell of fine weather was coming to an end. Friday morning dawned wet and windy with

the sea flouncing angrily against the rocks and with grey sweeps of
rain being hurried across the bay. When I went up to the village shop
to buy paraffin I espied Erchy, Hector and Tom-Tom leaning in
various attitudes of disconsolation against the gable of the latter's
house. All were gazing with equal gloom at *Wayfarer* who was plunging and rearing at her mooring.

'You're not going off today, then?' I observed.

'No damty fear,' replied Erchy. 'That sea is goin' to get bigger
before it gets smaller.'

'There's some big enough lumps out there already,' said Tom-
Tom. 'I don't fancy it myself.'

'We're safer where we are,' agreed Hector with glum acceptance of
the situation.

'Well, here's one who's mighty pleased we're not settin' foot on
the sea,' said Erchy with a wink and a nod towards a hunched figure
which squatted miserably beside him. 'Is that not so, Johnny?' he
shouted, and in answer the figure raised a face that would normally
be described as being of 'ashen hue'. However, when one has become
a burner of peat as opposed to coal it is a description one can no
longer use, for 'ashen' would imply the complexion of a Red Indian.

'Poor Johnny Comic,' I said. 'Is his toothache still as bad as
ever?'

'No,' denied Erchy. 'You cannot have toothache an' be scared out
of your life at the same time. You can only feel one or the other.'

We were joined by Morag who was also on her way to get paraffin.

'So my brave boys has decided it's too rough for them,' she said by
way of greeting, and the men turned away, discomfited by the derision
in her voice. I picked up my can and moved away. Morag walked
alongside me, a smug grin on her face.

'It doesn't look very nice out there, does it?' I remarked.

'Ach,' she said disdainfully. 'They're not much of sailors nowadays.
I've seen my father go out in seas three times as big as I'm seein' out
there an' their boats not half the size either.' She turned and gestured
towards the bay. 'I've known myself be out in more sea than there is
now.'

'Morag,' I demanded. 'Have you ever been out in a sea big enough to frighten you?'

'Only once that I mind,' she confessed with a slight grimace of shame.

'Was it very rough then?'

'Ach, it was all yon big green beasts that you can see through. Comin' straight at us they was till you thought with every one of them that the boat would never ride the next. My father made me lie down under one of the thwarts so that I wouldn't get thrown out.' She sighed. 'Aye, we were caught badly that day an' I believe I was as frightened as I've ever been. Mind you,' she added hastily, 'frightened though I was, I was never what you'd call inebriated with fear.' She chuckled. 'I was younger then, though, an' I daresay I hadn't as much sense as I have now.'

With our cans filled with paraffin we started off for home again, stopping frequently for me to change my can from one aching arm to the other. Morag, who was carrying twice the amount of paraffin, did not put hers down for an instant and only watched my struggles with a tolerant smile. Hector and Erchy were still propping up the end of Tom-Tom's house but by this time they had been joined by Old Murdoch and Yawn who had doubtless come to offer cautionary advice although at this moment they were engaged in conversation with a young girl who stood, slim and straight, between the two bent old men, like an 'I' in parenthesis.

'Yon's the lassie that's been stayin' with Mary Ann over the last few days,' said Morag in a low voice. 'You'll have seen her likely?'

'Only in the distance,' I admitted.

'She was askin' Hector last night would she get back to the mainland with him today an' he had to promise her he'd take her.'

'I should jolly well think he would have promised,' I muttered as we drew closer. She was quite the most beautiful creature I had ever seen, with huge brown, lustrous eyes, dark curly hair, exquisitely fine bones and a skin of such golden-ness that it looked on this dull day as though it was exuding sunshine. Even I felt momentarily stunned by her appearance. What she did to men I could only guess.

'But, Hector,' she was saying with wheedling fretfulness as we approached, 'you promised you'd take me. I would have gone on the bus this morning and caught the ferry if I'd thought your boat wouldn't be going. I've simply got to be back in the office in London on Monday morning or I'll get the sack.'

Hector only hunched his shoulders harder against the wall and looked sulky.

'Ach, you'll not get the sack,' consoled Erchy. 'Tell them you got held up by the storm an' it'll be all right.'

'I can't tell them that,' she retorted.

'Why not?' demanded Erchy.

'They wouldn't understand.'

Erchy grunted his scepticism.

'It'll maybe get a bit calmer by this evening yet,' Yawn prophesied, and the girl who, despite the fact that her teeth were chattering, still managed to look ravishing, brightened up visibly.

'Will you take me across this evening then, if it gets calm?' she coaxed, with a look at the men that should have sent them hurrying to launch any number of boats.

'Ach, no,' said the usually impressionable Hector, shuffling uncomfortably. 'Tse tide will be all wrong by tsis evenin' for gettin' the dinghy off the shore.'

The girl's expression as she turned to me was a mixture of chagrin and disbelief.

'Please,' she begged. 'They don't seem to understand how terribly important it is for me to get back. It's a new job I've landed—quite a good one and I wasn't really due a holiday yet but they kindly let me have these few days. Will you try to explain to Hector for me?'

I shook my head, understanding her frustration but by now almost as out of touch with her world as were the rest of the group.

'Well,' said Erchy with decision. 'You say you cannot get back to London by Monday morning unless you leave here tonight. An' you cannot leave here tonight so you cannot do anythin' else but wait.'

'They'll not take it so badly if you just explain to them that it was the storm that kept you back,' soothed Yawn. 'An' the tide,' he added as an afterthought.

The lassie drooped with dejection. 'I've told you,' she reiterated. 'You can't explain to people in London about things like that. They'll never believe it,' she finished with a grim smile.

Yawn was visibly staggered. 'They wouldn't believe you?' he demanded.

The lassie shook her head.

'Well, lassie,' he advised her with great gravity, 'I'm tellin' you, you'd best never go back at all to a place like that. If they don' understand about storms and tides and things they must be a lot of savages just.'

'Miss Peckwitt and Morag! Is it yourselves?' Tom-Tom's wife appeared round the corner of the house. 'Come away in now and take a fly cuppie with me. I have it ready.'

We followed her inside, and the men, anxious to evade the lassie's continued importunings, lumbered after us.

'Honest to God,' grumbled Erchy, as he seated himself on the bench. 'Some people thinks it's us that makes the weather.'

'Aye, an' tse tides,' rejoined Hector. 'Some of tsese folks tsat come in my boat, tsey say to me, "Can I leave tsis picnic basket," or some-tsing like tsat. "Will it be all right here on tse shore till we get back?" And tsen when I tell tsem no, tsey must take it up on tse rocks out of tse tide's way, tsey tsink I'm not bein' nice to tsem.' He shook his head sadly.

'It just seems as though they don't understand about the tides,' said Erchy wonderingly.

'They know the theory but not the practice,' I said. 'They learn about tides ebbing and flowing but they're not taught that this means the water is always moving up to or away from the actual bit of beach they're sitting on.'

Hector gazed at me with serious surprise. 'Tsey shouldn't need to be taught tsings as simple as tsat,' he assured me. 'Tsey didn't teach ourselves.'

As I drank my tea I studied Hector covertly, for I had just witnessed him do a thing which I had always thought him incapable of doing and that was to remain impervious to the charms of a young and beautiful girl. I was curious to know the reason for it.

'Isn't that lassie a beauty?' I hazarded.

'Eh?' said Erchy stupidly.

Tom-Tom's wife thought for a moment. 'I don't believe she's so bad at that,' she conceded.

Hector looked up from his tea. 'Ach, what good is she when she's tsat tsin you could use her for darnin' a sock,' he observed with a grin, and looked at the other men for confirmation.

Tom-Tom's wife, who had once been described to me as being 'not fat but needin' an awful lot of room when she sat down', chuckled appreciatively. I stared at Hector. He had never before struck me as being particularly figure conscious when selecting his female companions. What then, I wondered, was there about this girl that he should find her so uninteresting?

'She tsinks too much of herself, tsat one,' he explained, as though I had asked the question aloud. 'I was down on tse shore tse usser day,' he went on, 'and she comes along. She was after lifting tsese coloured stones from tse beach to take back wiss her and when she sees me she drops tse bag and she says: "Oh, Hector, I'm so glad I've met a big, strong man to carry my stones for me. Tsey're awful heavy," she says.'

'An' did you carry them for her?' questioned Morag with a wink at me.

'Indeed I did not,' responded Hector. 'I told her if she'd managed to carry tsem tsat far she must be stronger tsan she tsought she was, so she'd best carry tsem tse rest of tse way.' His blue eyes were impish as he looked at each of us in turn, expecting our approval. 'You know she was tsat vexed wiss me she hardly spoke to me all tse way home.'

'I don't understand it,' I said. 'I would have expected every man in the place to be following her. I'll bet she's used to plenty of attention in England.'

'Well, she'll no' get much of it here,' Erchy stated flatly.

'And yet she's what I'd describe as a real beauty queen,' I mused.

'I'm no' seein' it tsen,' scoffed Hector. He took a noisy gulp of tea.

'I believe she's only one of tsese foreigners anyway and she's queer.' He frowned down at his cup. 'I wouldn't want to take anytsin' to do wiss her anyway, for no religion has she at all but a bit of wood or stone.'

All weekend the clouds raced greyly above a shaggy sea but on Monday night there seemed to be a promise of calm in the night sky and on Tuesday morning I woke without the sound of rain on my windows or the wind bullying the roof. In Bruach one's life was so inextricably bound up with the weather that one got into the habit of waking with an ear cocked for the sound of wind much as, after an illness, one wakes to the expectation of pain. If there was no noise of storm in a morning one waited tensely, hesitating to believe the miracle and then when one had accepted it one would throw off the bedclothes and hasten to get started on the labours of a busy day.

By the time I returned from milking Bonny *Wayfarer* had left her moorings and was already a dark speck on the horizon. Within a few days Nelly Elly, the postmistress, had received a telephone message from Erchy saying that Johnny had been taken to the dentist and that Hector had bought himself a new boat in which they now proposed to sail back. She reported that he had sounded quite sober. For two or three days there was no word from the men and so it was assumed that they were already on their way. Those of us who had binoculars went frequently to lean our elbows on the stone dykes and stare out to sea, hoping to be the first to pick up a sight of the mariners and send the word round the village. For easily diverted people like myself it was an excuse to scan the outlying islands, trying to identify their varied peaks or, nearer home, to focus the glasses on the constant industry of the sea birds; on cormorants fishing greedily; on busy, bobbing guillemots and on the swift dipping flight of terns over the sea, contrasting their activity with the motionlessness of a stately heron standing beside the mouth of the burn, and then, ruefully, with my own idleness.

But a week went by without any sign of the boat and when on the following Tuesday morning the mist rolled in from the sea, thick as a sponge, and hid everything beyond the boundaries of the crofts, we

knew we could not expect to see them for some time. I wondered if
Morag and Behag, Hector's wife, were worrying about the lack of
news and felt I ought to go along and ceilidh with them for the
evening. When I pushed open the door of Morag's cottage there came
the sound of many voices.

'Come away in,' called Morag happily. 'Come in and see the
rascals.'

Erchy, Tom-Tom and Hector, their faces shining in the lamplight,
were seated at the table enjoying a meal of salt herring and potatoes.
There was a partly full bottle of whisky on the table and a couple of
empties down in the hearth. The men looked mightily pleased with
themselves.

'How on earth did you get home on a day like this?' I asked them.

'We came in Hector's new boat. How would you think?' replied
Erchy waggishly.

'Did you have a compass?'

'We did not, then. What would we be wantin' with one of them
things, anyway?'

'But isn't the mist as thick on the water as it is here on the land?'
I wanted to know.

'Twice as thick,' pronounced Erchy. 'We kept catchin' the boat
right bangs. Hector said they was only hard pieces of water but I
believe we hit every rock between here and Oban.' He broke open a
large floury-looking potato and stuffed almost the whole of it into his
mouth. He turned to Hector. 'She's a good strong boat you have
there,' he told him, with an accompanying slap on the back. 'She
must be or she'd be in bits by now.'

Hector smiled bashfully at the herring he was holding in his two
hands.

'Seriously,' I taxed them. 'How did you manage to navigate if you
didn't have a compass?'

'Ach, well, we was just goin' round in circles to begin wiss,' explained
Hector. 'Every time tse mist lifted a bit we saw tse same bit of coast one
side of us or tse usser. We was keepin' close in, you see, trying would
we creep round tse shore.'

'Aye,' Erchy took up the tale, 'and then I remembered how my father had told me about bein' caught in the mist on the sea once. He tore up a newspaper he had in the boat and scattered bits of it on the water as he went so he'd know if he was goin' in circles. We did the same just. We did that all the way and it got us home here, safe as hell.'

It sounded like a story I had heard before and ought to have more sense than to believe. 'Is that true?' I asked doubtfully.

'As true as I'm here,' asserted Erchy, and to this day I do not know whether he was pulling my leg.

'You didn't tell us yet how Johnny got on at the dentist's with his teeths,' said Behag quietly from the bench where she was sitting patiently with three alert kittens and the irrepressible Fiona all helping her to knit a fair-isle sweater.

The three men gave a concerted hoot of laughter. 'You should have been there to see it,' Erchy said. 'Johnny went and sat in the chair like a lamb and we didn't think he was goin' to give any trouble at all, but the dentist took one look at him an' decided he'd best give him gas. That was all right and he took the tooth out after a bit of a struggle, but then he must have taken the gag out too soon or some-thin'. Anyway, he had his thumb right inside Johnny's mouth when suddenly Johnny's teeths clamps down on it. My, you should have heard that dentist shoutin'. He started swearin' at his assistant an' the assistant swore back and told him what a fool he was to his face. He got his thumb out at last, but by God! he was in a state, I can tell you. Then Johnny comes too, an' feelin' his bad tooth's out an' not hurtin' him any more, his face lights up and he jumps up from the chair an' rushes at the dentist shoutin' "By God! By God!"' Here they were all overcome with laughter. 'The poor wee dentist mannie didn't know Johnny only wanted to shake hands with him and thank him for gettin' his sore tooth sorted for him,' resumed Erchy. 'He was terrified! He thought Johnny was after him to do him some hurt an' there he was runnin' round and round the surgery holding his thumb with Johnny chasin' after him still shoutin' "By God! By God!" like he always does when he's excited. "Get him out of here!" the dentist yells at us. Screamin' he was too. "Get the bugger out of here before he kills me." Well me and Tom-Tom manages to get hold of Johnny and drag him out. Poor man was that puzzled about it all so I went back an' told the dentist that Johnny had meant him no harm, it was only that he was wantin' to thank him.' Erchy disgorged a mouthful of herring bones on to his plate. 'Ach, but he wouldn't listen to me. "Don't you ever let him inside here again," says he. "I might never be able to pull another tooth the way my hand is now." '

'Poor man,' ejaculated Morag half-heartedly, but I did not know to whom she was referring.

'Did you bring any chickens?' I asked after a pause.

'Aye, so we did.'

'Black Leghorns?'

'Aye.'

'Black Leghorns!' shrilled Morag with an acerbity that was mellowed by the tot of whisky she had just swallowed. 'Drunk Leghorns more likely!'

'Drunk?' I echoed with a smile.

'Aye, drunk,' affirmed Morag, lifting the lids of two cardboard boxes near the fire.

'Aye,' Erchy started to explain. 'You see we got them three days ago when we first thought we was startin' back. Well, then we met up with some lads we knew and we had a good drink with them so we didn't wake up in time to get goin' the next day. The lads came again the next night so we stayed and had another good drink. We'd forgotten about the chickens, you see.'

'I didn't forget tsem,' repudiated Hector who was beginning to doze in his chair. 'I gave tsem a wee taste of oatmeal I scraped up from tse linings of my pockets.'

Morag snorted. 'For all the good that would be to them you might just as well have left it there,' she told him.

'Well, as I was sayin',' resumed Erchy, 'we didn't think about the chickens until sometime last evenin' when Hector says all of a sudden: "My God! What about them chickens?" So we fetched them out of the wheelhouse where they'd been all the time and we had a look at them.

They didn't look bad and they was makin' plenty of noise but they was huddled together just as though they was feelin' the cold.'

'Sure they was feelin' the cold,' interpolated Morag. 'The poor wee creatures.'

'What did you do then?' I encouraged.

'We didn't know what to do,' said Erchy. 'We had no coal on the boat to put on a fire and no other way of warmin' them, until Hector said we should try would we warm them with our own breath. So that's what we did. We took it in turns just to go and give them a good breathin' on every now and then. Is that not the way of it, Hector?'

Hector again roused himself to confirm his own brilliance.

'But how did they get drunk?' I persisted.

'Ach, well you know how it is, Miss Peckwitt. These lads we met, they came down again and they'd brought a few bottles with them, so we started drinkin' again. We minded not to forget the chickens though an' we kept openin' the lids of their boxes and givin' them a good warmin' with our breaths. I remember thinkin' one time that they looked to be gettin' sleepy. Their eyes was closin' and they started staggerin' and lyin' down with their legs stretched out. I thought they must be dyin' all right but Hector said no, they was lyin' down because they were goin' to sleep as they should.' He laughed. 'Ach, I think we was both pretty drunk then.'

'I would have expected Johnny Comic to have mothered them like a hen,' I said.

'He didn't know a thing about them,' said Erchy. 'As soon as he stepped back on the boat he rolled himself in his oilskins and lay in the bunk there and he stirred only to eat one of the hard-boiled eggs Kirsty had given him when he came away. Honest, she gave him three dozen of them!'

'They're no' lyin' down any more,' said Morag, taking another peep into the boxes. 'They're no' very strong but they're up on their feets.'

'Am I not after tellin' you it was just drunk they was. Drunk on too much whisky fumes,' said Tom-Tom who, since finishing his

meal, had sat smiling foolishly at the coloured plates on the dresser
as though he was watching a chorus of dancers.

'The poor wee things,' said Morag again. 'Day-old chicks and so
drunk I'm thinkin' they'll not reach a day older before they're dead.'

But she was wrong. 'The poor wee things' not only survived but
thrived exceedingly well. They seemed to be immune from all the
maladies that can affect young chickens and not even Morag had ever
known such wonderful layers.

Tourists

NELLY ELLY, her son Duncan, Erchy and Hector were all looking slightly baffled when I called at the Post Office.

'It's a glorious day,' I greeted them enthusiastically, and though they were emphatic in their agreement that it was indeed a glorious day and went on politely to acclaim the benefits such weather would bring in the way of increased crops and increased tourism there was an air of preoccupation about the four of them. I wondered if it had anything to do with the folder Nelly Elly had in front of her on the counter.

'Ask Miss Peckwitt what she thinks about it,' suggested Erchy.

'Yes, well,' said Nelly Elly hastily. 'I was about to do that just.'

I looked from one to the other.

'It's like this,' the postmistress began to explain. 'We've just had a telegram through for one of the young men that's campin' down by the burn there—yon dark boy who wears the thick glasses and chews bubbles when he talks, you mind?'

I nodded, puzzling as to what the difficulty might be.

'Well,' went on Nelly Elly, with a trace of reticence, 'it seems it's his twenty-first birthday and the sender's paid for one of those special birthday greetings forms for him and I haven't one left in the place.'

'And now,' Duncan continued for her, 'if we give it to him on a plain form just an' he finds out it was a fancy form that was paid for, somebody might be after puttin' in a complaint.'

'What sort of forms have you, then?' I asked, trying to be helpful.

'Just these,' said Nelly Elly, handing me two forms, one of which was decorated with wedding bells while the other was gay with storks.

'One's for weddings and the other's supposed to be for the birth of a baby,' she explained superfluously. 'Those are all I have except for the plain forms.'

'I'm sayin' she should send him tse one with tse birds on,' suggested Hector. 'Tse poor man might get a bit of a fright if he gets a wedding telegram right in tse middle of his holidays.'

'It depends on the message, I should think,' I said.

'It says just "Congratulations on your twenty-first",' Nelly Elly read out obligingly.

'In that case I should think he'd get much more of a fright if he got a telegram with storks on it,' I said with a levity that was not particularly well received.

'Which sort of tsings is storks?' demanded Hector.

'Those birds,' I told him, indicating the telegram form. 'They're the ones that are supposed to bring the babies.'

'Aye?' His expression was one of polite disbelief and I realized that of course Bruach had never indulged in such pleasant euphemisms.

'Well, will one of us go down an' ask the man which form he'd like best?' suggested Erchy.

'Ach, no.' She seemed doubtful. 'Maybe if Duncan took it down on a wedding form and explained to the fellow that it's all we have just at the moment, likely he'd take it all right?'

'Likely he would,' we comforted, and so she wrote out the message and gave it to Duncan. Erchy and Hector accompanied him so as to witness any possible reactions.

I gave my letters to Nelly Elly and she tried the date-stamp experimentally on her bare arm. 'Ach!' she ejaculated. 'Fiona was in last night and was playin' with my stamp.' She adjusted it and again applied it to her arm before stamping it on to the envelopes. 'There now,' she said, dropping the letters into the box.

She came round from behind the counter to close and bolt the door of the Post Office behind me. It was only three in the afternoon but she was going to hoe her potato-patch beside the road and from there she could see any potential customers. She was not to be left long undisturbed, for Bruach already had its first quota of tourists and I had left the Post Office only about a hundred yards behind me when I met a pair of sun-scorched and midge-bitten campers sauntering along the road, who demanded a little resentfully to know where the Post Office had hidden itself and if, when they found it, they could buy stamps there. They implied both by their tone and their remarks that they had found Bruach a little unaccommodating so far. I directed them on their way but their resentment had kindled a response in me, not against Bruach or the Bruachites but against the tourists themselves, for they were coming now in their coachloads and carloads, robbing the village of its privacy and awakening the hibernating avarice of the crofters.

The moment the first tourists arrived (always pronounced 'towrists' in Bruach) the crofters began to look more alert. Except for the old die-hards like Yawn, who would have nothing to do with tourists and only gave them a 'withdraw the hem of his garment look' when they ventured near him, they thoroughly enjoyed the colour and the air of prosperity the presence of the visitors imparted to the village. Soon notices began to appear outside croft houses adjoining the roadside, proclaiming that they were 'Tearooms' or offering 'Bed and Breakfast', and of these there were more than enough to cater for the number of people who came. Some drew more custom than others, perhaps because of their position, perhaps because of the fare they offered, but it was comforting to see how little rivalry there was between them. Admittedly, Hamish, having been dissatisfied one season with the amount of trade his wife's tearoom had attracted, had tried to increase it the following season by the added lure of a 'toilet', and with this intention he had erected a notice-board in his front garden. Painstakingly, because he was crippled with rheumatics, he had painted the word on it in large white letters, but unfortunately spelling was not Hamish's strong point and he was soon having to endure much mockery from his neighbours for having left out the 'i' so that the notice stated somewhat confusingly 'Tolet'. In an attempt to rectify his mistake he had hastily inserted an 'i' in the appropriate position but the letters were already so cramped that it merely looked like an emphatic full stop separating the words 'To' and 'let'. That at any rate is how the tourists interpreted it and throughout that season Hamish and his family were pestered by people anxious to rent their thatched cottage, until Hamish, almost beside himself with vexation, had resolved to clarify the position beyond doubt in time for the next season. This he had done by simply adding the letters 'W.C.' above the 'To.let' already on the board. I do not know if it brought increased custom to his tearoom but I do know that whenever I passed by Hamish's cottage there were groups of puzzled tourists studying the sign and debating among themselves as to its meaning.

However, on Sundays, despite the presence of tourists, Bruach reverted to its normal piety. Sheets put out to bleach were taken in if they were dry, or, if they were still wet, rolled up so that the sun should not be employed to whiten them. In some houses male guests might be asked if they would mind shaving on the Saturday night because the landlady could not allow the use of a razor on the Sabbath, and always, last thing on Saturday night, the 'Tearoom' and 'Bed and Breakfast' notices were draped over with sacking, though with such artful nonchalance that the words were never completely obscured.

'He Breeah!'

I paused and turned round in the direction of the hail to see Janet talking to Dugald who was at work in his potatoes. She waved an indication that she was about to join me and I sat down on the grass verge of the road while I waited for her. The hot sun was burning through my dress and the parched grass was warm and brittle against my bare legs. The breeze was soft as thistledown and spiced wih lark song, while out in the bay a school of porpoises plunged and tumbled with consummate grace. Close inshore a trio of shark fins cut lazily through the water. We were well into the second week of long days that began with the sun poking its fingers into one's eyes in a morning and ended, after molten sunset, in a calm and soothing twilight that all too soon merged into another dawn. The cuckoos, who all day answered their own echoes until it seemed they would drive themselves and everyone else crazy, only decelerated their pace during the night—they did not cease altogether.

'Ach, mo ghaoil,' puffed Janet as she struggled up the steep bank. 'Whenever are we goin' to see the last of this fine weather?'

'Are you tired of it?' I asked her.

'Indeed, I'm no tired of the weather but I'm tired of bein' short of water,' she grumbled. 'My brother's complainin' he has time for nothing else all day but going back and forwards to the well for me.'

It was always the same when we got a nice spell in Bruach. We could not really enjoy it after the first few days because by then we had begun to fret about our water supply.

'I have that many sheets to wash,' resumed Janet, 'an' there's more visitors comin' tonight. An' even when I get the water the well is that low it looks like I'm washin' the sheets in strong tea.' She swung her sack of bread over from one shoulder to the other. 'Indeed: that woman I have stayin' with me just now came out to speak to me while I was doin' my washin' yesterday an' you should have seen the look she gave to my water.' Janet chuckled tranquilly.

'Is that the woman from Manchester you were telling me about?' I enquired.

'It is so, mo ghaoil, an' that's what I was wantin' to ask you about. She's sayin' she feels it that strange here an' she's just longin' to meet another Englishwoman. I was wondering would you come over and have a wee crack with her this evenin' and cheer her up a bitty?'

'I can't come now,' I apologized, for in Bruach 'afternoon' receives no recognition. It is morning until about two o'clock and then it becomes 'evening'. 'I've promised to take Fiona for a picnic and I don't suppose I shall feel much like going anywhere but to my bed when I get back from that.'

'No, indeed,' agreed Janet understandingly, for Hector and Behag's small daughter was a notoriously intractable child.

'Will I tell her you'll come tomorrow, then?' Janet pleaded, and when I agreed she grasped my hand thankfully. 'She'll be fine an' pleased when she hears it, for she's like as if she thinks she's among a lot of savages.' Janet's laughter bubbled again. 'Indeed, d'you know she asked me the other day if there was coal mines beyond the hills because they reminded her so much of the "slack heaps" I think she called them she's after seein' in England.'

'Why ever did she come here?' I asked, feeling vaguely affronted.

'Ach, well, I believe her husband used to come to these parts an' he was always after praisin' it up to her so when she lost him she thought she'd best come here an' see what he liked so much.'

'What a good thing she didn't come with him and spoil it for him,' I said.

'That's just what I was sayin' there myself to Dugald. The woman's a right misery to herself because she can't see a single factory chimney no matter how hard she looks.'

The sandwiches and cake for our picnic were already prepared and I had only to pack them into a bag and then collect Fiona. She was bobbing impatiently in the doorway and as soon as she detected me she ran towards me, shouting all the way.

'Dugald's just away and he says you're to get rhubarb tonight on your way back.' She tugged at my hand, pulling me round so that we faced in the opposite direction to which I had planned. 'We're goin' this way,' she announced.

'No, we're going this way,' I told her firmly. The trouble with Fiona was that she was so used to getting her own way she was completely deaf to correction. She continued to pull me in the direction she wanted to go but on this occasion I had resolved that I must be equally firm.

'I am going this way, Fiona, and if you want to go the other way you may. We'll share out the food now.' It was a risk because she was quite capable of agreeing to go off by herself and I should then have had to trail surreptitiously in her wake to make sure she came to no harm. Her sudden capitulation appeared to stagger her as much as it did myself for she was too speechless to issue a single command while we plodded over the brittle dry moors and picked our way across the beds of dried-out burns.

'Why did you no' want to go the other way?' she demanded when she had regained her complacency, and while we helped each other to descend a narrow path that led to a beach which Fiona had never visited before and which I loved for its seclusion I explained to her why I had chosen to come this way. It was really to avoid Bonny, for when I had first bought her and put her out on the hill with the rest of the village cattle she had been friendless and alone for a time and so whenever she saw me she had got into the habit of following me. I had made the mistake then of packing a 'wee potach' for her along with my own picnic lunch and had then had to endure her standing over me ecstatically chewing a juicy green cud from which webs of saliva drifted all over my own food. The next time she had spied the lunch bag on my shoulder she had grown impatient for me to open it and had insisted on escorting me so very closely that when I had come to the stepping-stones of a burn and had stood poised hesitantly in the middle she had urged me on so eagerly with her horns in my back that I and the lunch bag had emerged in a wet and sorry state. Her devotion to me was touching and because of it I did not try too much to discourage her until she had progressed from being merely accepted by the other cattle to become the acknowledged leader of the younger set. Then I had to find a different location for my alfresco meals. It was one thing to take one's own cow for a picnic. It was quite another to take thirty or forty other cows, each one of them curious to discover what it was in my lunch bag that was so attractive to their leader.

Fiona stared at me expressionlessly as I talked and when I had finished she asserted flatly, 'See that boat out there,' as though she had not listened to a word I said. She was looking out across the listless water through which a ringnetter was tearing its way with emphatic urgency.

'She has plenty fish,' she added with adult self-assurance.

'How do you know she has fish, clever puss?' I teased.

'Because she has the gulls with her,' replied Fiona through tightened lips. She did not call me a silly old cailleach as she would have had I been her mother or aunt, but her tone was unmistakable. I stared out at the ringnetter. There was a trail of fuzzy smoke from her galley chimney and in it the gulls whirled and eddied with the sun glancing off their wing tips so that it looked as if the boat had thrown over herself a gauzy, sequin-studded scarf.

I suggested beachcombing, a pastime which the child revelled in and which I found at least as pleasurable as at one time I would have found a shopping spree in town. It added to one's feeling of self-sufficiency and independence to gather driftwood for one's fire and in addition there was always the exciting prospect of stumbling upon a really worthwhile find. Our progress was slow for Fiona demanded my attention for even her most trivial finds and her chatter was incessant. However at last we found for her a brightly coloured ball and then almost simultaneously a coir doormat and a perfectly good plastic pail. She was momentarily overawed by her good fortune until she recollected our picnic.

'When will we take our tea?' she asked with only partially concealed impatience.

I waited only to pick up my own finds—a brass porthole with glass intact that I thought would improve my front door and two aluminium net floats which Erchy would halve for me to provide four typically Bruach feeding bowls.

'We'll have it now if you like,' I told her. We sat down cautiously on the sunbaked rocks with our bare feet in a warm, tide-washed pool that was floored with pounded shells and studded with sea-anemones, and when we had eaten we played at sailing Fiona's ball until the sun had moved off the cliff-screened shore and the midges began to work up to their evening appetites. We climbed up to the open moors again, our feet disturbing hundreds of heather moths which fluttered up in front of us like petals chased by a gamin breeze. The sun was still shining with evening-tempered brilliance; the sheep were just beginning to rouse themselves from their siesta; a lamb bleated for its mother and was answered by the frustrated mew of a buzzard planing overhead. Fiona's fat little legs plodded sturdily beside my own but she had gone very quiet and I suspected that she was tired. I hoped she had forgotten Dugald's message and planned to deposit her back with her mother and aunt before I went to collect the promised rhubarb. But of course she had remembered and of course she insisted on accompanying me, although it would add another mile to our walk. I gave in without argument.

Dugald's croft ran alongside the road and was recognizable by a large notice stating that it was a 'Car Park, price 1/–', a notice which had been erected originally more as a piece of bluff than anything else but which was now appreciably augmenting Dugald's pension. It had been at a ceilidh one evening that Dugald had been complaining bitterly that the tourists' cars were ruining his hay and someone had then suggested that the best way to stop the cars from parking on his croft was to make them pay for the privilege. Dugald had thought it an excellent idea and had immediately erected the notice, but to his bewilderment instead of continuing along the road where there was ample free parking space the foolish drivers still came and parked on his croft. For some days Dugald had tried to look as though neither the house nor the croft belonged to him when he saw honest drivers looking for someone to pay their shillings to, but when, from the concealment of his byre, he had watched them go to the cottage and hand the parking fee to his wife, Dugald had been so shaken that, as he put it, 'I didn't know what to say to myself.' When he saw how the shillings mounted up he realized that he was on to a good thing and now Dugald was soon out of the house and waiting for his fee whenever a car so much as put a wheel on his croft. Except of course on Sunday.

Dugald was changing the calves' tethers when we saw him and made our presence known. He shouted that his wife was away on the bus but that there was rhubarb for me at the house if I would get it. Fiona and I opened the door of the porch and took the large bundle of rhubarb that would not only provide me with puddings for several days but would also be enough for a couple of jars of jam. I went over to thank Dugald and as he had finished the tethering he was ready and willing to spare a few minutes for conversation.

'She was sayin' you'd get more if you're wantin' it,' he told me. (Crofters when speaking English never seem to know how to refer to their wives, for in Gaelic it is 'cailleach' which is literally 'old woman' and they realize that this is not quite acceptable to polite English people.)

'If she has plenty I'd like some more,' I told him. 'I could use it for making wine.'

'Aye, she has that much of it we could do with throwin' some of it in the sea,' he told me. 'You'd best come up after you've taken your dinner tomorrow and get some more.'

'Not tomorrow I can't,' I replied. 'I've promised to go and talk to that woman Janet has staying with her. Janet say's she's lonely and miserable.'

'Is that the one they had out in the boat today to show her the scenery and she just sat with her head bent over her knittin' all the way so she didn't see a thing?'

'It sounds like her,' I agreed.

'Ach, well, likely she will be miserable,' said Dugald. 'She's from Manchester, isn't she?' he added, as though that explained everything.

'How's the parking business going these days?' I asked him with a grin, to which he responded with an oblique smile.

'Ach, no' bad, no' bad,' he said with studied offhandedness. 'Though there's some of these drivers that comes an' all they give me instead of a shillin' is a mouthful of argument.'

'I was hearing great praise of you from a motorist only the other day, anyway,' I told him.

'Which was that?' he demanded with sudden suspicion.

So I told him of a driver I had been talking to who had parked on his croft the previous Sunday, and who had gone to the cottage to pay his parking fee only to be confronted by Dugald who had refused the shilling with stubborn piety. The man had been so impressed that as soon as he knew I was not a Gael he had burst out with the story. He had never believed, he had told me, that he would actually meet a man so implacably devout as to forgo his rightful dues just because it was the Sabbath.

'Ach, that cheat,' said Dugald, when I had finished. 'He was English too, I mind.'

'Cheat?' I repeated.

'Aye, cheat, I said. He parked his car here all day from early in the mornin' till late at night an' not so much as a sixpence did I get out of it.'

'But he told me he had pressed you to take the money but you refused.'

'So I did,' said Dugald virtuously. 'I explained to him once or twice that I couldn't take the money from him because it was the Sabbath.'

'Well, in that case how can you say now that he was a cheat?' I demanded with a touch of amusement.

'Could he no' have left it on the window-sill for me?' replied Dugald with shattering apostasy. 'It would still have been there for me in the mornin'.'

Both Fiona and the midges were becoming increasingly persistent in their demands that we should move and, slapping at our bitten limbs, we fled down the road to Morag's cottage where Hector and Erchy were enjoying a strupak. This season the boats had swapped partners and now the two friends were happily running the *Ealasaid,*

Hector's new boat, together. Their greeting to me sounded slightly ironic.

'You don't sound too happy,' I told them. 'Haven't you had as good a day as you'd expected?'

'Good enough,' replied Hector. 'But we're only just back from our last trip.'

'That was a late one,' I said, taking the cup of tea Morag was holding towards me.

'Aye, and we didn't get paid for it either,' said Erchy.

I looked at them searchingly. An unrewarding boat trip so often meant that there had been a climbing accident. 'Ach, but these English are mean,' said Erchy with a slow shake of his head, and Morag and Behag shot placatory glances in my direction. I laughed.

'Goodness!' I said. 'I seem to be hearing nothing but stories of English meanness today. What has been happening to you two?'

'It was a fellow we took on the boat this mornin' that went climbin' in the hills. When we went back for him this evenin' we found him sittin' on the shore near crazy. He told us he'd come to a very narrow ridge and the only way he could cross it was on his hands and knees. When he was halfway across his wallet slipped out of his pocket an' fell down the steepest part. He said it had fifty pounds in it.'

'Didn't he go after it?' I asked.

'Ach, he was in no state to go after it,' retorted Erchy. 'He was shakin' all over like a leaf when we found him an' that must have been two hours after.'

'What happened then?' I prompted.

'Well, we had our people waitin' on the shore to go back an' we couldn't just leave them there so we brought them back an' him along with them. Then we went back to see would we find the man's wallet.'

'Could he describe where he'd lost it?'

'Aye, indeed we knew fine where it was likely, but that didn't mean it was any easier to get. Hector near broke his back tryin' would he reach it an' there was that many stones fallin' down we were both of us in fear for our lives.'

'But you got it?'

'Aye, we got it at last an' when we came ashore here there was the man waitin' on us. We waved it at him so he'd know to stop worryin' an' he came runnin' down the shore fast as a deer an' grabbed it out of my hand. Me an' Hector, we waited while he opened it, thinkin' maybe we'd get a bit of a reward or maybe the hire of the boat just for goin' back for it, but all that man did was to take out the notes there in front of us an' count them. When he'd finished he gave us a nice smile. "Fifty pounds," he says to us. "All intact, gentlemen. Thank you very much," an' away up the road he goes without leavin' us as much as the price of a dram between us for our trouble.'

Hector shook his head. 'It was him countin' tse money tsat made me feel so bad,' he said sadly. 'Just as tsough we might have been after stealin' some of it.'

'Aye,' said Erchy, 'but that's the English for you.'

'Maybe he was that glad to see his wallet he just didn't think to give you anythin' at the time,' interceded Behag.

'Ach, the man must have had no brains at all if he wouldn't think of a thing like that,' said Erchy.

'He had brains all right,' asserted Hector. 'Tse folks tsat came on tse boat with him was tellin' me he was a Doctor of Divinity.'

'Ach, but you don't need brains to be one of those sorts of doctors,' said Morag knowledgeably. 'You see, you don't need to have any practice.'

The following afternoon I put on my latest summer dress (made from material purchased through a mail-order catalogue), picked a bunch of flowers from my garden and set off for Janet's house prepared to do my bit towards entertaining the difficult visitor. Janet came out to the gate to meet me and exclaimed delightedly at the sight of the flowers.

'She's havin' a wee bitty lie down on the sofa,' she told me. 'Wait now till I get a wee somethin' to put the flowers in an' then I'll tell her you're here.' She found an empty jug and drained the cold contents of a teapot into it.

'Good heavens!' I ejaculated. 'Is water as short as that with you?'

'It's gettin' that way,' she confessed. 'My brother's sayin' we'll need to drink whisky instead of tea if the well gets much lower. It takes that long to fill a pail now he's there all day.' She twitched the flowers into position as an impatient dressmaker twitches at an ill-fitting dress, and then put the jug on the table. 'Beautiful just,' she murmured. 'Come away in now an' we'll see is she awake.'

In the other room a torpid figure, its face covered by a newspaper, lay along the couch beneath a window that framed a picture of islands dozing tranquilly in a wideawake sea that the sun was sowing with stars; of hills that were dreamily remote behind a tremulous haze of heat; of a sky that was blue and white as a child's chalk drawing, scuffed by a woolly sleeve. The figure pulled itself to a sitting position.

'Ee, luv,' she said in a voice that was so coarse it made me feel dishevelled, 'whatever made you come to live in a god-forsaken place like this after England?'

She said, 'I think I'd go daft if I had to live here among a lot of strangers.'

She said, 'You know, luv, just seein' you come through that door and knowin' you've lived near Manchester, it's just like a breath of fresh air to me.'

Erchy said the next day when I was down on the shore giving my dinghy a coat of paint: 'Here, I'll take back what I said about the English yesterday. I'm thinkin' some of them aren't so bad after all.'

'Oh,' I said, with only conventional curiosity, 'and what has changed your mind?'

'Yon woman that's come to stay this week.'

'Not,' I interrupted him, 'not surely the woman from Manchester?'

'No, but the one who's come to stay with Kirsty. Now she's what I call a nice woman. We took her for a trip in the boat this mornin' an' she gave us a good tip on top of her fare.'

'Good,' I said. 'I'm glad we're not all to be condemned.'

'Ach, some are all right, I suppose,' acknowledged Erchy grudgingly.

Hector sprackled up to us. 'Tsat Englishwoman's wantin' a boat for tomorrow to take her to see tse caves just by herself,' he said. 'She says she'll hire tse whole boat.'

Erchy looked startled. 'Did you tell her how much it will cost her?' he asked Hector.

'Aye, I did so, but she just said "money's no option".' Hector rubbed the back of his neck. 'I've never heard anybody say tsat before in my life.'

'She's away with Ruari this evening in his boat,' I observed.

'Aye,' agreed Erchy. 'She told us she likes goin' about on the water so she's goin' to share out her trips between the different boats. That's partly what I meant when I said she's a nice woman,' he explained as he moved away.

The children came out of school in a rush and with barefooted nimbleness picked their chattering way along the road. The day quietened as the boats disgorged their last passengers and the noise of labouring coaches receded into the distance.

'Did you get a tip from yon woman that's stayin' with Kirsty?' Erchy called out to deaf Ruari as they were making fast their dinghies for the night.

'Aye, I did that,' responded Ruari with all the power of his stentorian voice. 'I got a whole crown from the bitch.'

'I do envy you being able to understand the Gaelic,' said the 'nice woman', who had paused to watch me as I put the last touches to my dinghy and who was screened by a rock from the sight of the two men, 'it's such a quaint-sounding language.'

I do not know if Ruari's voice had diffused the sound so much that she had not been able to distinguish the words or whether she had chosen this way of saving all our faces but when Ruari and Erchy came abreast of the dinghy and saw her still there she talked them easily out of their confusion and was still talking to them with great animation as she walked between them to the brae.

'Here,' said Erchy anxiously when I next met him. 'D'you think that woman heard what Ruari said last night? Honest, I thought she was a mile away or I would never have asked the man.'

'I don't think she heard,' I assured him.

'I wouldn't like to think she was offended,' he said, 'she's such a nice woman.'

Whether or not she had heard the remark it seemed to have given no offence, for she continued to patronize the boats and to tip generously. In return the boatmen greeted her warmly whenever she appeared and even bestowed on her the accolade of an invitation to go with them on the free trips they sometimes ran in an evening for their friends. She confided to me one day that she had never before in her life had such a wonderful holiday and her praise for the boatmen was unstinted. When at length her holiday came to an end she astounded them by presenting each of them with a bottle of whisky.

'Didn't I tell you she was a nice woman?' demanded Erchy when I congratulated him on the gift. He took the bottle out of his pocket and gazed at it with great reverence. Then his voice changed and he seemed to recoil from the shock of his own words. 'A nice woman, did I say she was?' he questioned, with another fond glance at the bottle. 'No, indeed, but I should have said she was a nice *lady*!'

The Election

'DID you get a bit of venison from the Laird last week?' enquired Morag as we were returning from milking our cows one frost-still autumn morning.

'No,' I replied. 'Did you?'

'Surely we did,' she informed me. 'I thought everybody got a bit.' We parted company for a moment, she to pick her way round one

59

side of a patch of bog while I went round the other. 'It makes a laugh
the way he gives us a wee bitty venison as if he's givin' us a five-
pound note,' she continued as our paths rejoined. " 'I hope you'll find
this nice and tasty, Morag," says he, thinkin' likely that it's a rare
treat for us.' She giggled. 'An' so it would be I doubt if all the venison
we got was when he has a mind to give it to us.' Her face wrinkled
in an allusive grin. 'Indeed, many's the whole stag of his I've eaten
if he did but know it,' she confessed shamelessly.

'Why the generosity?' I wondered.

'Likely it's the Election,' explained Morag with her usual astuteness.
'Maybe you didn't get a piece because he thinks you're a Socialist,'
she added.

Until the announcement of the forthcoming General Election
politics had rarely cropped up as a subject for conversation at the
ceilidhs and when it had it had always been in a bantering and in-
conclusive way. Even after the announcement there was no vestige of
what could be termed 'election fever' in the village. Old men ventured
to make sketchy references to such subjects as tariffs and free trade,
and Murdoch, the village's only militant Tory, was once or twice
reduced to stuttering inarticulateness by the tauntings of a couple of
the younger blades with professed leanings towards Socialism, but
invariably the skirmishes ended if not in complete agreement then in
good-humoured laughter. The Bruachites did not have much time for
subjects from which they could not extract some fun one way or
another.

As the Election drew nearer it became apparent that Bruach was
going to vote almost exclusively Tory, for in contrast to their normally
uncompromising individualism the Bruachites displayed a curious
desire for conformity in superficialities. How often have I heard the
wily tinkers successfully inducing people to buy a child's dress or a
woman's overall simply by exaggerating the number of identical ones
they had already sold in the village. And when the biannual request
for donations to the church came round the sum shown against the
first name on the list was always dittoed for all the rest of the names.
Similarly, when the hospital appealed for eggs everyone was careful

to give the same number as his neighbour. Except for one uncomfortable occasion when the Grazings Officer sent round a list asking for the dates of bull servings and got it back with so many dittoes that a hundred and twenty seven cows were shown as having been served by the same bull on the same day, the duplication appeared to be perfectly acceptable to everyone.

However, when it came to deciding at the ceilidhs what advantages they wished the Government to provide the Bruachites reverted to their usual policy of amiable disagreement.

'What we're needin' before anythin' is a pier,' declaimed deaf Ruari with a combative look in the direction of any dissenters.

'We've been promised a pier by every government since I was a lad,' returned Yawn easily. 'But I didn't see it yet.'

'It'll come. It'll come yet,' soothed old Murdoch amidst grunts of disbelief.

'No, but what we're needin' first is a good road, the way we won't have to get the heavy things on the steamer and then have to carry them all the way up the brae,' argued Big John between gulps of baking-soda from a tin on the mantelpiece.

'Aye,' seconded the irascible Donald, who as the owner of a tiny motor boat chose to believe there existed between him and the steamship company as much rivalry as exists between competitors for the Blue Riband. 'We could finish then with Messrs. David MacBrayne and Company, nineteen twenty-eight limited,' he exulted with his accustomed preciosity. During the summer Donald ran trips in his boat to local places of interest. The steamer did likewise but with far more comfort and a great deal less hazard—hence the antagonism.

'If we got the watter we could ask them for a lavatory for the public,' piped up Sheena, who was unfortunate enough to live in a cottage which adjoined the road near a spot much favoured in the season for disgorging busloads of tourists. Glassy eyed with discomfort after the rough ride and too urbanized to trust themselves to the privacy of the moors, the tourists' first thought was to prospect for some shed they might break into and foul. 'I canna' gather but a handful of peats from the shed without there's dung or piss on it,' Sheena complained.

'Aye, that's the way of it,' confirmed Morag, with a nod.

'If it's a lavatory we're wantin' then it's in the burial ground we should be gettin' one first,' asserted Erchy. 'Never mind the tourists.'

'A laventory? In the burial ground?' expostulated old Murdoch. 'Whatever for, man?'

'They have them in other places,' Erchy told him. 'Two of them sometimes: one for men and one for women.'

'God knows what for, then,' said Murdoch, shaking his head bewilderedly. 'Surely they're not believin' the dead get up and walk?'

'It's for the folks who go to the funerals,' shouted Erchy above the tittering, and Murdoch's brow immediately cleared. 'You know how it is when you're at a funeral,' Erchy went on, 'you always feel you can't wait to drop your pants. If it's outside the gate you go then it's likely one of the women will get a hold of you so you can't get away. If you try inside the damty place is so full of graves somebody starts shoutin' at you for defilin' his grandfather or somebody.'

It struck me that in contrast to the demands of the more cosseted townsman they seemed to want very little from their government. There was no appeal voiced for factories to provide regular employment, no general desire for larger crofts, no agitation for higher pensions. Perhaps it was because in the cosy atmosphere of the ceilidhs the Bruachites were entirely honest with themselves. They did not want the discipline of industry in addition to that already imposed on them by storms and tides. Their crofts were as large as they could comfortably manage without mechanical aids. On the matter of pensions they kept wisely silent for in Bruach there was no pride about receiving Public Assistance. Rather was it a source of rivalry to see who could wheedle the most out of the authorities and at times one got the distinct impression that the recipients regarded the payments as in the nature of prize money for the best storyteller. Their avarice was both shocking and amusing and I well remember an occasion when, as I was waiting to board the train at the mainland station en route for a visit to Glasgow, I had suddenly been hailed by a lady whom I knew had been drawing Public Assistance for years.

She was dressed neatly in black with touches of that sparkling white-ness I believe only Highland rainwater can impart to a fabric, and had I not known her I should have thought from her dignified bearing and the quiet authoritativeness of her manner that she was at least a duchess. We greeted each other cordially and agreed it would be nice to travel together.

'There are some empty compartments down there,' I said, inclining my head towards the rear of the train.

My companion gazed at me with sorrow and surprise. 'Oh, but those are all second-class compartments down there,' she told me. 'You'll surely not be travelling second class, will you, Miss Peckwitt?'

'Why, yes,' I replied. 'Aren't you?'

'Oh, no, mo ghaoil,' she responded without a trace of embarrass-ment. 'I always think one meets such common people travelling second class.' She scanned the train and then turned to me again. 'Will you not change your ticket?' she begged with affected concern, for she had just spotted a more desirable acquaintance who was beckoning to her from the genteel end of the train.

'No,' I said firmly. She shook her head in mock reproof but her mouth relaxed into a lenient smile as we parted, she to step regally into a first-class compartment while I wilted into a second.

I recall too the time when there came to reside temporarily in Bruach an old lady whom the Bruachites invariably referred to as 'yon rich old fool'. However when the 'rich old fool' had been in the village for some months she revealed, with a discernible pride in her achievement, that she too had joined the ranks of those receiving Public Assistance. The crofters were scandalized and her revelation was tossed from person to person along with comments that were as disparagingly hostile as if she had gatecrashed an exclusive club. Of course they never for an instant believed that she was not still a rich old woman; but I never again heard anyone refer to her as a fool!

Though I once heard of a crofter who was too proud to accept Public Assistance or to allow his wife to accept it whilst he was alive, the story was accepted by the rest of the Bruachites with the same mocking half belief as they accepted such tales as of the man who had grown a third leg and of a child who had been buried out on the unhallowed moor because it was born with two heads.

It was not long before we began to hear of various election meetings being held in neighbouring villages more accessible from the mainland than Bruach itself, and if there was a pub and the owner of the bus could be persuaded to run a cheap trip then there was always a fair contingent from Bruach willing to listen courteously to anyone who might care to practise his rhetoric upon them. They would titter at all his witticisms, they would murmur appreciatively at the aspersions cast by party on party, but they rarely heckled and it was quite impossible for a stranger to guess in which direction their loyalties lay.

Inevitably the Election began to impinge on our lives. The postman arrived later and later. 'These bloody election letters,' he explained. 'Honest, they keep me back worse than the pools.' Eventually our ballot papers arrived.

'Here,' said the postman conspiratorially as he followed his bulging mailbag through the open kitchen door. 'Just you take these from me and put them under the kettle.'

'What are they?' I asked him, immediately suspicious.

'Ballot papers,' he replied. 'Put them under the kettle, I'm tellin' you.'

'I daren't!' I told him.

'Ach, they're only for my cousin Tearlaich,' he explained, 'and the bugger will only be after spoilin' them by votin' Socialist.' He held the envelope towards me, but I drew back shaking my head, and when he moved as though towards the stove I stopped him firmly. It was then that I caught the glint of laughter in his eyes so that I was not deceived by the air of disappointment he assumed as he slipped the envelope back into his bag.

'What would you have done if I'd snatched those papers out of your hand and put them under the kettle?' I taxed him.

He met my enquiry with a broad, delighted grin. 'Damned if I know,' he admitted unregenerately.

A brief spell of crisp bright days ended with bitingly cold winds that flung great sloppy raindrops at the frost-skinned earth. On the moors the bracken, so stately in its youth, so wanton in maturity, now lay brown and sad among the rocky outcrops while in the boglands the peat hags filled with dark water. It was while we were enduring this sort of weather that there came word that a representative of the Socialist candidate would be holding a meeting in the village schoolroom the following evening. Bruach was a little staggered.

'We must be gettin' well known,' said Yawn facetiously. 'Why else would they be botherin' to come out here when they didn't before?'

'Didn't come before?' ejaculated Morag. 'Indeed they did so.'

'I never mind them comin',' maintained Yawn.

'Aye, well they did so,' reiterated Morag. 'Murdoch will tell you, will you not, Murdoch?'

Murdoch, thus appealed to, looked thoughtful for a moment and then said with great confidence, 'Aye, of course I mind fine them comin' here.' He turned to Morag. 'Was that no' the year we salted the herrin' before we cut the corn?' he asked her.

'It was indeed,' confirmed Morag. 'An' it was good herrin'.'

'Aye, aye, it was good herrin',' agreed Murdoch, removing his pipe. There was a recognizable moment of nostalgia while Murdoch's spittle sizzled on the glowing peat.

'Will you be goin' to listen to the mannie tomorrow if you're spared?' Morag asked me as we were saying good night.

'I suppose so,' I replied. 'We should go and hear what he has to say.'

'Well,' said Morag, 'it would no' be very nice for him if people didn't go and take a look at him after him goin' to the trouble to come out here for us.'

So the following evening, braving the inexorable rain, I went along to the schoolroom which, by the time I arrived, was already nearly three-quarters full of chattering, chaffing adults interspersed by a sprinkling of sober, wide-eyed children. The mingled smells of damp peaty tweeds, stale dogs, dungy boots and pipe smoke, all shot through with the sharp, clean smell of wet oilskins, met me as I stood by the door looking for a suitable seat. Morag caught my eye and beckoned me over to a spare desk between herself and Behag and even as I compressed myself into it there was a chorus of warning coughs from the porch and a purposeful middle-aged man attended by two smug confederates made his way to the teacher's desk. A courteous hush fell as he was introduced to us by one of his aides.

'Here, but I know that man well,' confided Morag, who, I believe, attended all such gatherings as much to exercise her quite remarkable memory for faces as for any other reason.

'Who will he be, then?' whispered Behag with a sudden spurt of interest.

'Why, but that Willy John. His father used to live up at . . .' She and Behag went off into a mixture of reminiscent Gaelic.

'What does he work at now, then?' enquired Behag, obviously far more curious about the man's pedigree than in what he had to say.

'Ach, well, I believe he was a cobbler one time, but then he went away to the war,' Morag recalled. 'He was wounded in the hand I was after hearin' and he couldn't carry on with his cobblin'.'

'Poor soul,' said Behag. 'What does he do now?'

'Ach, they sent him off to one of these places where they rehalibutate people and now he's a fish buyer,' Morag told her. 'They're sayin' he's doin' well at it.'

'Whist you, Morag,' some of the people behind enjoined us after they were satisfied that Morag had completed her identification. The representative was standing up and we composed ourselves to listen to his address, but from the moment he opened his mouth we felt ourselves stiffening as if we were being coerced into a conflict, bewildered as to its cause and with the certainty of our own defeat. His words smote us; the breaths he occasionally paused to exhale seemed to sear us, and when the meeting came to an end we found ourselves feeling curiously sorry for him for having given us such a bad time—and wishing he would soon go so that we would have time to feel sorry for ourselves. Nevertheless we sat and clapped him dutifully and with confident smiles he left us.

'My, my!' exclaimed Morag as we emerged from the schoolroom, feeling bruised with politics and cramped and chilled after our damp contortions in the tiny desks, 'that man's voice was that rough I believe I could have struck a match on it.'

The following morning I awoke with all the signs of a vicious head cold and although I heard that the Liberal candidate was sending a representative to the school that evening I put out my light early to discourage ceilidhers and went to bed. My cold was little better the next day, so that I missed also the representative of the Tory candidate, who, not to be outdone, had arranged to hold a meeting that evening. By the evening of the third day I was feeling thoroughly wretched, my cold obstinately refusing to yield to my usual remedy ('It came itself, it can go away itself'), and I had resolved that as soon as my chores were finished I would take myself off to bed with a couple of aspirins, a large glass of hot milk and some extra blankets and try to sweat it out of my system. It was therefore with some dismay that I found Ishbel, the elderly spinster half-sister of Katy, the shepherd's wife, waiting for me when I returned to the cottage, but I managed to sniffle a tepid welcome. She seemed satisfied and sat down on the edge of a chair with her usual nervous hesitancy that reminded me of a fledgling just before it launches itself from the nest.

'I mustn't stay,' she demurred.

'Of course you must.' I tried to infuse some decision into my voice.

'No, but I heard you had taken the cold so I thought I'd best come along and see if you needed help.'

I thanked her warmly but assured her that it was really only the discomfort of the cold that worried me.

'It's that Socialist fellow gave it to you,' she declared with more asperity than I had ever heard in her voice. 'I knew the moment I heard him speak he'd brought the cold to us.'

'Possibly,' I agreed. In Bruach once the holiday season was over colds were infrequent and when one ravaged the village it could invariably be traced to someone who had 'gone to the mainland for a cold' or to some infected visitor.

'I'd never vote for him after that,' threatened Ishbel, whose childish rule of exacting indiscriminate retribution, however trivial the incident, was something of a joke in the village; she had once slipped on a piece of orange rind and broken her arm so she had never eaten an orange since.

'Are you takin' anythin' for your cold?' she asked, reverting to her normal timidity.

'Just hot milk and aspirins,' I told her.

She delved into her bag and brought out a half bottle of whisky which was at least two-thirds full. 'Now, I want you to take this,' she adjured me. 'A good glass of this tonight before you go to your bed an' it'll see your cold away by the mornin'.'

I was overwhelmed by her kindness. 'Thank you very much indeed,' I said, 'but really——'

'No, but I want you to have it,' she interrupted me. 'I've had this stuff in the house since I took the cold myself near thirteen years ago now. I didn't take the cold again to this day so I've not had but the one dose of it.' She put the bottle down on the table. 'Whisky keeps all right though it's been opened,' she assured me.

'Of course,' I murmured and thanked her again. 'But,' I objected, holding up the bottle to the light, 'I shan't want all this. I'll just take out a dram and you take the rest back with you.'

'No, indeed I will not.' She stood up, clutching her bag as if to prevent any attempt to foist the bottle back on her. 'I'll away now and let you get to your bed but you'll see and take a good dram of it before you go?'

I promised.

The following morning I was still snuffling when Erchy called to give me a bundle of dried carragheen and also the startling news that the Socialist candidate was proposing to address a meeting at eight o'clock in the Bruach schoolroom.

'The man himself,' Erchy emphasized. 'You'd best come an' listen to him.'

'Not unless my cold clears up a bit during the day,' I replied.

'Ach, but you shouldn't have a cold today,' he remonstrated. 'I was after hearin' you got some whisky from Ishbel last night to take for it. You couldn't have taken a right dram if you still have a cold. The whisky would have killed it.'

'I didn't take much of a dram,' I confessed with an involuntary shudder. 'And neither would you if you'd been in my place.'

'Why not?' enquired Erchy.

'The bottle had been opened thirteen years ago,' I began, but he cut me short.

'It doesn't matter. Whisky keeps all right,' he assured me with an authoritativeness that I felt sure could only have been based on hearsay.

'Oh, yes,' I agreed. 'I've no doubt whisky keeps all right but it also takes up the smell of mothballs.' I grimaced. 'It was the foulest-tasting mess I've ever tried to swallow. She must have had the bottle packed round with camphor for all of thirteen years.' I picked up the bottle and held it towards him. 'Here, smell it yourself.'

Erchy took a cautious sniff and then groaned. 'The daft old cailleach,' he commented.

But apparently one small mouthful of camphorated whisky had its effect on my cold for by evening my head had improved wonderfully. When eight o'clock came I wandered down to the school. There was not an empty desk to be had and I had to insert myself into the knot of men who were packed around the door. The candidate had already begun speaking, wooing the crofters with glib promises of prosperity but completely alienating them, if only he knew it, by predicting the setting up of rural industries so that they could supplement their croft incomes without recourse to Public Assistance. Nevertheless, he left happily assured of their support.

'I canna' understand that man. They tell me he has letters after his name so he must be clever. You wouldn't think he'd want to go spoilin' himself with Parliament,' opined Morag, who seemed to be under the impression that the nomination of a candidate was arrived at in much the same way as was the selection of the village 'bull tender' and that the field of choice was similarly limited to those with no aptitude for more exacting tasks.

In the wake of the Socialist candidate came the Liberal, who also held a well-attended meeting in the schoolroom. I had a date with my wireless set that evening so I did not hear his address but I have no doubt that he too was completely convinced that he had won the confidence of the Bruachites. I asked Erchy when I next saw him how the meeting had gone.

'Ach, that man!' replied Erchy scornfully. 'He didn't seem to know what to say to us at all. Indeed I don't believe he was sure if he was goin' to vote Liberal himself.'

It seemed that the Conservative candidate did not consider the votes of Bruach's small population vital enough to warrant a personal appearance and Morag and old Murdoch among others had to endure some innuendoes from those who feigned rebellion simply to take a rise out of the older folk. Then, on the afternoon preceding polling day, when I was mixing the evening mash for the hens, Morag came scuttling into my kitchen with the air of apologetic excitement that always assailed her when she had urgent news to impart.

'The Conservative candidate is here,' she burst out enthusiastically, 'an' he has a loud halo.' She had predicted all along that he would come. 'Come away outside and listen to him,' she insisted. I put down the bowl and followed her out into the garden where the booming voices of the first loudspeaker van to visit Bruach could be heard wafting an invitation to everyone to be present at eight o'clock at the school that evening to meet the candidate in person.

'Well!' I ejaculated. 'So you were right. But imagine Bruach having a loudspeaker van. They must think we're important.'

'Aye,' agreed Morag, 'but I wonder at them goin' to all that expense when our own Ruari could have shouted it just as well without any batteries to work him.'

Whether it was the 'loud halo' or the reputed wealth and social position of the candidate that animated the village I do not know but by a quarter to eight (unprecedented punctuality for the Bruachites) the school classroom was packed as full as only Gaels can pack themselves, and people overflowed into the porch and even, though it was a chilly night, out into the playground. Everyone appeared to be present from the oldest grandfather to the youngest child and the air shimmered with expectancy.

'I see even Angus's father has managed to get here,' I observed to Morag, who had pushed her way to my side. Angus's father was an obstinate old man who spent the periods of relative mobility between crippling attacks of rheumatism sitting on the grass verge beside the road and would not be cajoled or coerced away from it.

'Aye, well, he's no' so bad when he's on the flat bit of road,' Morag told me. 'It's when he comes to the ingredients he canna' manage.'

The candidate was very late, but there was no audible discontent, and when he did arrive the company clapped him with a vigour that was strangely out of keeping with their normal show of reserve. As he rose to address us an almost servile silence descended and everyone listened with apparent avidity, though many eyes wandered frequently from his rather long hair to the casual dandiness of his clothes, only to be arrested again and again by his expansive gestures. At the end of his speech one or two people ventured to ask questions, but he answered them with nimble assurance and when the meeting officially came to an end he remained behind, still affable and approachable, ready to discuss the trials of a crofting life.

'My,' observed Erchy reverently at the ceilidh which followed, 'that's a nice fellow if only he'd get his hair cut.'

There was exultation among the old folk. 'That's our man,' they all agreed. 'You mind what he promised us about the pier?'

'What does it matter what he promised you?' young Hamish demanded. 'Once they get into Parliament they don't bother what they said to folks before.'

'Maybe so, maybe so,' admitted Murdoch, hurrying to prevent Yawn from voicing scepticism.

'An' supposin' he does get us a pier from the House of Commons then it only needs the House of Lords to throw it out and we're back worse off than when we started.' Hamish was becoming eloquent in his dissatisfaction. 'The first thing the Socialists will do is to get rid of the House of Lords,' he promised. 'There's no damty good at all in that place.'

'Here, no,' Murdoch rebuked him.

'Indeed, yes,' responded Hamish, with increasing fervour. 'What good does it do, anyway? Tell me that now.'

Murdoch pondered for a moment or two, rolling his unlit pipe in the palm of his hand. 'Well,' he began, 'what I say is, the House of Lords is just a big ceilidh house; sometimes they have a wee bit talk over things, sometimes maybe a wee song and maybe a dram at times or a wee strupak, just like ourselves here.'

'An' what the hell use is that?' Hamish's voice was shrill with derision.

'Ach, well,' said Murdoch. 'I'm thinkin' many's the time there's been troubles in this place but when they've been talked over at a couple of ceilidhs likely they've soon been sorted.' It might be as well to explain here that in Bruach everything is 'sorted'. You go to the dentist to get your teeth 'sorted'. Similarly you go to the doctor to get your ailments 'sorted'. And if the engine of your boat gives trouble you send for someone to come and 'sort' it.

Hamish gave an ironic grunt and moved towards the door. 'The trouble with you lot is you won't give a man your vote unless he has plenty of money,' he flung at them as a final taunt.

Had he stayed he would have found me in wholehearted agreement with him, for I am convinced the crofters prefer their M.P. to be wealthy, their attitude seeming to imply that whereas there is a possibility of a rich man being satisfied with what he already has, a poor man is inevitably a greedy one.

Polling morning brought a perceptible rise in temperature with a sun-tinted wind chasing a genial haze of rain through the glen. Voting was scheduled to start at nine o'clock in the morning but not until all the croft work was finished and the bus driver had taken his tea did the crofters trouble to get themselves ready. The polling station was in a neighbouring village at a tiny disused school and the bus was ready to take the voters at sixpence per head, but I chose to walk, for the uncertain day had matured into a perfect autumn evening with the hills hardly more than a murmur of golden serenity behind shrouds of gauzy mist. My path lay along the coast and below me the bay spread out like a broad blue apron, ruched with dark rocks and dotted with resting gulls like white French knots. Earlier in the year the evening would have been marred by swarms of rapacious midges so that one would have needed to smother oneself in protective lotion or envelop one's face in fine veiling, but now the midges had disappeared and one could swing along heedlessly and rejoice in the beauty that was everywhere.

Angus, short, wizened and briskly genial, called to me as he was shifting the tether of a cow to a fresh patch of grass. He was wearing polished shoes instead of his usual gumboots.

'Are you away to the votin'?' he asked.

'Yes,' I replied. 'Are you and Jeannie going?'

'Ach, Jeannie'll no' be comin', she's near dead with the cold,' he answered. 'But I'm goin' along myself.'

'What about your father? Is he going to triumph over his rheumatics to vote?'

'Ach, my father could get over his rheumatics right enough,' said Angus, 'but he says he's no' puttin' in his teeths just to go and put a wee cross on a piece of paper.'

The bus, packed with passengers who waved with decorous condescension, passed me, but it had to stop so often along the road to pick up hesitant or late voters that it arrived at the polling station only a few minutes before I did. The crofters, self-conscious in their best clothes, were just alighting and there were shouts and imprecations as ecstatic sheepdogs, who had chased after the bus all the way from the village, greeted their owners and tried to insist on following them into the school.

The schoolroom was very small and was tastefully decorated with jars of white, strongly scented flowers which I had never seen growing anywhere but in the most sheltered corner of the burial ground. The two bored voting officers sat cuddled together at the teacher's inadequate desk on which cups of tea, a plate of buttered scones and a dish of jam reposed hospitably between the box containing our voting slips and the official black ballot box. The polling arrangements would have made wonderful propaganda for an enemy. To mark our cards we were in turn directed to a cupboard which stood against the wall at right angles to the window. The cupboard was just large enough for a small person to get inside but if one closed the door it was too dark to see what one was doing. If one left the door open then everything one did was easily visible to the prospective or spent voters who loitered with carefully assumed indifference outside the window.

When I came outside again Big John, who stood six foot three and was of pugilistic build and yet the mildest of men, was leaning nonchalantly on the sill watching a confused Sarah peering in her short-sighted way at the voting slip which she held in her two hands. Sarah frowned; she pulled at her lips. John gave a commentary on her predicament and there was a stir of laughter. We all knew Sarah couldn't read anyway. At last she held her card up to the window and her mouth framed a question. Big John pointed. Sarah nodded and smiled with relief and bent over her card, the pencil grasped in her shaky fingers. John rapped peremptorily on the window and Sarah's perturbed head bobbed up. John gesticulated. Again Sarah nodded and bent over her paper. John relapsed into nonchalance.

'Silly old cailleach nearly voted for the wrong fellow,' he told us.

Tinkers' Wedding

THE following summer was drearily wet and was succeded by an autumn that was distinguishable only by the shorter hours of daylight and by the waning appetites of the midges. For those of us who had not been hardy enough to ignore the constant rain (the less resilient under-sixties, it seemed) croft work dragged on interminably. Most of my potatoes were as yet undug. My peat shed was only a third full, the rest of the peats being still in their stacks on the moors waiting either for me to carry them home, creelful by slow and heavy creelful, which I had been endeavouring to do all summer, or for the track to dry out sufficiently for them to be loaded on to a lorry. I even had hay still out on the croft in sad, dark cocks which were so soaked with rain that they were able to resist the teasings of the strengthening winds.

'I doubt a right gale will come before long an' put your hay away for you, but not where you're wantin' it,' predicted Yawn smugly as he passed the croft where I was working. I answered him with a feeble grin, recalling how savagely a gale the previous autumn had dealt with almost the whole of Donald Beag's carefully made stacks of hay. Into a night of mist and calm the gale had come suddenly, announcing its arrival by a staccato rattle of the new tiles of my cottage roof. By the time I had shut the bedroom window and buttressed the front door with a shaft of wood it was already thumping against the windows, blasting noisily into the chimneys and hissing venom at the leafless elder bushes. For two hours it had blown turbulently and then, with only two or three faint whispers of apology for the commotion it had caused, it had gone, leaving the unsettled night to be soothed by the dolorous tick of the rain. Daylight had revealed that all that was left of Donald's hay harvest were the wisps and shreds that were caught in the wire netting of neighbouring hen-runs. The Bruachites secretly gloated. Donald was easily the hardest working man in the village and the fact that he made his croft pay caused some resentment. They had lost no time in seeking him out to witness his dismay whilst at the same time offering perfidious commiseration.

'What happened to all your hay, Donald?' they asked him innocently, and Donald, who was perfectly aware of their feelings, only laughed and, waving a facetious hand towards one of the outlying islands, replied, 'It's all in Sandy's barn over there, I reckon.'

The end of October drew near and then it was Halloween. Stags were roaring in the hills. The rams were already among the sheep. The Department of Agriculture bull had been caught and sent to his winter home. Through wind and rain I worked desperately at my potatoes so as to have them all lifted before November came. Admittedly, unlike my neighbours, it was not so much the disgrace of having croft work still unfinished on the first of November that spurred me on. It was the knowledge that, though a date well into the middle of November was always decreed by the local Grazings Officer as being that on which all cattle could be brought in from the moors and allowed to roam the crofts, as soon as a few of the more idle or less tolerant inhabitants had themselves fenced their haystacks and put away their spades for the winter, moor gates were liable to be left insecurely latched so as to swing open at the nosing of a curious cow, or after dark they would be deliberately opened so that one was apt to wake up to find cattle driving their horns deep into one's carefully stacked hay or fighting one another over one's precious potato patch. Resolutely ignoring my stiffening back I plunged the fork into the earth, lifting the roots and picking off the potatoes one by one, examining each for signs of blight before throwing it into the pail which in turn had to be carried to the shed where they were to be stored. The floor of the shed was already covered with dry peat dust and on top of this had gone a layer of heather and dry bracken. On to this cosy bed went the potatoes, to be covered, when the lifting was finished, with more heather and bracken and then with a layer of old sacks. I was assured my potatoes would now be safe from everything except pilfering mice.

Mercifully, all my hay was in the barn and by tea-time on Halloween I had reached the final row of potatoes, digging in a deepening twilight that was aided by a mist of fine rain and enclosed in a silence that was pierced only by the occasional lament of a homeward-bound gull, the scrape of my fork into the stony ground and the thud of potatoes into the pail. The musty autumn smell of the moors was strong in my nostrils, reminding me of how the village children would even now be excitedly rummaging into musty sheds and spidery lofts for even mustier clothes in which to dress themselves for their evening ploys. Their simple Halloween 'false-faces', made from a sheet of cardboard bent round the face and tied with string at the back of the head, would in snatched and secret moments already have been chalked or painted with fearsome white fangs, staring multi-coloured eyes and then liberally trimmed with fleece from the spring shearings, before being hidden away to await the great night. I recollected that some parents had expressed doubt as to whether the children would have the courage to go out this year because of the reported presence of a 'white beast' or as some described it 'a wee white man' in the hazel copse which filled a cleft of the moor between my own croft and the skirts of the hills. In the autumn the copse was a favourite nutting place not only for the children when they came home from school but for any adults who had time to pick or teeth to crack the nuts, but this season, after the first pickers had returned visibly shaken to tell their stories, the copse had been completely neglected.

'D'ye believe in the wee folk yourself, Miss Peckwitt?' Old Anna had asked, and because I refused to be drawn she went on, 'Are ye no' afraid, livin' all by yourself down there?'

I had told her that I was not afraid but now, straightening my aching back for a moment and looking across to the copse looming spectrally through the drifting mist, I wondered if it was still the truth. No, I was not afraid, but there is no denying that in the twilight of a still evening the moors, wild and deserted yet full of whispers, can have a disquieting effect. They seemed to breathe their mystery down my neck as I picked up a full pail of potatoes and carried it up the croft to the shed, refusing to let myself hurry yet conscious that my torso seemed to be well ahead of my legs. I emptied the pail and resolutely went back to my lonely digging.

'I see you're busy.' I jumped so much that I stuck a tine of the fork through the toe of my new gumboots and turning round saw the postman grinning at me from under his peaked cap. He was wearing uniform but there was a rifle under his arm and the mailbag was full of dead rabbits.

'I'm about finished,' I told him, indicating the half dozen or so sticks of withered haulm still unlifted.

'They're no' bad,' he complimented me after he had rubbed one or two of the potatoes in his hands. 'Are they nice and dry?'

'No' bad,' I admitted. 'They're not waxy, anyway.'

'My own are, but you should see the size of them,' he told me. 'I planted them in that boggy patch that's never been ploughed before, and I used nothin' but seaweed for them. My God! I'm tellin' you, I can tuck just one of them under my arm and it'll do a dinner for the four of us.' He gathered up one or two potoatoes that had missed the pail and put them in. 'I'd best be gettin' along, I suppose.' He sighed. 'She'll have it in for me if I'm not there on the dot.' He swung his mailbag into a more comfortable position and started off, but changing his mind he came back to stand beside me again. 'Did they tell you about yon white beast?' he enquired anxiously.

'Yes,' I admitted, with a surreptitious glance towards the hazel copse.

'Well, if you should see one be sure and chop it in two with your graipe,' he instructed, and even while I gaped at him in astonishment he dove forward and picked up something from the soil. 'That's the beastie,' he told me, triumphantly displaying on the palm of his hand a fat grub that might have been white beneath its film of earth. 'Make sure you kill it properly now or it'll play hell with your potatoes next year.'

He loped off, whistling a Gaelic air to which the thudding of the mailbag against his bottom provided an erratic accompaniment. I threw the last potato into the pail, forked the dead haulm into heaps ready for burning and, heavy with weariness yet full of satisfaction, went back to the cottage.

The kitchen was warm and while I waited for the torch, soaked in methylated spirit, to heat the tube of the pressure lamp, I looked out across the darkening bay to where the pattern of lighthouses were already flinging their charted beams over the furrowed water, the most powerful of them kindling a fleeting window-patterned reflection of itself on my kitchen wall. The lighthouses always served to emphasize the change in my life, for in town at this time in the evening it would have been the ordered queues of street lamps flicking on to contemplate the drab pavements with stark suspicious glare. I drew the peony-flowered curtains and pumped the lamp until it hissed into brightness.

The kettle was steaming on the stove when there was a rattle at the door and Morag came in. I put aside the grocery list I had been studying with its quotations for bolls (140 lb.) of flour and oatmeal, for sugar by the hundredweight, pot barley, rice and coconut by the stone, for syrup in fourteen-pound tins.

'Ach, now, seein' you doin' that reminds me Neilly was askin' me to get some of that tobacco for him,' said Morag, nodding towards the list. 'I'll not be sendin' there for a whiley yet so perhaps you'll order it along with your own,' she suggested.

I took up the list. 'What kind does he like?' I asked, having always been intrigued by the esoteric attraction of 'Black Twist', 'Bogey Roll', 'Warhorse' and 'Warlock'. To my delight she plumped for 'Bogey Roll'.

'I wonder,' I mused as I wrote it down, 'just what "Bogey Roll" has that the others haven't got?'

'Indeed I don't know,' responded Morag, 'but when he hasn't any tobacco from the shop Neilly will smoke nettle leaves, or dockens, or I've even known him stuff his pipe with brown paper and smoke it, so I shouldn't think it's anythin' particular.' She wriggled herself into her chair like a hen into a dust bath before taking the cup of tea I was holding out to her.

We sipped in silence for a while, half listening for the furtive whisperings or stealthy footsteps of children who, on their one night of jollity in the year, might be rigging a booby trap outside my door or climbing on to the roof to drop empty tins down the chimney.

'Did you hear about the sod-hut tinkers?' Morag burst out suddenly.

'No,' I admitted. 'What about them?'

'They're goin' to have a marryin',' she announced exultantly, 'in the church with the minister.'

I stared at her incredulously. During the spring and summer months Bruach, in common with most of the Hebrides, was beset by tinkers selling every kind of merchandise and of more recent years by the collectors of scrap-iron—still called 'tinks'—who poked uninvited around our crofts and sheds discovering our assets and then, with irritating insistence, making offers for everything we did not wish to dispose of. I have never forgotten one filthy old man who had stood glowering at me through a draggle of grey beard while a confederate of his was glibly proposing to 'take out of my way' an old trough with which I had not the slightest intention of parting. During a slight pause the old man had jerked suddenly into the conflict by asking, 'Is they your own teeths?' with such an air of covetousness that I expected him to immediately make me an offer for them.

These 'scrap tinks' were considered by the crofters to be of a much lower class than the rest of the tinkers, largely, I think, because they indulged in no courteous Highland preamble before they got down to business, a neglect the Bruachites found distasteful. But they became, like the other 'tinks', an unavoidable adjunct to the Hebridean way of life, and in the early mornings throughout the spring and summer one could see their tents or their dejected old lorries parked in some green and pleasant spot just off the road while nearby a kettle hung over a crackling twig fire. On clear sunlit mornings when the air was splintered with birdsong and the faces of the breakfasting tinkers seemed to reflect the sunshine, the life appeared to be not without a certain glamour, but any hankering for it was dispelled on dreary mornings of storm when the camping place was sleeked by rain and dotted with dismal heaps of scrap unloaded from the lorries so as to make sleeping space for the family. There was no crackling fire then but only a pile of twigs which a drape of gloomy faced men took turns to fan with their hats into some semblance of flame.

Bruach normally saw the last of its tinkers well before the end of September but this year a company of them had decided to stay for the winter and had built for themselves a substantial hut of sods, covered with tarpaulins which were weighted down with boulders from the bed of the burn. Although the encampment was a good two miles from the village the Bruachites at first seemed to find the presence of the tinkers a trifle disturbing, partly, I suspected, because they could never completely dissociate them from the stories of witchcraft and magic with which a Hebridean child is surrounded. It soon became obvious from the blue smoke that sprouted from a hole in the tarpaulin that the tinkers were burning peat, so peat stacks were examined

frequently, though even had pilfering been observed it is unlikely
that anything would have been done about it except to carry all the
peats home to the safety of the shed at the side of the house. When
two of the more incautious of the villagers reported that the tinkers
had opened up a couple of hags close to their encampment the relief
was general. No one really wanted to have any cause for complaint
against the tinkers. Of course, they admitted, they had no right
whatever to cut peats without permission from the village. 'Ach, but
what's a few yards of peat in hundreds of acres of the stuff!' they
exclaimed in tones that would not have been half so tolerant had it
been one of themselves who had so flouted tradition. It was exactly
the same with the driftwood on the shore. In Bruach the men went
regularly to the beaches, putting up above high-tide mark all manner
of flotsam and jetsam ranging from small pieces of driftwood which
would make good kindling to large hatch covers which might provide
solid supports for a new byre or shed. All along the shore these dog-
in-the-manger piles of wood were dotted, constantly being added to,
rarely being depleted. Sometimes the larger pieces would have initials
roughly scratched on them to proclaim the finder but this was unnecessary, for in the village it was an unwritten law that a man owned
whatever he put above high-tide mark and it was considered to be the
depth of treachery for another to lay a finger on it, even if it had been
lying rotting there for much of the claimant's lifetime. They were
able apparently to memorize not only each heap they had gathered
but each individual piece and I have witnessed an old man who had
not moved from his fireside for several years describe after a few
moments' meditation a piece of wood of a particular shape and size
and then give an importunate relative reluctant permission to abstract
it from one of his caches on the shore. Yet now came the tinkers who
with smiling indifference and without a sign of remonstrance from
the owners indulged in day-long sorties, looting the stores of wood
with a rapacity that, had they been ordinary villagers, would have
resulted in months of bitterness and recrimination.

There appeared to be at least a dozen of the 'sod-hut tinks' and
from the sounds of laughter one could always hear in the vicinity of

their abode they seemed to pack a great deal of jollity into their un-fettered lives. The grocer reported that they were ideal customers in that they bought unstintingly, paid cash and carried their purchases away with effortless good humour. The barman was quoted as having said much the same thing.

'Which of them is going to marry which?' I enquired of Morag, being as much enchanted with the news as she was.

'I believe it's yon little one Erchy's after sayin' has the "come-to-bed eyes".' She gave a wry chuckle. 'Aye, an' I mind our own Hector tellin' him, "Well, Erchy," says he, "if it's come-to-bed eyes she has then I'm thinkin' it's a been-to-bed walk her legs has." '

'Oh, that one,' I exclaimed, recalling a young girl with rather bandy legs, bounteous chestnut hair and shadowed lazy eyes, who had called at the cottage a couple of times and with liquid mendicant chant had tried to flatter, wheedle and coax me into buying bowls and ladles made from dried milk tins, roughly soldered.

'Aye, that one,' confirmed Morag.

'And who is she marrying?' I demanded.

'And who but that one they call "Hairy Willie",' she declared with great satisfaction.

'Hairy Willie!' I ejaculated. 'But he's too old for her, and anyway he's in Canada.'

'He may be too old for her but he's not in Canada,' contradicted Morag with smug emphasis. 'He's back at the sod hut.'

I was overcome with curiosity. The rumour a month or so earlier that Hairy Willie's sister in Canada had sent him the money for a three-month trip by plane to visit her had caused a great sensation in the village. No one had at first believed the story but gradually signs of unusual excitement became apparent among the tinkers themselves. Several bachelors in the village reported having been asked for cast-off underwear to fit a 'big, big man'. (Hairy Willie was a clothes-bursting six foot two.) Others were asked if they could spare a suit-case. Then when interest had been whipped up to its peak Hairy Willie himself did Erchy the great honour of appearing at his door and asking 'would he be havin' a kind of tie or two he wasn't wantin' to go to Canada?' Erchy had obligingly produced a couple of cherished ties and in return for the gift had asked Hairy Willie point blank if the story of his flying to Canada was really true. Hairy Willie had been delighted not only to show Erchy the letter from his sister (he himself could not read) but also the money order she had enclosed for his fare. ('An' the size of it near knocked me over!' Erchy confided afterwards.)

One day the following week a bevy of tinker children was seen climbing over and under, inside and outside Hairy Willie's ramshackle old van, racing each other with pails of water from the burn, washing it and polishing it and making it fit for the journey down to Glasgow where he was to catch the plane. The very next day Hairy Willie, dressed in a lovat-green tweed jacket which had come from the Laird via the gamekeeper; a pair of homespun trousers, furtively supplied by the shepherd's tender-hearted wife; a pious black hat begged from the minister, and a pair of ex-R.A.F. flying boots from an entirely unaccountable source, had climbed into his van beside a battered portmanteau and amidst a chorus of good wishes, spurts of delighted dancing and waving of arms and hats started on his adventure. Since then the village had heard no news of him and it had been assumed by everyone that he was safely in Canada with his sister. Now, here was Morag saying that he was already back at the encampment.

'Didn't he like Canada?' I asked.

'Indeed the man never got to Canada,' she replied. 'You mind he was drivin' himself down?' I nodded. 'Well, they're tellin' me he collected that many drunken drivin' summonses on his way to Glasgow that all the money for his fare had gone on fines before ever he got there.' Morag was outraged by my laughter. 'A waste of good money,' she scolded, and then added thoughtfully, 'not but what it was a waste, anyway. How did she know he was her real brother? You canna' tell with tinks.'

'So now he's proposing to get married,' I said.

'Aye, an' it should be worth seein'. She's been around tryin' to find somebody will give her a dress for the weddin'. Indeed she was at my own house yesterday but I had nothin' would do for her.'

'Poor kid,' I said. 'I wish I could help her.'

'Ach, she's no needin' help,' replied Morag. 'Mary Anne's promised her a white dress she has by her.'

'Her own wedding dress?' I asked.

'Ach, no, mo ghaoil, it's just a dress of some sort she inhabited from her granny when she died. It's been up in a box in the loft long since.' I felt even sorrier for the girl. 'It's queer all the same,' Morag went on, 'the likes of them tinks wantin' to get marrit in a church.'

'Why?' I asked. 'How do they usually get married?' I was thinking of the traditional gypsy ceremony.

'Indeed I'm thinkin' they don't usually bother themselves,' said Morag.

There was a sudden thump on the door and it flew open, revealing a group of masked children clad in a variety of old seamen's jerseys, yachting caps, long black skirts and tattered dresses. They blundered into the kitchen and silently stood in an aura of mildew and excitement, waiting for us to guess their identities, greeting our deliberately wrong guesses with anonymous snorts and giggles and reluctantly acknowledging correct ones by removing their masks. Eventually all the masks were removed and we gave them each a threepenny bit. I put out a bowl of water in which lurked quartered apples and rolling up their voluminous sleeves the children ducked for them with eager deliberation. When the apples were finished they put on their masks again and securely tucking up flapping skirts and trouser legs ran off gaily to repeat the performance at the next house.

'I'm thinkin',' said Morag, 'the tinks will be after some of them dresses the children was wearin' tonight if they see them. They'll want to be dressin' themselves up for the weddin' as well as the bride.'

A few days after Halloween the prospective bride called at the cottage. Trying to conceal her excitement she told me wistfully that she had tried 'everywhere just' (she implied by her tones every reputable store in town) but could not get a pair of white shoes to fit her. Had I such a thing as a pair? She would be so full of thanks to me if I could but just find her a wee pair. I knew I had absolutely nothing suitable. I also knew that she would not believe me if I told her so. I invited her inside to inspect my shoe cupboard to see if there was anything else that might do. There were no light shoes at all, my Bruach footwear being limited to gumboots, brogues and carpet slippers. She smiled at me ingratiatingly. She understood, of course, I wouldn't want to part with them; they were nice anyway and that cool in the summer for the feets. I wondered at first which particular pair of shoes she was going to try to win from me and then I saw that her glance kept going to a pair of grubby old tennis shoes in the bottom of the cupboard. I bent down and rooted them out. There was a small hole in the toe of each.

'These?' I asked incredulously. 'You want these?'

Ach, it was too much to ask of me. She tried to look contrite, but her eyes returned greedily to the shabby shoes I was holding. I handed them to her.

'Have them by all means if you want them,' I said, and poking about found a tube of whitener not completely hard which I also pushed into her hand. Full of smiles and dramatic predictions of good luck that would follow my generosity she rushed off clutching the shoes to her and leaving me with an inexplicable sense of guilt which was not dissipated until Morag told me that she had heard the bride's mother only that day pestering the grocer to get her some coloured toilet rolls.

'Aye, I thought that would surprise you. I was surprised myself,' she told me, with cheerful disapproval. 'Toilet rolls for tinks!' she scoffed, 'and coloured ones at that! "What's wrong with a handful of grass the same as we use ourselves?" I says to her, and do you know what she was wantin' them for?'

I shook my head and waited.

'She said she must have coloured paper for makin' the flowers for the bucket the bride was goin' to carry.' She snorted. 'Fancy that now. Not satisfied with a white dress my fine lady must have a bucket to carry like brides in the papers and her mother's havin' to make her the flowers for it.'

An ancient dress, a pair of old tennis shoes, a bouquet of paper flowers!

I announced my intention of going to see the wedding, and Nelly Elly was quick to say that she would come with me if she could get someone to see to the Post Office for her. Mary Anne, delighted at the possibility of seeing the bride in her grandmother's dress, planned that she too would come if Jamie would get back from the cow in time. Morag indicated that she would come if the Lord spared her.

The day of the wedding brought a sunwhite morning encircled with gull cries and harried by a bluster of wind. The wedding was to be at twelve o'clock in a church some twelve miles distant so there was time only to rush through the morning's chores before embarking on a wrestling bout with Joanna, my car, who with age was becoming an increasingly slow starter. I was late and all three of my friends were walking along the road towards the cottage when I met them.

'My, they're sayin' there's tinks come from as far as Inverness for this weddin'!' exclaimed Morag as soon as we had started off.

'Indeed and so they have,' agreed Nelly Elly. 'Did you no' have them round yesterday just? Beggin' me to buy they were, just so they could give the bridegroom a wee bitty somethin' for his weddin'.'

'I'm knowin' fine what the wee bitty somethin' would be, too,' observed Morag sagely. 'It'll be a rough weddin' if there's many from Inverness there.'

'There's a dozen came from there yesterday,' reported Nelly Elly. 'An' I'm after hearin' that the little boy they brought with them was a wee monster. He was swearin' that bad on the train they had to lock him in the guard's van all the way.' She sucked in a horrified breath. 'Folks was sayin' they'd never heard anythin' like it.'

'If there's a dozen of them from Inverness there's as many from other places,' put in Mary Anne. 'There must be near forty of them all together in that sod hut. Dear knows where they're all to sleep.'

'Ach, they'll no' be carin' where they sleep,' said Morag disdainfully. 'An' they'll have that much drink inside them they won't know where they are anyway.'

'Erchy was past their camp yesterday and he was sayin' there was good smells for a mile either way,' supplied Nelly Elly. 'They were after cookin' the chickens they got. He says they had three or four fires goin' and he reckoned they had about fifteen birds there of one sort or another. They're doin' well out of it. I know the cockerel my mother gave them was near as big as a goose.'

'My own was as big,' countered Morag with pride. 'I was thinkin' maybe I'd keep him till the New Year, but ach, when they asked me would they get somethin' for the weddin' feast I felt I'd best give it to them.' She smoothed her gloves complacently. 'All the same,' she went on, 'I believe they've done well for meat from Lachy's cow that fell over the cliff a day or two back. He says they were runnin' back and fro with pails and basins to it all day long till the tide took it away.'

'Indeed I heard that too,' confirmed Mary Anne. 'So I didn't give them a bird at all. I wasn't for givin' then anythin' at first but the hens are layin' well just now so Jamie said to give them a few eggs.'

'Somebody told me you gave them a pound of tea, too!' accused Morag.

'Aye,' admitted Mary Anne self-consciously. 'I had plenty so I thought I'd not be missin' it.'

'I'm glad everyone didn't give them a chicken,' I said, regretting that I had put only half a crown into the toe of each of the tennis shoes.

'Why do you say that?' asked Morag.

'Because I didn't,' I replied.

'Ach, well, I daresay you gave them eggs or potatoes or somethin',' she suggested. 'There was no call for everybody to give them chickens.'

'I didn't give them anything at all,' I confessed. 'The bride asked me for a pair of old tennis pumps I had and when I gave them to her I popped half a crown into the toe of each of them, but I wasn't asked to contribute anything to the feast.'

'No indeed, and that was plenty to give them,' comforted Nelly Elly. 'They were havin' a struggle to carry home the food they collected when I saw them. What with all they'd have from Lachy's cow and them havin' got a whole sack of potatoes from Roddy they'll be feedin' like kings and queens anyway—not but what they don't always,' she added.

'Better than the rest of us,' agreed Morag, with a tremor of indignation. 'An' not only that. Did you hear how he's been gettin' the petrol so they can go for a honeymoon?'

We all admitted that we had not heard.

'Why, he's been takin' his van to a different spot each day an' there he leaves it an' stands himself beside it with an empty can. He stops every car and lorry as it comes by an' tells them he's run out of petrol and asks will he get a bit to see him home.' She paused for our exclamations. 'Some of the drivers feels that sorry for him they'll give him near a canful,' she continued, 'an' my fine fellow has a fifty-gallon drum in the back of his van so as soon as they're out of sight he nips round an' puts the petrol into it.'

'Oh, my, my, he's the wily one,' chuckled Mary Anne appreciatively.

'Hear that now!' said Nelly Elly with envy-tinged disapproval. 'What will those tinks be after thinkin' of next?'

'I wonder?' I murmured, as I was assailed by a sudden recollection. 'I wonder if that's what he was up to the other day when Hamish saw him, broken down, as he thought, beside the road?'

'Likely it was,' said Morag.

I started to chuckle as I recounted for the amusement of my companions the story Hamish had told me. It seemed he had been walking back to Bruach after delivering some sheep to the mainland when he had come across Hairy Willie, looking rather grimier and sweatier than usual, bending over the engine of his van. When Hamish had drawn alongside the tinker had proceeded to give him a brief but vitriolic description of the misdeameanours of the ancient engine and while he was in full spate a car drew up and a gentleman got out to ask if help was needed. Hairy Willie promptly replied that it was 'Nothin' but a wee bitty petrol she was after wantin'.' But the gentleman, according to Hamish, had already started his own investigation and, to the tinker's very obvious surprise, had discovered that the tank contained ample petrol. He had continued his examination of the engine, poking and prodding, screwing and unscrewing, and eventually he had told Hairy Willie to try to start it. The engine had responded

to the first pull. The mystified expression of the tinker had changed
to one of such relief that the gentleman had asked anxiously if he had
been stranded for long and how far away his home lay, to which
questions Hairy Willie replied with his customary glib mendacity.
'Thank you, thank you, sir,' he repeated again and again. 'What
would I have done now if yourself hadn't come along?'

'It isn't I you should thank but God Almighty,' replied the gentleman. 'It is He who sent me here to help you.'

'Hairy Willie's face looked as though he had two tongues and had
bitten both of them,' Hamish reported, 'an' he turned to the man.
"You must be a minister," says he. "I am indeed," says the man. "Is
there anything wrong with that?" "Wrong!" shouts Hairy Willie.
"Wrong? Man! Why the bloody hell didn't you tell me you was a
minister, I might have started swearin' in front of you".'

My companions exchanged looks before they permitted themselves
to giggle demurely.

By this time we were rounding the head of the loch where the wet,
black hills gloomed over acres of shore which the tide had left to a
shifting mosaic of seabirds. Hooded crows swaggered uneasily among
the fringes of salt weed and an occasional heron stood in aristocratic
aloofness, with feathered 'widow's weeds' lifting gently in the breeze.

'Here comes the boys!' announced Morag, and I drew in to the side
of the road. There had been a cattle sale at the loch side that morning
and the Bruach men had started out at two o'clock to walk their
cattle to it. They were trudging their long way back now, driving
before them either cattle they had bought at the sale or cattle they had
refused to sell because of poor prices. Morag put down the window.
'How did the sale go, boys?' she demanded eagerly.

'No' bad,' they admitted.

'Good prices?'

'Ach, no' bad.'

'What did our own Ruari make on his beasts?' It was not done to
ask a man outright what he got for his cattle. You asked him about a
neighbour's or a friend's beasts and hoped he would volunteer to
tell you how he himself had fared.

'I believe he got seventy for the two of them.'

'The dear knows!' exclaimed Morag noncommittally. 'An' is he after buyin' a beast in for himself?'

'Aye,' was the disdainful reply. 'A right queer beastie, too, that looks as if it's been crossed with a camel.'

'The fool!' said Morag with derision. She turned her attention to wee Shamus, who at eight years old had achieved the status of manhood by being allowed to walk his widowed mother's cow through the night to the sale. His valiant efforts to disguise his tiredness were not helped by the fact that he had a black and swollen eye.

'Shamus!' Morag taxed him. 'You've not been fightin', surely?'

'I have not then,' replied Shamus with flushed stubbornness.

'You haven't? Then how is it you have such a black eye?'

Shamus kicked his gumbooted feet in the grass. 'Well, you see,' he said profoundly, 'somebody struck somebody.' But before she could question him further he had darted off to turn a cow who was trying to dodge past him.

Erchy, red-faced with exertion, came hurrying up to the car. 'Here,' he told us, 'I'm thinkin' I'll come back with you.'

'You will not,' we told him. 'We're cramped enough as it is.'

'I could sit on top,' he coaxed.

'No.' We were adamant.

'Ach, well, I'm comin' back tonight yet,' he told us as we were moving off. 'I'm feelin' I need a good drink after all the runnin' about I'm after doin' today.'

'You'll be needin' your bed, more likely,' Morag said, but he too was running to head off a recalcitrant cow.

'If they get the Bruach men with their cattle money and the tinkers after the weddin' they'll have a wild night at the bar tonight,' she prophesied.

We arrived at the church a little before twelve, but though there was a fair number of people standing in coy groups outside the church they were obviously not the wedding party. I pulled Joanna in behind a parked van close to the church gates before I realized with a shock that it was an ambulance. With a look of dazed enquiry I turned to

Morag. Bruach modes of transport were often wildly unorthodox but surely, I thought, not an ambulance for a bride!

'Ach, no,' Morag reassured me. 'Likely it's the driver himself come to take a look at the weddin'.'

'We'll not go into the church, will we?' asked Nelly Elly.

'Why not?' I replied. 'I thought that was why we came.'

'Ach, no indeed, I could never go into the church with the tinks,' she giggled.

'You're not goin' in yourself, are you, Miss Peckwitt?' Mary Anne enquired.

'If Miss Peckwitt's goin' in I'll go along with her,' said Morag venturesomely.

'Of course I'm going in,' I said, and getting out of the car made for the church door, whither they all followed me with eager resignation.

Just as we reached the entrance someone shouted, 'Here they come!' and pausing to look back along the road we saw the disordered procession of tinkers coming towards us. The bride and all the female tinkers, frequently impinging on one another as they walked, headed the procession, while the groom with the equally undisciplined male tinkers followed close on their heels. Untrammelled children dove in and out with a liveliness that was in no way affected by their lengthy walk.

A thought struck me. 'What happened about the bouquet?' I enquired. 'Did the grocer get any coloured toilet rolls?'

'Not him,' replied Nelly Elly. 'Why would he do that when it's just left with them he'll be?'

'Did she manage to get hold of some coloured paper, then?'

'Well, indeed but didn't Enac and Fiona go over to the mainland to get themselves some boots last week, an' them feelin' that sorry for the tinker girl not gettin' her bucket they went into all the hotel lavatories and took a bit. They even went through the train while it was in the station and took some of them paper towels. Aye, but the old tinker body was well pleased when they gave it to her. The girls was well pleased too because she told them they'd have rich husbands and good luck for the rest of their lives through it.' She chuckled. 'Ach, but the men are sayin' we're all goin' daft over this weddin'.'

Distinct sounds of hilarity were now reaching us from the distance, but as they neared the church the tinkers hushed their children and their own voices and allowed their features to resume the masks of mendicancy we knew so well.

We slipped into the church and took our seats on a back pew and, taking courage from our example, most of the onlookers followed suit. So quickly did the church fill that when the tinkers arrived there were only a few front pews vacant. Embarrassed and bewildered, they squeezed themselves in, waiting vainly under the unrelenting eye of the minister to be told what to do. Hairy Willie came in and stood surveying the congregation with an artificially induced benignity. He was resplendent in his 'Canadian trip' clothes, his battered black hat being crushed under his arm. His normally shaggy hair had been cropped so close to his head that it looked as though he was wearing a nylon skull cap. Morag nudged me.

'I believe that's the haircut all the men is gettin' in Glasgow,' she whispered. 'I believe they call it the "cruel cut".'

The minister beckoned and in response Hairy Willie and his best man loped eagerly up the aisle towards him shaking the minister's decorum perceptibly. He fended them off with a rigidly held prayer-book and indicated where they should stand. Hairy Willie complied and stood with his hands clasped nonchalantly behind him. There was a hissing in the front pews and the bridegroom turned round and bestowed on his supporters a jaunty smile accompanied by a convivial wink to which they responded with such uninhibited whisperings that the minister, no doubt apprehensive of blasphemy, spoke to him quietly. Hairy Willie obligingly faced the chancel and stood to attention until perhaps recalling that the black hat crushed to shapelessness under his arm had been given to him by the minister, he reached for it and, holding it behind his back, proceeded to remould it to its original shape.

The stir of excitement that always precedes the entrance of the bride was by no means lacking at this wedding. One of the tinker children who had no doubt been held captive to this moment in the porch burst through the door, ran up the aisle and pummelling his two fists into the bridegroom's broad back yelled, 'She's comin' for ye!' He was quickly seized by a tinker at the end of the pew and pushed protestingly out of sight among the packed bodies, and all eyes turned towards the door as the bride' appeared holding determinedly on to the arm of a vacillating old man who I at once recognized to be a spruced-up version of the tinker who had coveted my teeth.

I was astonished. She looked as pretty as any young bride I had ever seen. The warmhearted Mary Anne had not only washed and bleached her grandmother's dress but had re-made it so that the bodice fitted perfectly and the long skirt draped itself to conceal all but the toes of my old tennis shoes which peeped out a little dustily as she walked. Her bouquet, which she held in front of her much as a housewife might hold a flue-brush, was most artistic, though the green foliage betrayed itself by its hygenic pallor. As she walked up the aisle she turned to smile with delighted appraisal at the congregation on either side of her. She looked radiant and I do not think there was a single person present who was not extremely touched by the whole event.

Rescues

ERCHY was mucking out his cow-byre when I called on him to ask if I could borrow his saw.

'My God! but I had a good laugh out of them tinks the night of the weddin',' he said.

I looked at him searchingly. Erchy had been to a cattle sale on the day of the tinkers' wedding and on such occasions his stories of subsequent happenings were not usually very lucid, due to his own inebriation.

'Aye,' he went on. 'That Hairy Willie was as drunk as I don't know what an' when one of them pulled his trousers away from his backside an' poured a pint of beer down inside Hairy Willie didn't even feel it.' Erchy leaned on his fork and smiled out at the pewter-grey sea.

'What I'd like to know is whether they got away on their honeymoon as they were supposed to?' I asked. 'There were quite a few people here who didn't believe they'd ever get away.'

'He got started all right,' said Erchy.

'Where was his bride?' I asked.

'I believe she was with him some of the time,' replied Erchy after a moment of doubt. 'Ach, but she was drunk as he was himself.' He threw out a couple more forkfuls of manure. 'I was tellin' you about them gettin' started on their honeymoon.'

I nodded.

'Aye, well we all saw him go, with his bride sittin' beside him. He set off an' he was drivin' all over the road. It's a damty good thing the pollis knew to keep out of the way or they would have had to take him in. The rest of the tinks was laughin' and dancin' away in front of the hotel. Honest, I didn't want to get drunk myself, I was enjoyin' watchin' them so much.' He looked a little wistful. 'I can tell you I saved myself a packet of money that way too,' he added. 'Did I not, Cailleach?' I turned to see that his mother had come up behind us. She smiled warmly at the two of us. 'I wish you could be always savin' your monies like that,' she chided him gently, for he was the apple of her eye and she did not really begrudge him his occasional wildnesses. 'You'll see and take a wee strupak with me before you go,' she said to me and I promised that I would.

'I was tellin' Miss Peckwitt about the tinkers' honeymoon,' Erchy told her.

'Oh, my, my,' whispered his mother disapprovingly. 'It was terrible just, was it not?'

'Why, what happened?' I asked with mounting curiosity.

'Well,' said Erchy, continuing with his story. 'About an hour after they'd gone we was sittin' in the kitchen of the hotel havin' a bite of somethin' to eat with the cook, for it was well past closin' time. There comes a bangin' on the door and when the cook goes to open it, there on the step is Hairy Willie. "For God's sake, help me!" he bursts out. "Here, here," she says to him. "Help you what way?" for she thinks he's still pretty drunk. "To get my van out of the ditch," he tells her. "Find me some men and some ropes before the pollis sees it." "How did it get into the ditch?" she asks him. "Woman," says he, "I'm thinkin' I must have put it there myself," he says, "an' now the bloody thing's turned right over." The cook brings him in to the kitchen an' she was tellin' him how lucky he was that we were all there still. Ruari and óne or two of the others went off to see would they find a rope. Suddenly the cook says to Hairy Willie, "Where's your bride?" "My bride?" says he as though he's never heard of her before that minute. "Yes, indeed," said the cook, "the girl you married today in the church and was with you in the van." "Ach!" Hairy Willie tells her, as though it doesn't matter, "she's still under the van." "Still under the van?" the cook screams at him. "My God! what are you thinkin' of? You should never have left her. All you're thinkin' about is gettin' your old van out of the ditch before the pollis sees it, when that poor lassie might be lyin' there dead." Hairy Willie looked at her as though she's goin' daft. "I know fine she's not dead," he tells her. "I could hear her swearin' after me all the way along the road." '

'Oh, the monster!' gasped Erchy's mother in horrified tones.

'Ruari had the hotel car out by then,' continued Erchy with un-abated enthusiasm. 'An' when we got to the place there was Willie's van upside down in the ditch with half of a stone dyke on top of it that he'd knocked down. There was no sound from the van so we told Willie he must talk to the girl and see if she was all right.' Erchy's eyes glittered with remembered amusement. 'As soon as he opened his mouth there was such a stream of swearin' would have turned your stomach to hear it. From a lassie, too.' He succeeded in looking shocked.

'Dear only knows,' murmured his mother piously.

'Anyway,' he went on, 'we got the van out an' the lassie was all right seemingly, only drunk still.'

'Well, thank goodness for that,' I said with a chuckle.

'Wait you,' warned Erchy. 'I haven't finished yet.'

I looked at him expectantly and his mother put a hand over her mouth in an effort to hide a smile.

'We'd hardly got the van out but the fellow who has the croft came shoutin' at us. He'd seen all the lights and he'd been wonderin' what was happenin'. When he sees his wall's all broken down, by God! there was more swearin' and cursin' from him. "My cows will get out through that," he shouts at Hairy Willie, "an' if they get lost it's you that will pay for them. And you'll pay for me to mend that hole in the dyke," says he, "or I'll have the pollis on you." Hairy Willie was that scared I believe I could hear his moustache rattlin'. "Where's your cows now?" he asks the man. "In there," says the man, pointin' to the dyke, "but as soon as they find this hole they'll be through it. You'll just stay yourself and see that they don't get out." Hairy Willie was lookin' that bad I felt sorry for him right enough. An' then, before anybody knew what he was at, he got into his van, started it up and ran it straight back into the ditch again so that it filled up the gap in the dyke. "There," he tells the man, "will that not keep your cattle in?" "Aye," says the man, and you should have seen the look on his face. Then he starts to laugh. "All right," he tells Hairy Willie. "Seein' my cattle's safe I'll not say any more about it," and he went off home.'

'And what happened to the tinkers then?' I asked.

'Ach, they was just goin' off back to their camp, holdin' each other up, the last I saw of them,' said Erchy, as he bent to lift a spilling forkful of manure. 'I expect that's where they're goin' to spend the honeymoon if there's room for them to get in yet.'

I went back to the house with Erchy's mother, had my strupak and collected the saw, which she seemed a little hesitant to give me. It was not until I was on my way home that I realized it was a Saturday and that she would have preferred to keep the saw in her own house until the Monday so that there should be no possibility of its being used upon the Sabbath day.

'What are you goin' to do with that, now?' asked the grocer facetiously, when I went to buy a tin of meat from him. 'Build yourself a new house, are you?'

'I'm going to have a good go at those old blackcurrant bushes,' I told him. 'They never produce a crop and I think it's because there's too much old wood there.'

'I wouldn't be surprised,' said the grocer with only tepid interest. 'Did your butcher meat not come that you're buyin' a tin of meat on a Saturday?' he asked curiously.

'I didn't order any this week,' I told him. 'That tink they call Phillibeag promised he'd bring a rabbit for me for the weekend, but I doubt if I'll get it now.'

'Ach, you're better not to get anythin' from that man anyway,' the grocer warned me. 'He wouldn't care what sort of a beast he'd sell you. Why, they tell me if he finds a cat in his snares he just skins it and sells it along with his rabbits. He says folks can't tell the difference.'

'Oh Lord!' I said, and my appetite even for tinned meat vanished completely.

'You'd be as well to keep some tins of meat in the house in case we get snow,' the grocer counselled. 'It's lookin' as though it's not far off.'

'Oh, surely not yet,' I said, thinking of my meagre fuel supply.

'Aye, indeed. My brother was sayin' only last night he was seein' plenty of that thick snow waitin' at the back of the hills. It'll be here before long, likely.'

His prediction had me a little worried and as I hurried home I mentally reviewed the contents of my store cupboard and the quantity of feeding stuffs left in the barn. I resolved to write once again to the coal merchant to ask him to speed up the delivery of coal I had ordered some time ago. So engrossed was I in my calculations that although I was vaguely aware of a male figure approaching I was not shocked into the realization that it was a stranger until I saw him take out a large white handkerchief and blow his nose on it. Recollecting myself in time to stifle the usual chaffing remark or specific comment on the weather I wished him 'Good afternoon', to which he replied with stilted cordiality and continued on his way. I was curious. Now that the tourist season was over any stranger in the village was usually something to do with an official body so that it was almost a duty for everyone to discover the reason for their visit. I turned into Morag's cottage to find her in the act of taking a large steaming dumpling off the fire.

'I've just seen a strange man!' I announced.

'A strange man?' echoed Morag and Behag together and even little Fiona stopped trying to tie the tails of two cats together to stand and stare at me in unblinking surprise.

'Who would that be, I wonder?' went on Morag. 'It's late for anyone to be here. What like was he?'

I described him as well as I could.

'Had he an open or a closed collar?' demanded Morag.

The expression was new to me and I had to ask her what she meant. 'I mean, did he have a closed collar like a minister or an open collar like a tourist?' she explained.

'Open,' I said.

'Ach, well, then, likely he'll be that student fellow has been preachin' at the Seceder church these three Sundays past,' interpreted Morag. 'He'll be stayin' with Kirsty, the poor mannie.'

'That'll be the one that Euan was praising up so much?' suggested Behag with a titter.

'Aye, he will be indeed,' agreed Morag, a reciprocal smile on her lips.

'Does Euan go to the other church now?' I asked in surprise. Euan, the half-wit brother of 'Padruig the Daftie' had, until recent months, been kept away from any church because of the profanity of his language. However the two female 'pilgrims', to whom I have referred in a previous book,[1] found in Euan not only a devoted admirer but also a proselyte who made up in susceptibility for what he lacked in intelligence. During their relatively short stay in the village they had undertaken both his lay and his religious education with such a degree

[1]. See *The Sea for Breakfast*

of success that he no longer referred to a chicken as a 'feathery bugger'
but was content to indulge his passion for epithets by the use of such
mildnesses as 'that damned-by-God hen'. They had even taught him
to sing a hymn and now whenever one passed by Padruig's cottage
the lusty voice of Euan could be heard rendering adagio, prestissimo,
pianissimo or fortissimo, the words of 'When He Cometh' with
tuneless assiduity. It was shortly after the departure of the 'pilgrims'
that Padruig had been taken ill and had gone to be nursed by his
married sister on the mainland. Euan had shortly afterwards asserted
his right to go to church and there he had since attended regularly,
sitting in his pew rigid with importance except when the hymns were
announced when, handing his book to a neighbour, he would request
that the right hymn should be found for him, although he could not
read a single word. When the singing commenced no matter what the
hymn might be Euan joined in vociferously with 'When He Cometh',
remaining aloofly indifferent to the nudgings and objurgations of those
in close proximity.

'Euan's been goin' to the other church for three or four weeks past
now,' Morag told me. 'There's no tellin' my fine lad what he's to do
now that Padruig's not keepin' the upper hand of him.'

'Why has he left your church?' I asked her.

'The dear knows why,' she replied, 'unless it's just that he's feelin'
he needs a change.' She cut off a large hunk of hot dumpling and
wrapped it in a cloth for me to take home for my supper.

'I really must ask Euan next time I see him why he's changed
churches,' I told them as I said goodbye. 'It would be interesting to
hear what he has to say.'

It was not until the following Monday afternoon when I was
returning from a session of beachcombing that I met Euan. He too
had been beachcombing and the creel on his back was piled high with
driftwood. I complimented him on his industry and then went on to
question him about his apostasy. 'It's quite a long way further for
you to have to walk to your new church,' I suggested.

'Yes, Missed,' he agreed eagerly. 'But when I gets there it's a nice
carpet I have to my feets an' a good stove to warm me. I's not goin'

to shiver in that dirty old church when I can go a bit further an' sit back like a gentleman.' He leaned the creel against the dyke, folded his arms in front of him and adopted the pose of a stiff Victorian gentleman.

'What about the new student preacher,' I asked him. 'Is he good?'

'God's hell!' he exclaimed with blasphemous piety. 'I believe he has the Lord in him okay.'

'You enjoy his sermons, then?'

'God's hell, but he's a good preacher!' reiterated Euan passionately.

The evening grew increasingly cold and towards nightfall a boorish wind, laden with sleet, sent everyone hurrying to find their cattle and chase them into their stalls for the night. The following morning I awoke to find my bedroom full of a strange pale light and when I went to the window I found the hills masked with snow with only a few dark patches pricking the sheet white moors where the most robust heather clumps had shrugged through the thick mantle. I fed Bonny and drove her out through the moor gate where with the wisdom of her breed she would nose at the snow until she could get at the heather beneath. For a few minutes I leaned on the gate, watching the sluggish dark clouds piling themselves around the startlingly white hills and thinking how strange it was that snow, which falls so white and clean, should yet be heralded by such a dirty-looking mess of cloud. In the Hebrides snow, when it comes, assumes a recognizable personality. There is that which steals in with ballerina lissomeness on a north wind to leave the hills poised and breathless as a corps de ballet awaiting the re-entry of their star. By comparison the snow that the south wind brings is clumsy and sluttish and lies dispiritedly over the land until it abandons it to slime and drabness. Then there is the noisy, second-hand snow that has been wrested off the mountains by a tyrannic gale and is flung at us in crisp particles that needle into our skin.

There came a muffled flurry of wind threaded with snowflakes and I hurried home to get the byre cleaned and hay put out in readiness for Bonny's evening feed, for she would need to be brought in earlier than usual. Despite the cold I was glad to be outdoors, for between the snow showers, which became more reticent as the day progressed, the sun smiled benignly, the snow shimmered and above the silence of the land came the tinkling whisper of the wind-ruffled water. Immediately after a late lunch I went to collect Bonny for, though the last snow shower had been hardly more than the flick of an angel's duster, as evening approached there was an increasing frostiness in the air and already there was a rasping under my boots as I slithered along the path from which my own and Bonny's footprints of the morning had been obliterated. It was a nuisance having to go out on the moors to bring home a cow, though there was solace in the beauty of the shadow-edged loch, coldly blue except where it reflected a few tatters of an elusive sunset, and in the sight of Rhuna tip-tilting its corners up from the water like a smiling mouth, an accepted sign of frost. But when one knew that nearly everyone else's cattle needed only to hear a once-bellowed invitation or even the clang of a moor gate to go hurrying through to their byres where shelter, hay and a warm 'potach' awaited them, and that even those cows which did not enjoy the luxury of a byre would range themselves hungrily along the fence waiting for their owners to bring them hay, it was infuriating to have to go and seek my own cosseted cow. Cows are perverse creatures and for some curious reason Bonny and Morag's cow Milky and Tearlaich's Bracty had of late formed a passionate attachment for one another, with the result that every evening, whatever the weather, we three unfortunate owners had to trudge out to the moors, separate three reluctant cows and coerce them homewards through three separate gates. Morag and Tearlaich were already making their way towards the loving trio when I reached the moor and they waited for me to join them.

'Ach, but there's no sense in this weather, no sense at all,' grumbled Morag as we got behind the cows and started them moving towards the fence. 'Me feets gets that cold, though I have on three pairs of stockings under them an' it hurts to take off my boots. I'm wishin' sometimes I could be goin' to bed in them.'

'You should put cow dung mixed with a wee bitty straw in your boots first,' advised Tearlaich. 'Aye, aye, aye, cow dung. That's what I said, cow dung.' Tearlaich was always known as 'Tearlaich-a-Tri' because of his habit of repeating a thing three times before he could be sure he had said it.

'Is that what you use yourself?' Morag asked him with a show of surprise.

'Aye, I do, I do, I do,' he replied. 'An' I'm no' after feelin' the cold a wee bitty, not a wee bit, I say.'

'I wouldn't fancy washing your socks,' I murmured.

'Socks? You dunna' need socks at all, at all; no, not at all.'

'Then surely your feets must be awful tender,' suggested Morag.

Indignantly Tearlaich turned on her and proceeded to instruct her in the acquiring of a pair of warm and comfortable feet. I gave scant attention to their conversation, being engrossed in tracing the pattern of shrew prints that interlaced one another on the snow like the strands of a necklace. The three cows were lumbering along in front of us, their great bellies bumping from time to time and their protesting moos mingling with the grumbling of the snow as it packed down beneath their hooves.

Suddenly I became conscious of a thick sucking splash just in front of us and of Tearlaich shouting in Gaelic. I looked up just in time to see the hind-quarters of Morag's cow disappearing into a bog. Panic-stricken I ran forward with the others, urging the cow to extricate herself before she sank deeper. The beast's two front feet were still on ground that seemed firm enough but as we tried to drive her forward by slaps and prods, by pulls on her horns and by continuous male-diction from Tearlaich her hind-quarters only sank deeper and deeper. We bared our arms and plunged them into the bog, trying to grasp a leg and aid her in her struggles but despite our efforts the cow only seemed to settle herself until she was in the ludicrous position of sitting upright with her forelegs stretched out in front of her, like a begging dog.

'I doubt we're only makin' things worse,' panted Morag. 'We'd best go an' get help.'

We paused dejectedly for a moment, assessing the situation. It looked as if it should have been easy enough to extricate the beast when she already had two feet on firm ground but the bog was a narrow hole and by now her hind-quarters were deeply embedded. Morag, looking white and strained, swept the hair from her eyes with a peaty arm. The light would not last much longer and by the time we got help from the village the cow might have lost the will to live.

'You and Miss Peckwitt had best take your own cows home,' Morag advised in desperation. 'You can get help then, while I stay here with my beast.' Tearlaich said he would put his beast 'through the gate just', but I raced Bonny home in record time. However by the time I had made my first plea for help Tearlaich had told Morag's deaf brother Ruari who had simply raised his voice and acquainted the whole village with the news. When I got back to the moor there were half a dozen men with ropes and boards in attendance round the cow, who had become distinctly more apathetic than she had been when I left. With much excited Gaelic argument and much impedance from excited dogs, a rope was tied to the cow's horns and boards were pushed down into the bog to try and give her a firm footing. But by now the cow had lost the will to struggle and the position began to look hopeless.

'Give her a dose of whisky,' suggested Ian. 'I have some here in my pocket.'

'Here, no,' said Murdoch. 'I'll drink that myself. Wait till you get the beast out before you give her the whisky and make sure it won't be wasted.'

'Ach, give her some anyway,' insisted Ian, and a generous dose was poured down the cow's throat. This was followed by several more fruitless attempts to heave her out, but the struggle became increasingly difficult as what had at first been firm ground softened under the continuous treading and slithering of many feet. Even the boards which had been placed under the cow's front hooves had become slimy so that they now provided only a treacherous foothold. The men were becoming tired.

'I doubt we'll not get her out,' said Morag with weary despair.

'She has such small hooves for the size of her, that's what's the trouble,' said Murdoch. 'If she had a good big foot that wouldn't cut into the ground we maybe might get her out.'

There was a general shaking of heads in abandonment of the cow's prospects, and yet I knew they would not leave her while there was the remotest chance of her survival. I turned to see Johnny Comic, who must have been ceilidhing in the village and who now stood forlornly among the group of helpers. He suddenly looked about him, lumbered over to a small hillock and sat down. Then he proceeded to take off his very large boots. I was still staring at him perplexedly when he got up and walked through the snow towards the cow, holding out his boots.

'Here,' he told the men, 'put my boots on the poor creature's feets.'

Murdoch stared at him, bereft of speech for a moment, and Johnny, thinking they were going to refuse, bent down and struggled the cow's front hooves into each of his boots. 'Give her a pull now,' he instructed and derisive but obedient the men pulled. There seemed to be a slight sound from the bog. Immediately everyone became excited. 'Take off your own boots, Murdoch, you old bodach, you have the biggest feets here. See an' give us your boots an' we'll try will we get her out with them.' Almost bodily they carried the old man over to the hillock and took off his boots and then, returning to the cow, they plunged their arms into the bog once more and lifted. The bog seemed to release its hold a little more and the cow, feeling the firmness of Johnny's boots on her front hooves, heaved her body again. Everyone became cautiously jubilant. 'Be ready with them boots!' shouted someone. 'When we give her another heave see can you get them on to her feets.' They heaved altogether, the cow responded and there was a shout of triumph as her hind-quarters suddenly came up out of the bog. Murdoch's boots were jammed on her hind hooves, and with boots on all four feet she was pulled and pushed to firm ground.

'Ach, but she's in a pretty bad way,' said Ian, as the cow swayed from side to side and looked as though she would fall back into the bog. 'Get her a wee bit further away and give her another dose of whisky, that'll warm her,' he instructed. With men on either side of her to prevent her falling over the cow was persuaded slowly forward. 'Now, pour this down her throat,' said Ian. I think it was Erchy who seized the bottle and, making a pouch of the cow's mouth, poured down the rest of the spirit.

'By God!' he said to Morag and me as we rubbed the cow with handfuls of the hay someone had brought, 'that was a damty queer place for a cow to be. How did she get there?'

There followed a great deal of explaining until there came a shout from Murdoch who was still sitting on the hillock, trying to cradle first one foot and then the other in order to keep it warm. Johnny Comic seemed hardly to notice the loss of his boots.

'How am I goin' to get home without gettin' my death of cold?' demanded Murdoch irately. 'Somebody had best go and get my Sunday boots and bring them to me.'

'Tearlaich will go, an' he'll fill them with dung for you first,' returned Morag, laughing now with relief.

'Here, no!' expostulated Murdoch. 'They'll not let me into the house.'

'You'd best get that beast movin',' Ian told us, seeing the cow shivering with cold and fright. 'Miss Peckwitt, give the cow a wind to see will it start her off,' he commanded me.

'A wind?' I repeated stupidly.

'Aye, indeed so.' He leaped over the bog and pushing me aside seized the cow's tail which he began to crank as though it were the starting handle of a car. Whether it was the maltreatment of her tail or a sudden bellow from Tearlaich's cow on the other side of the fence that provided the impetus I do not know but the beast gave an answering bellow, lunged forward and started to lumber erratically away from us.

'By God, she's drunk! I must have given the beast too much whisky,' shouted Erchy with a jubilation that was tempered by horror.

'By God, but she has on my boots!' shouted Murdoch. 'Take them from the beast before they're lost to me.' But no one heeded him for the relief of tension had brought laughter and sh᷾ ᷾ comments and also an awareness of our cold and tired bodies.

If a stranger had seen our procession that night as it wound its way over the still moors that were silvered with moonlight and in the wake of a drunken cow wearing tackety boots, with one bootless old man being carried 'piggy back' by big Ian and the other trudging in his stockinged feet through the snow, he surely must have thought we were engaged in some pagan ritual. As Erchy put it, 'It's a damty good thing this didn't happen in the summer when there's folks about or they'd have said we was as mad as I don't know what.'

The snow lasted for nearly three weeks, and every day the sun shone brilliantly during the brief hours of daylight and then sank in an extravagant splendour of gold and crimson that rippled and pulsed across the sky.

'How about a trip in Hector's boat tomorrow?' Erchy asked me one day as I was breaking the ice that formed each night on the water butts.

'I'd love to,' I said with alacrity.

'There's a message come through to the Post Office that the folks over at the Glen is gettin' short of food an' they canna' get to them by road yet. Nelly Elly was askin' would Hector take some there to-morrow.'

The snow had made it impossible to use any sort of vehicle even on the Bruach road and so Hector and Erchy and Duncan, the post-mistress's son, were well loaded with parcels of every shape and size when they passed the cottage on their way down to the boat. Morag and Behag, grumbling good-naturedly, shuffled behind them carrying their own offerings of homebaked oatcakes and scones in a sack thrown over the shoulder and held there with one hand. The other hand shielded their eyes from the sparkling brightness of the snow. I plodded after them, resting my eyes from the brilliance of the land by looking out to sea where *Ealasaid*, Hector's new boat, lay serenely at her moorings, at this distance looking like an ivory carving set in a polished sea. On closer inspection the effect was spoiled by the girdle of old motor-tyres with which she was draped, for though boats are ever more elaborately equipped and piers are ever more elaborately designed the fishermen still raid the shores and village dumps for old motor-tyres to prevent the two from becoming too familiar.

It was bitterly cold up in the bow of the boat where I chose to stand, but had I gone aft I should have been forced to breathe the fumes from the fo'c'sle fire which Morag was already lighting. Erchy noticed my teeth chattering.

'I don't know why you don't go in there with Behag and Morag,' he chided me. 'You'll be after gettin' perished with the cold out here.'

I indicated my binoculars. 'I want to keep a watch out for the deer,' I explained. 'This weather will have driven them down to the shore, don't you think?'

'Aye,' agreed Erchy morosely. 'But what good is it goin' to do you to see the deer, anyway?'

'I'm just interested,' I said.

'I'll give you a shout if I see them,' he promised. 'Now for God's sake, woman, go down into the fo'c'sle before you freeze to death in front of my eyes.'

The fo'c'sle was damp and odorous and untidily snug, the bunks full of a jumble of tarpaulins and sails and ropes, while two or three elegant whisky glasses co-existed happily with a collection of enamel cups and plates. Morag had the folding table erected so that she and Behag could sort through the more homely women's magazines which comprise the library of so many Scottish fishing boats. The table itself had intrigued me from the first time I saw it, for though it was made of only two rough and many-knotholed boards, six of the best-placed knotholes had been knocked out to provide the crew with some of the most stable egg-cups ever devised.

'Here's your deer!' shouted Erchy appearing momentarily in the entrance and I scrambled up on deck to see a herd of deer, apprehensive and poised for flight yet reluctant to leave the kelp on which they had been feeding.

'I can count three stags and twelve hinds,' I turned ecstatically to Erchy. 'How many can you see, Erchy?'

He flicked an unenthusiastic glance towards the shore and then huddled back into the wheelhouse with Hector.

'Erchy!' I reproached him. 'Aren't you interested in the deer?'

'The only deer I'm interested in just now is piping hot on a plate,' he retorted with a nod of dismissal.

I returned to the fo'c'sle and my two still-engrossed companions and after about twenty minutes we heard the engine note of the boat change as she was put out of gear.

'We must be there,' said Morag, so we collected our parcels and went up on deck. There was a swirling of water as the engine stopped and a dinghy, rowed with quick, excited strokes, came out to meet us. There was an exchange of Gaelic as we and the parcels were unloaded into the dinghy but though they were obviously glad to see us their greetings were at first a little strained. It was obvious that the family were much ashamed of having to admit that they had not laid in sufficient stocks of food to tide them over only three weeks' isolation. 'We've been spoiled with these vans comin',' they confessed after a glass or two of whisky from a bottle produced by Erchy had lessened the slight tension. 'We just let ourselves get slack but we'll see and not let it happen again.'

It developed into a very convivial ceilidh (whisky was the only form of sustenance our friends had not run short of) and by the time we came out again into the snow it was dark. I was faintly puzzled when I looked up at the full moon to discover that not only had it grown a waist but that it also seemed to have sprouted fuzzy whiskers. I realized with a fleeting sense of shame that the whisky had made me light-headed. Morag and Behag too showed signs of unusual elation and as soon as she had clambered aboard Morag went to lie down on one of the bunks, complaining of a 'frosted stomach'. I too eased myself down on to an unyielding lump of tarpaulin and stared with great contentment through half-shut eyes at that strangely shaped moon which was now wearing the porthole as a halo. The engine of the boat started; there was a rattle of chain as the anchor came aboard; 'goodbyes' were shouted. *Ealasaid* dipped gently as she was brought round and with the quickening of the engine the water thumped and swished against the stemhead. The fo'c'sle was full of a misty light and only an occasional sniff from Behag broke the steady pulsing of the engine and its accompanying clatter of enamel plates. It was with regret that I heard the home mooring being picked up and the engine switched off.

'I'm feelin' a change in the weather tonight,' said Erchy as we walked up from the shore.

'That's not what the forecasters are saying on the wireless,' I told him. 'They said only this morning that there was no sign of a break yet.'

'Ach, I don't care what the forecasters is sayin',' Erchy maintained. 'I can feel it kind of different an' your feelin's is a lot better than forecasts.'

'Aye,' agreed Hector soberly, 'an' tsey feel a lot furszer ahead.'

Two mornings later I awoke feeling that there was indeed a change. The light in my bedroom was sad and grey and there was the old familiar dripping of rain. Pulling back the curtains I saw that in the night the thaw had come leaving the moors as full of tracks as an up-turned palm while the hills wept snowy tears. It rained relentlessly the whole of that day and the next day, which was a Sunday, the rain was accompanied by a truculent wind which came at us in great rushes that nearly caught us off balance as we trudged the sodden ground. Work done, I stayed snug in my cottage with a Howard Spring and a box of marshmallows for company and saw without contrition the good folk of the village trailing drably through the semi-dusk to church.

'I came to bring you this skart,' said Morag on Monday morning. 'Hector shot it on Saturday so you'll be able to cook it tomorrow.'

I thanked her and, taking the bird from her, hung it behind the kitchen door.

'An' do you know who lowered himself to come to our church last night?' she demanded with scarcely concealed amusement.

I shook my head.

'Well then, it was Euan! Him that's been sayin' ours is a dirty old church an' has been takin' to goin' to the other one at the far end of the village.'

'Good gracious!' I exclaimed. 'What's made him change back again, I wonder?'

'That's what I said to him just. "Euan," I asked him, "why are you not at your own church tonight when you've been sayin' it's so much better than ours an' that the missionary student fellow is such a good man?" An' do you know, Miss Peckwitt, he just blinked his eyes at me an' he said: "What would I be doin' walkin' all that bloody way on a night like this? Is it daft you think I am?" '

The Nurse

THE nurse was extremely irate.

'What I don't do for these people here,' she complained loudly in a voice that sounded to me to be permanently pitched to a tone of grievance. 'And what thanks do I get for it? The way they treat me sometimes anybody would think I was trying to make them worse instead of better,' she elucidated with unwitting accuracy.

Our nurse was a fussy, prudish little woman with an occupational flush on her face and a halo of springy white curls that were only partly repressed by the severity of her dark blue felt hat. She must, when she was young, have been extremely pretty. She was still, if you took her feature by feature, a pretty woman but at fifty she had already achieved an appearance of senility by her splayed-foot walk, her habit of peering over the tops of her spectacles and by the looseness of her pouting mouth.

I tipped the pail of shingle I had just carried up from the shore on to the path I was making and invited her inside for a 'strupak', the resentment I felt at having to leave off just when I was full of energy for my work being somewhat mitigated by the prospect of a couple of hours of indiscreet but very revealing gossip about my neighbours.

Though a Scot, the nurse was, like myself, a 'foreigner' in Bruach and despite the fact that she had been residing among them for over twelve years she was not perceptibly nearer dispelling the prejudice of the crofters than she had been during her first twelve weeks. Undoubtedly for a stranger the task of nursing Bruachites was a difficult one—they could be testy enough on occasion—but so far as the crofters were concerned the nurse's chief disadvantage was that she did not speak their language: she 'hadn't the Gaelic'. If they became ill it might be too much of an effort to translate their needs into English, a complaint I felt was justified as it was obvious that however good their English they still thought in Gaelic and then effected the translation. Had the language difficulty been the only obstacle there is little doubt that time would have established a sufficiently cordial relationship, but time had elicited the fact that the nurse's shortcomings included an insatiable curiosity and an incorrigible tendency to gossip, so that despite her assiduous attentions when she was called in many of the Bruachites preferred to keep quiet about their ailments and to recover or die without her aid in either direction.

'Did you hear what Alistair Beag had the cheek to say to me yesterday?' Nurse challenged me shrilly when she was seated.

I had heard, and like everyone else had been secretly delighted at its aptness but, turning my back to her while I filled the kettle, I professed ignorance.

'He told me I'd been here too long,' she declared, her voice brimming with outrage. 'In fact he shouted after me as I was leaving the house so that everybody could hear. "Away back to your bosses," he yelled at me. "Away back and tell them they should change the nurse here every three years the same as they do the bull!"' Her rather guileless blue eyes filled suddenly with tears and I felt a great pity for her. It was my impression that she had come to the village originally with the genuine aspiration to become a loved and respected figure— an Alma Mater to whom everyone would unhesitatingly turn in sickness or in trouble. The mixture of tolerance, pity and open antagonism that she had achieved must have been for her a bitter disappointment.

'I expect he was only saying it in fun,' I consoled. 'He says the most offensive things to me sometimes. It's just the sort of man he is.' I went on to tell her how a few days previously, having been particularly forgetful, I had been coming home from the village shop for the third time within a few hours when old Murdoch, who had been surveying the life of the community from the vantage point of his storm-damaged roof, had called out: 'Why, Miss Peckwitt! What are you at? You're here, there and everywhere today, just like the mavis.' Even while I was bestowing upon him a grin of fatuous appreciation the voice of Alistair Beag, who was hidden from me by the stone dyke he was rebuilding, had corroborated chummily, 'Aye, aye, she's been dodgin' about like a fart in a colander.'

The nurse appeared to be shocked. 'That's what I dislike so about them!' she exclaimed. 'They're so coarse! And they're immoral,' she went on. 'They blaspheme something terrible, and if they get near a pub they drink themselves silly. And then when the missionary comes round they sit there with their bibles on their knees and pretend they'd never think a dirty thought nor use a bad word. They're utter hypocrites!' She paused only while I refilled her cup. 'Of course,' she added, 'I see a lot more of what goes on than you do.'

'Of course,' I agreed.

'Hypocrites,' she repeated distastefully.

'Some of them aren't so bad,' I demurred.

'They're still hypocrites, even the best of them,' she insisted. 'Look at Anna there. She's what I'd call a really good woman. Yet you know she gets her water from the well out on the moor on Sundays instead of from Murdoch's croft right beside the road.'

I nodded. 'I know that,' I said.

'Well, isn't that sheer hypocrisy? She runs out of water but it's wicked to carry water on Sunday. So, sooner than let folks see her, she goes to the well out on the moor.'

I defended: 'But Anna does get extra water in from the well on a Saturday night. I see her regularly. And,' I went on, 'there are so many righteous people with nothing to do on a Sunday except just to pop into Anna's and have her give them tea. That's why she runs short of water.'

'Indeed it is,' agreed the nurse emphatically. 'But honestly, you'd think the Lord never knew a thing about what these folks do except what the missionary tells Him.' She took two or three quick sips at her tea and continued. 'You know Willy who I'm having to go and visit six and seven times a day? It's cancer, of course, and he's dying, as I daresay you know?'

I admitted that I knew, the village having diagnosed Willy's illness and assessed his probable expectation of life before the doctor had been called in, so that they were already speaking of him as though they were reading his obituary notice.

'Well, here's hypocrisy for you,' went on the nurse. 'Willy's in dreadful pain and there's no hope for him whatever but he's a Seceder and their religion doesn't allow the use of drugs. Every time I get near the door of that man's room his wife waylays me. "Now, Nurse," she says, "don't you be givin' him any of those drugs. We believe they're wicked." And then she leans over Willy. "Now, Willy," she says, "don't be askin' Nurse for drugs, you know you'll go to hell if you do." As soon as she's gone out of the room Willy turns to me with the tears and the sweat running off his face. "For God's sake, Nurse," he begs, "give me somethin' to stop the pain, I canna' bear it." '

'How awful,' I murmured. 'What do you do?'

'I give him a shot of morphia,' returned Nurse without hesitation. 'I'm not going to stand by and see a man suffer unnecessarily, religion or no religion.'

'Thank goodness!' I exclaimed. 'It would be awful to think of dear old Willy suffering like that.'

'His wife came in and caught me at it the other day—and nearly snatched the hypodermic from me.' She gave a dry little chuckle. 'She told me I was a vile and sinful woman bent on sending her husband to hell. I'd have laughed at her if I hadn't been so angry myself. Instead I told her to calm herself, it was only water I was giving him.'

'Do you think she believed you?' I asked incredulously.

'No, I don't think she did,' replied the nurse, 'but that's what they're like, these Seceders. They just want somebody else to take the responsibility of being the sinner.' She blew her nose to show she was feeling happier.

I said thoughtfully: 'There must be quite a lot of doctors and nurses who are Seceders. What happens then?'

She gave me a long knowing look from over her spectacles. 'I've worked for one,' she admitted. 'And never again, I hope. Of course, if their patients aren't Seceders they're doomed for hell anyway, so they get whatever drugs the doctor thinks they need. It's when the patient is a Seceder I don't like it.' She shuddered.

'They just let them suffer?' I prompted, hoping for her denial.

'Well, I'll tell you. Maybe you remember Ian Beg, who died not long after you'd come here? Now he was a Seceder, and so was the doctor we had at the time. When Ian was taken ill with cancer he said to the doctor, and I was there beside the bed at the time, "Now, Doctor," he said, "I know I'm dying and I want you to promise me that no matter how much pain I'm in and how much I beg for relief you'll not prescribe drugs for me." The doctor warned him he would probably be in great pain, but Ian was adamant. So the doctor promised. Now I nursed that man till he died and there were times he nearly wrecked the bed in his agony and on a still night you could hear him moaning and crying with pain all over the village. It was

terrible for his wife because she wasn't a Seceder. And it was terrible
for me. I used to beg the doctor when he came to let me give Ian a
shot of morphia but he wouldn't go back on his word. I've known me
and Ian's wife to bury our heads in the hay in the barn to shut out the
sound of his screaming when it was getting towards the end, and the
hay would be wet with our tears after it.' She sighed a tired reminiscent
sigh. 'Dear Lord, how that man suffered,' she said, 'but not one shot
of anything did he have throughout his illness.'

She stared reflectively out of the window and for a few moments
the kitchen was sad with our thoughts. 'Mind you,' she began again,
'there aren't many like Ian. Most of them are firm enough at denying
others the use of drugs but when they get a wee twinge of pain themselves they're soon after me to do something about it.'

While we had been talking the still water of the bay had become
progressively shadowed and I could hear my hens questioning the
delay of their evening feed. I asked the nurse to excuse me while I
attended to them. She looked at the clock. 'I suppose I ought to be
going, really,' she said with obvious reluctance, 'but I'm enjoying my
wee ceilidh, and I've got to go and see to Willy again in an hour's
time. It doesn't seem worth going home in the meantime.'

I suggested she should stay.

'Well, I'll need to use your toilet,' she said. 'That is if you've got
one.'

'Of course,' I said, a little indignant.

'There's no "of course" about it,' she retorted. 'I had a friend of
mine staying with me last year and I left her in one of the houses while
I was attending to a patient. She'd been drinking a lot of tea of course
and when she got uncomfortable she asked if she could use their
toilet. The woman looked at her and said straight out, "I'm afraid we
haven't one." My friend was a bit put out and I suppose she couldn't
help showing it. "You haven't one?" she gasped. The old woman
gave her a haughty look and said, "No, we never felt the need of one
yet." Of course that made my friend think they'd only just moved into
the house so she said, "Oh, I see, you haven't been here long, then?"
"Why, yes indeed," the old woman replied. "We've been here twenty-

five years." I just got back into the kitchen then and saw the look on my friend's face. We got out of the house and she turned to me. "Nurse," she said, "that old woman's just told me they've lived here for twenty-five years and they've never needed a lavatory. Aren't they peculiar?" ' Nurse laughed. 'I had to hurry up and explain that their peculiarity wasn't biological, it was just that they always used the calf shed.'

'It amuses me the way they just cut a hole in the front and back of the little boys' pants so that they don't need to use nappies or train them to pot,' I said. 'It's certainly very effective.'

'Sheer bone-idle laziness!' snorted the nurse, who had water laid on in her own house and so was not burdened with the task of carrying every drop needed for washing.

I showed her my 'wee hoosie' as I rushed off to feed the hens and put out hay, praying that Bonny would be waiting at the moor gate when Erchy went to let in his own cows, so that she would come home alone without my having to go looking for her in the dark after the nurse had gone.

'My goodness!' said Nurse admiringly when I came back into the kitchen. 'You're quite civilized with your toilet.'

I laughed. 'It seems a bit barbaric to me still.'

The problem of sewage disposal in Bruach was, as it must be in every sewerless and waterless village, a difficult and distasteful business. Chemical lavatories are not the answer, certainly where there is no man available for emptying them. They are too heavy for a woman to lift when they are even half full and somewhat wasteful of time and chemical if they are emptied more frequently. I had solved the sewage problem by having two adjoining lavatories; an ordinary chemical one for serious visits and an invention of my own for the more flippant occasions. The idea had come when I had started keeping a cow and found that though she was put into her byre sometimes about four o'clock in an afternoon and not let out again until ten o'clock the following morning the shingle bottom of the trench behind her was always completely dry. At first I had thought of calling in the vet but after being adequately reassured by Bonny herself I realized that from the byre the land sloped down to the shore so evidently her urine just ran into the shingle and seeped its way into the sea. I worked on this principle for my second lavatory. First I dug a hole in the shingle floor of my 'wee hoosie' and into the hole I lowered a section of chimney lining that I had begged from old Murdoch. An old galvanized pan with holes punched roughly in its bottom sat in the chimney lining and this was then topped with a substantial box seat. In the 'wee hoosie' I also kept a pail of sea water so that it could be 'flushed' immediately after use. It was a simple arrangement but it worked beautifully, and I use the adverb deliberately for on nights when the sea water was full of 'noctiluca', those minute organisms which give the sea its phosphorescence, I have waited entranced until the last of the scintillating water has gurgled down from the pail, leaving it transformed by a luminous coating that still glowed greenly as I shut the door.

'I'll be coming here more often now that I know you've a nice little place like that,' threatened the nurse. 'I usually have to wait until I get to Janet's up the road there. She lets me use the toilet they have for the tourists in summer,' she explained. 'But you know, Miss Beckwith,' she continued, 'that's where you have it with these people. They've gone to the trouble of building a "wee hoosie" so that the tourists have somwhere to go and they even keep a toilet roll in it. But they have the toilet roll fixed to the ceiling instead of the wall.'

'That's a funny place for it,' I commented.

'Isn't it?' agreed the nurse. 'I said to her: "Janet," I said, "why on earth do you keep the toilet roll up on the ceiling? It's awful hard for a wee body like myself to reach up there when I want it." "Well, Nurse," she told me, "it's like this. Shamus keeps his pet sheep in there at night and if I don't have the toilet roll way up out of its reach the beast has eaten the lot by morning." '

'If they have a shed it mustn't be wasted,' I observed with a smile; 'and really I suppose it's understandable. A "wee hoosie" is only a status symbol that their children insist on when they come home from university. You'll notice that a house where there are no young folk doesn't usually have even the crudest of privies. The old folk seem to find it unnatural to shut themselves up in a confined space to relieve themselves.'

'Yes.' The nurse nodded vigorously. 'But when they're getting older and they don't want to face the storms, that's when the trouble begins. Then it's "Nurse, Nurse, I haven't cacced for days, will ye give me a dose?" You'd wonder too at the amount of calomel it takes to shift them.' She sighed. 'Oh, well, I suppose I must go and give Willy his injection——' She broke off. 'Goodness, I've just remembered I'd promised the teacher I'd go down and inspect the children's heads today. She's been complaining about them.'

I looked at her without speaking.

'They were in a shocking state when I attended to them before.'

'How do they get them?' I asked. 'Most of the houses seem to be pretty clean.'

'It's just the one or two that aren't that cause the trouble,' she said. 'I always have to undress on a sheet when I've been anywhere near them.' She moved a few steps towards the door, still loath to say good night. 'Dear knows what time I'll get home tonight,' she said with her hand on the latch. 'I have to go and see Barabal yet. I suppose you've heard about Barabal?'

'No!' I said with some surprise. 'Is she ill?'

'No,' replied the nurse with a look that was meant to convey something out of the ordinary. 'She's not ill but the doctor went to see her last week.'

'But why did the doctor go to see her if she's not ill?' I felt foolish the moment the question was off my lips.

'Well, I mustn't say in my position, must I? But you'd think she'd have had more sense at her age.' The nurse's mouth collapsed into a droop of disapproval but her eyes regarded me eagerly from above the spectacles.

'Well, I never!' I said, lapping it all up without a qualm of conscience. 'Is Barabal married?'

'Not at all.' The nurse's tone implied that no man would have been fool enough to marry Barabal.

'Who's the father supposed to be, then?' I asked, overcome with curiosity.

'Nobody here anyway. They say she went to Glasgow for it.' The nurse was still contemptuous. 'She was there for a couple of months in the summer, anyway.' She opened the door and stepped out into a drizzle of dusky rain. 'I wish I'd remembered about Barabal being Alistair Beag's sister when he was shouting insults at me the other day,' she said. 'I could have told him if anyone had been anywhere too long it was his sister in Glasgow.' She got halfway down the path and I stood in the doorway watching her. 'Change the nurse like they change the bull, indeed,' she was muttering as she went out through the gate. 'I wish I'd remembered it.'

Kirsty

'ACH, that woman!' commented Morag.

I had just told her that I was on my way to visit Kirsty, Johnny Comic's sister, to see if she would sell me a bag of potatoes.

'Aye,' went on Morag, 'I doubt she'll sell you a bag, though she'd have but one left to do herself. Let her see your money an' she'll not be able to say no to you.'

Morag was standing in the doorway of her cottage, bending over a rubbing-board which stood in a zinc bath of soapy water. The washed clothes she had flung aside into another tin bath which stood outside catching the wind-harried douche of water from a piece of leaky guttering, for it was still raining torrentially. (In Bruach where there was no piped water we washed on wet days and, if it was calm enough, optimistically hung out the washing on the line to wait for the dry day that would come. With this treatment—sometimes hours, sometimes days, of crystal clear rain coursing through them—our clothes needed no artificial bleaches to get that 'extra whiteness'.)

'You do dislike Kirsty, don't you?' I said. Morag looked shocked.

'Ach, it's no' that I mislike her at all. It's just the way of her.'

'What way?' I asked.

'Well, mo ghaoil, I'm tellin' you, she's that grand seemin' an' whenever any of us women hereabouts that's been in service go to speak to her we always get the feelin' that the first thing she's goin' to say to us is, "And can you do a little flannel washing, my dear?"' She stretched her neck and screwed up her lips to convey the condescension of a duchess and looked at me to see if I understood. 'It's what the mistresses always used to ask when I was girl in service,' she supplied by way of explanation.

'Was Kirsty never in service herself?' I asked.

'No, indeed, she was not. Not service as we knew it, anyway. All my fine Kirsty did was to push one of them rich invalid ladies around in a wheelbarrow.' She tossed her head haughtily. Drawing aside the bath so that I could step round it, she resumed, 'I saw you comin' so I called to Erchy to pour out a cup of tea for you.' Erchy was sitting on the bench under the window with his elbows resting on the back of it. He had taken off his oilskins but his cap was still on his head, pushed well back so that it would not drip over his face. With a limp gesture of acknowledgement he indicated that the cup of tea beside him on the bench was for me.

Opposite Erchy and within convenient spitting distance of the fire sat Neilly Ally, an old uncle of Morag's, who had arrived unheralded on the bus one evening, as crofters' relatives appeared to have a habit of doing, and who had been in semi-residence with her ever since. He took his pipe out of his mouth briefly to say 'Aye' by way of greeting. Although Neilly had lived in Glasgow for over fifty years he had not shed the aura of the croft and, sitting there with his disordered white hair, his blue seaman's jersey and his dark crumpled trousers he looked as though he might just have come in from the shore after hauling his boat. There was a bowl of soapy water on the floor beside him—another acknowledgement of the bounteous rain—and his newly washed feet resting on the slab of driftwood that did duty as a kerb looked as though they had been more accustomed to paddling in peaty burns than treading Glasgow's pavements. In the intervals of puffing his pipe and spitting uninhibitedly he was engaged in scraping the tar off a netting needle, a task which appeared to require a disproportionate amount of concentration.

'Well,' said Erchy, rousing himself, 'are you pleased with the weather?'

'I am not,' I replied. 'I'm tired of this rain, rain, rain, day after day. I can't get anything done.'

Neilly Ally ceased his scraping momentarily. ' 'Tis no' as bad as in the Bible when it rained forty days and forty nights,' he soothed.

'How do you know? You weren't there,' said Erchy pertly.

The old man stared aloofly through the window above Erchy's head. 'Was I no', then?' he enquired in a tone that implied there could be some doubt about it, and glancing again at his white spongy-looking feet I almost believed there might be.

Morag came in, wiping her hands on the edges of her coat. 'You're not sittin' down, Miss Peckwitt,' she chided me.

'Not as wet as I am,' I told her. 'I'm more comfortable standing.'

She picked up the teapot and tilting it drained the remains of the tea into her own cup.

'This weather,' she grumbled. 'You'd think the sky would have got tired of flingin' the rain at us the way it's been doin'. I don't remember weather like this when I was a girl. Wind we had, but not all this rain.'

'They say the bombs has changed it all,' put in Erchy, 'but ach, I don't believe it's that at all.'

Neilly, who had been sitting in an offended silence since Erchy's previous remark, now sat up. With great deliberation he put the netting needle on the table and placed his pipe beside it.

' 'Tis no' the bombs,' he pronounced, fixing us with an impressive blue gaze. 'It started before the bombs, I can tell you.'

'Aye?' encouraged Erchy.

'I'm tellin' you, what spoiled the weather altogether was when that ship the *Titanic* hit that iceberg. The weather's never been the same since that day.' He fitted his pipe back between his lips and took up his netting needle again, indifferent to our varied expressions.

'Aye?' murmured Erchy politely.

'Aye?' repeated Morag curiously.

'Aye?' I echoed faintly.

Erchy changed the subject. 'Did I hear you sayin' you was goin' to Tornish?' His voice was only faintly interrogative.

'Yes, I'm going to call on Kirsty.'

'Ach, that woman!' spluttered Erchy through a mouthful of tea.

It was always the same whenever anyone mentioned the name of Kirsty. 'Ach, that woman!' would be the rejoinder. The tone might be disparaging, combative, outraged or contemptuous but the phrase prefaced any further comment no matter how her name cropped up in the conversation, and it amused me that the woman should appear to go out of her way to get herself so much disliked.

Sooner or later Kirsty mortally offended everyone with whom she came into contact and yet the strange thing was that she was never ostracized. It would be safe to say, I think, that she was completely unloved but never hated. The women disliked her intensely during the few minutes' altercation she permitted herself to have with them from time to time and from which she always emerged victorious. The men detested her temporarily and mumbled epithets for a few days after she had humiliated them, which she did with great deliberation but without apparent malice. But her acid comments on neighbours were too much relished for enlivening the ceilidhs for there to be any risk of her being ignored for long and her reputation for always providing a 'good dram' for any man who did an odd job for her ensured that she was well looked after.

A rigid Presbyterian, she had been known to refuse point blank a lift from church in a visitor's car one stormy Sabbath with the words: 'Some may not care what becomes of their souls but others know what is right from what is wrong.' And when the much discomfited minister had put his head out of the window of the car and assured Kirsty that it was no sin—'Wasn't he himself taking the chance of it?' —she had shrivelled him back into his seat with the retort, 'Maybe it is no sin for you, but I'm takin' no risks with my soul.' The rest of the congregation still within earshot had been quietly outraged. As they said afterwards, 'Wasn't it a wild wet night anyway for such a walk an' after all wasn't the minister himself only gettin' a lift to Kirsty's own house where he always lodged on a Sunday night because there was no bus back to his village until the Monday morning, poor man.' I have often wondered which of them asked the blessing on the cold supper they would have shared that night.

Erchy stood up. 'Ach, if you're goin' that way I suppose I might just as well come with you,' he volunteered, setting his cap with the peak at the back in deference to the wild weather. 'I was thinkin' it was time I went to see Dugan about some rams an' it's on my way.'

'See and take care Kirsty doesn't get a hold of you,' Morag called out to him insinuatingly as we started off.

'Hell, no!' returned Erchy. He bestowed upon me what from someone less unsophisticated might have been a leer but from him was only a crumpled smile.

'You heard about that?' he asked me.

'No,' I said, 'tell me.'

'Well, I'd just done a bit of cementin' for her. That bit of path you mind, down by her shed. When I'd finished she had my strupak ready an' we had a wee ceilidh an' then she poured me out a good dram. She didn't take one herself an' I was sittin' by the fire drinkin' mine down an' feelin' good inside when she said all of a sudden, "Erchie, did I ever tell you about the time I saw a naked man?" God! I near

dropped the glass out of my hand I was that scared, an' I was sweatin'
that much I thought the drops would run down an' spoil my whisky.'
(I should perhaps mention that in Gaeldom there is no age at which
a woman ceases to be regarded as a seductress.) 'Then she went on
tellin' me that when she was a girl she was standin' on the shore an'
she saw a man come out of the water an' walk up the beach an' he had
nothin' on at all! She ran all the way home an' told her mother an' all
her mother did was to give her a good thrashin' for not shuttin' her
eyes. I can tell you,' said Erchy with a grunt, 'I finished my whisky
an' grabbed my coat an' was off out of the house as fast as I could go,
an' that old cailleach just stood in the door an' watched me an' she was
laughin' that funny way she has, you know? Indeed, I believe she did
it on purpose, just to see me sweat.'

We picked our way through the rivulet that was normally a dry
sheep-track to the open moor where the wind, still full of the smell of
tangle, doubled its strength, threatening to tear the buttons off our
oilskins, whipping our clothes against our legs and rattling the rain
against our sou'westers, so that all other sound than the plodding of
our boots was shut out. With chins tucked resolutely down into our
coat collars and gloved hands hooked into pockets (the latter filled
with rain too easily to plunge our hands deep into them) we battled
to the comparative shelter of the glen where the track was less exacting
and I was able to forge ahead of Erchy. Although I never found the
prospect of walking the moors in a storm remotely inviting there was
at times, I confess, something almost pleasantly hypnotic about it once
I had accepted the necessity for my journey and was well and truly
embarked upon it. Shut inside oilskins and sou'wester and hearing
nothing but the rain, one has the feeling of being insulated not only
from the weather but from the world in general. Because superfluous
movement would expose chinks in the carefully disposed insulation
one limits one's gaze to the path immediately in front of one's feet. In
any case there is no perceptible movement to distract one's eye. The
ubiquitous rabbits, the busy shrews, the sinuous stoats, are all snug
in their secret places. The cattle and sheep, having found a sheltered
corrie, lie there, patiently cudding. There are no trees on the moors

to be lashed into dervish dances; no tatters of bracken whirling on the wind. Everything that is not securely anchored has been wrested away in the first few hours of the storm. So, one plods on tranquilly, building and rebuilding a lifetime of dreams while one's feet seem to stride without conscious effort over the stiff black heather roots and the flayed grass, so abject in its surrender.

'Hi!'

I halted guiltily as I heard Erchy's shout, for I had forgotten all about him.

'My,' he grumbled as he panted up to me. 'You're a fast woman.'

I smiled at him.

'Aye, you can laugh, but folks shouldn't rush like that over these moors. You'll get heart trouble or somethin'. That's why people here live so long, you know. It's because they never hurry.' His face was peony red with exertion and polished by the rain.

Realizing that I too was breathless, I slowed my pace and so it was nearly half an hour later than I had reckoned before we started to come down the hill and could see the stone dykes and croft houses of the village.

'Kirsty's croft isn't a very big one, is it?' I asked Erchy, for now we were in the shelter of the hill and could converse without too much effort.

'Ach, she's no' needin' a very big one. She only keeps the one cow anyway an' if she thinks her hay's a wee bit short she just helps herself to what's on other people's crofts.'

'No!' I protested.

'Aye, she does indeed. My uncle used to have the croft next to her but he gave it up because of her. When he'd go to cut his hay he'd find Kirsty had cut that much of it over his boundary—an' the best of it, too.'

'But he could have stopped her, surely?'

'You cannot stop that woman doin' anythin' she's set her mind to,' said Erchy. 'When he spoke to her about it she just reared herself up the way she does an' told him she'd cut hay wherever she wanted.

"But that's my own croft I pay rent for," my uncle told her, "an' that grass you've cut was growin' on my own land." "Indeed," Kirsty says to him, "supposin' it was growin' on your own chin, I'd still cut it." My uncle was that mad about it but there was nothin' he could do except complain to the Land Court an' they wouldn't have been able to stop her from doin' it. They would only have told her not to.'

We came in sight of Kirsty's cottage, easily identifiable by its pie-bald appearance. Johnny had been directed to cement-wash it during the summer and had almost completed the task when he had discovered a large and beautiful spider's web suspended from the guttering. Unable to bring himself to destroy it he had left that part of the wall uncemented and by the time Kirsty had returned to coerce him the rain had started and it had been raining off and on ever since.

'Poor Johnny Comic,' I said, for in contrast to the excessive gentleness of Johnny's nature Kirsty was rock hard. She had been twelve years old when her brother was born and, perhaps because her mother had never fully recovered after the event and had died less than a year later, it seemed as if she had never forgiven him for the presumptuousness of being born at all. Six years later their father had died and Kirsty at eighteen had been left to cope alone with the infant Johnny. People said that from that time she seemed to have become obsessed with the idea of thwarting his every wish, and though she had fed him adequately, clothed him and kept him clean, his presence in the house had irritated her and thus Johnny's wanderings had begun at an early age. When he returned home he was given his porridge and boiled egg meal and unrelentingly sent to bed, no matter if it was only six o'clock in the evening. He had been so repressed that even when he was a grown man he was too docile to protest at the arrangement and so it had continued for nearly sixty years. He was allowed no money of his own although Kirsty's income, thanks to a small annuity left to her by the 'lady in the wheelbarrow', was more than adequate for their standard of living. The only indulgence she permitted her brother was a grudging access to the tin of baking-soda in her cupboard, and even this small comfort was hidden away if she considered his consumption excessive.

'You'd think she'd let Johnny keep a pet of some sort,' Erchy said. 'It wouldn't do her any harm an' it would be good for Johnny.'

'Someone did give him a baby rabbit a little while ago,' I said. 'Wasn't he allowed to keep that?'

'No, indeed. Kirsty killed it as soon as she could get a hold of it.'

'She's a real bitch!' I said feelingly, recalling the rapt expression on Johnny's face when he was fondling a cat or a dog and his anguish when he found an injured bird.

'Look at the way she was last year with that bird's nest,' continued Erchy. 'While she was away seein' her cousin last spring the birds built a nest in the chimney of "the room". Johnny was up to it every day on a ladder watchin' it. When the birds was just about ready to fly Kirsty came home an' sees it, an' though I believe Johnny went down on his knees pleadin' with her to wait only a couple of days for them to leave the nest Kirsty just took paper an' paraffin an' lit a roarin' fire in the grate an' roasted the poor wee things to death.'

We opened the gate to the grassy plot that Kirsty kept trimmed so expertly by means of a hay scythe and she herself appeared on the doorstep. Her face expressed surprise but I suspected she had seen us coming. She had in her hand a barometer which she held up in the rain.

'Look at that!' she addressed it crossly as we came within earshot. 'Take a good look at it, will you, an' then dare to tell me it's fair weather!' Giving it an admonitory shake before hooking it savagely back on the wall in the porch she turned to us. 'That thing has a face full of lies,' she said.

Erchy turned and winked at me, while Kirsty, satisfied she had given him a good story for the next ceilidh, bade us take off our dripping oilskins and 'come away inside'.

The kitchen into which she led us was blatant in its discomfort. The wooden walls were painted a shiny gasometer green and were completely unrelieved by pictures or hangings of any sort except for an embroidered cloth bag which bulged with mail-order catalogues. These, with the Bible and hymn-book prominent on the window-sill, were the only literature Kirsty permitted herself. The linoleum too was shiny and green and sketchily patterned with small dark circles that reminded me of the eyes of a moribund sheep. The table was covered with American cloth, white and new-looking; the big black range gleamed with polish; the cushionless wooden chairs and the bench shone with many coats of varnish. The whole place looked almost sterile in its cleanliness and about as comfortless and un-inviting as a fishmonger's empty slab.

Kirsty swung the big kettle over the huddle of peats which were smouldering apologetically in the grate. She next dipped some pieces of driftwood into a can of paraffin that stood in a corner of the room and then poked them carefully between the peats. Bending down she blew with big capable breaths, quickly coaxing them into flame. The kettle began to send forth a subdued spout of steam.

'I'm sayin' the peats didn't get properly dry at all this year, the weather's been that bad,' Kirsty said.

Erchy and I looked at each other understandingly. We knew that she claimed more peat hags, cut more peats and yet used fewer than anyone else in the village. We knew that the big shed at the back of the house was bulging with dry peats left over from the previous year's cutting and that the complaint of wet peats was only an excuse for the meagreness of the fire.

She set out one of her best cups for me and an old chipped one for Erchy. Let it be said that neither he nor I felt we could manage an-other strupak coming so soon after the one we had taken with Morag but we sat and meekly watched Kirsty brewing tea and buttering oat-cakes without so much as a whisper of protest from either of us. She poured out a cup of tea for herself but as it was an inflexible rule with her never to eat or drink anything while there was still steam coming from it she took up some crochet work and talked to us with con-descending affability while we sipped and ate. She appeared to do a great deal of crocheting although there was no evidence of a finished article to break the austerity of the room. I wondered how she dis-posed of it as I watched her large male-looking hands weaving the fine threads into intricate patterns of scrolls and scallops with enviable dexterity.

Kirsty was an impressive woman, now in her seventies yet still standing nearly six foot tall. Like her brother she had a pale, fine skin and very large hands but there any resemblance between them ended. Kirsty's pale grey eyes could have been put in by a glazier. Her mouth was like a tight-drawn thread. Her black hair which one felt had never had the temerity to turn grey seemed only to have rusted at the ends and was clamped to her head, pancake fashion, and stuck with so many pins it made one think of an ancient cow-pat that the starlings had been foraging in. She was dressed, as always, in black relieved only by a chit of white at the throat on which a jet brooch was pinned with geometric care, and it was this slight adornment, I think, as much as anything else that underlined her appearance of hauteur and made it easy to understand Morag's reference to 'flannel-washing'.

I was about to broach the subject of potatoes when Kirsty gave a faint exclamation of impatience and withdrawing the crochet hook from her work she pushed it between her lips.

'Miss Peckwitt,' she said, 'I have what is like a soreness in my teeths here. I believe it must be what they call "the toothache".'

I was a shade surprised to hear Kirsty admit to any physical discomfort and was temporarily at a loss for words.

Erchy came to the rescue. 'You'll need to go to the doctor and get it sorted,' he told her.

'Indeed I will not then,' she replied with asperity.

'It'll be much better to get it seen to,' I murmured. 'The doctor will surely see to it as you're so far from a dentist.'

Kirsty crocheted industriously for a few moments and then she said: 'The last time I went to the doctor I was twelve or thereabouts. I'd cut my thumb near off on the scythe, for we'd been cuttin' the corn. Look at that, now!' She showed us the distorted thumb on her right hand. 'It was hangin' right back against my hand, if you can believe it,' she continued, 'and my father said I was to go and see the doctor with it. He walked with me himself to the surgery and that's near fourteen miles, and there I had it put back on and stitched into place. The doctor gave me nothin' to help the pain and he said I was so quiet about it he'd give me a sweetie to suck to help pass the time while I was walkin' back home. It was one of them big sweeties, I forget what you call them, but I mind I didn't feel like eatin' it until I got nearly home again. When I did put it into my mouth and bit it, it was that hard I broke two of my teeths on it and my mouth started to bleed like I would bleed to death. My father just turned me round and walked me all the way back to the doctor's again. I've never been near their kind since.'

At that moment there was a stamping of feet in the porch and Johnny Comic came into the kitchen. He had obviously tramped a long way home and the rain was dripping from his cap and running from his oilskin wrappers. He greeted us off-handedly and went straight to the dresser, took down a cup and taking it over to the fire lifted the teapot which Kirsty had refilled with water from the kettle.

'Where's the cow?' Kirsty asked, fixing him with a glacial stare.

'She's at the moor gate,' Johnny replied, pouring tea that was like singed water into his cup.

'Then away and get her,' commanded Kirsty imperiously.

'I'll take this drink first, I'm thirsty,' said Johnny with a bravado that we knew was buttressed by our presence.

'You'll away and get her,' repeated Kirsty. Her expression did not change, her fingers did not falter over her crocheting but her voice had an undertone that apparently was not lost on Johnny. He put down the teapot obediently, took his stick and was about to go through the door when Kirsty called him back.

'You'll not be needin' your stick,' she told him.

'But the bull's there with her,' Johnny began pleadingly. 'I'll never get her away from him without a stick.'

'You'll leave your stick,' repeated Kirsty.

Johnny's face crumpled but he left the stick by the door and shambled out. 'If he takes the stick I cannot trust him not to lay it across the cow,' she explained.

Erchy and I exchanged glances. It was ridiculous for her to suggest that gentle old Johnny would beat an animal. We knew and Kirsty knew that he wanted the stick only for brandishing in front of the

bull if the animal was determined to follow, for he was timid where
the larger animals were concerned. But there revealed was Kirsty's
one weakness. Her cow. It and it only had found the one flaw in her
petrified emotions. It was an odd beast of nondescript breed, swag-
bellied, small-hoofed, and with horns that looked like malignant
growths but she had reared it from a calf and she still lavished upon
it all the care and affection that less eccentric natures would have
bestowed upon an only child. She was constantly feeding it tit-bits
from the house and it ate them all. Biscuits, chocolate, cake, cheese,
bread and jam. 'Ach, it's no' a right beast at all to eat them things,'
people were apt to comment. It did seem, even to a tyro like myself,
that the cow was unnatural and many times when I had passed the
cottage I had paused in wonder when I saw its great behind sticking
out of the doorway, only the narrowness of the entrance and the
width of its belly seeming to prevent it from pushing its way into the
spruce kitchen.

So far as Kirsty was concerned the cow could do no wrong. So far
as Johnny was concerned it could do no right. If Johnny had been
capable of hating anything at all he would have hated that cow. As it
was he merely accepted philosophically its domination of the household. He had to cut hay for it, he had to carry water for it, he had to
muck out its byre and drive it to and from the moor when Kirsty did
not fancy the weather and he did it all uncomplainingly and under a
constant barrage of sarcasm from his sister. The only times Johnny
became exasperated were when the cow broke into his beloved flower
garden. In Bruach, where gardens were invariably feeding grounds
for poultry or bone-chewing sanctuaries for the dogs, Johnny's love
of flowers was considered to be just another of his queernesses. It was
quite understandable that Kirsty should have a garden, surrounded by
a barricade impenetrable even for a cow, where she grew excellent
vegetables for sale to the summer tourists, but Johnny's anthomania
they found incomprehensible. It was a pity that the only land he was
allowed to have for his hobby was a small plot at the windward side
of the house where a few sad blackcurrant bushes brooded over the
mouldering stones of a derelict shed. Laboriously he had dug out

enough stones to give him a little soil in which to transplant wild
primroses from the moors or seeds and plants he begged from the
Laird's gardener; but as soon as the plants grew into a green and
tasty mouthful Kirsty's cow would come and with calculating greed
work at his shaky stone dyke until she could break in and devour the
lot. Every year Johnny tried, indifferent to his sister's upbraidings for
wasting his time. Every year the cow outwitted him. Not having any
money to buy fencing he would scrounge old pieces of wire netting
wherever he could and carry shafts of driftwood of formidable size
for miles from the shore to reinforce the dyke, but he never once
succeeded in keeping out the cow until the flowers came into bloom.

There was a bellow from outside of a cow demanding attention.
Kirsty put down her crochet. Erchy and I got up and started to put
on our oilskins. I mentioned the subject of potatoes. She could, it
seemed, let me have a bag to 'see me on'. Much relieved, I took out
my purse.

'Are you wantin' them in a hurry?' she asked.

'Well, yes,' I admitted. 'I've only enough for a couple of days at the
most, and I haven't much else in the way of vegetables either. I wish
I knew your secret of getting vegetables to grow,' I told her.

'They're too damty scared not to,' whispered Erchy in a languid
aside.

I really was envious of Kirsty's garden for in return for all the
attention I bestowed on mine it yielded little more than a few weary
lettuce, half-hearted cabbage and wind-shrivelled beans while hers
seemed to produce near prize-winning specimens with Kirsty doing
little else but act as overseer.

Her thread of a mouth tautened into the vestige of a superior smile.
She more than anyone else had always despised me as too weak and
incompetent to tackle the crofting life and doubtless my admission
confirmed her opinion.

'You'll get your potatoes tomorrow, then,' she promised, and then
as we were leaving she said with sudden cordiality, 'You should come
and ceilidh with me more often.'

'I would,' I told her with shocking insincerity, 'but it's such a long tramp over the hill.' I was conscious of a whimsical look from the corner of Erchy's eye.

' 'Tis nothin' at all,' she scoffed. And as if to prove her statement she arrived at my cottage the very next day with a hundredweight of potatoes strapped to her back. She had carried them all the way over the hill track because she had promised I should have them and the carrier's lorry had broken down.

The Green Halo

It was a ripe, red berry of an autumn day, bloomed with haze and tinged with sunshine and I was busy in my kitchen making jam from brambles which had grown fat and tasteless from the superabundance of summer rain.

'Here, did you hear the news?' demanded Erchy, standing in the doorway and swinging in his hand a large hammer with which he was expecting to do some repairs to Bonny's byre.

'About Peggy?' I asked, for all the village had been laughing yesterday because poor Peggy, who was known to be over ninety and who still worked all the hours God sends, had waylaid the doctor when he was visiting in the village and asked him why she should have become so bent. She never used to be, she told him ingenuously.

'No, indeed. Not about Peggy at all but about Johnny Comic's accident?'

'No!' I said, immediately serious. 'What's happened?'

'He was knocked down by a lorry on the road yesterday an' they've taken him off to hospital.'

'Was he much hurt?' I asked him.

'The nurse didn't seem to think so,' Erchy supplied. 'But they won't know for a day or two till they get the X-rays.' He stayed in the doorway, his sturdy peasant body enclosed by the sunlight. 'Come an' tell me what I'm to do,' he ordered.

'I can't leave this at the moment,' I said, glancing anxiously at the full pan which was bubbling to within half an inch of the rim.

He came over and stood beside the stove.

'You haven't much freeboard there,' he commented. 'I only hope it'll keep calm for you.'

'If, instead of being clever, you would go and look inside the byre you'll see for yourself what needs doing,' I told him with mock severity as I carefully slid the preserving pan away from the heat. He left me to my task and when the jam had achieved a 'jell' I poured it into jars, labelled them and put them in the larder and then stood back to admire. I derive more pleasure from a well-stocked larder than from a well-stocked wardrobe, particularly if the shelves are packed with the result of my own labours, but in Bruach I was denied the satisfaction of attaining a really adequate supply of preserves because there was too much wind for fruit growing and rather more than most vegetables can stand. As a consequence they were always scarce and expensive and so it was a matter of making use of the more despised representatives of the earth's bounty. Elderberries I had already made into jelly and wine and this year the blaeberries which hid themselves in squat leafy clumps in sheltered parts of the moor had been so plentiful that even after the children had sated themselves on them the smell of the neglected berries fermenting in the moss had come to us on a wine-scented breeze. For the brambles I had searched the freckled moors diligently, finding the bushes squandering themselves over and into abandoned peat-hags. Now I awaited the fast-ripening rowan-berries, and hoped to outwit the starlings which each evening gathered in the tree behind the house and smacked their beaks over the feast that was to come.

Morag and the fat and jovial Anna Vic, each with a creel of peats on her back, went past the cottage as I was carrying the preserving pan outside to fill it with rainwater from the tank.

'Put those down a minute and come and have a wee strupak,' I called. 'I'm just going to make one.'

They lowered their creels on to the stone dyke and came through the gate. 'My, but your garden is beautiful just,' Anna Vic observed, and added, 'You English are the great ones for your flowers right enough.'

My garden was certainly looking its best now that a spell of calm weather had at last allowed the flowers to bloom unmolested and, though the winds had shrivelled some plants beyond resuscitation and delay had paled the vividness the rest would have revealed had they managed to flower earlier, they nevertheless made an attractive display. There was variety in the colour of the late lupins and in the gold and yellows of the calendulas while large clumps of honesty held out their flat pods to be silvered by the sunshine. The lupins had been sent to me from England. The seeds of the calendulas and honesty too had been purchased from an English firm and yet, though they may be exactly the same variety and from the same nursery, the flowers in a Hebridean garden never seem to achieve the poise and glamour of the flowers in an English garden. Their stems grow stockier, perhaps because of their continual struggle with the storms. The blooms are always either wind harried or rain stressed but when they do burst into flower there is about them a buoyancy and virility which suggest that they too might have shed some of the constraint of English life.

My two friends sat down and when I had brewed tea I called Erchy to come in for a cup. With him came Donald Beag who had, surprisingly, mislaid the hook that did duty for one of his arms and who had been on his way to the shore where he thought he might have left it.

Erchy was glancing ruefully down at the bottom of his trouser leg which he had caught on a nail in the byre and torn. He asked whether there were any tinkers in the vicinity from whom he might get a new pair.

'There was one in the village yesterday,' Anna Vic told him. 'But he had nothin' but things for the children except for some nighties.' Her voice became shrill. 'He was wantin' me to buy a nightie from him. "I don't want a nightie," I told him. But ah, he kept on at me, "Buy a nightie from me, mistress." "I don't want another nightie," I said, "my drawers is stuffed with nighties." '

'Is that what it is?' interpolated Erchy with a mischievous glance at her well-padded hips. 'Well, all I çan say is, it's a damty funny place to keep your nighties.'

'You wretch!' Anna Vic flung at him, hovering between amusement and vexation.

'I'll bet you bought a nightie from him all the same,' I challenged her, for her heart was pure gold.

'Ach, well, you don't like to send them away without takin' anythin' from them an' it was no use me buyin' children's clothes.'

'I wish I could hear of the same tink as I got this pair from,' said Erchy, looking down at his torn trousers again. 'Maybe he doesn't look much good now but he was a good trouser when he was new.'

The talk soon switched to Johnny Comic's accident.

'However did he come to be knocked down by a lorry?' said I, thinking of the deserted Bruach road which saw a lorry about three or four times a week at its busiest.

'Ach, the driver says he wasn't there one minute an' the next he's just down in front of the wheel. He thinks Johnny was standin' up on the dyke beside the road there an' either a bit of the dyke slipped or Johnny just tripped an' fell down,' said Morag.

'It's a bad business, anyway,' said Donald. 'An old man like that havin' to go to hospital.'

'The nurse said she didn't think anythin' was broken,' Morag assured us.

'If he's nothin' broken yet then they'll break somethin' for him in hospital,' said Donald, with conviction. 'They'll not have him in there with nothin' wrong with him.'

'Ach, likely they'll give him a dose of castor oil an' send him home in a day or two,' said Erchy. 'I believe that's an awful lot of what they do in hospitals.'

'Castor oil,' said Donald reminiscently. 'I mind when I had my arm off the surgeon said I'd had too much castor oil. Likely I had, too, for I used to take a couple of big spoonsful of it every few days then. I reckon that's what kept me fit while I was at the war, anyway.'

'A couple of spoonsful of it every few days!' remonstrated Anna Vic. 'Surely a body had no need of that amount at all?'

'Aye, well, the nurses tried to stop me but I didn't take any notice of them. Then when this surgeon was takin' the dressin' off my arm he said to me, "Donald," he says, "have you been taking castor oil?" "Aye," I told him, "I have a dose every now and then." "Good God, Donald!" he says. "You've been taking that much you've got it all through your system and it's comin' out of your arm here. You must stop it right away or it'll never heal." He showed me the dressin' with all this oil on it—you could see it plain as anythin'. That's as true as I'm here an' I've never taken another dose of castor oil since,' Donald concluded, taking a hearty bite out of a scone.

'Johnny wouldn't be needin' castor oil so long as he can get bakin'-soda,' said Morag, when we had digested Donald's story. 'The way that man eats it you'd surely wonder he had a stomach left.'

'It's a damty good stomach when you think what he puts into it,' Erchy defended as he got up to go and resume work.

Donald too stood up. 'I'd best go an' seek my arm,' he told us, 'for if I don't find it I'll need to get the doctor to give me a new one.'

'Best get him to give you a new head, then, while he's at it,' suggested Erchy impudently.

I was still thinking of Johnny Comic and of an article I had recently read which claimed that a Russian doctor had discovered that a daily dose of bicarbonate of soda prolonged life, and I mentioned this as we all straggled out into the garden, Morag and Anna Vic to take up the burden of their creels once more and Donald to continue his search for his hook.

'If that's true then Johnny Comic should live for another hundred years,' said Morag with a chuckle.

The next day Bruach was dumbfounded by the news that Johnny Comic had passed away during the night.

'An' did you hear what Kirsty said when she heard it?' Erchy demanded. 'She said, "Ach, he was always the same, any little thing killed him." '

We exchanged horrified glances.

'Aye, well,' resumed Erchy with complete matter-of-factness, 'I'm glad he's died in hospital so I won't have to go and shave him.'

'Why do you always go and shave people when they're dead?' I asked him curiously. 'Is it some superstition you have?' I was remembering that when Sandy had died Erchy had gone up to shave him on the day he died and then again on the eve of the funeral.

'But the beard grows after they're dead,' Erchy explained. 'An' these Seceders don't like the nurse to touch them once they've gone.'

I asked when the funeral was to be.

'It should be tomorrow,' he told me, 'but the undertaker sent word this mornin' that he was at a dance last night so he couldn't get the coffin ready in time. Now they're goin' to bury him on Thursday. We have to go tonight to dig a grave for him, though God knows where we'll find a place for him.'

'This village really does need a new burial ground,' I agreed. 'It's more like a rabbit warren than a cemetery.'

'Aye, an' the way you can hear the rabbits runnin' over the coffins in the graves there! It's terrible just.' He lit a cigarette. 'Aye, well, I expect we'll find a place for him up by the trees there. It's a bit away from the rest but I daresay there'll be others to keep him company soon enough.'

Thursday morning was full of early mist and when it had dispersed the heather clumps still held their nebulous quota in innumerable spiders' webs. Early mist usually presages a fine day and I hurried back from milking Bonny for, partly to see for myself Kirsty's reaction to the death of her brother and partly to please Morag, I had promised to go to the funeral. It was arranged that I should call for Morag at eleven o'clock but as I turned in at the gate of my cottage there was an agitated flutter of starlings from the rowan tree and I realized that, funeral or no funeral, unless I gathered my rowanberries right away the birds would have stripped the lot before I returned. I put down the milk pail, grabbed a step-ladder and started to pick. There can be few sights more beautiful, more arresting, than a rowan tree in autumn with its profusion of red berries glowing against the tawny foliage. And Hebridean rowanberries seem to be so much more colourful than any others. As I harvested them I thought I had never seen them so vibrantly red as they were this year and looking at them in the palm of my hand I half expected to see their tiny pulses beating. When the basket was full there were still plenty left for the starlings and when, at the garden gate, I turned to look back at the cottage, the roof was spiky with birds awaiting my departure before re-commencing their banquet.

The first thing I noticed when Morag and I came in sight of Kirsty's cottage was the patch of bright colour where Johnny's garden had always been. I remarked on it to my companion.

'Aye, well, you mind Kirsty's cow has been that sick for two or three weeks past an' she's not had it stirrin' out of the byre.'

I didn't 'mind' for no one had thought to mention it.

'Poor Johnny,' I said. 'This must be about the first time he's managed to get flowers to bloom in his garden and now he's not here to see them.'

'Aye, it's a shame right enough,' agreed Morag. 'An' it's a shame about the beast too, for I'm hearin' she's not wantin' to eat anythin' let alone break into Johnny's garden to spoil his flowers for him.'

'They're lupins too,' I said as we drew near enough to identify them. 'I remember him telling me how the laird's gardener had given him some plants and he was so thrilled about it at the time.'

'An' just look at them,' Morag said. 'It's as though they know Johnny's dead for they're screamin' out loud with their bloomin'.'

The tiny kitchen of Kirsty's house was packed and overflowing with women all supporting or being supported by one another for everyone had been exceedingly fond of Johnny. The older women were dressed in black but the clothes of the younger women made a startling knot of colour in their midst. In front of the house the coffin lay across two kitchen chairs and the men stood in a semicircle round it, chattering among themselves and hunching their shoulders against a brisk breeze that burned their cigarettes away too quickly and scattered fragments of glowing red tobacco from their pipes. A couple of sheep dogs kept a wary eye on their masters and scratched themselves dispassionately. There was no sign of Kirsty.

A car drew up and the missionary got out and greeted the assembled crowd with what seemed to me to be unseemly levity. As he walked towards the coffin cigarettes and pipes were stubbed out. Swiftly there fell a silence that was broken only by the mournfully assertive song of a robin, the liquid call of an oystercatcher and the practised whimpering of a weep of Seceders who had detached themselves from the rest of the mourners.

'Where's Kirsty?' the missionary asked.

Everyone glanced about them as though they had not missed her until now and then someone spotted her coming away from the byre. She was dressed in black but her sleeves were rolled up and before she joined us she bent down and wiped her hands on the grass. We all guessed she had been ministering to her cow and there were whispers of enquiry to which she replied with a negative shake of her head. The missionary must have overheard them.

'Is your cow sick, then, Kirsty?' he demanded.

'Aye indeed,' replied Kirsty. 'I'm thinkin' she'll not last the day out.' Her voice was sufficiently funereal to convince everyone of her utter dismay.

'Oh, my, my,' said the missionary in shocked tones.

This particular missionary had often been described to me as 'a good missionary but a better cow doctor', so I was interested to see his reaction. He seemed to consider for a moment, and when he had made up his mind he snapped shut his book and laid it down on top of the coffin. 'Johnny has passed on,' he told us seriously, 'an' he'll take no harm from waitin' there while I go an' take a look at Kirsty's cow,' and rolling up the legs of his good black trousers he picked his way across the dungy path to the byre. Everyone followed in that direction.

'What ails the beast, d'you think, Kirsty?' he asked her.

'Indeed, but I don't know. She must have eaten somethin' strange, I'm thinkin'. She's been stuck fast for the last five days now an' nothin' the vet's sent will move her. I've been expectin' to find her gone each time I've come out to look at her.'

The byre was small and dark but we saw the missionary step over to the cow and feel her bones. Then he stepped back, pulled his black hat over his eyes a little and stared at the beast, biting his lips. Kirsty watched him intently and the mourners crowded closer to the door.

'Kirsty!' said the missionary at last, 'you're surely goin' to lose this beast.'

'Surely,' agreed Kirsty philosophically.

'Well then, as you're goin' to lose her in any case you'll no mind takin' a bitty risk with her?'

Kirsty nodded.

'Now, have you any Epsom salts?'

'Aye, I have some,' Kirsty told him.

'Well, you'll take two pounds of Epsom salts.' There was a gasp from the crowd. 'Now, repeat it as I say it so you'll not get it wrong,' the missionary instructed testily.

'I'll take two packets of Epsom salts,' faltered Kirsty, with un-accustomed submissiveness.

'Two pounds, woman!' the missionary shouted. 'Yon packets you get from the grocer is only about two ounces. You'll need sixteen of them. It's got to be kill or cure.'

'Two pounds of Epsom salts,' repeated Kirsty, meek as a child.

'And four pounds of margarine.'

'Four pounds of margarine.'

I felt Morag gripping my arm and there was no sound from the tense crowd round the door.

'Four pounds of treacle,' the missionary continued inexorably. 'An' when you've mixed them all together you can make it into balls and dip them into oatmeal and give them to her.'

'When will I give it to her?' Kirsty asked.

The missionary looked at the crowd and his eye lighted on Alistair. 'Alistair Mor Ruari!' he addressed him. 'You have long arms and no wife to be girnin' if you mess up your clothes so you can give her the dose right now while I'm here.'

The crowd relaxed and some of the women rushed off to collect the ingredients for the medicine. It seemed only a short time before they were back with a sticky-looking mess in a pail which Kirsty moulded into balls and handed to Alistair who rammed them down the cow's throat one by one.

'Now,' said the missionary when that was done. 'See that the last thing before you go to bed, Kirsty, if the beast's still alive, you'll give her a quart of linseed oil mixed with a pint of turpentine. Now promise you'll do that.'

'Tonight,' Kirsty said with steady emphasis, 'if the Lord spares me, I'll give her a quart of linseed oil and a pint of turpentine.'

'You mean if the Lord spares the cow,' murmured a familiar voice behind me. ' 'Tis no' you, Kirsty, who's takin' the dose.'

There was a faint titter from the crowd which was hushed immediately as the missionary rounded upon them.

'I'm thinkin',' he said, with gruesome practicality, 'if this beast dies in the night she'll be that swollen by mornin' you'll never get her out of this narrow doorway without cuttin' her to pieces first. You'd best just get her down to the bog where there's plenty of soft ground that'll make the buryin' of her easy.'

The men rallied round the cow and carried and pushed the poor emaciated creature down towards the bog. By the time they returned the missionary had reassumed an appropriately obsequial air and commenced to read the burial service.

'I was wonderin',' said Janet hesitantly to Morag and me as we watched the men carrying away the coffin for burial, 'Johnny bein' so fond of his flowers, would we pick them and put them on his grave?' As we approved her thought she suggested it to Kirsty who apparently agreed for a few moments later we saw them gathering armfuls of the blooms and then following the cortège down the road.

We walked home in the September sun, discussing the remarkable 'dose' the missionary had prescribed.

'I doubt the linseed oil alone will be enough to turn the beast inside out,' Morag predicted.

Early on Friday morning I began the rather tedious process of making rowan wine and was putting a great deal of energy into pulping the berries when Erchy arrived.

'Come an' we'll get your cupboard while the tide's high,' he said. 'It'll not be so far to carry it down the shore.'

On one of my beachcombing expeditions I had found washed up a very nice ship's locker which I thought would do very well for a cupboard in my kitchen. It was much too big and heavy for me to carry home alone so I had asked Erchy if he would come with me some time and we would get it home by boat.

We dragged the dinghy down the beach and while Erchy took the oars I huddled in the stern. The morning held the threat of rain over the grey water and the hills looked cold and snuffly with shreds of white cloud clinging about them like discarded paper handkerchiefs. Erchy was uncommunicative and the boat nosed forward with only the squeak of the oars in the rowlocks and the splash of the blades on the water for an accompaniment. A few lethargic raindrops fell, pitting the slack surface of the sea like the enlarged pores in an old woman's face.

Erchy's eyes suddenly became focussed on the land. 'That looks like Kirsty on the shore there,' he said. I twisted round on the thwart and espied a figure hurrying along the edge of the cliff and stopping every few minutes to peer down at the shore. 'I wonder what she's after,' Erchy mused.

'I think she's beckoning us to go in,' I said. 'Do you think she's all right?'

'We'd best go in and see, anyway,' Erchy replied. He steered the boat towards the shore and Kirsty scrambled agilely down the cliff and came towards us. Erchy got out and held the dinghy, greeting her with taut interrogation.

I was struck by her woebegone expression and the muted urgency of her voice. Only once before had I seen Kirsty looking so thoroughly discomfited and that had been when Erchy, stung by some innuendo she had made, had boldly taunted her in front of several people that he 'didn't believe she'd ever had a man up her skirts in her life'. Kirsty, utterly shamefaced, had admitted that she 'didn't believe she ever had'. Now it seemed, as she had not looked much affected by Johnny's funeral yesterday, that something equally disconcerting had happened.

'I've lost my cow,' she informed us in a stricken voice.

'Ach, well, you expected to. The missionary told you that yesterday,' retorted Erchy.

'I don't mean that. I'm sayin' I can't find her anywhere.'

Both Erchy and I stared at her with extravagant surprise.

'You cannot find her?' Erchy repeated.

'I've looked everywhere an' I cannot find the beast. Come an' see for yourselves.'

We pulled the dinghy above the tide and followed Kirsty to the bog where the cow had been left the previous evening.

There was no sign of the beast.

'My God! What's these?' ejaculated Erchy, bending down to peer at some hoofmarks scored deep into the bog. He scratched his head bewilderedly.

'It's as though somebody was after chasin' the beast,' suggested Kirsty.

'Indeed, if that dose has worked her I doubt she'll think she had the devil himself chasin' her,' he vouchsafed.

Together we followed the hoofmarks and they led us strangely enough towards the burial ground. I think even before we came in sight of it that Kirsty and I suspected what had happened.

'Somebody's left the gate open,' Kirsty said, and there was dread in her voice.

'Them damty flowers!' Erchy upbraided her. 'I said yesterday it was a daft idea an' I say it more so now.'

We stood in the open gateway of the burial ground and looked towards Johnny's grave, a little apart from all the other crowded graves. The cow stood beside it, sublimely chewing her cud. There was no sign of the lupins but all round and completely covering the grave there were seas and seas of manure, and the smell was appalling.

'Look at that, now,' said Erchy in an awestruck voice. 'You cannot say she's stuck now, anyway.'

'The defiler!' breathed Kirsty. 'What will folks say of me when they see I've let my cow defile my own brother's grave?' She became almost human in her anguish. 'What will the missionary say?'

'Ach, if you say nothin' the rain'll get rid of the manure for you, but you'd best get the beast out of the way pretty quick,' Erchy advised. Kirsty 'stood not upon the order of her going' and in a trice the cow was out of the burial ground and being driven up the road towards her byre.

Without a word Erchy closed the gate of the burial ground after us and we returned to the boat. When he had rowed a few strokes he rested on his oars. 'That's the queerest dose ever I heard of to cure a sick beast,' he said, his voice full of wonder. 'Man! But that must be a good cow doctor.' He resumed rowing again but his perplexed expression betrayed that he was still pondering the miracle of the cure.

By the time we reached home with the cupboard the rain was pouring unstintedly from a sagging grey sky. It continued over the weekend and on Monday morning Erchy, who had been doing some careful reconnoitring, reported that there was no longer any trace of manure to be seen at the burial ground. The village, if they noticed anything amiss, refrained from comment but the next time the missionary came out for a funeral he was heard impressing on Kirsty what a good man her brother must have been because the Lord had made the grass grow so much greener over and around his grave than anywhere else. He likened it to a 'green halo'.

Now in case any interested farmer should read this account perhaps I ought to mention that Kirsty's cow lived for seven years after this event had taken place and during that time she produced four good calves.

As though it may have some significance, Erchy insists that I also mention that the missionary died within two years!

All Mod. Cons.?

THERE was no sound of rain on the roof when I woke but the morning was damp and shot with chilliness, as though winter were already licking its chops. Blessedly the wind had dropped away to nothing so that, released from the necessity of physical combat with it when I went outside, I felt unburdened and relaxed. The cattle who had so long confined themselves to grazing the sheltered corries in the hills had moved upwards during the night so that they now stood elegantly silhouetted along the skyline, a sight which is locally believed to foretell a spell of fine weather. In a sheltered corner of my garden a few bedraggled plants that had waited so long for stillness opened their petals warily in response to the tremors of sunlight that managed to evade the glowering clouds.

I had planned a busy morning and was outside giving the kitchen mats a thorough beating and shaking when I became aware of the sound of voices and, slipping with typical Bruach curiosity to the end of the house, saw Morag, Yawn and Erchy, each carrying a sack and a pail and looking very workmanlike in their whelking clothes, coming down the path.

'My, but you're starting the whelks early,' I called to them.

'Aye, indeed. But they're sayin' there's a good prices on them already,' returned Morag happily. 'You should be leavin' that an' comin' with us.'

I detest picking whelks. 'I'm going to do some washing while the rainwater tank is full,' I told them. 'I've left it far too long as it is.'

Morag accepted my excuse without comment. Yawn treated me to a sardonic stare.

'They're sayin' we're goin' to get the water at last,' rushed in Erchy consolingly, 'so you'll be able to wash whenever you feel like it then.'

'Are we really?' I demanded. 'Is it really true?'

'As true as I'm here,' declared Erchy with an air of misgiving. 'Did you no' have the wee mannie round askin' for your signature on a paper?'

I had indeed had the 'wee mannie' round but he had been almost gloatingly pessimistic as to the chance of the authorities piping water to my cottage in less than five years' time at least. The main obstacle, he had told me, was that the village was too scattered, thus making any scheme so far proposed too costly to be approved. Also, he had confided, not all the Bruachites considered piped water necessary, some of the more rigid Presbyterians maintaining that the Good Lord made the water to flow where He wanted it and therefore it was not right for Man to try to deflect its course, an attitude that I would have found too preposterous to believe had I not previously come up against it when the draining of a patch of boggy land had been proposed.

The 'mannie' had suggested that it might be worth my while to install a ram pump at the well down by the shore and pipe water to the cottage from it.

'I don't know if the supply would be adequate,' I had told him. 'It's a very shallow little well.' Very obligingly he had come with me to inspect it.

'I daresay the supply might be good enough if it was dug out a bit,' he suggested. 'But wait, now, till I test it.' Full of enthusiasm he had hurried back to his car, returning with a thin metal rod about four or five feet long with which he had proceeded to probe the depth of the well. It went down eventually to about two-thirds of its length.

'Just as I thought,' he told me cheerfully. 'You'd have plenty water there if you could get it dug out a bit more. It's just that it's all silted up with not being used for so long.'

I had been grateful for his encouragement and as we walked back to the car he had very kindly worked out for me the probable cost of the installation. 'Of course, you'll understand mine's only a very rough estimate,' he had cautioned. 'I don't really take anything to do with the water department at all. It's only that somebody's been badgering the Council about getting the water here and seeing I was coming out this way they asked me to collect signatures.'

'You're not from the water department then?' I had asked.

'No, no. Water's not my job at all.'

'Oh,' I said innocently, 'I assumed that you carried that rod with you for testing the depth of the wells so that you could advise people as to their suitability for providing a piped supply.'

'This rod? Oh, no indeed. This is a grave poker.' He wriggled it carefully into position across the seats of his car. 'You know,' he explained chattily, oblivious of the tenseness of the moment, 'there's a rule now that corpses must be buried four feet down. But they won't take any notice of it hereabouts if I don't go round all the burial grounds every so often and prod the graves to see how deep they've put them.'

'A grave poker?' I echoed.

'Yes, indeed.' He darted a suspicious glance at my face. 'I suppose it sounds kind of funny to you, being a stranger.'

I agreed that it did.

'Well, goodbye,' he said brightly, getting back into his car. 'I'm very pleased to have been able to help you.'

Back in the kitchen I had fortified myself with a cup of tea—made from rainwater.

'I don't believe they mean to give us the water at all,' said Morag, her voice full of scepticism. 'We've been promised it now for twenty-five years that I know of an' there's still no sign of it. I doubt I'll never see it in my time, anyway.'

'Damty sure you will,' replied Erchy with a surge of confidence.

Yawn still continued to stare at me with sardonic amusement but as the conversation seemed to have petered out and Morag and Erchy were starting to move away I began to shake some of the mud from my mats. Yawn still made no move to follow his companions, so I grinned at him fatuously, wishing he would say something or else go. A few more moments under his embarrassing scrutiny and I would be driven to asking him what was wrong. Suddenly he spoke.

'I'm thinkin' you must be one of them arishtocrats.'

It was my turn to stare. Anything less like an aristocrat than I looked at that moment in my gumboots, soiled overall, rubber gloves and with a muddy mat clutched in either hand I could not have imagined. 'Why do you say that?' I asked in undisguised bewilderment.

' 'Tis only arishtocrats that wears rubber gloves to shake mats,' he admonished me. 'Next thing we know you'll be takin' to cuttin' your peats with a knife and fork.' He permitted himself a short grunt of laughter. 'I knew some people once from hereabouts and they went to live for a time in Edinburgh. When they came back here they was that arishtocratic they put on gloves to eat their salt herrin'.' Satisfied now that he had made his criticism, but still mumbling condemnation, he turned to follow the other two.

I continued with my chores, speculating again as to the financial possibility of having my own piped water supply but it was indeed futile speculation for I had already come to the decision that it would cost more than I could afford. I argued with myself that the energy used in carrying water could be so much more profitably spent in doing other things. I had learned to be frugal—water that had been used for my own toilet was then re-heated to wash towels, etc., and then tipped into a pail for washing floors. But it was not just the energy I grudged, it was the time it all took. I am not blessed with single-mindedness so that more often than not when I took up my pails and started to hurry to the well I would catch a glimpse of a strange bird, so that I had to freeze while I tried to identify it. Or, enchanted by the sight of greenfinches feeding on the seeds of the burdock plants that grew against the stone dykes, I would ignore the urgency of my task. Sometimes it was a new flower among the heather that caught my attention, or the particular shades and patterns of a mossy bank. Always there was so much wildness and beauty accompanying even the most mundane outside work and I could not bear to let myself pass it by.

Not for the first time I wished that the powers-that-be would get their priorities in order. It seemed to me ludicrous that electricity, which was well on its way to Bruach, should come before there was a prospect of a water supply, but that was what was happening in other less inaccessible villages so that it was not unusual to see bent old women tottering from a well, which was often no more than the most rudimentary depression in the ground, carrying the full pails of water back to their old-fashioned croft kitchens and there shakily ladling the water with the traditional tinker-made dipper into a shiny new electric kettle.

One or two families in Bruach already had a water supply, but they were the luckier ones who had wells close to their houses yet on higher ground so that it was an easy and relatively inexpensive matter to pipe the water. It is doubtful if even they would have bothered had they not intended to cater for summer tourists. The rest of the crofters, having carried water all their lives, suffered little frustration from the lack of it and though they would agree wholeheartedly, when the subject was mentioned at the ceilidhs, that it would 'indeed be wonderful to have the watter', their desire for it was never as fervent as my own. They professed to want bathrooms but more, I suspected, as a status symbol than a genuine need. Their attitude was in fact epitomized for me by old Murdoch who having heard he could get a grant to have a bathroom built on to his house applied for it immediately. Now Murdoch and his niece had been doing very well out of taking in boarders for bed and breakfast—'nighter's' they called them—and the wily Murdoch thought that if he could, without much cost to himself, get another room built on he could offer even more accommodation. He reckoned that once the bathroom was built he would only have to turn round to the authorities and tell them there was no water supply and they would just pay the grant and let him get away with it as an extra bedroom. It was unfortunate for Murdoch that a new inspector was appointed just about the time his so-called bathroom was completed and although it was furnished with a bowl on a stand, a pail of water and a towel rail Murdoch found it impossible to convince the inspector that the new building merited the description 'bathroom'. To the old man's dismay he was informed that the grant would be withheld until the room was equipped with a conventional bath, toilet basin and W.C. Vociferous with indignation Murdoch grudgingly complied and again approached the authorities, assuring them, no doubt in good faith, that he was willing to sign an undertaking that as soon as piped water was available in Bruach he would have it connected to his bathroom. He naturally did not disclose that in the meantime he intended to store the unusable mod. cons. in a shed and let the room as a bedroom to help pay for them. But the authorities were adamant. To qualify for the description 'bathroom' there must be running water. The inspector came to deliver the ultimatum to Murdoch when the old man was perched on a ladder repairing for the third time that season the damage the storms had done to his roof. Murdoch almost exploded. The inspector waited for him to subside and then pointed out helpfully that there was a good well not far away which could supply ample water without a great deal of expenditure. Murdoch, still spluttering with wrath and argument, descended the ladder and faced the inspector aggressively and then in truly Gaelic fashion, he flung out his arms in a dramatic gesture. 'Look at that!' he cried, pointing up at the roof. 'Look at it, will ye! Over fifty years me an' my father before me has been tryin' to keep the water from comin' into this house, an' now you're after forcin' me to take it in.' He had spat his disgust into the wind, chuckled appreciation of his own joke, and then invited the inspector inside for a strupak.

So Murdoch had 'taken in the watter' and no one was more proud than himself when it was finally installed. He had even announced his intention of taking a bath some day, the first in his long life. It was about six months afterwards that he had sprackled up to me when we were both out on the hill feeding our cattle in the misty quiet of the evening.

'Here, Miss Peckwitt,' his voice was hardly more than an awed whisper. 'Did you ever take a bath?'

'Yes,' I answered, knowing that if I betrayed the least surprise or amusement I should never know what lay behind the question.

'Well, tell me, when you came out of it did you no' feel like a herrin' that's been stripped of its scales just?' His blue eyes were anxious and expectant.

'I don't think so,' I said and this time I could not control a slight tremor in my voice.

'An' did you no' feel for a week or more after it as though your clothes was full of wee, wee splenters?' He wriggled with a suppleness that belied his age. I shook my head.

'Ach, well that's just the way I felt myself after it. Ach, I enjoyed it right enough when I was in it but I never want another one the way it left me feelin'.'

The day stayed calm and patchily bright. After lunch I got out Joanna, having promised to drive Katy, the shepherd's wife, and her half-sister, Ishbel, to a neighbouring village to visit a friend who had just moved into a newly built house. It had been arranged that I should pick them up at 'the back of three' and Ishbel was already waiting for me by the croft gate, dressed regally in her best clothes and carrying a string bag which contained a couple of small parcels. Whenever she visited a house, however briefly, Ishbel always took along some little gift. It was usually something quite trivial, perhaps a hank of darning wool, or a packet of envelopes, perhaps a magazine or even a packet of needles, just some little thing she found she could spare, so that she should never go empty-handed. Nervous, as always, she got into the car filling it with the evidence of her unstinted and relentless combat with the moths which she imagined campaigned against her with a vindictiveness that was purely personal.

At the shepherd's cottage we picked up the plump and voluble Katy who seemed to burst into chatter with every bump of the rough road. Ishbel said little and she was too shy even to respond to the convivial knots of workmen we passed, who took their weight off their spades to raise them in excited greeting—which, Katy observed derisively, was probably the most strenuous work they'd be doing that day. Despite the indolence of Highland labourers, however, progress was stalking rapidly towards Bruach, leaving a wake of tall poles which were to carry the electricity to the village. There were more signs of change too, for there was an extremely favourable grant and loan scheme for building new houses to replace the old croft dwellings, and the younger folk, though perhaps exiles themselves, had been quick to take advantage of it. The squat, tiny-windowed old croft houses, usually built in the most sheltered corner of the croft, were becoming byres for cattle while beside them desirable two-storey residences with modern steel windows were appearing, looking as exposed and uncomfortable as someone who has just been kicked out of a warm bed. Into these the old people moved reluctantly, complaining of their coldness and temporarily overawed by their comparative spaciousness and by the sight of the bathrooms and up-to-the-minute sink units complete with mixer taps—though of course they still had neither water nor drainage.

It was beside such a cluster of raw-looking houses that I brought

Joanna to a stop and Maggie, a dumpy, merry-voiced little woman
with almost no inhibitions, rushed out to greet us effusively. Ishbel
presented her gifts—a packet of biscuits and a tin of condensed milk—
both of which were opened immediately and offered to us. We sat in
the white glossy kitchen and drank tea while Maggie entertained us
with a fluent and descriptive recital of all the events that had taken
place in the village of recent months. She told us, with many inter-
polations from Katy, of Padruig Mor, who had been to the mainland
to attend an auction sale where he had bought himself an old grandfather clock.

'Ach, it was no bloody good at all,' said Maggie. (It is not usual to
hear a Hebridean woman swear but the fact that Maggie did so unrestrainedly seemed, so far as her neighbours were concerned, to
enhance her attraction as a hostess.) 'Indeed,' she continued, 'the works
was all gone out of it long since but he brought it home with him
on the train as proud as a cockerel.' I recollected Padruig Mor's tiny,
dark old house, commonly described as a 'wee but and ben', and so
was not surprised when Ishbel asked: 'How in the world did he get it
into his house?'

'He didn't to begin with,' replied Maggie, shrill with ridicule. 'The
ceilin' was too low, so what did my fine fellow do but dig a hole in
the floor till the clock would fit it. It's daft he is surely.'

'So grandfather has one foot in the grave already,' I murmured.

'So he has. You should go and see it for yourselves. It looks crazy
just but he's that pleased with it,' said Maggie. 'Aye, but it was a
laugh, I can tell you.'

Ishbel, Katy and she fell to discussing the rest of the neighbours,
politely drawing me into the conversation when it seemed I had been
silent too long, although most of the names they referred to I had
heard of only vaguely, if at all. Despite the fact that I had not taken
off my coat I felt cold, for the room was too large to be heated adequately by the discreet little grate that peeped out of the ultra-modern
tiled surround, although Maggie had it piled high with peats. The
room was full of such contradictions. The fireplace was flanked by
battered pails of peats and the miniature mantelpiece was decorated

with imposing silver ornaments that looked as though they might have been filched from a hearse. On the spotless hearth two black iron pans stood and a bundle of hen feathers lay ready for sweeping up any fallen ash. The centre of the room was taken up by a plastic-topped table with metal legs but the solid old croft-house bench was backed along one wall, throne-like in its austerity. Above it a bundle of rabbit skins hung from the ceiling. Everywhere looked scrubbed and clean, the new linoleum on the floor being still smeared with damp from a recent washing and even as I watched a grey-looking cat sidled apprehensively from under the bench and then streaked out through the open door as if it too expected to be picked up and scrubbed.

Maggie filled an old black kettle from one of the enamel pails which stood in the stainless steel sink and poised it delicately half on, half off the fire with the remark that she didn't see the use of these sort of fireplaces anyway, what was the use of a fire that didn't boil the bloody kettle?

'Don't you use the electric kettle?' Katy asked.

'I can never find a match to light it with,' retorted Maggie, and when we had finished laughing, she went on: 'The bugger won't let me use it. He says I'll likely burn the bottom out of it.' The outrage in her voice was only for our benefit.

'The bugger', her son Seoras, appeared in the doorway at that moment. He was a dark, wiry young man with a permanently satirical expression on his face and a tongue even less inhibited than his mother's. However, he greeted us with perfunctory politeness as he threw off his jacket and sat down at the table. Maggie scooped a steaming bowl of unpeeled potatoes from one of the pots on the hearth and ladled a mound of boiled fish on to a plate from the other one and placed them in front of Seoras. He bent to his repast with great concentration.

'Will you come and see over the house?' invited Maggie, and led us first to the blue and white tiled bathroom which contained, besides an aridly futile-looking W.C., a bath so narrow that anything but the slimmest of figures would have needed the aid of tyre levers to get in or out.

'That's a useful cupboard you have there, under the washbasin,' I observed. 'Much better than being able to see all the pipes.'

'Indeed it is,' agreed Maggie, and opened the door to reveal a broody hen sitting tight on a clutch of eggs. 'It's a grand little cupboard,' she enthused.

We followed her into a downstairs bedroom and then into another room, not yet furnished.

'Which room is this to be?' I asked.

Maggie hesitated a moment or two before replying.

'Indeed, I don't know just what he called it,' she admitted. 'Seoras!' she screamed back into the kitchen. 'What did they call this room on the plan?'

'Damned if I know,' responded Seoras thickly.

'Wait now till I get the plan and then you'll tell me,' said Maggie, rushing off. She returned and handed me a rolled-up plan which we studied for a moment together.

'This will be the sitting-room, then,' I hazarded.

'The sitting-room?' she repeated guilelessly. 'Is that what they call it? Indeed, God knows what we'll put to sit in here unless it's more clockin' hens.'

'D'you hear that, Seoras—it's the sitting-room,' she called.

'No, it is not, then—the shitting-room is the one with the bath in it,' retorted Seoras.

Upstairs there were three bedrooms, more than Maggie had known in her life although she had brought up seven children. 'It's kind of lonely, though,' she said regretfully when we exclaimed over their proportions. All the windows were curtained with net, shutting out the glorious view and to me it seemed a pity that the crofter wife should emulate the townswoman in that the bigger windows she aspires to the more curtaining she buys to screen them. I drew aside one of the bedroom curtains to look out across the shaggy moors, smouldering with autumn colour, to where the mist-wreathed hills looked down sulkily at the restless water. My three companions came up behind me.

'I see old Flora and Jamesie didn't take to livin' in their new house yet,' observed Katy, pointing to a brash new dwelling beside an old croft house on which a sagging roof seemed to have settled with much the same brooding determination as the hen I had just seen on the clutch of eggs in the bathroom.

'No, and I don't believe they ever will,' Maggie asserted.

'I wonder why?' I mused.

'Ach, I think they're afraid of dirtying it,' was Maggie's pert rejoinder.

It was time for us to go, and we returned to the kitchen to collect Ishbel's bag and my gloves.

'I must pee before I go,' announced Ishbel with perfect naturalness.

'Of course,' said Maggie hospitably, and led us out to the back of the house where a new concrete cattle byre of approved hygienic design had replaced the former dry-stone byre. Straddling the dung trench behind the incurious cows we relieved ourselves.

'It's handy, this,' Katy approved.

'Ach, aye, it's better by far than the old place,' replied Maggie seriously.

Seoras was standing beside the rainwater tank, scrubbing at his face with a tatter of towel.

'If you're goin' back to Bruach now, I was just thinkin' I might get a lift with you,' he said. 'It's time I got myself a haircut.'

'Seoras!' expostulated his mother, 'you can't go yet, you didn't milk the cow.'

'Milk her yourself, you lazy old cailleach,' replied Seoras with complete bonhomie. He picked up a bottle of beer from the kitchen table and followed us outside.

'Seoras!' his mother screamed after him. 'You didn't get the peats.'

Seoras responded with a spate of Gaelic too fluent for me to understand.

'Seoras, you're a b . . . ,' Maggie clapped her hand over her mouth and looked contrite. 'Oh, Seoras boy, I nearly called you a bad name.'

'Aye, I know,' Seoras returned with a bleak smile. 'You nearly called me a bugger.'

'Oh, no, Seoras,' she rectified, 'I nearly called you a bastard.'

They were still hurling insults at each other with perfect good humour when we drove away with Seoras in the back seat beside Ishbel.

'Isn't it a good thing there's a right barber now in Bruach after all these years,' offered Ishbel timidly, for the presence of a male always overawed her. 'Is he a good barber would you say?'

'I don't know,' interposed Katy, 'but,' she added as if in commendation, 'they all say he's a good sheep shearer, anyway.'

It was only during the last year that Bruach had acquired a barber when a crofter exile who claimed to have had barbering experience in Glasgow came home to spend his retirement on his sister's croft. Some said he had never been more than temporary lather boy and that fifty years ago, but whatever qualifications he may or may not have possessed he had announced his willingness to give any man a haircut or a shave. So as to run no risk of his earnings interfering with his pension he would accept only a pint of beer in recompense for his services. To the gratification of his lonely widowed sister and the corresponding envy of neighbours the barber's house had soon become a popular ceilidh house where there was always a good gathering of men not only from Bruach but from other barberless villages desiring to have their hair cut. His shaving was not nearly as much in demand, and those who had undergone the experience did not choose to repeat it, complaining that the barber 'kept a bloody cuckoo in a clock that burst out every quarter of an hour and made you jump so much you were feart where the razor would land next.'

As we were depositing Ishbel outside her home a sauntering figure approached us. It was Erchy, just returning from his whelking. Seoras poked his head out of the car to talk to him.

'Are you here just to ceilidh then, or are you goin' some place?' Erchy asked him.

'I'm here to see will the barber cut my hair for me,' replied Seoras.

Erchy lifted his cap and felt his own mop of hair experimentally. 'I could do with a haircut myself,' he admitted, 'an Johnny's supposed to be bringin' me out some of that stuff on the bus tonight.' He nodded towards the bottle of beer in Seoras's lap.

'A bottle of beer is very cheap for a haircut, isn't it?' I asked.

'I got a haircut and three dirty stories for my pint last time,' said Seoras. 'That's good value if you like.'

'Aye,' admitted Erchy cautiously, 'it's good value right enough but all the same, sometimes if there's been a few there before you so you're at the end of the queue, it's a damty queer haircut you get out of it.'

Love and Coal

'THERE,' said Yawn, with a satisfied grunt. 'You'll not take those out with your teeths.'

I concealed a smile. 'No,' I agreed, though I doubted if his handiwork was really any more robust than my own. Yawn had found me trying to repair the drooping boards of my peat shed when he had come to deliver a piece of his sister Sarah's home-made haggis. With uncharacteristic gallantry he had seized the hammer when I laid it down for an instant and, without comment, had continued to hammer in the nails himself.

'That should stand for a while,' I acknowledged by way of gratitude, having learned that to offer Yawn direct thanks only embarrassed and confused him.

He walked around the shed, aiming experimental kicks at the walls. 'You'll be needin' a new shed anyway before long,' he warned me. 'You cannot expect this one to stand up to much in the way of weather.'

I shrugged my shoulders. 'It'll have to stay until it blows away or falls down,' I told him. 'I can't afford to build a new one.'

'If you could put some stones round it just, to strengthen it,' he suggested. 'It might do you a wee bitty longer.'

'And where do I get the stones?' I asked him resignedly.

Yawn plunged his hands into his pockets with an air of finality. 'Aye,' he conceded, 'that's the way of it just.'

Despite the rocky ground, the craggy cliffs and the boulder-strewn shores, suitable stones for building were scarce enough in Bruach. There was an abundance of round stones, or oval stones, or sausage-shaped stones, all moulded to smooth symmetry by the sea or by the rushing burns, but flat stones such as could be built into a wall were precious and if you had any on your croft you hoarded them jealously for the day when you would surely need them. They might be required in times of storm for weighting down haystacks or perhaps the roof of your house (it is difficult for an amateur to tie a rope successfully to a round stone). One of pleasing shape and size might even be used as a headstone for a grave for few Bruachites wasted money on expensive tombstones. And of course the local lobster-fishermen were constantly on the look-out for good stones for their creels. Indeed so rapacious were they that it had been reported from some villages that the fishermen were suspected of helping themselves to headstones from the burial grounds. Erchy maintained the report was more than suspicion and claimed to have seen a creel newly hauled from the sea in which a couple of good-sized lobsters were crawling over a stone roughly carved with the words 'Isobel C . . . aged 89 yrs'. Erchy said he couldn't have eaten those lobsters 'supposin' you'd given him a bottle of the "hard stuff" [whisky over-proof] to wash the taste out of his mouth afterwards'. And yet though stone in Bruach was so scarce there was on nearly every croft at least one tumbled ruin of a dry-stone house or shed which, curiously enough, no one ever tampered with. There was just such a ruin in a corner of my own croft, now smugly canopied with many decades of moss and fern growth, but when I had one day embarked on the task of levering up some of the stones from their settled positions with the avowed intention of strengthening my peat shed in just the way Yawn was now suggesting, he himself had soon appeared on the scene to exhort me not, on any account, to disturb the stones.

'But they're not doing any good there, are they, Yawn?' I had argued, suspecting that it was either sheer sentiment or the possible disturbance of the 'wee folk' that prompted his concern.

'Aye, but you'd best not lift them,' he had insisted. 'You'll lift those stones and you'll lift a fever.'

'A fever?' I echoed. 'Why?'

'Ach, well, that was one of the houses that was left at the time of the big fever when it was in these parts,' he had explained. 'They set fire to all those that had it but the fever still stays in the stones so they say.' His voice was exceedingly grave. 'Nobody about here believes in touchin' them, anyway.'

'Do you remember this big fever, Yawn?' I had asked him.

'No, but I mind my father tellin' me of it. He remembered it from when he was a lad just.'

As soon as Yawn had gone I had dismissed his warning as absurd and had carried the few stones I had already prised out over to the peat shed. They were extremely heavy and the muscles of my back began to object so strongly that I had given up work for the rest of the day. That night I had been unable to sleep because of the agonizing pain in my back and next morning I had felt as though I was develop-ing all the symptoms of a severe cold. However, within a day or so I was perfectly all right again and I returned to the task of further depleting the ruin. I had succeeded in dislodging several more stones before my back had again begun to trouble me and a sneaky chillness had insinuated itself between my shoulder blades. I had left off work and gone back to the cottage to get warm but though there were no other recognizable symptoms of a cold the chillness refused to be thawed by hot drinks sipped before a roasting fire with my back as the main target for the heat, and it remained icily indifferent to a 'poultice' of a hot-water bottle tucked under my bedjacket; for three days I was subject to sudden fits of shivering. As soon as I had recovered I resolved that when a reasonable day came I would continue work on the ruin, and told myself with great firmness that my aches and pains were either the direct result of perspiring freely while working in heavy clothes and then standing about in a bleak wind, or else they were of psychological origin. For how, I asked myself, could fever linger in stones to remain a source of infection a century or so later? There had come a day of relative mildness with a ragged sky that looked like old sheep's fleece and a spectral breeze that breathed moistly on the rusty sedge. I approached the ruin with waning confidence, for it seemed to my doubtless prejudiced eye to have taken on a slightly sinister aspect, the dark cavities from which I had already removed the stones looking like resentful scars on the ageing skin of moss. It is easy enough to shrug off apprehension or superstition in the warm comfort of one's own kitchen when one has just switched off 'Woman's Hour'; not so easy when one is completely alone with the wildness of the moors where even the straightening of the trodden grass dogs one's footsteps with stealthy whispers. Strangely loath to start work I prospected for a place where the dislodging of one stone might release several more and thus quicken my labours but they seemed to be embedded more firmly than I remembered and when I thought I had found such a place I had not the strength to move a single stone. My back began to ache in anticipation and I could have sworn I felt the first vestige of a shiver. I had looked sourly at the ruin and then sorrowfully towards my flimsy peat shed. Then I had gone back to the cottage and started to bake bread.

'Aye,' repeated Yawn, pushing vigorously at the peat shed again.

'There's not many stones hereabouts that you can use.' We had care-fully turned our backs on the ruin, which I never interfered with again. 'You could get a few from the shore maybe if you looked long enough,' he added.

'It isn't often one sees a flat stone on the shore,' I objected.

'Ach, you'd find flat ones if you looked for them. Other folks does. Look at Alasdair there,' he went on. 'Every day he goes to the shore and finds himself a good stone or two to carry up in his creel for this wall he's after buildin'.' There was a glint of amusement in Yawn's eye.

'That's so,' I admitted. Every day, whatever the weather, one could see the indomitable Alasdair struggling up the cliff path from the shore with one or two stones each weighing nearly half a hundredweight in a creel on his back. These he would painstakingly build into the very substantial wall that had been destined originally to protect the tiny flower garden his Glasgow-born wife had once dreamed of planting. Perhaps, when he had dedicated himself to it over fifty years ago as a young man of twenty-four, the task had not seemed to him so stupendous but even now though he rarely missed a day during all that time the wall still needed many stones to complete it. But, though his wife had been dead for some years, he still plodded doggedly on. Perhaps he was impelled by the desire to fulfil a promise made to his deceased wife; perhaps it was too difficult to break the self-imposed routine of a lifetime, but whatever the reason Alasdair's wall still continued to grow by that daily quota of hard-won stones.

'It passes the time for him,' Yawn said with true Gaelic under-standing of his need. I suspected that if the wall were ever completed Alasdair might find there was no purpose left in living.

Being blessed with neither Alasdair's rugged physique nor the Bruachites' subjugation of time I knew that any flat stones I might find on the shore would stay there long enough to be washed into round ones before I would exert myself to carry them. My peat shed would have to take its chance in the gales.

'Well, are you thinkin' of buildin' Miss Peckwitt a new shed?' Morag came upon us in the midst of our ponderings and Yawn, no doubt fearing that I might take her remark seriously, hastily left us.

'I've brought you a wee bitty meat will do for your dinner.' Morag handed me a basin with half a dozen fresh chops in it.

'It's wonderful to have fresh meat,' I said gratefully, thinking how lucky I was to have a respite from the limp and unidentifiable chunks of flesh with gory paper clinging tenaciously that came to us through the post each week from the mainland butcher.

'Aye, mo ghaoil,' she rejoined devoutly, 'an' once you've eaten heather-fed lamb you're spoiled for any other meat for the rest of your life.'

Together we walked back to the cottage. 'I'll take the bowl back with me just,' said Morag. 'I'm thinkin' I'll take a wee taste over to Willy's wife, the poor soul.'

'How is Willy?' I asked as I rinsed out the basin. 'The poor man seems to be lingering on a long time, doesn't he?'

'Aye,' she agreed, with an anxious frown. 'He doesn't just seem as though he can make up his mind to die.' We heard the latch of the gate click and both turned to look out of the window. 'Here's Erchy,' she announced unnecessarily, 'an' I daresay he's come to bring you a piece of meat from his own beast. He was after killin' it a day or two since.'

'My goodness!' I said, 'I shall be able to feast for a week.'

As soon as the weather was cold enough for the flies to have disappeared and for meat to be kept safely for two, perhaps three, weeks in an ordinary shed, each Bruach family liked to slaughter a sheep. It was the custom then to give joints to one's friends who had not yet slaughtered and they would reciprocate when their turn came to kill. In this way the supply of fresh meat was prolonged for several weeks. I had no sheep but that did not deter my friends from bestowing upon me more than adequate joints as well as generous slices of haggis or blackpudding as they made them, for when a sheep was slaughtered the thrifty Bruach housewives saw that the entrails were eaten before the carcase was cut into at all. Yawn's sister, Sarah, easily the thriftiest woman in Bruach, had once told me that she used every bit of a sheep except for the ears and teeth and when I had asked for a demonstration she had taken me, in company with two pailsful of internal organs, down to the burn which bounded ˋ ˗. croft. There, standing in icy cold water with the noisome contents of several stomachs and many yards of intestine swirling greenly around our gumboots, I was initiated into the mysteries of making haggis and blackpudding.

'There,' approved Sarah, when we were back in her kitchen and the lungs of the sheep were simmering in a saucepan and dribbling pink froth from the trachea which was draped over the side of the pan, 'you'll be able to call yourself a right crofter now that you've helped clean a sheep and make a haggis.' I managed a wan smile but not until the blood had been mixed with oatmeal and poured into one stomach bag to be boiled into blackpudding, and the lungs and a selection of other dubious-looking morsels had been chopped up and stuffed into another stomach bag to be boiled into a haggis had I felt sure enough of my legs to rise from my chair and go to the door, desperate to breathe unfouled air again. But Sarah had been determined that I should witness every aspect of her skill and economy and the two collaterals were rubbing tumid shoulders in an enormous cauldron under the scrutiny of a singed sheep's head awaiting its turn beside the fire before she had allowed that the demonstration was over.

The following day when the haggis was cooled and set Sarah had sent me a thick slice of it which I crisped in the frying pan and then ate with some mashed potatoes. To my great surprise I had enjoyed every scrap of it and from that day on have been a devotee of the beast.

Erchy came into the kitchen and deposited a now familiar-looking parcel on the table. 'There's your ration,' he said to me and then, so as to foil any attempt at thanking him, he went on quickly: 'I'm just hearin' that Murdoch's been taken awful bad and they've had to send for the nurse.'

'Oh, be quiet!' ejaculated Morag with startled incredulity.

'Aye, it's right enough,' affirmed Erchy.

'Indeed, he was tellin' me only yesterday he'd been conscripted for the best part of a week and the nurse had given him five calomel to shift him,' Morag remembered. 'Would it be to do with that likely?'

Erchy shook his head. 'I don't know at all,' he said. 'But what I'm after wonderin' now is whether the third one's not goin' to be Willy as we've all been expectin'.'

'Here, here,' murmured Morag in a horrified voice.

Erchy was of course referring to the old belief that graves were always required in threes. 'Once you've opened up the burial ground you'll need to open it up twice more,' he had told me. Although it was uncanny how often it came true it was a cruel superstition for once the first of the cycle of deaths had occurred the old folks in the village would begin to show distinct signs of uneasiness, even panic, until the third grave was satisfactorily filled when those that were 'spared' would shed their fears and with them many of their years and begin what was literally a new lease of life.

During the previous few weeks the Bruach burial ground had been opened twice—once for a young baby who had 'died of an open window' and once for Johnny Comic. Willy, who everyone knew could not last much longer, had been confidently accepted as the likely occupant for the third grave but in view of Erchy's news it was possible that Murdoch might be the third corpse and when Willy died he would likely be the first of another trio. Both Erchy and Morag looked very serious indeed. I tried to take their minds off the subject.

'I wish there was something I could do for you in return for all this lovely meat,' I said, with genuine wistfulness.

'Ach, 'tis nothin' at all,' Morag dismissed the suggestion instantly.

'Well, you can do somethin' for me,' said Erchy with a boldness he sometimes assumed in company. 'You can bake me a loaf of that nice bread you make. I reckon it agrees with my stomach better than shop bread.'

I had never known Erchy to refuse at least one slice of my home-made bread even if he had just taken his dinner when it was offered to him. 'I'll certainly do that,' I told him. 'But I'll let you into a secret, Erchy.' He looked at me curiously. 'The reason for the nice flavour of my bread is that I mix a handful of the hens' bran into the flour when I make it.'

'Is that right?' queried Morag.

'That's right,' I told her.

'I'd still eat it supposin' it was a handful of the hens' dung you mixed in with it,' said Erchy staunchly. 'It's damty good bread anyway.'

'Talkin' of bakin',' said Morag with careful offhandness. 'Were you no speakin' of givin' a party a while back.' She enunciated the word 'party' with the awkward amusement she assumed when she used a word she regarded as being 'swanky'.

'Yes, I was,' I replied. 'I've been wondering about the best time to have it.'

'Wait you, now,' said Erchy. 'If you go an' get all ready to have a party an' then Willy goes an' dies, there's nobody would be able to come to it.'

I had already thought of that, Willy being related to every family in the village so that no household would be unaffected by his death.

'Ach, but that would be awful spiteful of the man to go an' die on you like that,' said Morag with just a trace of outrage in her voice.

'Aye, but he might do it, just the same,' Erchy warned her.

'Aye, so he might,' agreed Morag.

'Perhaps I'd better put it off altogether,' I suggested.

'Here, no!' said Erchy. 'There's no need to do that. Will your cakes no' keep for a wee whiley after you've baked them?'

'Yes, of course,' I told him; 'they'd keep for a few days anyway.'

'Well then,' said Erchy, 'you go ahead an' have your party and supposin' Willy dies we'll have him buried in a day or two an' then we could all come.'

Thus encouraged I went ahead and arranged to have what I had to refer to as a 'good ceilidh' on the Thursday of the following week. I started the necessary baking on the Tuesday so that there would be plenty of time for icing and decorating the various cakes. On the Wednesday morning Erchy called in to tell me that Willy had 'passed on' in the night. The funeral was to be on Friday.

'You'd best put off your party till Friday night now,' he advised me.

'But will people come to a party the same day as the funeral?' I asked him, more to reassure myself than from actual doubt in the matter.

Erchy's eyes opened wide in surprise. 'Surely they will,' he replied without a trace of hesitation. 'What would be keepin' them back then?'

I was about to comment on Willy being the occupant for the third grave when Erchy observed with great satisfaction: 'Well, we've got our third corpse all right. I'm tellin' you it always goes in threes.'

'You'll have another grave to dig tonight, then, will you?' I asked him.

'No,' he answered surprisingly. 'He's not to be buried here at all. Seemingly he left a wish to be put over in a burial ground on the mainland where his mother and his brother is buried already.'

'Does that mean you'll still be expecting to have a third grave to dig soon? You've always said it was the burial ground that had to be opened three times.'

'Aye, well,' he excused himself. 'When anybody dies I just straight-way think of diggin'. It's just my own way of speakin' of it.'

My mind flashed to the other invalid. 'By the way, how's old Murdoch?' I enquired.

'Ach, there's nothin' wrong with him at all. Nothin' that a day out in the heather didn't cure anyway. He was there squattin' that long he took his oilskin with him an' made a tent of it. By God! but those calomel went through him. He was feelin' pretty bad when he got back an' didn't move from the fire until he heard this mornin' that Willy was dead. As soon as he heard that he was away out to see to his horse. His niece said she couldn't keep him back at all.' Erchy chuckled. 'I saw him myself out there, so I called out to him, "Murdoch, what are you at? I thought you was dyin'." He turned on me an' he shouted: "I'm no' dyin' yet. I'm owed too much money to die yet." "Who's owin' you money?" says I. "The government," he says. "Haven't I been payin' into that pension scheme for most of my life an' I'm damty sure I'm not goin' to die till I've had every penny of it back again." ' Erchy shook his head. 'He's a hardy all right,' he said admiringly.

I left Erchy to spread the message that the ceilidh was to be post-poned until the Friday evening and though I carried on with the preparations I could not help wondering if he had really spoken for the rest of the crofters and if I and the hens were to be left to eat our way through batch after batch of cakes and scones and tarts. Experience had shown me that there was always a terrific sense of relief in the village after a corpse was buried and that the subsequent ceilidhs were perceptibly more animated than usual but whether an arranged party would be considered too frivolous to follow directly upon a funeral I had yet to discover.

At about twelve o'clock on the Friday morning, whilst I was replenishing Bonny's manger with summer-smelling hay pulled from the middle of the stack I noticed an unfamiliar vehicle on the road and guessed that it was something to do with the funeral. A little later a few solemnly garbed people trickled homewards across the crofts and there was a busy hurrying of smoke from chimneys as everyone put their potatoes on to cook. The afternoon settled itself tranquilly over Bruach, the breeze of the morning having died away so that the cottage chimneys smoked in sleek blue plumes and the stilled moors relaxed for an hour in the discreet wintry sunshine. Only the figures of the women were to be seen going about their chores until just before dusk the small troupe of children straggled up the brae from school, their clamorous voices striking shrill echoes from the rough stone walls of the dykes.

At nine o'clock in the evening with the furniture pushed to one side and the refreshments laid out I was waiting a little tensely for the arrival of the first of my guests. The fire was sluggish for despite frenzied appeals to the new coal merchant I had received no delivery of coal for nearly six months and was having to make do with dross fortified by that summer's damp peats. It is a great disadvantage to have a coal merchant who is also a fish-salesman and a caterer for tourists, for when there is an abundance of either he cannot be per-suaded to bother himself with the far less profitable coal. Fretfully I picked up the bellows which, like my copper warming pan, I had once bought as an antique but now found I needed to use frequently. I

blew steadily on the fire and was soon rewarded by the sight of little
spurts of flame that irradiated the shaggy peats into racing patterns of
sparks. I was still blowing when my ears caught the noise of an engine
in the distance and, throwing on a coat, I went outside to look. A pair
of headlights was glaring down the road towards the cottage and a
few minutes later a heavy lorry swung through the entrance to my
croft. The driver, a blond young man with an impudent smile, jumped
down.

'I've brought you the half-ton of coal you were wanting,' he
told me in a voice that was as spiky as if he habitually dined on
cactus.

'Oh, bless you!' I exclaimed with a delight that was not wholly
due to the fact that I now had some coal. Since coming to live in
Bruach where one had to fetch and carry so much for oneself the
delivery of even the most utilitarian commodities filled one with
excitement.

'Will you give me a light?' he asked and when, with slightly less
excitement, I agreed, he pressed a torch into my hand and hauled
himself up into the back of the lorry. There he commenced shovelling
out the coal into a heap on the frosty grass. It was bitterly cold to be
standing about and it seemed to take hours before the last shovelful
of coal had clattered on to the heap and the shovel had been thrown
back into the lorry.

'I must fill a pail and put some on the fire,' I said, shivering. 'You'd
better come in and have a strupak.'

Chivalrously he offered to fill the pail for me and just as I was
handing it out to him we discerned several torch flashes. From somewhere along the road came bursts of shouting and laughter. 'There's
people comin' here,' the driver informed me needlessly.

'Yes,' I told him. 'They're coming to ceilidh with me. Stay if you'd
like to.' I set the already singing kettles back on the stove and within
a few moments heard the approaching thud of boots on the frosty
ground followed by a heavy thump on the door. 'Come in!' I called,
and they all pushed one after another into the tiny porch, their faces
frost-whipped into enviable ruddiness. Whispering and commenting

excitedly, those who wore coats took them off, dropped them on the
stairs and then spread themselves over the room until all the available
seats were taken and some of the girls were perched awkwardly two
on a chair. The lorry driver dumped the pail of coals beside the fire
and then sat himself on the floor beside the pouffé on which the
attractive Mora was sitting. I met smiles with smiles and tried to make
everyone as comfortable as space would allow but I was rather disappointed to note that except for the lorry driver and the old men—
Yawn, Ian and an exceedingly sprightly Murdoch—the rest of my
guests were female. The best ceilidhs were always those where the
numbers were more or less equal and I hoped it would not be long
before the rest of the men arrived.

'Where are Erchy and Hector and the rest?' I asked Morag as we
handed round refreshments.

'Indeed I don't know at all,' she replied, genuine mystification in
her voice. 'I don't believe they got back from the funeral yet.'

'Trust Erchy,' I said with some asperity. 'It was he who insisted
on my going ahead with this party.'

'Here, mo ghaoil, but there's plenty of time for them yet,' she
soothed.

After an hour or so had gone by and there was still no sign of the
younger men the girls, except for Mora who was flirting modestly
with the lorry driver, were beginning to look anxious, and though
there was plenty of chatter and laughter it was possible in odd moments
to hear the hiss of the pressure lamp which, to me anyway, meant
that the party was not as successful as I had hoped it would be. However, Morag coaxed Murdoch into giving us a song and soon we were
all joining in the choruses rapturously, the girls throwing back their
heads and swaying and the old people beating their hands into their
laps in time to the music. It was nearing midnight and we were in the
middle of a particularly nostalgic Gaelic air when the door was flung
open and Erchy and Hector and a bevy of the young men of the
village tumbled in, their eyes shining, their caps pushed back on their
heads and the pockets of their best suits bulging with bottles of
various sizes.

'I thought you'd been to a funeral,' I commented as they sat themselves on the floor, their backs against the wall, and tucked hungrily into the food that was offered them.

'So we have,' responded Erchy happily. 'An' a right time of it we had too.' He looked at Hector and they grinned at each other with amiable understanding. 'We got that much of a surprise when we saw it was a bus that came to take the coffin to the funeral,' Erchy confided in a voice that effectively silenced everyone else in the kitchen. 'We was thinkin' it would be only a small car just to take the coffin and maybe one or two folks along with it. When we saw it was a bus an' we could all go, we rushed away home to get a pound or two to put in our pockets. Seein' we was all dressed up anyway we thought we might as well go an' have a good drink.' He filled his mouth with a sandwich and spoke thickly through it. 'I'm tellin' you, Miss Peckwitt, if it hadn't been that I remembered about your party there's not one of us would have been back yet.'

'How did you get back?' I asked.

'We hired a car from that Farquhar man,' Erchy told me. 'I believe we started off fairly early but Farquhar would have us keep stoppin' for a drink. Honest,' he said in awestruck tones, 'I've never known a car that does more pubs to the mile than that one of his.'

'Aye,' chimed in Hector, 'and tse more Farquhar's had to drink tse slower he drives. Indeed I was tsinkin' we'd get back sooner if we pushed. You'd tsink it was goin' to a funeral we was instead of comin' back from one, tse way he was drivin'.' He held his cup of tea at arm's length and looked at it with much the same expression of distaste as I have seen on the face of a publican when he looks at a glass of his own beer.

With the arrival of the more virile men the girls shed the last remnants of lassitude and the inevitable teasing and chaffing began. Bottles were flourished, glasses were demanded; the singing became progressively louder and less tuneful until at two o'clock in the morning everyone was complaining of a dry throat and clamouring for tea again.

'Well,' said Yawn, as we all relaxed for tea drinking. 'I'm thinkin' it's a good thing you got over all those colds and fever you had when you was tryin' to lift those stones. We wouldn't be after havin' such a good ceilidh as this one.' It was the first allusion he had made to my having been observed defying his warning.

'I've left them now, anyway,' I admitted ruefully.

'You should never have touched them at all,' reiterated Yawn, 'for you went to look real poorly after it.'

'Indeed so she did,' agreed Morag. 'I didn't like the look of you at all,' she said to me.

'Ach, I don't believe myself it was anythin' to do with the fever,' put in Behag with surprising conviction. 'I think Miss Peckwitt just got herself a good cold and that was the start of it all, likely.'

The old men shook their heads, knowingly.

'Ach, these colds,' grumbled Ian. 'I never had no trouble with all this catarrh an' sinuses as the doctor says I have until I started to use a handkerchief.' He darted a lugubrious glance at his sister, a very refined lady, who was sometimes to be heard chiding him for not using one. 'It's my belief it's handkerchiefs that's the cause of all these colds that are going about nowadays,' he said.

'Anyway,' interjected Morag, evidently deciding there had been enough censure for the time being, 'Miss Peckwitt's all right now, are you not?' She turned to me for confirmation.

'More or less,' I replied. 'I'm still having trouble with my chest, though. It's pretty uncomfortable at times.'

'Well then,' commented Erchy. 'You know what you must do for that?'

'No,' I said, hurriedly trying to recollect some of the old cures about which I had heard from time to time during my residence in Bruach. 'What should I do?'

'You should get yourself a bottle of Stallion Mixture and rub yourself with it. It's the finest thing in the world for bad chests.'

'Stallion Mixture?' I echoed blankly, and one of the girls giggled.

'What would Miss Peckwitt be wantin' with Stallion Mixture?' demanded Morag, indignant on my behalf. 'It's her chest that's troublin' her not her horse.'

'I know that fine,' retorted Erchy. 'But you mind my cousin Ruari had awful trouble with his own chest? He tried everythin' for it just, until he found he had a bottle of Stallion Mixture left in the house from when his horse was sick. He rubbed himself with that very day for a week an' he's never had a spot more trouble since.' He turned to me. 'You should get a bottle from the grocer tomorrow,' he urged me. 'That'll see your bad chest off for you.'

'I shouldn't like to risk rubbing myself with Stallion Mixture,' I told him, smiling.

'What's the risk?' he demanded. 'It never did my cousin any harm. Indeed,' he resumed with increasing enthusiasm, 'you should have seen the way the hair grew on his chest with the stuff. Just like a Highland bull he was, an' he fathered three fine sons after it.'

'Surely it must have dribbled a bit, then,' observed the irrepressible Morag, while several of the girls shrieked with coy appreciation.

Yawn stood up stiffly. 'I'm away home to my bed,' he said, and there was a murmur of assent from the rest of the old folk that the younger people affected not to hear.

'I'm sure Miss Peckwitt must be tired,' announced Katy, with a solicitousness that was belied by the mockery of her smile.

'I am,' I admitted unashamedly, well accustomed by now to being teased about my habit of liking to go to bed on the same day as I got up. There was a general if reluctant movement to go, the old folk saying good night with seeming abruptness as they were met by the icy air that came in through the open door. Apparently impervious to the cold the lassies clustered round the doorway waiting for the men to arouse themselves from the alcoholic drowsiness into which they had fallen. Becoming impatient, they grasped the men bodily and pulled them to their feet and together they all stumbled out into the night, singing and arguing their way along the road into the darkness. I waited only to tidy the room before going to bed where I fell into a deep and contented sleep from which I was aroused somewhere around six o'clock in the morning by the sound of the coal lorry being driven away.

'Well, I enjoyed my ceilidh fine last night,' said Morag, and then she went on to pay me the Hebridean's supreme compliment, 'I didn't feel the time passin'.'

'Good,' I replied.

'Was that the coal lorry I heard away at the back of six this mornin'?' she enquired.

'I believe it was. I wonder where he was until that time?'

'He'd be with Mora,' said Morag with complete certainty. 'My, but she's the one for the lads all right.' She made a disparaging noise in the back of her throat. 'You'll no' go short of coal for a while till she's tired of him,' she added.

'Well that's good to hear,' I said. We were nearing the entrance to my croft and Morag could now see the heap of coal the lorry had dumped. It looked pitifully small.

'Here, but that's surely not half a ton,' she declared.

'It's supposed to be,' I told her, though I too had been suspicious about the quantity when I saw it by daylight.

'It's never half a ton,' she insisted. 'You should tell him that when you see him next. You know how it is with these lads at the yard?'

I nodded. The loading of coal, unless it was being delivered direct from the boat, was a homely affair. As each half hundredweight of coal was decanted on to the lorry from a large scoop a stone was placed on a convenient window-sill and when there were twenty or forty stones on the sill there was considered to be half a ton or a ton of coal in the lorry. This method generally worked quite well but as the loading was rarely conducted with much seriousness on the part of the loaders it was not wholly reliable. Any distraction, such as an incipient dog fight might be prevented by someone picking up a stone from the sill and hurling it at the combatants; or perhaps a wandering child, unnoticed by the loaders, would appropriate a couple of the more interesting-looking stones. In either case you got jolly good measure for your money but, as it was just as likely that the child might decide to add a few stones to the array on the window-sill or even that one of the ubiquitous loiterers would take an impish delight in surreptitiously adding a stone or two to confuse the loaders, your delivery of coal might be quite seriously short.

'I'll tell the driver about it next time I see him,' I said to Morag. 'And you'll be able to corroborate, won't you?'

'Indeed I will,' she promised.

It was only two evenings later, but well after dark, that the lorry driver turned up at the cottage.

'Morag's after tellin' me you got short weight with your coal,' he began.

'Yes, I'm sure I did,' I told him. 'I honestly don't think there was more than about six hundredweight in it. Here,' I handed him my big torch, 'go and have a look for yourself.'

He went, and came back sucking his breath disapprovingly. 'I was kind of thinkin' that it was short myself at the time,' he acknowledged. 'I suppose it was the lads got larkin' about. I was takin' my tea at the time.' There was a deep frown between his eyes and he seemed a little uncertain what to say next. I asked him inside for a cup of tea but he refused it hastily. 'I'll tell you what I'll do,' he said, making up his mind. 'If you'll take another half-ton of coal I'll load it myself and see there's extra put on to make up for last time.'

As I have said, coal had been in short supply for some time and the prospect of another half-ton was extremely attractive. 'Of course I'll take it,' I told him, unable to disguise my eagerness.

'Right, then, I'll try will I bring it out tomorrow.' He jumped into the lorry and drove off and, much to my amazement, about the same time the following evening I heard the lorry approaching and soon another load of coal was being added to the heap on my croft. The sight of it glistening in the light of the torch filled me with satisfaction.

'It's wonderful to have a nice stock of coal,' I said. 'I've had so many colds this year and I've found it impossible to keep warm with just peats no matter how high I build the fire.'

The driver looked sympathetic. 'How long d'you reckon it takes you to get through half a ton of coal?' he asked me.

I thought for a moment. 'About six weeks,' I told him.

'Then that lot you have will no' last you very long,' he pointed out. 'Twelve weeks at the most.'

'That's true,' I agreed.

'I'll not be makin' any promises but if I can get you more coal will you take it?' he asked.

'I'll be only too glad to,' I said rashly.

'Right then. Cheerio, I'll be seein' you,' he called and was away again, racing his lorry over the bumps of the road and leaving me to wonder why I had suddenly become such a favourite. It took Morag to put me wise.

'Didn't I tell you you'd get plenty coal after your ceilidh?' she asked. 'I could see then the way it was goin' to be between him and Mora.'

'Oh, I don't think it's just Mora who's bringing him out here so often with coal for me,' I said. 'I think he feels sorry for me because I've been so long without coal.'

Morag smiled compassionately at my ignorance. 'Sure it's Mora,' she averred. 'The only way he can get out to see her at night is on the lorry an' the only way he can get hold of the lorry is by sayin' he's bringin' folks coal. Indeed isn't he after everyone in the village swearin' that it's the hardest part of the winter to come yet.'

'Oh, I see,' I said. 'But,' I added brightly, 'good luck to him. I've told him I'll take all the coal he can bring me.'

'Maybe you'll be sorry yet, then,' she said, but I laughed her warning away. I could always use more coal, I told myself with a feeling of light-heartedness. In that way I differed from the rest of the crofters for they used little coal, some of them none at all, and they seemed to find all the warmth they needed in a few peats smouldering greyly in the grate, but then they wore much the same clothes indoors and outdoors, even leaving on their gumboots. I, who felt a slattern unless I changed when I had finished my outside chores, liked to stoke up the fire lavishly in the evenings so that I could move about the room without finding myself in a cold corner. I had told the lorry driver half a ton of coal lasted me about six weeks. Half a ton lasted most of the crofters a year or more.

The obliging driver turned up with another half-ton of coal the following week and within a few days there was yet another half-ton. Gloatingly I regarded the growing heap. My winter's supply of coal secured within easy reach of my cottage! The weather could do its worst now and I need not worry. I was extremely grateful to the driver. So much so that the following week I was confronted with yet another half-ton of coal. I began to feel faintly perturbed. Although I told myself it was a good idea to have a reserve of coal against the time when it might be unobtainable—a circumstance that was all too familiar in Bruach—I had to face up to the fact that coal cost money and my own resources were strictly limited. It was with dismay that I heard the coal lorry turn on to the croft the very next week and, like 'the sorcerer's apprentice', I began to wonder when the flow was going to stop.

'Look,' I told the driver, with affected joviality. 'I'll take up to five tons and then you must marry the girl or else give her up. I can't afford to buy any more.'

He grinned self-consciously and when he bade me goodnight his voice was distinctly regretful.

'Here,' said Erchy some time later in the month. 'You want to be glad now you've plenty of coal. You'll not be gettin' any more for a while. That lorry driver's quarrelled with his boss so he's not workin' for him any more.'

I felt a sense of relief, which was shortlived for, not many evenings later I again heard a lorry approaching with a very familiar rumble and on going outside I found myself confronting my driver friend. My heart plunged to my boots.

'Not more coal?' I asked apprehensively.

'No, indeed,' he assured me. 'I've finished with that man.' He came into the kitchen and sat down uninvited. As he seemed prepared to stay for a while I offered him tea and as he drank it he described to me the various jobs he had tried. When he had finished his tea and was about to leave he asked, 'Did I no' hear you sayin' somethin' at the ceilidh about wantin' a new peat shed?'

'You might have heard me say that I was wanting to strengthen the one I already have,' I told him.

'Aye, well, what I was thinkin' was, I'm workin' now for a fellow has good slabs of wood—you know, the outside of the trees, I'm meanin'. They're good and cheap and if I brought you a load out here in my spare time the carriage would cost you nothin' at all.'

He was an exceedingly persuasive young salesman. It seemed a good idea, and I fell for it. A load of slabs was soon delivered and Erchy went to work on the shed.

'You know,' the driver told me, 'you should take advantage of these slabs while they're so cheap and get yourself another load. You could build yourself another shed with them and make new stalls for your cow byre. There's no end to what you can do with them and you won't be able to get them for much longer.'

The stalls in the byre were sketchy indeed; I succumbed and ordered another load.

'Well,' said Morag, when she saw them lying on the croft. 'You only just got your slabs in time. He's quarrelled with the slab mannie, so he's not workin' for him any more.' She shook her head, lamenting upon the fickleness of the young driver.

'Who is he working for now, then?' I asked.

'Indeed, I'm hearin' he's gone to that place that's sellin' the lime,' she told me.

During my residence in Bruach the village had been visited by one expert after another, all sent by some official body to advise on methods of improving croft land. Lime, they had invariably insisted, was the basic and most urgent necessity. Lime, lime and lime again, they adjured us. The crofters were frankly disbelieving; lime cost money, so they preferred to retain their faith in dung and seaweed. I think I was the only person who accepted the findings of the experts at that time, so that when the lorry driver eventually presented himself at my door with the offer of a load of lime brought out at cheap rates in the evening I was not too unwilling to accept. He generously offered to help me spread the first load, an offer which, had I suspected the reason for it, I should not have accepted with so much alacrity. The experts had said two tons to the acre but the driver spread his share so prodigally that the ton he had brought out did not cover nearly half that area.

'Ach, but I'll be bringin' you out another ton tomorrow,' he comforted. 'You can't give this land too much lime,' he added with an air of superior knowledge.

'And anyway,' he added shrewdly, 'you'll want to qualify for the subsidy on it.'

We spread another ton the following night.

'You would be the better of twenty tons of lime on this croft,' the driver observed briskly flapping his overalls.

'I'm liming only two acres of it for a start,' I told him with a firmness that was no doubt accentuated by my chalk-white face. 'That means I'll need four tons altogether. I'm not taking any more than that.' But after he had brought me the third ton the deliveries ceased abruptly.

'I'm thinkin' you'll need to wait a good whiley for the rest of your guana,' Morag crowed. Everything used to fertilize the land that was not recognizable as seaweed or honest dung, Morag persisted in describing as 'guana'.

'Why?' I asked. 'Has he quarrelled with the lime merchant now?'

'Indeed he has,' she replied.

'Oh, well, I suppose he'll soon get a job with someone else and be out here again coaxing us to buy things at cheap rates.' I laughed.

Morag gave me an odd look. 'An' he's after finishin' with Mora, too,' she said.

'Really?' I exclaimed.

'Aye, so he has,' she told me. 'An' it's glad you ought to be for that, mo ghaoil, for the new job he has is with the undertaker.'

Ladies in Distress

THE woman in the bed next to mine swung her legs cautiously over
the side while the nurse waited, holding her dressing-gown.

'They're letting me home on Friday,' she told me.

'Where is home?' I asked her and she described to me a little
village, the name of which, along with many others, I had glimpsed so
often in the *Oban Times*.

'Where's yours?' she asked, and when I told her she was immediately sympathetic. 'That's an awful way away,' she said. 'No wonder you don't get many visitors.'

My one and only visitor had come the previous evening and then it had been well past visiting hours. The evening meal had been served and there had been the usual period of comparative inactivity before we were bedded down for the night. The patients were meditative and only the rustling of paper as presents were inspected and the light quick footsteps of the nurses broke the lazy silence of the ward. All at once we became aware of the heavy, unsure tread of rough boots. Everyone turned to look at the tall, embarrassed man, clad in homespun suit and cloth cap, who stood at the entrance. With a glow of pleasure I managed to lift my arm in an attempt at a wave and he came towards my bed, hesitantly at first and then with clumsy haste, his boots skidding on the highly polished floor.

'Hector!' I said, and my eyes filled with tears. 'Hector, this is wonderful.'

'Why, Miss Peckwitt,' he said, obviously dismayed at my wasted appearance. 'I just couldn't believe it was you till you spoke just. Oh dear, dear,' He shook his head and looked so distressed that I had to smile reassuringly.

'I'm getting along fine,' I told him, though so far he had been too overcome to ask how I was. 'But tell me, how did you get here, Hector?'

'I heard the carrier was comin' wiss some sheeps tsis way, so I said would he give me a lift and here I am.' He gave me a rueful little smile. 'Behag said I was to get you tsese.' He put a bag of fruit down on my bedside table. 'An' I tsought maybe you'd like tsis.' He laid a copy of the *Football Times* down on the bedcover.

'Tell me all the news,' I begged, when I had expressed my pleasure over the gifts. He rubbed his hand over his chin and frowned with concentration. After a few moments the frown lifted.

'Tsere's a lot of people told me to tell you tsey was askin' after you,' he said and reeled off a list of names. 'An' Morag said to tell you your cow and hens is doin' fine,' he finished up.

I nodded gratefully. 'And how is everyone in Bruach and what
have they been doing?' I asked him.

'Ach, tsey're fine,' he said. 'An' tsey're just where tse tide left
tsem when last you saw tsem. I don't know tsat tsey've been doin'
anytsing at all.'

I had been in hospital for some weeks and even in Bruach I was
sure something would have happened in that time. Surely someone
had bought a new cow, or lost an old one. Or someone's hay had
blown away or someone's horse had fallen over a cliff?

'Have the storms been very bad?' I prompted.

'Och, aye. Some of tsem. Daft Donald lost his dinghy in tse last
one. Smashed up properly she was. Mind you, she was as rotten as
shit.'

'Poor Donald,' I commiserated. 'He'll miss not having the *Swallow*
to fuss over, even though he never went out in her.'

'Aye, but he has anotser one already,' Hector said. 'He got it from
a man on tse mainland a few days ago just, an' he was round tse otser
day askin' my aunt what name would he put on it.'

'And did she suggest one?'

'Aye, well all she said was, "What's wrong wiss callin' her *Swallow*
again, Donald?" So tsats what he did. I was down on tse shore yesterday and tsere across tse transom of his boat he's painted *Swallow
Again* in big letters.' He smiled a swift, urchin smile. 'It kind of gives
you a funny feelin' in your tsroat just to see it,' he said, and we
exchanged a grin of understanding.

'No cows died? No calves born?' I asked.

'No, but tse stallion was out tse otser day for Tearlaich's mare—
tse one tsat didn't die. Tse mannie tsat brought him was sayin' he was
pretty fed up, too.'

'Why?'

'He was girnin' because he'd had to walk all tse way from tse pier
wiss tse beast an' he'd be after havin' to walk all tse way back again
tsat night for tsere was no place to keep him.'

'I should think he would be fed up,' I murmured.

'Aye, well tse minute tse stallion had served tse mare tse mannie grabbed a great bunch of nettles an' rammed tsem under tse mare's tail. My God! he was quick about it too. An' he needed to be, for she kicked up her heels to witsin an inch of his head. "Tsere now," he says to Tearlaich an' givin' him a wink, "tsat'll make sure she holds an' I don't have to come back here again." Tearlaich turns on him. "Man," he says, "you're lucky to be alive not to have to come back again." ' Hector's eyes were wide. 'An' I can tell you he was, too.'

Hector had not taken off his cap when he came into the ward and now, becoming conscious of the questioning looks of the night nurses just coming on duty, he pulled it down over his eyes so that he should not see them.

'Has no one died or been ill?' I asked him.

He shook his head and sucked in his breath, trying to remember something that might interest me.

'Hamish's sister is back,' he suddenly recalled.

'Is she really? Is she any better?'

Hamish's sister had developed, in addition to other peculiar habits, one of hiding behind any convenient shed or house whenever she saw anyone approaching and giving a very life-like imitation of a duck quacking. A few months ago she had been taken to a home to be treated.

Hector pondered my question. 'Well I don't know tsat she's better,' he said doubtfully. 'She's different tsough.'

'How different?'

'Well, she doesn't quack any more, but now whenever she sees you comin' she gets behind sometsing and crows away like a cockerel. She's damty good at it, too,' he said with an appreciative smile.

The nurse came to the foot of the bed and though Hector gave her his most enraptured smile she was not to be beguiled. He shrugged and cast a furtive glance along the rows of interested faces. I thought he was going to kiss me goodbye but his courage failed him. Instead he patted my hand.

'Never mind,' he said, 'you'll be better off for tsis operation, you'll see. Our own Hamish had an operation on his stomach at one time an' he never had any more trouble wiss it till he died.'

He lingered a moment or two longer. 'You'll be home for New Year?' he predicted questioningly, and when I shook my head he made a grimace of sympathy. I watched him with great affection as he skidded out of the ward and turned to wave to me before disappearing along the corridor. Then I lay back on the pillows, reflecting on his parting words.

Would I be home for New Year? Not, I planned, if I could help it. Out of hospital, I hoped, but not in Bruach where New Year was just a drinking orgy in which, because I loathe undisciplined drinking, I had perforce to play the part of observer. The first New Year I had spent there in Morag's house I had been so nauseated by the intemperance of the crofters that I had resolved when I got a house of my own I would withdraw completely from the celebration. Morag, who always had my interests at heart, had then made it her duty to come and explain to me how much New Year meant to them and how important it was that I should take a drink with my friends even if it was only a 'wee tastie'. I was never able to understand the Scots' preparatory bracing up for their complete abandonment to sottishness on this one night of the year but I was made to see how churlish and unsociable was my own attitude. So I had relented and bought a bottle of whisky and stayed up to entertain such revellers as were sober enough to stumble to my cottage. It was for me a long night of unmitigated boredom but since then I had become more acclimatized and had found that the best way of coping with the celebration was to set out myself just before midnight and go the rounds of my friends' houses taking my own bottle and wishing everyone a 'Happy New Year' and accepting only a 'wee tastie' in return. It still meant a long and tedious night but I preferred it to sitting at home and perhaps being surrounded by limp carcasses singing, praying, crying or just being horribly sick.

And yet, even at New Year, there were moments of fun. I remembered how it had been last year.

It had begun when 'postie' had burst into the cottage, decanted some very muddy envelopes on to the table and pulled a bottle of whisky out of his mail-bag. His eyes were Hogmanay bright.

'It's a bugger of a night for a New Year,' he began sociably. 'The wind lifted the mails out of my bag just, an' it took them half way up the brae before I could catch them again.' He paused for breath. 'Indeed I doubt I wouldn't have got them at all if they hadn't been caught in those bushes at the back of Sandy's house.' He bade me get two glasses and when I put them on the table he poured a generous quantity into each. He tossed off his at one gulp. 'I'll be seein' you again tonight yet,' he threatened as he girded his bag to him in preparation for the resumption of his battle against the storm. 'I'm goin' up to Erchy's when I've finished an' then we'll be startin' on the rounds.'

'Well don't leave it too late,' I warned him. 'I'm going up to Morag's before twelve.'

'Ach, we'll be there by then,' he promised.

I slammed the door after him and sagged into a chair. I had not been feeling too well for over a week and I really had no intention of going up to Morag's. I hoped that round about midnight there would be a quiet spell when I could put out the light and creep off to bed and let everyone think I was following my usual plan of having my New Year ceilidh in other people's houses. Throughout the evening there came a sporadic trickle of visitors coming and going in varying stages of inebriation. Whisky poured by crapulous hands was slopped on the table and on the floor and in the brief intervals between drinks the talk was senseless and repetitive.

At half past eleven the cottage was mercifully deserted and I was just about to put out the light and bolt the door when there was a peremptory knock on the window followed by a thump on the door and Morag came in.

'What, is there nobody here?' she asked, peering under the table and behind the chairs where she would expect to find New Year revellers. I told her who had come and gone. 'An' has our own Hector an' Erchy not been yet?' I shook my head. 'Well, I may as well sit myself down and wait till they do,' she announced, seating herself beside the fire, 'for they'll surely be here before the mornin'.'

I got out the bottle again and a couple of tots but she insisted that it must be 'only a wee tastie', just so that it could never be said she had refused to drink with me. The women of Bruach rarely took more to drink than they needed just to make themselves merry. It was only the men who insisted on quantity. We sat and talked until two o'clock and still there was no sound of approaching 'first footers'.

'It's a pity you don't take to New Year like the rest of us,' said Morag. 'Did you never make anythin' of it when you was in England?'

'Not really,' I told her. 'We had all our fun at Christmas.' I smiled reminiscently. 'The only difference New Year made at home was that my father used to stay up to let the New Year in and he used to have a bottle of wine and a cigar for company.'

'A cigar! There now.' Morag was visibly impressed.

'Yes,' I said. 'My mother used to buy him two three-and-sixpenny cigars for Christmas every year and he smoked one on Christmas day and one on New Year's Eve.'

'Three and sixpence for one cigar?' expostulated Morag. 'That seems a terrible waste of money.'

'Oh, no,' I replied. 'It was only two in the whole year. The rest of the time he smoked a pipe.'

'The dear Lord help us!' responded Morag fervently. 'If I paid three and sixpence for a cigar for a man I'd be after makin' sure he ate the ash of it.'

Even the small amount of whisky I had drunk was making me sleepy and I was unable to suppress my yawns. Morag too seemed to be a little tired. The clock struck three.

'I was thinkin' maybe Erchy wouldn't have all that much money to spend on drink after him losin' so much this week already,' Morag said.

'Erchy losing his money?' I asked. 'That's the first I've heard of it. How did that happen?' My sleepiness was temporarily abated.

'Did you not hear? He went off on Monday to the mainland with some of his beasts he was takin' to a sale there, an' Hector was supposed to be goin' with him. Erchy went on the cattle float, but our own Hector—ach! you know what like of man he is.' She made a gesture of hopelessness with her hands. 'Didn't he tell Erchy he'd meet him at the ferry because he was gettin' a lift in with the nurse in the mornin' to go and see the blacksmith about a thing for his boat. Well, he goes to see the blacksmith an' then he's outside waitin' on the bus to take him to the ferry when a car pulls up beside him. "You're Hector, aren't you, from Bruach?" says the driver. "I've met you before when I took a trip on your boat." Hector just can't remember his face but the man asks him would he like a lift. So Hector gets in, well pleased with himself.' Morag gave a dry chuckle. 'My, but he got a right drop when the car turns round an' comes back here to Bruach.'

'But didn't Hector say anything when he saw which way it was going?' I asked.

'Indeed he did not. The fool said he didn't like to when the mannie had been so kind to him.'

Hector was so afraid of hurting anyone's feelings that I sometimes used to amuse myself by imagining him driving a car on a busy road. I used to feel sure that if he received a polite 'pass' signal from the car in front he would, sooner than appear discourteous, obediently overtake even though doing so would mean that he would drive straight past the turning for his own destination.

'Anyway,' Morag resumed. 'Hector didn't get to the sale so Erchy was there by himself an' he made two hundred pounds on his beasts. Of course, Erchy bein' who he is, he had to go an' get drunk an' when he wakes up it's mornin' an' he's cold an' shiverin' in the waitin' room of the station. He puts his hand in his pocket an' there's his wallet missin'. All his cattle money's gone.'

'Poor Erchy,' I said. 'Whatever did he do?'

'That's not the end of it,' said Morag. 'He has to go an' borrow a pound or so from a man he knows to get him home.' I watched her avidly, waiting for the climax which I knew by her manner I could expect.

'Ach, the way poor Erchy was feelin' an' havin' to face his mother an' tellin' her what he'd done! An' the poor old soul hearin' him!'

'And is there no trace of the wallet?' I asked.

'Well, comes twelve o'clock,' went on Morag, nodding me into silence, 'an' what should draw up outside Erchy's house but a taxi.

An' what does this taxi do next but to start unloadin' parcels of groceries an' cakes that the driver gives to Erchy.

'"Here's the messages you ordered," the driver tells him. "Oh, God!" says Erchy, frettin' about what other foolishness he might have been up to. "Did I order these?" For he has no mind of it at all. "You did indeed," the driver says, quite sharp. "An' you ordered my taxi to bring them out here to you at twelve o'clock today." "An' how much did I pay you for doin' it?" Erchy asks him. "You didn't pay me," says the driver. "You promised you'd pay me two pounds ten if I brought them all to you safely at twelve o'clock today, an' there's the sheet of paper where you wrote down your name an' address." Erchy looks at the paper an' there's no mistake about it at all. He's just swearin' off the drink for the rest of his life when the driver pulls out a wallet an' hands it to him. "An' there's your wallet you asked me to keep for you," he said. "You'd best check what's in it. A hundred and ninety-five pounds you told me it was last night so it should be the same now." Erchy could scarce believe his ears an' he takes the wallet an' looks in it, an' there's a hundred an' ninety-five pounds.' Morag finished with an exclamation of incredulity.

'Oh good! So he didn't lose his money after all,' I said with as much relief as if it had been mine.

'None but twenty pounds of it,' said Morag. I raised my eyebrows enquiringly and she carried on with her story.

'"Now," says the driver, "I'd be glad if you'll pay me an' I can get back."

'"How much did you say I promised to pay you?" Erchy asked.

'"Two pounds ten," said the driver, thinkin' Erchy was goin' to argue.

'"Man," says Erchy, "I'm that damty glad to see you I'll give you twenty-two pounds ten!" An' he made the driver take it, too.'

'My goodness! I'll bet Erchy said his prayers after that little lot,' I said.

'Maybe he's still celebratin' his luck,' she said, standing up. 'I'm thinkin' the best thing we can do is to go and find out where he and that Hector are, anyway,' she suggested. 'They're sure to be somewhere if it's only the ditch they're in. But there's one thing certain, mo ghaoil, if you don't have a drink with them some place tonight then there's no use in you goin' to bed for they'll be here yet an' get you out of it, no matter what time it is.'

So instead of seeking my warm bed I had put on oilskins and gumboots and blundered with Morag out into the rumbustious night. We had called and taken our 'wee tastie' in several houses before we finally caught up with Erchy and his crowd at Dugald's cottage and there men were sprawled all over the kitchen, some with their heads on the shoulders of the long-suffering girls who, though it was past four o'clock in the morning and they had been celebrating since early evening, were as dewy-eyed and fresh-looking as if they had just come in from the hill. The Highland complexion has never, to me, ceased to be a source of envy and wonder. Dugald himself sat on the bench buttressed on either side by his chief cronies while in the recess bed behind drawn curtains his stone-deaf wife alternately snored and screeched objurgations at the assembled company. There was an ominous belch from the floor by the dresser and a frenzy of catarrhal sobs interspersed with protestations of remorse for his misdeeds came from Tearlaich, whose religion made him very conscious of the fact that he often sinned but never stopped him from doing so. Hector lurched over and waved a bottle of whisky over an empty glass which he pushed in my direction. With great solemnity we wished each other a happy New Year. Then it was Erchy's turn and then Ruari's and so on until they were all satisfied that they had poured me out a drink and had seen me raise the glass to my lips. Dugald attempted a song but before one line was completed his head had sunk on his chest and he was sagging with sleepiness.

I was assessing my chances of making a stealthy retreat when I found Erchy teetering over me.

'Your hair smells lovely of boiled onions,' he remarked with an ardent sniff, and without giving me time to accept his compliment he went on, 'Miss Peckwitt, I want you to help me.'

I indicated that I was quite willing to help him if I could.

'It's this Dugald here. He's that drunk an' somebody's got to get

him home tonight,' he explained. He swayed sideways and steadied
himself against the back of my chair. 'I'm thinkin' you an' me are
the only two here that's sober enough to be any good to him.' I
suppose I looked as mystified as I felt. 'Come on, now,' he invited. 'I
daresay we can manage him between us.'

'But, Erchy,' I remonstrated, 'this is Dugald's house. He's in his
own home.'

Erchy recoiled from me with a look of anguished incredulity.
'Woman!' he upbraided me, 'you must be bloody drunk if that's
what you're thinkin'.' He shook Morag's shoulder. 'You'd best get
this woman to her bed,' he adjured her, 'for she's that drunk she
doesn't know where she is.'

And the next day, looking like something the mice had been
nibbling at during the night, he had come quite early down to the
cottage to commiserate with me on my 'sore head'.

The woman in the next bed said: 'It's wonderful to think I'll be
sleeping in my own room again on Friday night—and I won't have
to wake up in a morning and see all those memorial tablets over the
beds. They fair give me the creeps.'

I agreed most heartily with her, for it is disturbing and disheartening to come out of an anaesthetic with one's body a tangle of pain to
be confronted by a well-polished but sombre plaque stating that one's
bed is dedicated to the memory of a deceased relative by a loving
family. Seen vaguely, in conjunction with massed flowers and the
white draperies of the nurses, the plaques give one the feeling that one
is attending one's own funeral.

'It'd be far better if they had a few pictures over the beds instead of
those things,' said my neighbour. 'The adventures of Tarzan all along
the walls would do more to cheer us women up than a lot of old
memorials.'

'It's pretty awful psychology, I should think,' I said. 'And I'm
sure a few delectable pin-ups would benefit the men's ward.'

She laughed. 'Ach, well, you've done your little bit, anyway, dearie.'
She laughed again and I darted her a look of venom while very nerve
in my body cringed with embarrassment.

'Your blessed brother-in-law,' I commented.

I had been lying stark-naked on my bed under the infra-red lamp the previous day and though the screens were around me the nurse had left a gap so that I could watch the ward clock and call her when my cooking was completed. I was basking contentedly in the soothing heat from the lamp and so paid little attention to the tall man in a dressing-gown who had just come into the ward and was talking to the nurse. I had not taken particular notice when, guided by her pointing finger, he made his way along the line of beds in my direction and it was not until a second or two before he reached my bed that I realized his proximity. Immobilized by an intravenous feeder and in any case too weak to move quickly I could only stare with agonized horror as he leaned his arms on my screens and greeted me with startled affability. I screwed my eyes tight shut and a moment later heard my neighbour's voice lifted in rebuke.

'Andrew! This is me over here.'

His head had disappeared by the time I could endure to open my eyes again and there was much awed whispering from the direction of the next bed. When he had gone and, my cooking over, I was settled beneath the bedclothes again, my neighbour called to me. 'That was my brother-in-law. Seemingly they brought him into the men's ward yesterday for an X-ray.'

'I don't care if he is your brother-in-law,' I stated flatly. 'He's a blundering oaf.'

She laughed with irritating complacency. 'He just made a mistake in thinking the nurse was pointing to your bed,' she excused him. 'But he told me to tell you he was awful sorry for coming on you like that.' She tried hard to look solemn.

'I feel so ashamed,' I grumbled. 'And I shall always be dreading the possibility that I may meet him again somewhere. Imagine how I shall feel if I ever come face to face with a complete stranger who's seen me in my birthday suit.'

'Ach, but you have no need to worry, dearie. He'll never recognize you.'

'I sincerely hope not,' I said.

'Oh, no, he won't honestly,' she assured me with artful positiveness. 'He told me he didn't bother to look at your face.'

On Thursday evening my neighbour sat on my bed and chatted with me for as long as the nurse would allow. I always thought of her as 'Rosie' because her offhand geniality, her voluptuous figure and her habit of calling everyone 'dearie' made me think of a typical English barmaid. In fact she was the post-mistress of a village that, when she described it, sounded to me to be only a little more sophisticated than Bruach. Speaking of her own illness she said: 'My man was saying he didn't believe they would have needed to keep me so long in here had we been able to get the doctor when I first felt ill. But it's the same every year in our village.' She gave a sigh of resignation. 'It's no use wanting the doctor once the grouse-shooting season's begun for he's always too busy.' She fed me a segment of orange. 'You know, people never like to make a complaint against the doctor,' she said. 'There are doctors in the Highlands can get away with murder and people wouldn't say a word against them. The last doctor we had was asked to go to a man once that was sick and he promised to go but he forgot all about it. A few days later he was passing the house and he sees there's a funeral. He suddenly remembers the sick man and gets out of his car to ask after him. He finds it's the very man they're burying, so he just follows behind the bier to the burial ground. Afterwards all the relatives were saying, "Ach, there we were miscalling the poor doctor for not coming out to visit the man but it seems he's not so bad after all. He did come to the funeral." '

'We're luckier than that where I live,' I told her. 'But I do remember one doctor we had who loved to buy cattle. If he saw a nice-looking beast anywhere along the road he couldn't rest until he'd found the owner and bargained with him for the cow. It would take hours sometimes and it didn't matter at all if he was supposed to be going to an urgent case.'

'Rosie' got up. 'Oh, well, I suppose I'd best get to my bed. The morning will come all the quicker for it.'

'What time is the ambulance to take you?' I enquired.

'Ambulance? I'm having no ambulance,' she asserted. 'My man's hiring a car for me since he heard what happened to the last woman from our village that was supposed to be sent home by ambulance.'

'Did it break down?' I asked.

'No, oh, no! But the woman said she was greatly taken with the way the ambulance driver kept turning round to ask her if she was feeling all right. She kept telling him she was fine. Then he said would she like a cup of tea at the next hotel they'd pass. She told him she would, so he took her inside and bought a nice tea for her. Then she got back into the ambulance and they started off again and when they were about half way home the driver asked her again if she was sure she felt all right. So she told him again she still felt fine. "In that case," he asked her, "would you mind going home by train for the rest of the way and I'll pay your fare for you?" She looked at him wondering what was the matter with him and he said, "You see, I have a girl friend lives just about here and if you'll go home by train I can go and spend the time at her house before I have to get back to the hospital." '

'And did she go home by train?'

'Oh, yes. She didn't like to say no, seeing as he'd bought her tea, but my man says he's not taking the risk of it happening to me.' She was climbing into bed as she finished her story and there was a crackling of paper as she commenced her supper of biscuits, for 'Rosie's' large appetite was not to be satisfied with hospital rations.

The lights in the ward were dimmed and when I had managed to wriggle my poor bottom, that was punctured like a sieve with injections, into the least agonizing position, I drowsed first into the short segments of dreams that precede sleep and then into the drugged doze from which I was awakened well before five in the morning so that my bed could be made. More than at any other time this early-morning eruption into activity, just when sleep was deepest, made me yearn for my own bed and the lazy, undemanding winter dawns in Bruach.

When morning came 'Rosie' was claimed by a smugly delighted husband and a gently fussing sister and her bed was soon occupied by a little girl who reminded me so much of Fiona that, except for the colour of hair, they might have been one and the same person. She was just as perverse, just as imperious and before she had been in the hospital more than a few hours she had acquainted herself with the complete genealogies of every nurse and every patient in the ward.

The long days dragged increasingly in proportion as my recovery speeded up. Each morning the surgeons, anonymous in their white coats, came and smiled down at me with cool, detached smiles and prodded my body with deft fingers. They applied stethoscopes to my stomach that was as bloated as a Botticelli angel's and congratulated me solemnly on its reboant rumblings. When I was not asleep I lay and listened to it with the same sort of clinical satisfaction and when, thinking to amuse myself, I put a piece of toilet paper (stamped 'Government property') over a comb and started to play it, it was some time before the rest of the patients in the ward realized that the noise I was making was intentional. And when a storm came out of a ragged sky, bullying the tall trees in the hospital grounds and rattling the ward windows, it was some consolation to know that all the wind in the world wasn't inside my stomach as in moments of agony I was willing to believe.

At last my own day for leaving came, but it was only to go on to a convalescent home and there I spent a blessedly sober New Year.

Morag had a fire going and my cottage warm and bright with welcome when I returned at last to Bruach and the overwhelming kindness of my neighbours.

'Did they tell you what was wrong with you?' Morag asked at last. 'We were told you were very poorly but nobody rightly seemed to know what it was.'

'I don't know myself,' I replied. 'They weren't very forthcoming at the hospital.'

So a few weeks later when the nurse called I asked her if she knew what had been wrong with me.

'All they told me was that you were terribly constricted and it was a very big operation,' she replied.

'I wonder just what that means?' I asked, but she shrugged her shoulders.

It was not long after my conversation with the nurse that I met Hector and Erchy coming up from the shore with paint brushes and scrapers in their hands and looking as though they had put in a full day's work. 'We've had *Ealasaid* up on the beach,' they told me in reply to my glance of enquiry.

'Why, was there something wrong with her?' I asked.

'Och, aye, she was terrible constricted.'

'Constricted?' I repeated, almost choking on the word. 'How do you mean?'

'It means she had a terrible dirty bottom,' elucidated Hector. 'Covered all over wiss weeds and tsem big barnacles. It's days we've been now scrapin' tsem off her and scrubbin' at her. It's been a right big job we've had wiss her.'

'And is she all right now?' I quavered, stifling the wild laughter that was threatening to shatter me.

'All right?' repeated Erchy. 'I'll say she's all right. Just you wait till you see her gettin' goin' again. You'll hardly know her she'll be that much faster.'

I too am a lot faster now.

A Selection of Arrow Bestsellers

ARROW BOOKS, BOOKSERVICE BY POST, PO BOX 29, DOUGLAS, ISLE OF MAN, BRITISH ISLES

NAME ....

ADDRESS ....

....

....

Please enclose a cheque or postal order made out to Arrow Books Ltd. for the amount due and allow the following for postage and packing.

U.K. CUSTOMERS: Please allow 22p per book to a maximum of £3.00.

B.F.P.O. & EIRE: Please allow 22p per book to a maximum of £3.00.

OVERSEAS CUSTOMERS: Please allow 22p per book.

Whilst every effort is made to keep prices low it is sometimes necessary to increase cover prices at short notice. Arrow Books reserve the right to show new retail prices on covers which may differ from those previously advertised in the text or elsewhere.

Bestselling Women's Fiction

☐	Destinies	Charlotte Vale Allen	£2.95
☐	Hester Dark	Emma Blair	£1.95
☐	Nellie Wildchild	Emma Blair	£2.50
☐	Playing the Jack	Mary Brown	£3.50
☐	Twin of Fire	Jude Deveraux	£2.50
☐	Counterfeit Lady	Jude Deveraux	£2.50
☐	Miss Gathercole's Girls	Judy Gardiner	£2.50
☐	Lisa Logan	Marie Joseph	£1.95
☐	Maggie Craig	Marie Joseph	£1.95
☐	A Long Way From Heaven	Sheelagh Kelly	£2.95
☐	The Gooding Girl	Pamela Oldfield	£2.75
☐	The Running Years	Claire Rayner	£2.75
☐	The Pride	Judith Saxton	£2.50

ARROW BOOKS, BOOKSERVICE BY POST, PO BOX 29, DOUGLAS, ISLE OF MAN, BRITISH ISLES

NAME ....

ADDRESS ....

....

....

Please enclose a cheque or postal order made out to Arrow Books Ltd. for the amount due and allow the following for postage and packing.

U.K. CUSTOMERS: Please allow 22p per book to a maximum of £3.00.

B.F.P.O. & EIRE: Please allow 22p per book to a maximum of £3.00.

OVERSEAS CUSTOMERS: Please allow 22p per book.

Whilst every effort is made to keep prices low it is sometimes necessary to increase cover prices at short notice. Arrow Books reserve the right to show new retail prices on covers which may differ from those previously advertised in the text or elsewhere.

Bestselling Fiction

☐ Dancing Bear	Chaim Bermant	£2.95
☐ Hiroshima Joe	Martin Booth	£2.95
☐ 1985	Anthony Burgess	£1.95
☐ The Other Woman	Colette	£1.95
☐ The Manchurian Candidate	Richard Condon	£2.25
☐ Letter to a Child Never Born	Oriana Fallaci	£1.25
☐ Duncton Wood	William Horwood	£3.50
☐ Aztec	Gary Jennings	£3.95
☐ The Journeyer	Gary Jennings	£3.50
☐ The Executioner's Song	Norman Mailer	£3.50
☐ Strumpet City	James Plunkett	£3.50
☐ Admiral	Dudley Pope	£1.95
☐ The Second Lady	Irving Wallace	£2.50
☐ An Unkindness of Ravens	Ruth Rendell	£1.95
☐ The History Man	Malcolm Bradbury	£2.95

ARROW BOOKS, BOOKSERVICE BY POST, PO BOX 29, DOUGLAS, ISLE OF MAN, BRITISH ISLES

NAME ....

ADDRESS ....

....

....

Please enclose a cheque or postal order made out to Arrow Books Ltd. for the amount due and allow the following for postage and packing.

U.K. CUSTOMERS: Please allow 22p per book to a maximum of £3.00.

B.F.P.O. & EIRE: Please allow 22p per book to a maximum of £3.00.

OVERSEAS CUSTOMERS: Please allow 22p per book.

Whilst every effort is made to keep prices low it is sometimes necessary to increase cover prices at short notice. Arrow Books reserve the right to show new retail prices on covers which may differ from those previously advertised in the text or elsewhere.

A Selection of Arrow Bestsellers

☐ Voices on the Wind	Evelyn Anthony	£2.50
☐ Someone Else's Money	Michael M. Thomas	£2.50
☐ The Executioner's Song	Norman Mailer	£3.50
☐ The Alexander Principle	Wilfred Barlow	£2.95
☐ Everything is Negotiable	Gavin Kennedy	£2.95
☐ The New Girlfriend & other stories	Ruth Rendell	£1.95
☐ An Unkindness of Ravens	Ruth Rendell	£1.95
☐ Dead in the Morning	Margaret Yorke	£1.75
☐ The Domesday Heritage	Ed. Elizabeth Hallam	£3.95
☐ Elvis and Me	Priscilla Presley	£2.95
☐ The World of Placido Domingo	Daniel Snowman	£4.95
☐ Maria Callas	Arianna Stassinopoulos	£2.50
☐ The Brendan Voyage	Tim Severin	£3.50
☐ A Shine of Rainbows	Lillian Beckwith	£1.95
☐ Rates of Exchange	Malcolm Bradbury	£2.95
☐ Thy Tears Might Cease	Michael Farrell	£2.95
☐ Pudding and Pie (Nancy Mitford Omnibus)	Nancy Mitford	£3.95

ARROW BOOKS, BOOKSERVICE BY POST, PO BOX 29, DOUGLAS, ISLE OF MAN, BRITISH ISLES

NAME ....

ADDRESS ....

....

....

Please enclose a cheque or postal order made out to Arrow Books Ltd. for the amount due and allow the following for postage and packing.

U.K. CUSTOMERS: Please allow 22p per book to a maximum of £3.00.

B.F.P.O. & EIRE: Please allow 22p per book to a maximum of £3.00.

OVERSEAS CUSTOMERS: Please allow 22p per book.

Whilst every effort is made to keep prices low it is sometimes necessary to increase cover prices at short notice. Arrow Books reserve the right to show new retail prices on covers which may differ from those previously advertised in the text or elsewhere.

Arrow Health

☐ The Gradual Vegetarian	Lisa Tracy	£2.95
☐ The Food Scandal	Caroline Walker & Geoffrey Cannon	£3.95
☐ The Alexander Principle	Wilfred Barlow	£2.95
☐ The Complete Book of Exercises	Diagram Group	£4.95
☐ Yoga for Women	Nancy Phelan & Michael Volin	£2.50
☐ Health on Your Plate	Janet Pleshette	£2.50
☐ The Zinc Solution	Professor D. Bryce-Smith	£3.50
☐ Goodbye to Arthritis	Patricia Byrivers	£2.95
☐ Natural Pain Control	Dr Vernon Coleman	£3.50
☐ The Natural Dentist	Brian Halvorsen	£2.95
☐ Ageless Ageing: The Natural Way to Stay Young	Leslie Kenton	£2.95
☐ The Joy of Beauty	Leslie Kenton	£5.95
☐ Raw Energy	Leslie & Susannah Kenton	£2.95
☐ A Gentle Way with Cancer	Brenda Kidman	£2.95
☐ Yoga for Backache	Nancy Phelan & Michael Volin	£2.95

ARROW BOOKS, BOOKSERVICE BY POST, PO BOX 29, DOUGLAS, ISLE OF MAN, BRITISH ISLES

NAME ....

ADDRESS ....

....

....

Please enclose a cheque or postal order made out to Arrow Books Ltd. for the amount due and allow the following for postage and packing.

U.K. CUSTOMERS: Please allow 22p per book to a maximum of £3.00.

B.F.P.O. & EIRE: Please allow 22p per book to a maximum of £3.00.

OVERSEAS CUSTOMERS: Please allow 22p per book.

Whilst every effort is made to keep prices low it is sometimes necessary to increase cover prices at short notice. Arrow Books reserve the right to show new retail prices on covers which may differ from those previously advertised in the text or elsewhere.

Arena

☐ The Lives of the Indian Princes	Charles Allen	£4.95
☐ Confessions of an Irish Rebel	Brendan Behan	£2.95
☐ Dancing Bear	Chaim Bermant	£2.95
☐ Let It Come Down	Paul Bowles	£2.95
☐ The After Dinner Game	Malcolm Bradbury	£1.95
☐ Eating People is Wrong	Malcolm Bradbury	£2.95
☐ Rates of Exchange	Malcolm Bradbury	£2.95
☐ So the Wind Won't Blow It All Away	Richard Brautigan	£2.95
☐ Ten Years in an Open Necked Shirt	John Cooper Clarke	£3.50
☐ The Wit and Wisdom of Quentin Crisp	Quentin Crisp	£2.50
☐ Thy Tears Might Cease	Michael Farrell	£2.95
☐ Boys on the Rock	John Fox	£2.50
☐ Selected Letters of E. M. Forster	Ed. Mary Lago & P. N. Furbank	£4.50
☐ Pudding and Pie (Nancy Mitford Omnibus)	Nancy Mitford	£3.95
☐ Mourners Below	James Purdy	£2.95

ARROW BOOKS, BOOKSERVICE BY POST, PO BOX 29, DOUGLAS, ISLE OF MAN, BRITISH ISLES

NAME ....

ADDRESS ....

....

....

Please enclose a cheque or postal order made out to Arrow Books Ltd. for the amount due and allow the following for postage and packing.

U.K. CUSTOMERS: Please allow 22p per book to a maximum of £3.00.

B.F.P.O. & EIRE: Please allow 22p per book to a maximum of £3.00.

OVERSEAS CUSTOMERS: Please allow 22p per book.

Whilst every effort is made to keep prices low it is sometimes necessary to increase cover prices at short notice. Arrow Books reserve the right to show new retail prices on covers which may differ from those previously advertised in the text or elsewhere.